Physics - Mechanics

VERSION 3.1

AMERICAN MODELING TEACHERS ASSOCIATION

Transforming STEM Education

PHYSICS MECHANICS, version 3.1, Third edition.
American Modeling Teachers Association (AMTA)

ISBN-13: 978-0-9990735-5-1 ISBN-10: 0-9990735-5-9
https://modelinginstruction.org/
http://socraticbrain.org/

Acknowledgements

This student Course-book uses readings, worksheets and review problems from the AMTA Curriculum resources for Physics, Mechanics, 2013 version 3.1. These resources are based on materials produced with generous support from 16 years of NSF funding for the Modeling Instruction Program at Arizona State University.

Principal Investigator - Dr. David Hestenes, Arizona State University

Project Director - Dr. Jane Jackson, Arizona State University

Dr. Malcolm Wells, Marcos de Niza HS, Tempe, AZ (deceased) originated the Modeling Method of Instruction as a part of research he conducted for his PhD in Physics Education Research.

Since their initial writing, these resources have undergone 6 major revisions; the current version was edited by Mark Schober.

This manual has been used for the course PHS 530: Methods of Physics Teaching I at Arizona State University. The materials are based upon work supported by the National Science Foundation grants MDR-895461, ESI-9353423, PHY-8919461, DUE-9910458, and ESI-0138561. Any opinions, findings, and conclusions or recommendations expressed in these materials are those of the authors and do not necessarily reflect the views of the National Science Foundation.

AMTA copyright Acceptable Use Policy

The AMTA readings, worksheets and review sheets in this Course-book are intended for AMTA member classroom use. These materials are designed to be used by instructors who have had professional development in Modeling Instruction though an AMTA approved summer workshop (60-90 hours) or a distance learning course (45 hours). They are compiled from the Modeling Mechanics materials that are available to AMTA members in a single electronic or printed document. The AMTA readings, worksheets and review sheets in this Course-book remains the copy-written intellectual property of the AMTA and is subject to distribution restrictions. It may not be copied and redistributed without AMTA purchase.

The materials in this Course-book may not be shared or distributed in ways that allow them to become part of the public domain. Renderings of this documents, to include solutions keys, may only be posted on password protected websites that cannot be indexed by search engines. Under no circumstances may solutions to these documents be posted on any publically accessible website. Documents may be posted on a password protected website as indicated above, but the copyright statement must remain on the page footer. Materials displayed on password-protected sites should be posted for a limited amount of time and it is suggested that solution keys them be removed within a few days of posting.

The American Modeling Teachers Association will respond to policy violation complaints and search the web for posted documents. Educators violating these policies will be asked to take them down in compliance with the policy. School/district/site administration may be notified and the pursuit of legal action taken.

Introduction

Congratulations – consider yourself fortunate! The book you are holding indicates that you are enrolled in a Modeling Physics course, with an instructor trained by the American Modeling Teachers Association to deliver instruction using an award winning, research-validated approach to teaching. Unlike traditional science teaching approaches, where students memorize facts about seemingly unrelated topics, Modeling Instruction organizes courses around the students' own construction, validation and application of a handful of scientific models that form the content core of physics.

The Modeling approach will help you develop a coherent framework for thinking about and making sense of physical phenomena, while developing scientific investigatory abilities. With your teacher's guidance, you will build useful, flexible conceptual tools for thinking, and practices for solving real problems.

To support this kind of instruction, this Course-book is full of resources designed for engaging classroom instruction and student discourse. As you flip through the pages, you will notice that there is little resemblance to a traditional textbook. If this is your first experience with Modeling Instruction, you'll learn why. The content of this Course-book mirrors the instructional approach of the course: you will be working collaboratively with your peers to construct your own understanding, rather than trying to learn what is written on the pages of a book.

Get ready to discard some of your old ways of thinking, and change the way you see the world!

Table of Contents

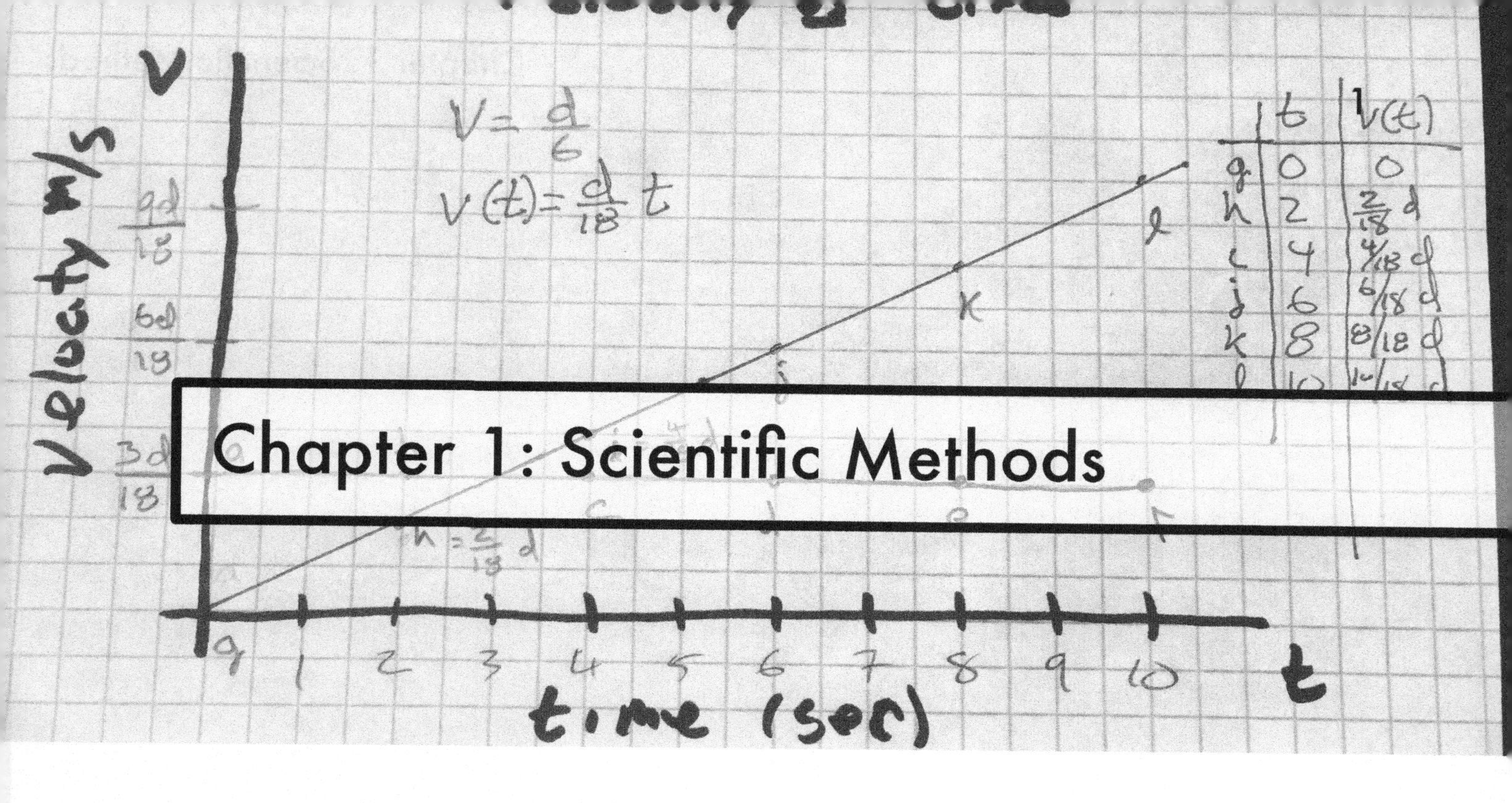

Chapter 1: Scientific Methods

Chapter Sections

chapter 1 online help

Lab Notes

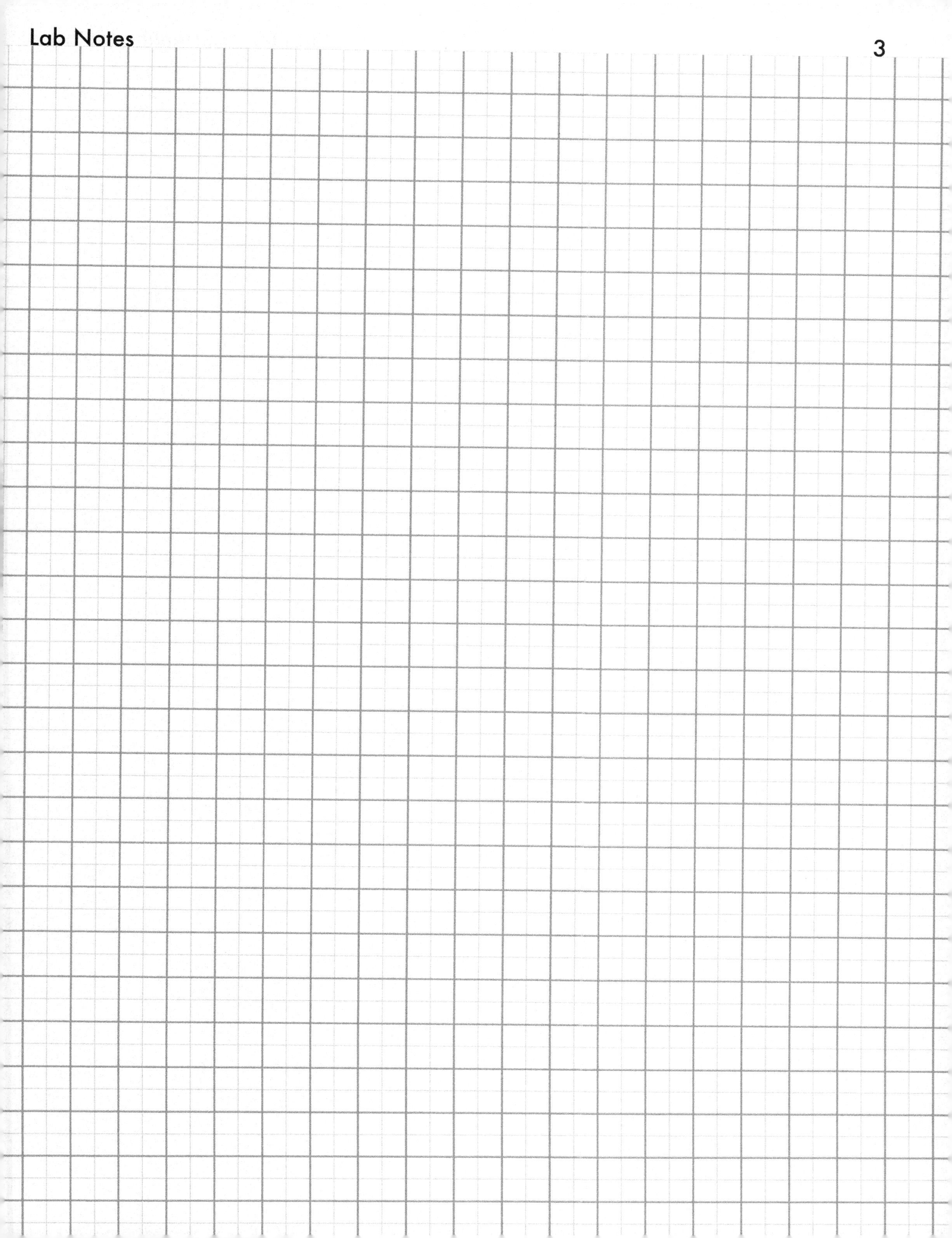

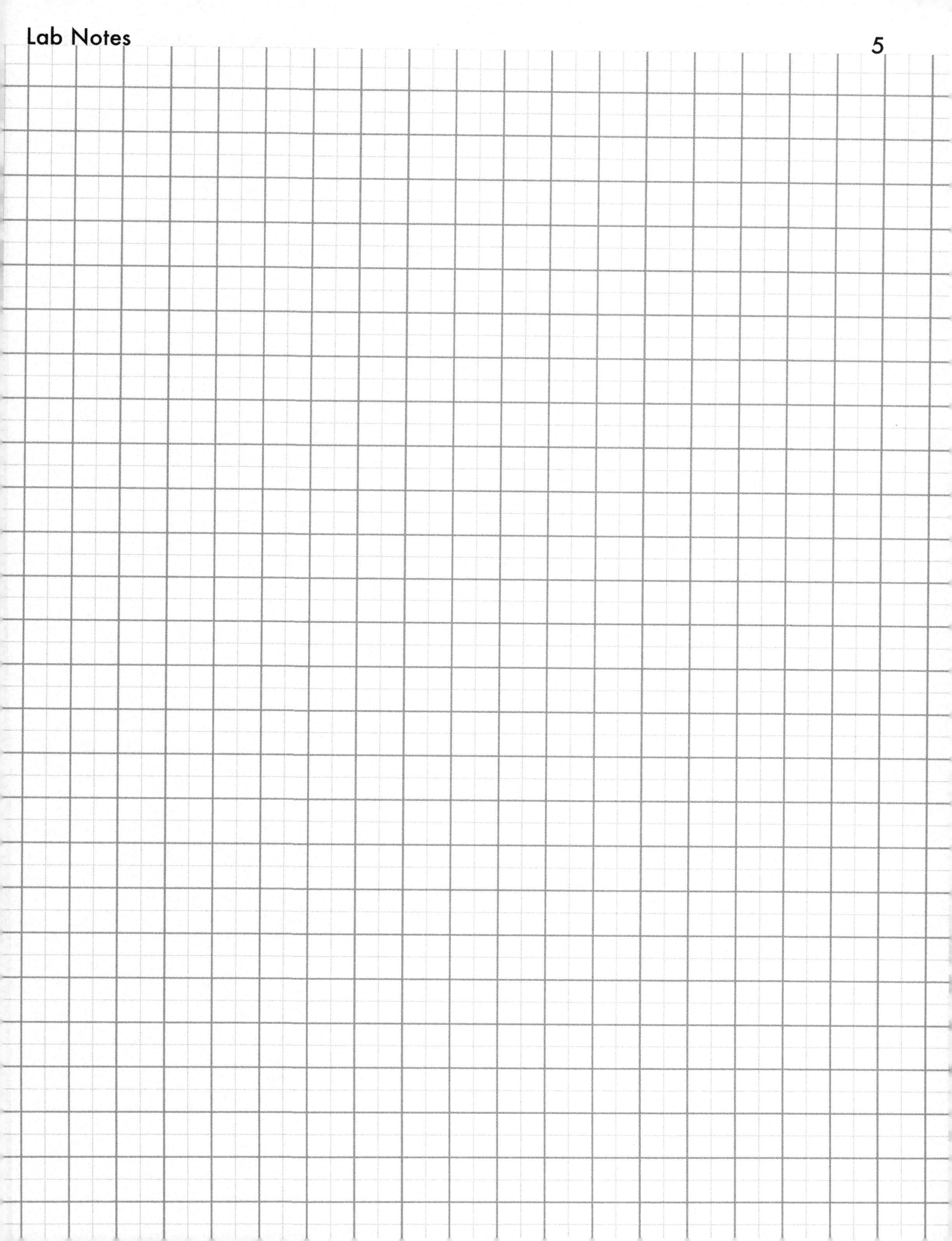

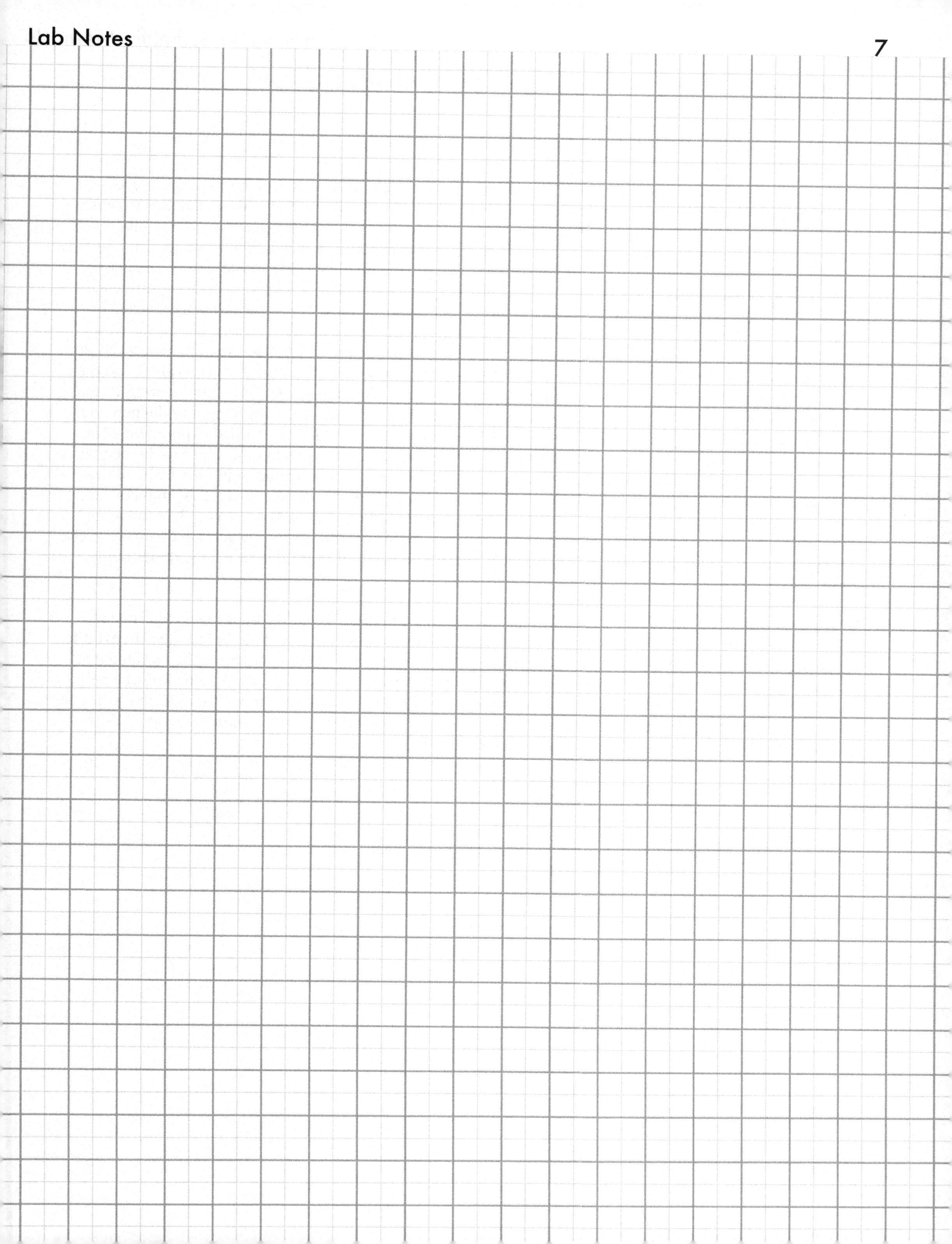

Reading: Experimental Design and Graphical Analysis of Data

A. Designing a controlled experiment

When scientists set up experiments they often attempt to determine how a given variable affects another variable. This requires the experiment to be designed in such a way that when the experimenter changes one variable, the effects of this change on a second variable can be measured. If any other variable that could affect the second variable is changed, the experimenter would have no way of knowing which variable was responsible for the results. For this reason, scientists always attempt to conduct **controlled experiments**. This is done by choosing only one variable to manipulate in an experiment, observing its effect on a second variable, and *holding all other variables in the experiment constant.*

Suppose you wanted to test how changing the mass of a pendulum affects the time it takes a pendulum to swing back and forth (also known as its period). You must keep all other variables constant. You must make sure the length of the pendulum string does not change. You must make sure that the distance that the pendulum is pulled back (also known as the amplitude) does not change. The length of the pendulum and the amplitude are variables that must be held constant in order to run a controlled experiment. The only thing that you would deliberately change would be the mass of the pendulum. This would then be considered the **independent variable**, because you will decide how much mass to put on the pendulum for each experimental trial. There are three possible outcomes to this experiment: 1. If the mass is increased, the period will increase. 2. If the mass is increased, the period will decrease. 3. If the mass is increased, the period will remain unchanged. Since you are testing the effect of changing the mass on the period, and since the period may depend on the value of the mass, the period is called the **dependent variable**.

In review, there are only two variables that area allowed to change in a well-designed experiment. The variable manipulated by the experimenter (mass in this example) is called the **independent variable.** The **dependent variable** (period in this case) is the one that responds to or depends on the variable that was manipulated. Any other variable which might affect the value of the dependent value must be held constant. We might call these variables **controlled variables.** When an experiment is conducted with one (and only one) independent variable and one (and only one) dependent variable while holding all other variables constant, it is a **controlled experiment**.

B. Characteristics of Good Data Recording

1. Raw data is recorded in ink. Data that you think is "bad" is not destroyed. It is noted but kept in case it is needed for future use.
2. The table for raw data is constructed prior to beginning data collection.
3. The table is laid out neatly using a straightedge.
4. The independent variable is recorded in the leftmost column (by convention).
5. The data table is given a descriptive title which makes it clear which experiment it represents.
6. Each column of the data table is labeled with the name of the variable it contains.
7. Below (or to the side of) each variable name is the name of the unit of measurement (or its symbol) in parentheses.
8. Data is recorded to an appropriate number of decimal places as determined by the precision of the measuring device or the measuring technique.
9. All columns in the table which are the result of a calculation are clearly explained and sample calculations are shown making it clear how each column in the table was determined.
10. The values held constant in the experiment are described and their values are recorded.

C. Graphing Data

Once the data is collected, it is necessary to determine the relationship between the two variables in the experiment. You will construct a graph (or sometimes a series of graphs) from your data in order to determine the relationship between the independent and dependent variables.

For each relationship that is being investigated in your experiment, you should prepare the appropriate graph. In general your graphs in physics are of a type known as scatter graphs. The graphs will be used to give you a conceptual understanding of the relation between the variables, and will usually also be used to help you formulate mathematical statement which describes that relationship. Graphs should include each of the elements described below:

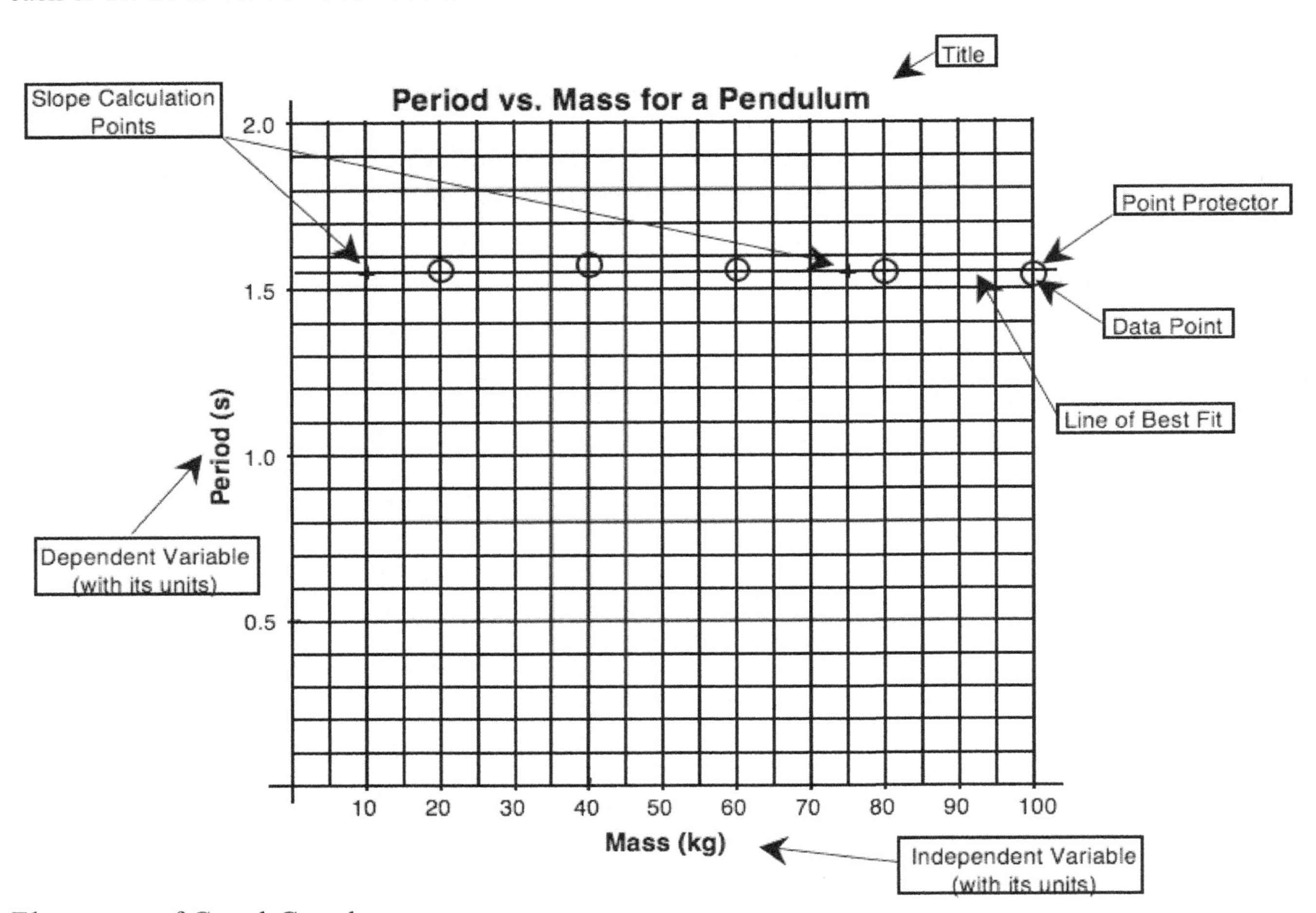

Elements of Good Graphs

- A **title** that describes the experiment. This title should be descriptive of the experiment and should indicate the relationship between the variables. It is conventional to title graphs with DEPENDENT VARIABLE vs. INDEPENDENT VARIABLE. For example, if the experiment was designed to show how changing the mass of a pendulum affects its period, the mass of the pendulum is the independent variable and the period is the dependent variable. A good title might therefore be PERIOD vs. MASS FOR A PENDULUM.
- The graph should **fill the space** allotted for the graph. If you have reserved a whole sheet of graph paper for the graph then it should be as large as the paper and proper scaling techniques permit.
- The graph must be properly **scaled.** The scale for each axis of the graph should always begin at zero. The scale chosen on the axis must be uniform and linear. This means that each square on a given axis must represent the same amount. Obviously each axis for a graph will be scaled independently from the other since they are representing different variables. A given axis must, however, be scaled consistently.

- Each axis should be **labeled** with the **quantity** being measured and the **units** of measurement. Generally, the independent variable is plotted on the horizontal (or x) axis and the dependent variable is plotted on the vertical (or y) axis.
- Each data point should be plotted in the proper position. You should plot a point as a small dot at the position of the of the data point and you should circle the data point so that it will not be obscured by your line of best fit. These circles are called **point protectors**.
- A **line of best fit**. This line should show the overall tendency (or trend) of your data. If the trend is linear, you should draw a straight line which shows that trend using a straight edge. If the trend is a curve, you should sketch a curve which is your best guess as to the tendency of the data. This line (whether straight or curved) does not have to go through all of the data points and it may, in some cases, not go through any of them.
- Do not, under any circumstances, connect successive data points with a series of straight lines, dot to dot. This makes it difficult to see the overall trend of the data that you are trying to represent.
- If you are plotting the graph by hand, you will choose two points for all linear graphs from which to calculate the slope of the line of best fit. These points should not be data points unless a data point happens to fall perfectly on the line of best fit. Pick two points which are directly on your line of best fit and which are easy to read from the graph. Mark the points you have chosen with a +.
- Do not do other work in the space of your graph such as the slope calculation or other parts of the mathematical analysis.
- If your graph does not yield a straight line, you will be expected to manipulate one (or more) of the axes of your graph, replot the manipulated data, and continue doing this until a straight line results. We will address the details of linearization later in the course.

D. Graphical Analysis and Linear Mathematical Models

When the data you collect yields a linear graph, you will proceed to determine the mathematical equation that describes the relationship between the variables using the slope intercept form of the equation of a line. Consider the following experiment in which the experimenter tests the effect of adding various masses to a spring on the amount that the spring stretches. The development of the mathematical model is shown on the next page.

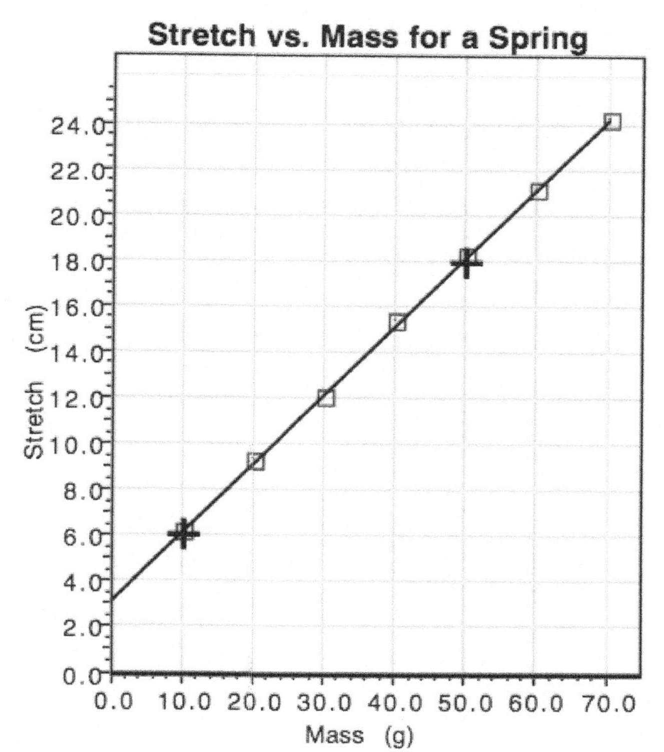

Begin with the equation for a line:

$y = mx + b$

Determine the slope and y-intercept from graph slope (m) = 0.30 (cm/g); y-intercept = 3.2 cm

Substitute constants with units from experiment $y = [0.30\ (cm/g)]x + 3.2\ cm$

Substitute variables from experiment

Stretch = S; mass = m

$S = [0.30\ (cm/g)]m + 3.2\ cm$

Final mathematical model:

$S = [0.30\ (cm/g)]m + 3.2\ cm$

The result of this experiment, then, is a mathematical equation which models the behavior of the spring:

$$\textbf{Stretch} = \mathbf{0.30\ cm/g \cdot mass + 3.2\ cm}$$

With this **mathematical model** we know many characteristics of the spring and can predict its behavior without actually further testing the spring. In models of this type, there is physical significance associated with each value in the equation. For instance, the slope of this graph, 0.30 cm/g, tells us that the spring will stretch 0.30 centimeters for each gram of mass that is added to it. We might call this slope the "wimpiness" of the spring, since if the slope is high it means that the spring stretches a lot when a relatively small mass is placed on it and a low value for the slope means that it takes a lot of mass to get a little stretch.

The y-intercept of 3.2 cm tells us that the spring was already stretched 3.2 cm when the experimenter started adding mass to the spring. With this mathematical model, we can determine the stretch of the spring for any value of mass by simply substituting the mass value into the equation. How far would the spring be stretched if 57.2 g of mass were added to the spring? Mathematical models are powerful tools in the study of science and we will use those that you develop experimentally as the basis of many of our studies in physics.

When you are evaluating real data, you will need to decide whether or not the graph should go through the origin. Given the limitations of the experimental process, real data will rarely yield a line that goes perfectly through the origin. In the example above, the computer calculated a y-intercept of 0.01 cm ± 0.09 cm. Since the uncertainty (±0.09 cm) in determining the y-intercept exceeds the value of the y-intercept (0.01 cm) it is obviously reasonable to call the y-intercept zero. Other cases may not be so clear cut. The first rule of order when trying to determine whether or not a direct linear relationship is indeed a direct proportion is to ask yourself what would happen to the dependent variable if the independent variable were zero. In many cases you can reason from the physical situation being investigated whether or not the graph should logically go through the origin. Sometimes, however, it might not be so obvious. In these cases we will assume that it has some physical significance and will go about trying to determine that significance.

Graphical Methods - Summary

A graph is one of the most effective representations of the relationship between two variables. The independent variable (one controlled by the experimenter) is usually placed on the x-axis. The dependent variable (one that responds to changes in the independent variable) is usually placed on the y-axis. It is important for you to be able interpret a graphical relationship and express it in a written statement and by means of an algebraic expression.

Graph shape	Written relationship	Modification required to linearize graph	Algebraic representation
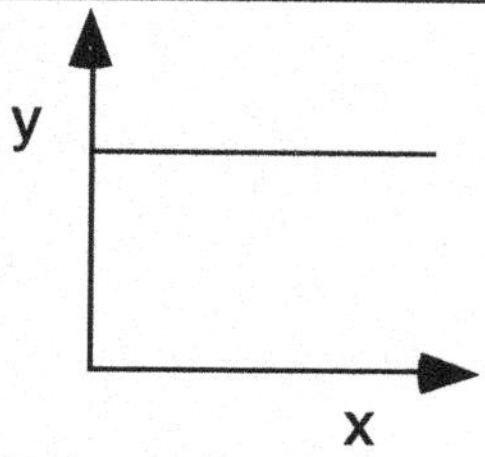	As x increases, y remains the same. There is no relationship between the variables.	None	$y = b$, or y is constant
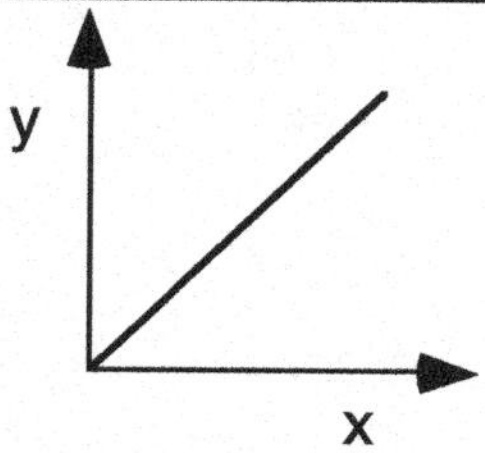	As x increases, y increases proportionally. Y is directly proportional to x.	None	$y = mx + b$
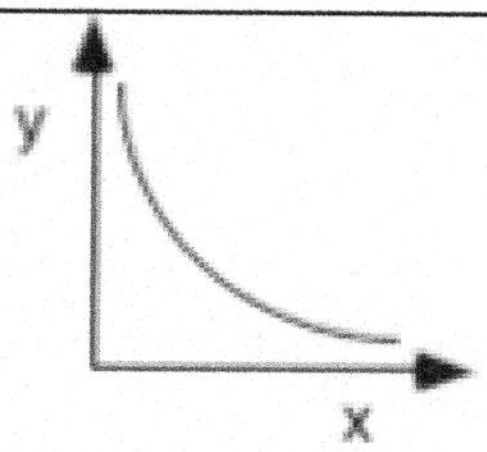	As x increases, y decreases. Y is inversely proportional to x.	Graph y vs $\frac{1}{x}$, or y vs x^{-1}	$y = m\left(\frac{1}{x}\right) + b$
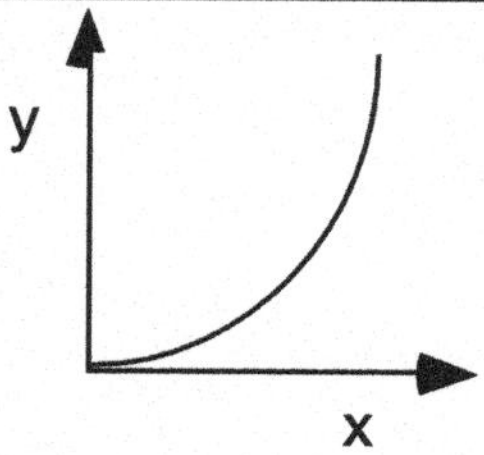	Y is proportional to the square of x.	Graph y vs x^2	$y = mx^2 + b$
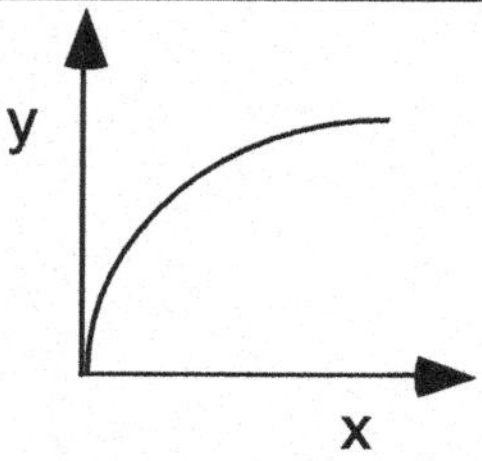	The square of y is proportional to x.	Graph y^2 vs x	$y^2 = mx + b$

When you state the relationship, tell how y depends on x (e.g., as x increases, y …).

Worksheet 1: Graphing Practice

For each data set below, determine the mathematical expression. To do this, first graph the original data. Assume the 1st column in each set of values to be the **independent** variable and the 2nd column the **dependent** variable. Taking clues from the shape of the first graph, modify the data so that the modified data will plot as a straight line. Using the slope and y-intercept of the straight-line graph, write an appropriate mathematical expression for the relationship between the variables. Be sure to include units!

Data set 1		Data set 2	
Volume (m^3)	**Pressure (Pascals)**	**time (s)**	**position (m)**
0.1	40.0	0.10	0.03
0.5	8.0	0.20	0.12
1.0	4.0	1.0	3.0
4.0	1.0	2.0	12.0
5.0	.80	3.0	27.0
8.0	.50	4.0	48.0
10.0	.40	5.0	75.0
Sketch of original graph:		Sketch of original graph:	
Sketch of test plot: (Print your graph and test plot, too.)		Sketch of test plot: (Print your graph and test plot, too.)	
Mathematical expression #1:		Mathematical expression #2:	

Data set 3		Data set 4	
mass (kg)	**velocity (m/s)**	**time (s)**	**velocity (m/s)**
1.0	22.4	0.0	0.0
2.0	19.6	2.0	10.5
3.0	16.5	4.0	14.0
4.0	13.3	6.0	18.0
5.0	10.4	8.0	21.0
6.0	7.7	10.0	23.5
7.0	4.6	12.0	26.0
8.0	1.1	14.0	28.0
Sketch of original graph:		Sketch of original graph:	
Sketch of test plot: (Print your graph and test plot, too.)		Sketch of test plot: (Print your graph and test plot, too.)	
Mathematical expression #3:		Mathematical expression #4:	

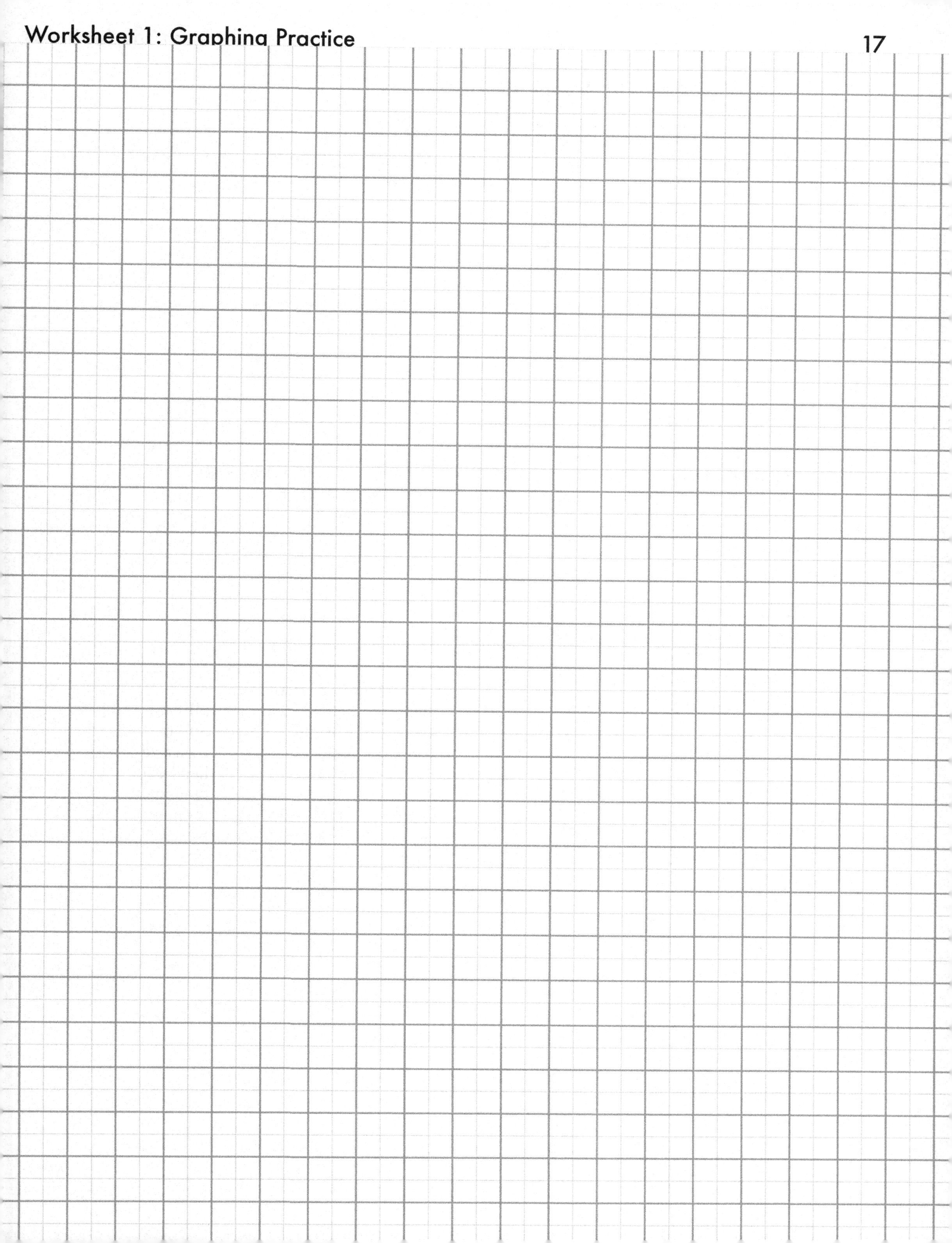

Worksheet 2: Proportional Reasoning

Some problems adapted from Gibbs' Qualitative Problems for Introductory Physics

1. 100 cm are equivalent to 1 m. How many cm are equivalent to 3 m? Briefly explain how you could convert any number of meters into a number of centimeters.

2. Forty-five cm are equivalent to how many m? Briefly explain how you could convert any number of cm into a number of m.

3. One mole of water is equivalent to 18 grams of water. A glass of water has a mass of 200 g. How many moles of water is this? Briefly explain your reasoning.

Use the metric prefixes table to answer the following questions:

4. The radius of the earth is 6378 km. What is the diameter of the earth in meters?

Metric prefixes:

giga	= 1 000 000 000	billion
mega	= 1 000 000	million
kilo	= 1 000	thousand
centi	= 1 / 100	hundredth
milli	= 1 / 1000	thousandth
micro	= 1 / 1 000 000	millionth
nano	= 1 / 1 000 000 000	billionth

5. In an experiment, you find the mass of a cart to be 250 grams. What is the mass of the cart in kilograms?

6. How many megabytes of data can a 4.7 gigabyte DVD store?

7. A mile is farther than a kilometer. Consider a fixed distance, like the diameter of the moon. Would the number expressing this distance be larger in miles or in kilometers? Explain.

8. One US dollar = 0.73 Euros (as of 8-07.) Which is worth more, one dollar or one Euro? How many dollars is one Euro?

9. In 2012, Germans paid 1.65 Euros per liter of gasoline. At the same time, American prices were $3.90 per gallon.
   a. How much would one gallon of European gas have cost in dollars?
   b. How much would one liter of American gasoline have cost in Euros?
   (One US dollar = 0.76 Euros, 1 gallon = 3.78 liters)

10. A mile is equivalent to 1.6 km. When you are driving at 60 miles per hour, what is your speed in meters per second? Clearly show how you used proportions to arrive at a solution.

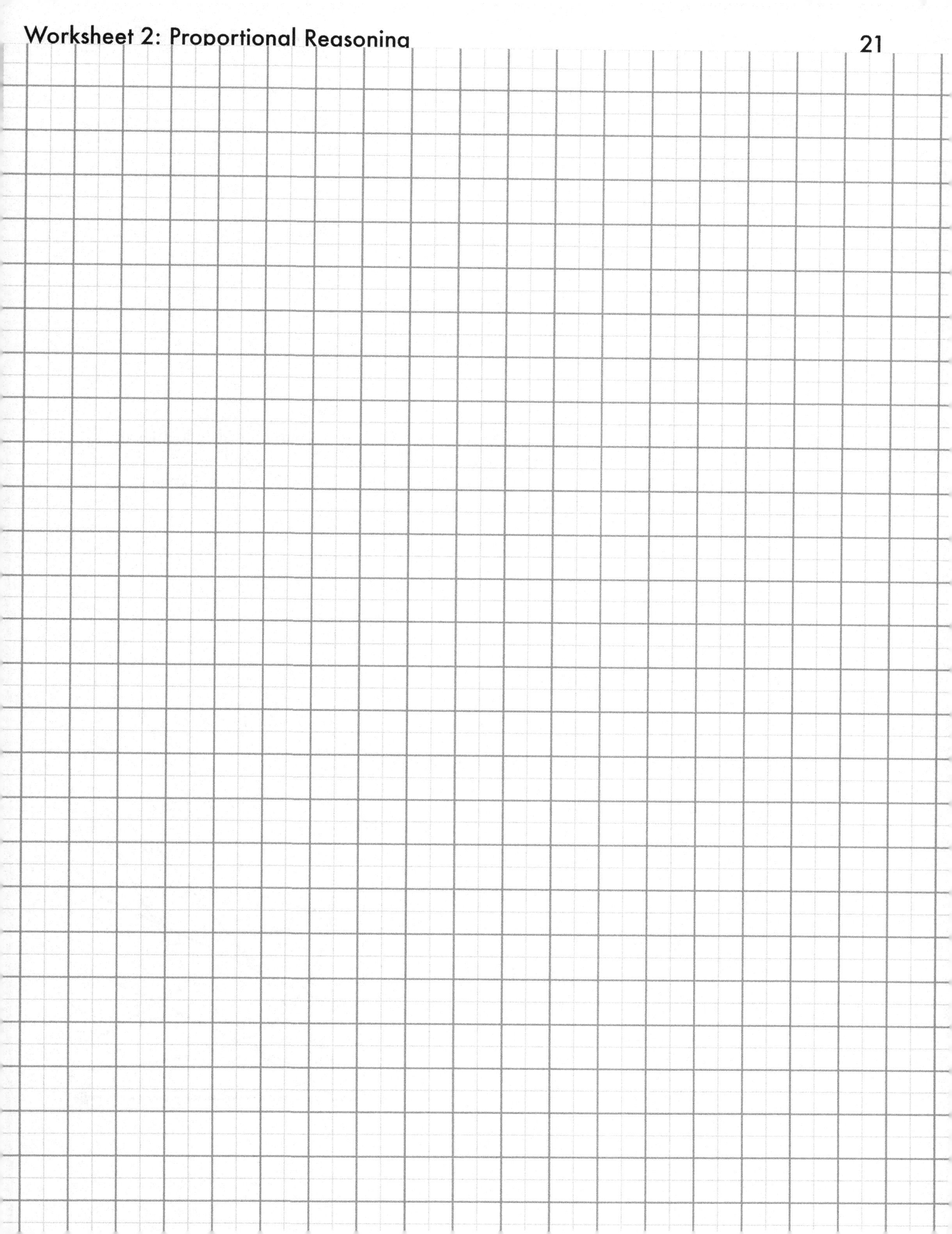

11. For each of the following mathematical relations, state what happens to the value of y when the following changes are made. (k is a constant)

a. $y = kx$, x is tripled.

b. $y = k/x$, x is halved.

c. $y = k/x^2$, x is doubled

d. $y = kx^2$, x is tripled.

12. When one variable is *directly proportional* to another, doubling one variable also doubles the other. If y and x are the variables and a and b are constants, circle the following relationships that are direct proportions. For those that are not direct proportions, explain what kind of proportion does exist between x and y.

a. $y = 3x$
b. $y = ax + b$
c. $y = x$
d. $y = ax^2$
e. $y = a/x$
f. $y = ax$
g. $y = 1/x$
h. $y = a/x^2$

13. The diagram shows a number of relationships between x and y.

a. Which relationships are linear? Explain.

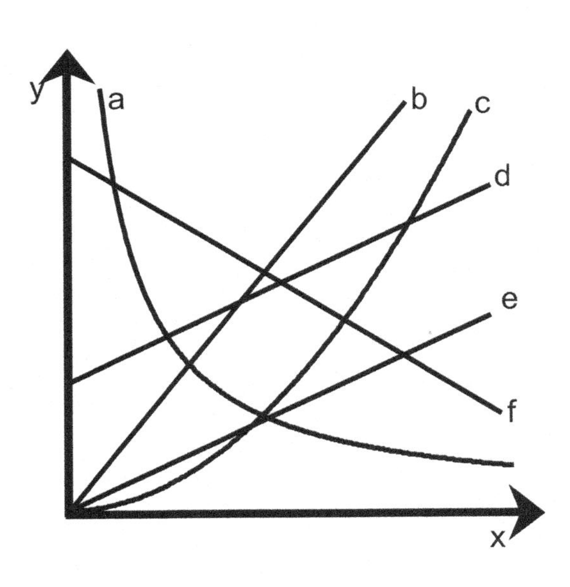

b. Which relationships are direct proportions? Explain.

c. Which relationships are inverse proportions? Explain.

Worksheet 3: Graphical Analysis

1. A friend prepares to place an online order for CD's.

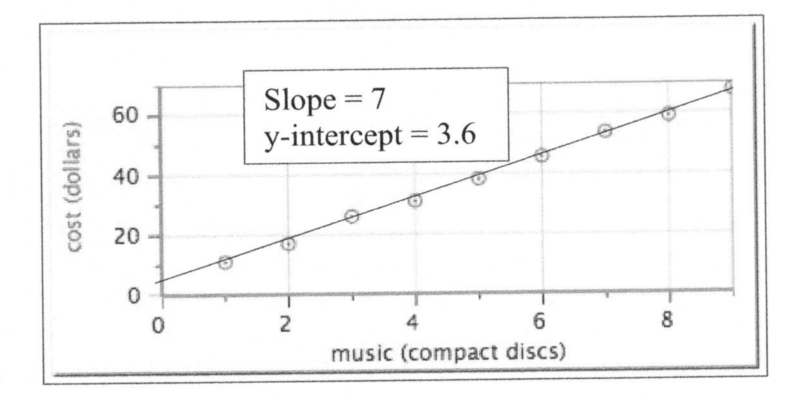

   a. What are the units for the slope of this graph?

   b. What does the slope of the graph tell you in this situation?

   c. Write an equation that describes the graph.

   d. Provide an interpretation for what the y-intercept could mean in this situation.

2. The following times were measured for spheres of different masses to be pushed a distance of 1.5 meters by a stream:

Mass (kg)	Time (s)
5	10.2
10	17.3
15	23.8
20	31.0

   a. Graph the data by hand on the grid provided and write a mathematical model for the graph that describes the data.

   b. Write a clear sentence that describes the relationship between mass and time.

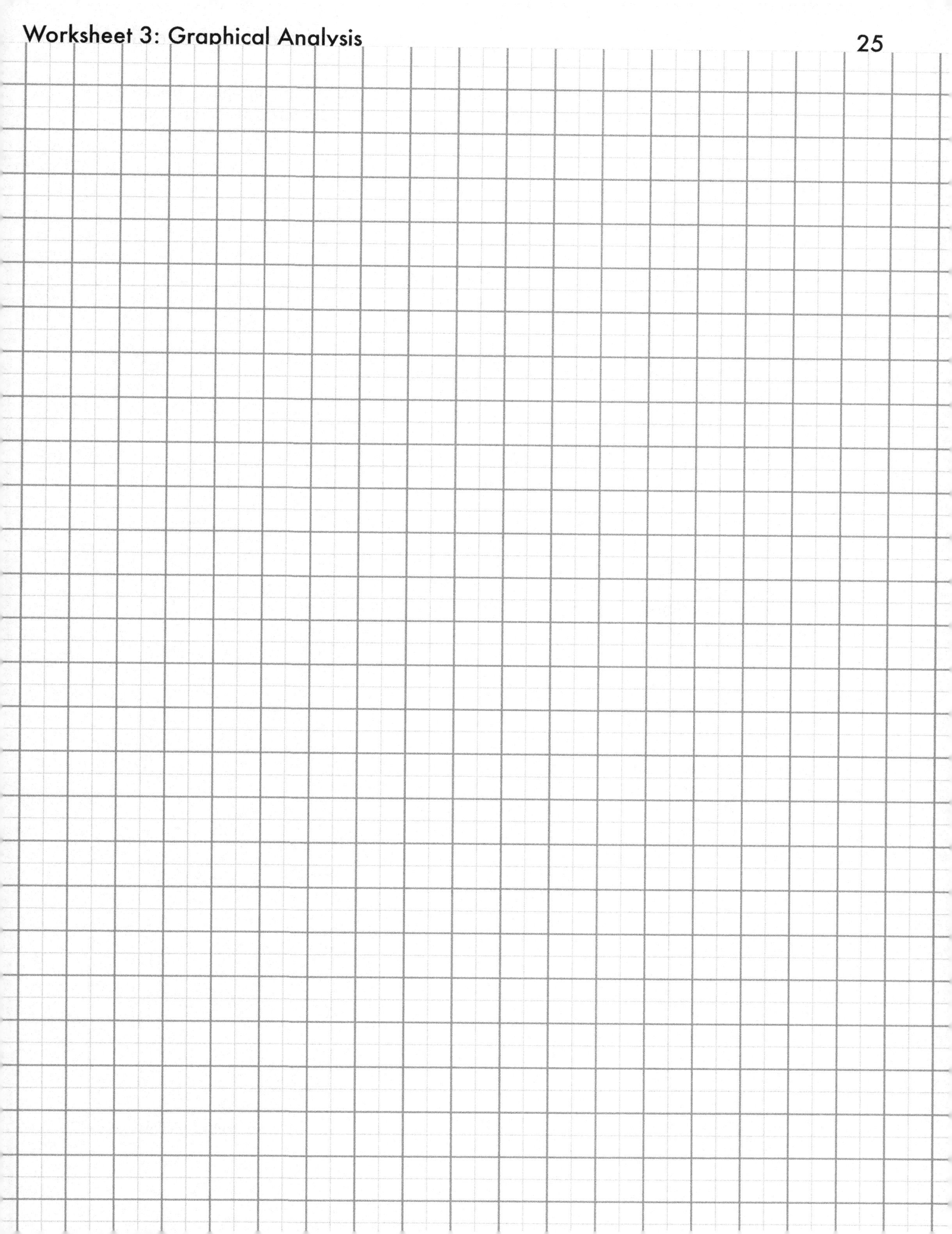

3. A student performed an experiment with a metal sphere. The student shot the sphere from a slingshot and measured its maximum height. The sphere was shot six times at six different angles above the horizon.

   a. What is the relationship being studied?

   b. What is the independent variable in this experiment?

   c. What is the dependent variable in this experiment?

   d. What variables must be held constant throughout this experiment?

4. a. What type of relationship does this graph suggest?

   b. What variables would you plot to linearize the data?

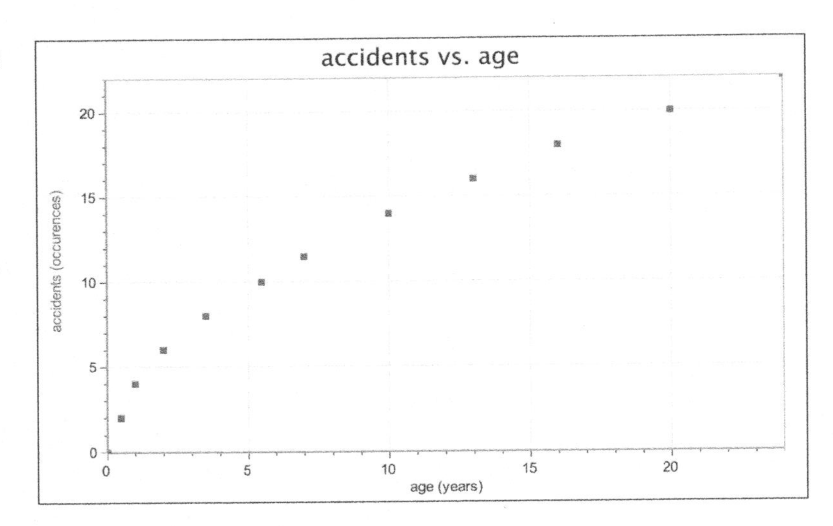

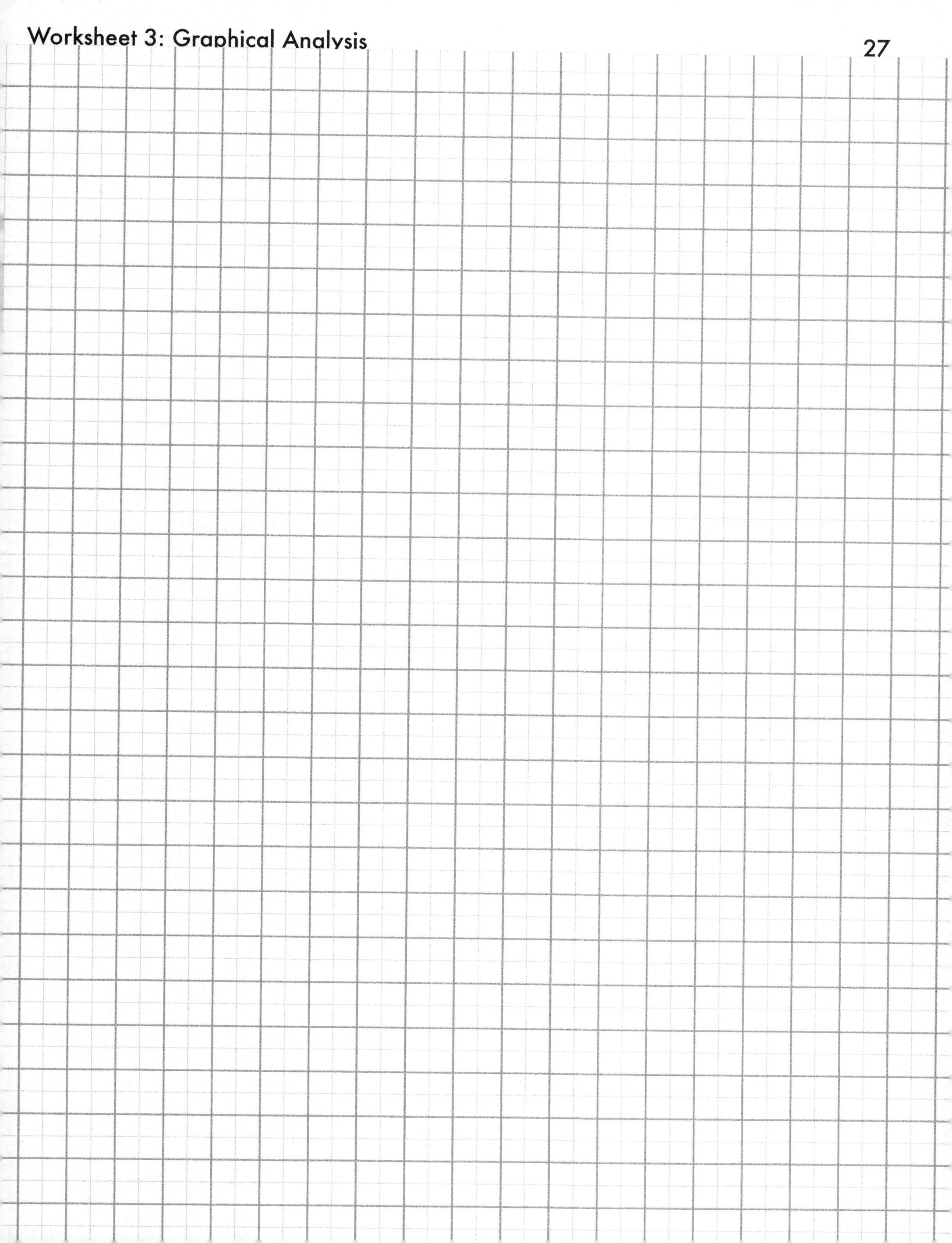

5. Consider the graph at right.

a. Write a mathematical expression that describes the relationship.

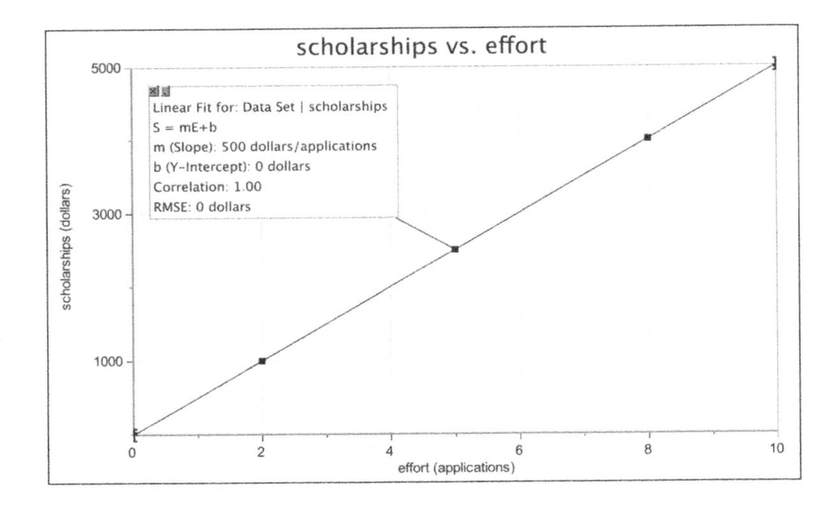

b. Provide an interpretation for the y-intercept.

c. Using the equation, predict how many applications would be needed to earn $8000.

6. For each of the following graphs:

- Describe how you would linearize the graph.
- Assuming a linear test plot results, write the equation that would describe the straight line produced.

a.

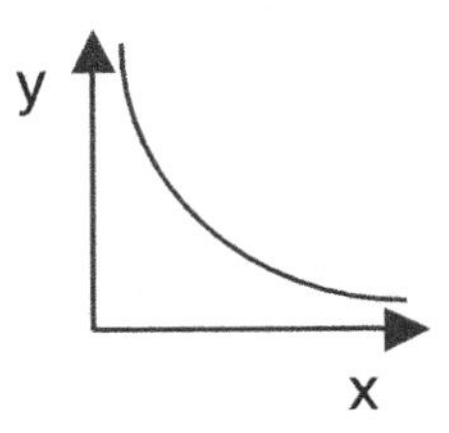

b.

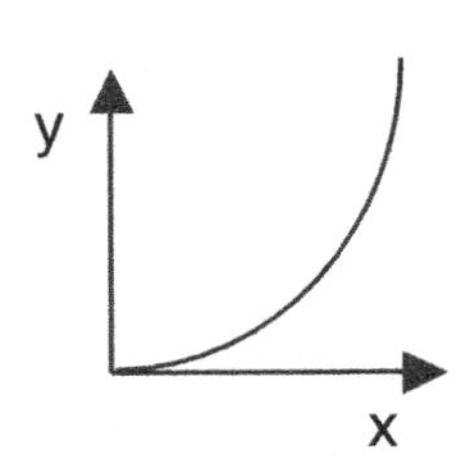

c.

y

x

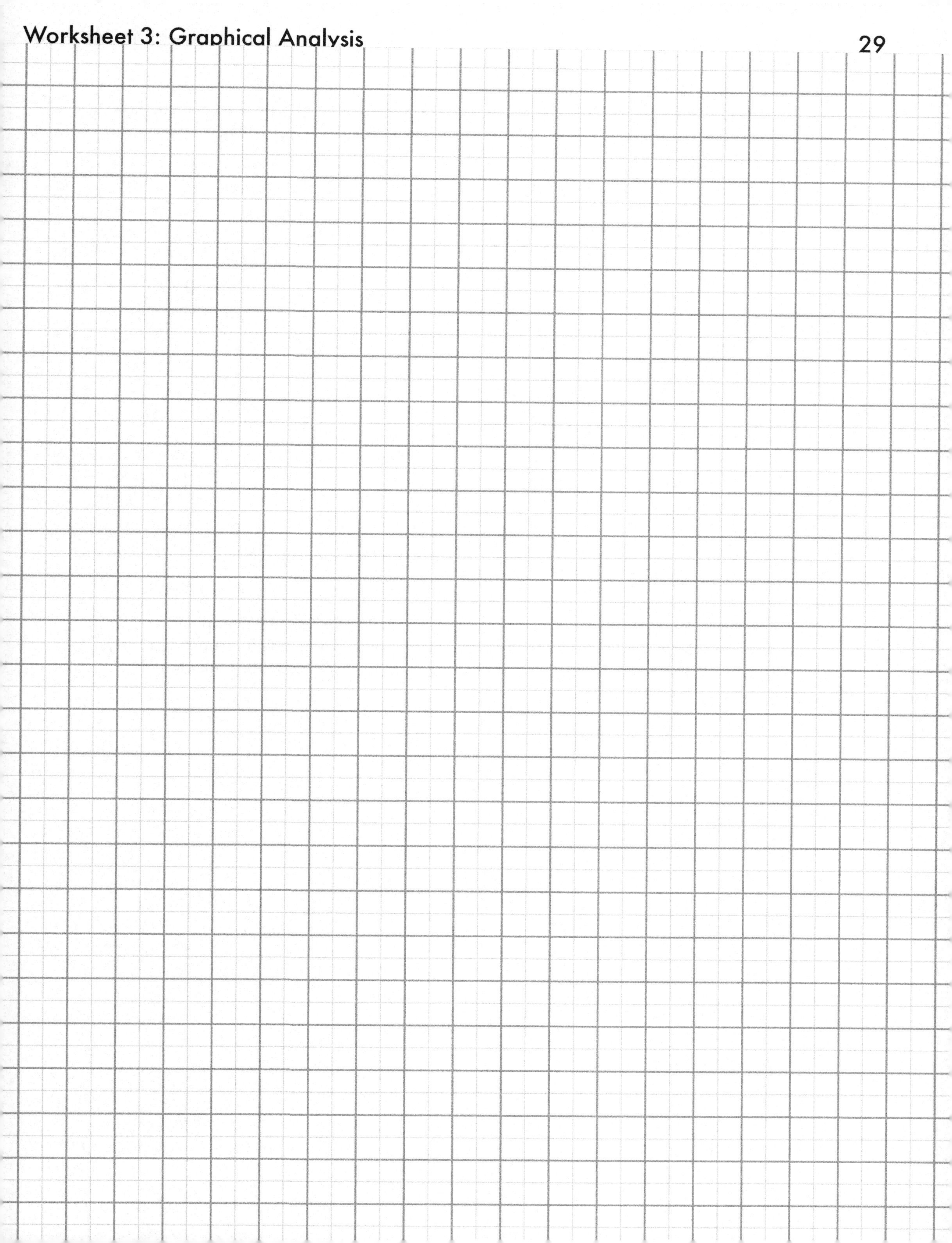

7. The graph below compares the amount of time it takes a planet to orbit the sun (in earth days) versus the distance the planet is from the sun, measured in Astronomical Units. (1 AU = earth to sun separation.)

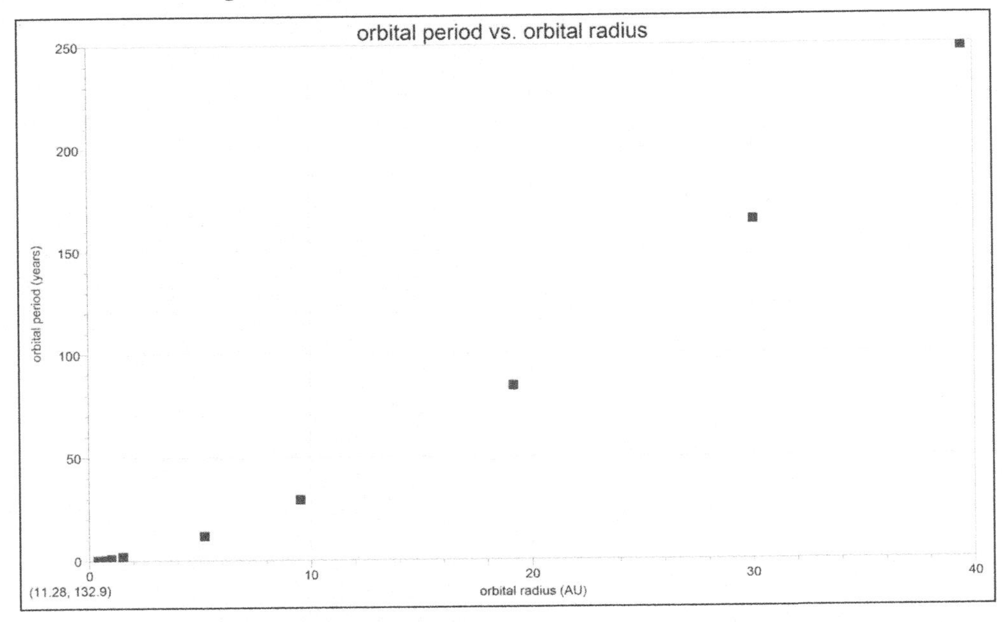

a. What test plot would you try first in order to linearize the relationship below?

b. In this case it turns out that several test plots need to be made before the graph is linearized. (Johannes Kepler was the first person to work out this relationship in the early 1600's.) Write the equation for the graph below. Does the same equation apply to the graph above? Why?

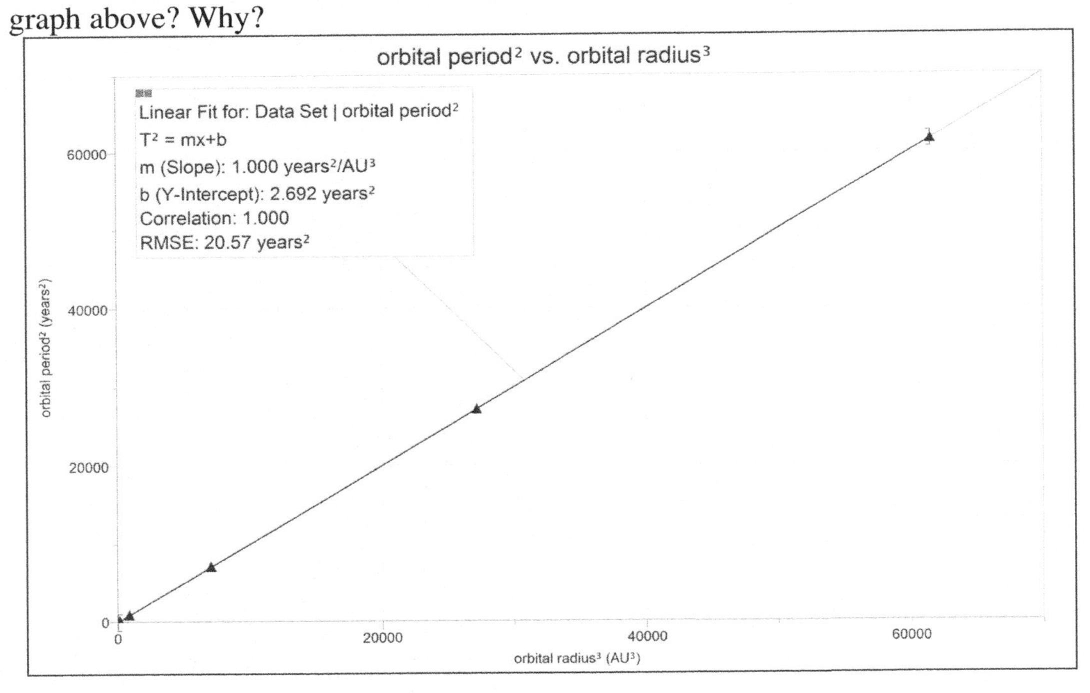

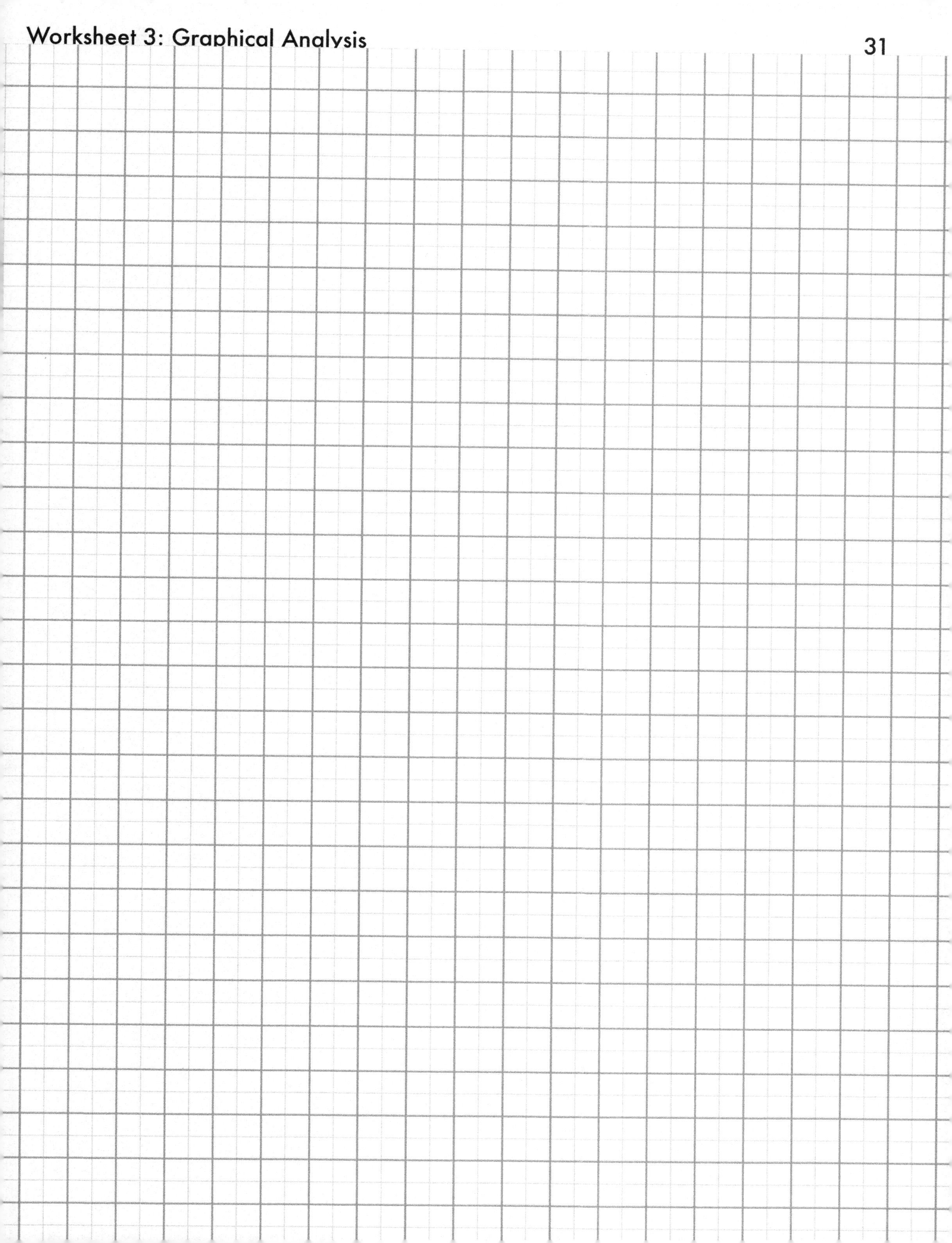

Model Summary

This is a place to summarize the big ideas in this chapter.

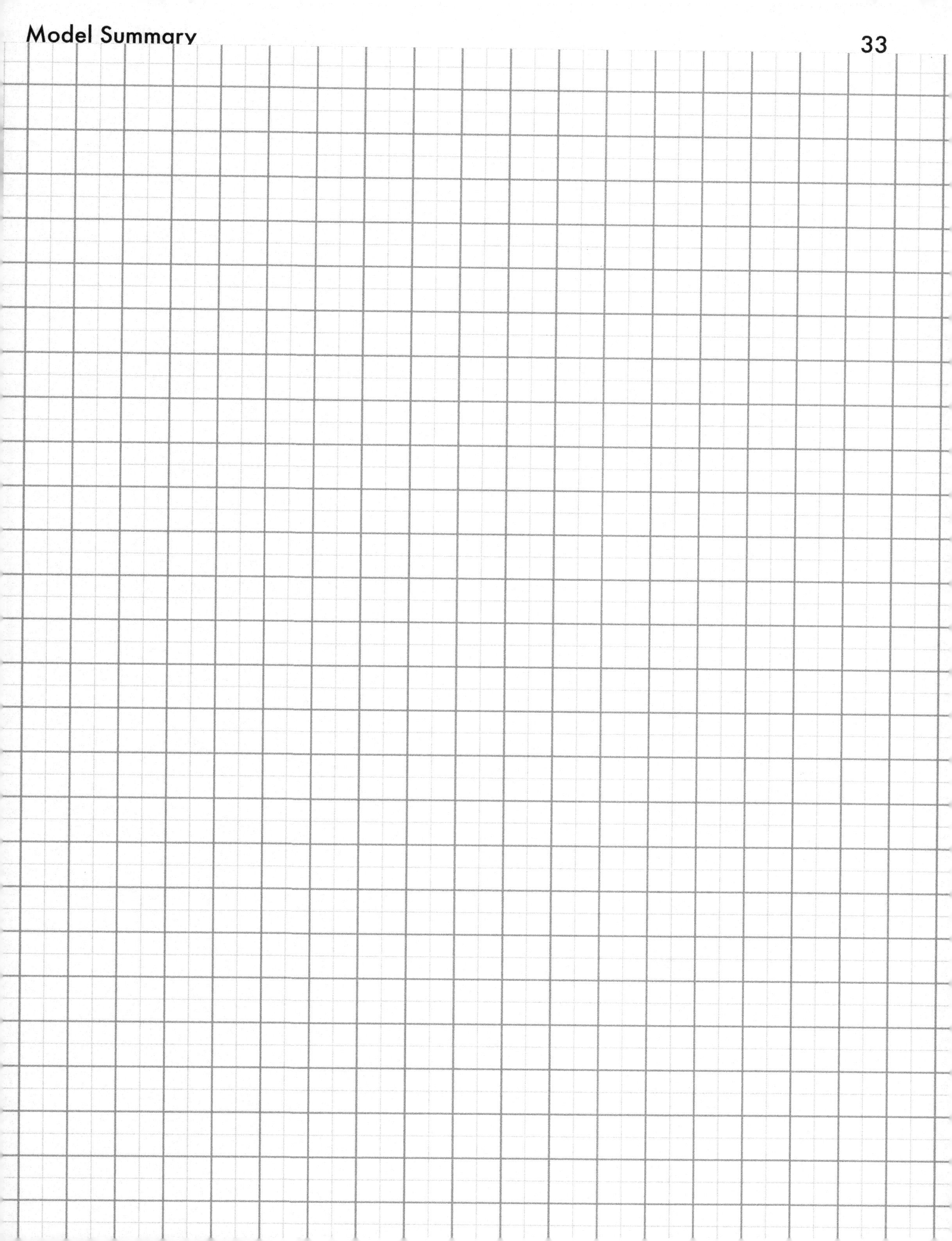

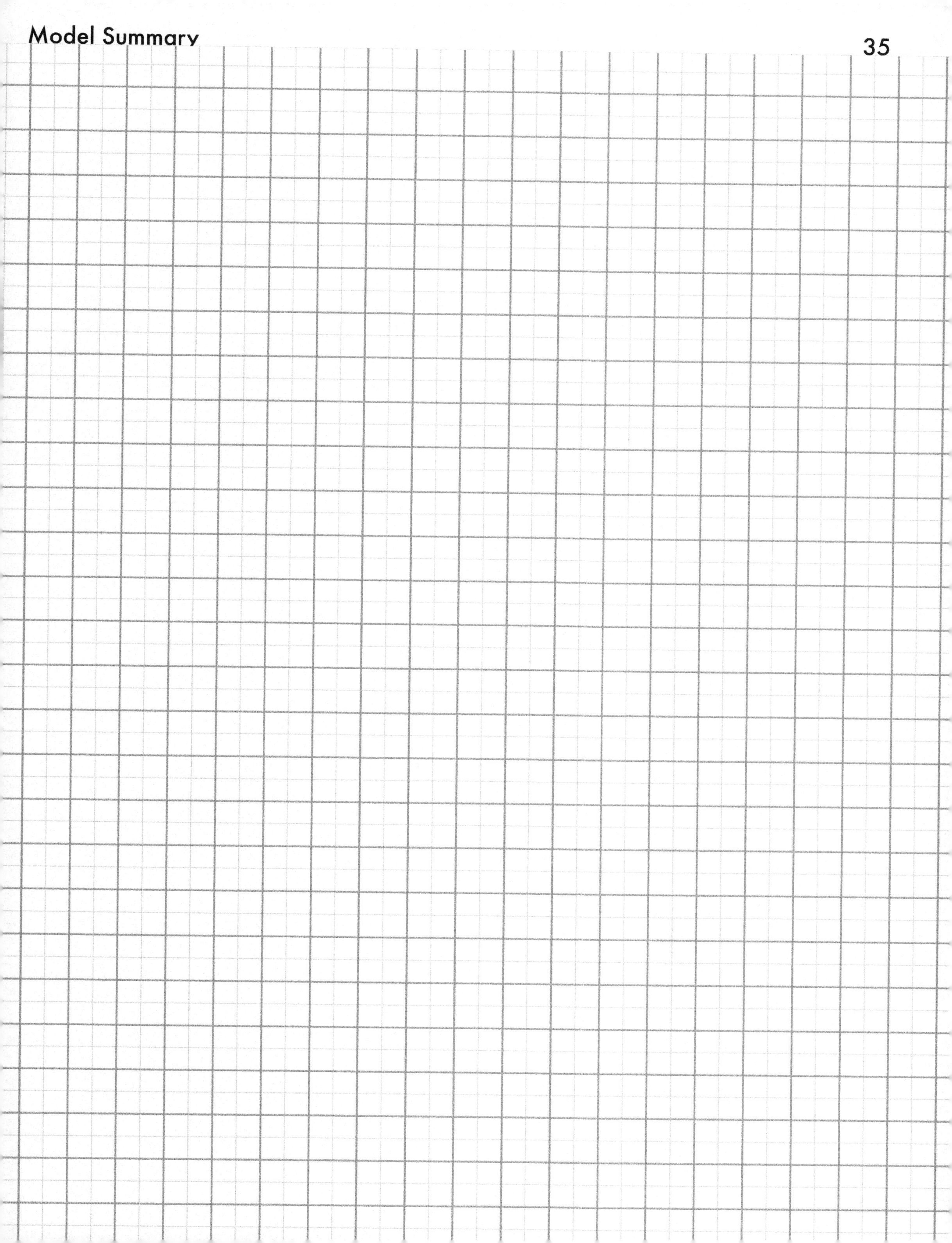

Chapter 2: Constant Velocity Particle Model

Chapter Sections

chapter 2 online help

Lab Notes

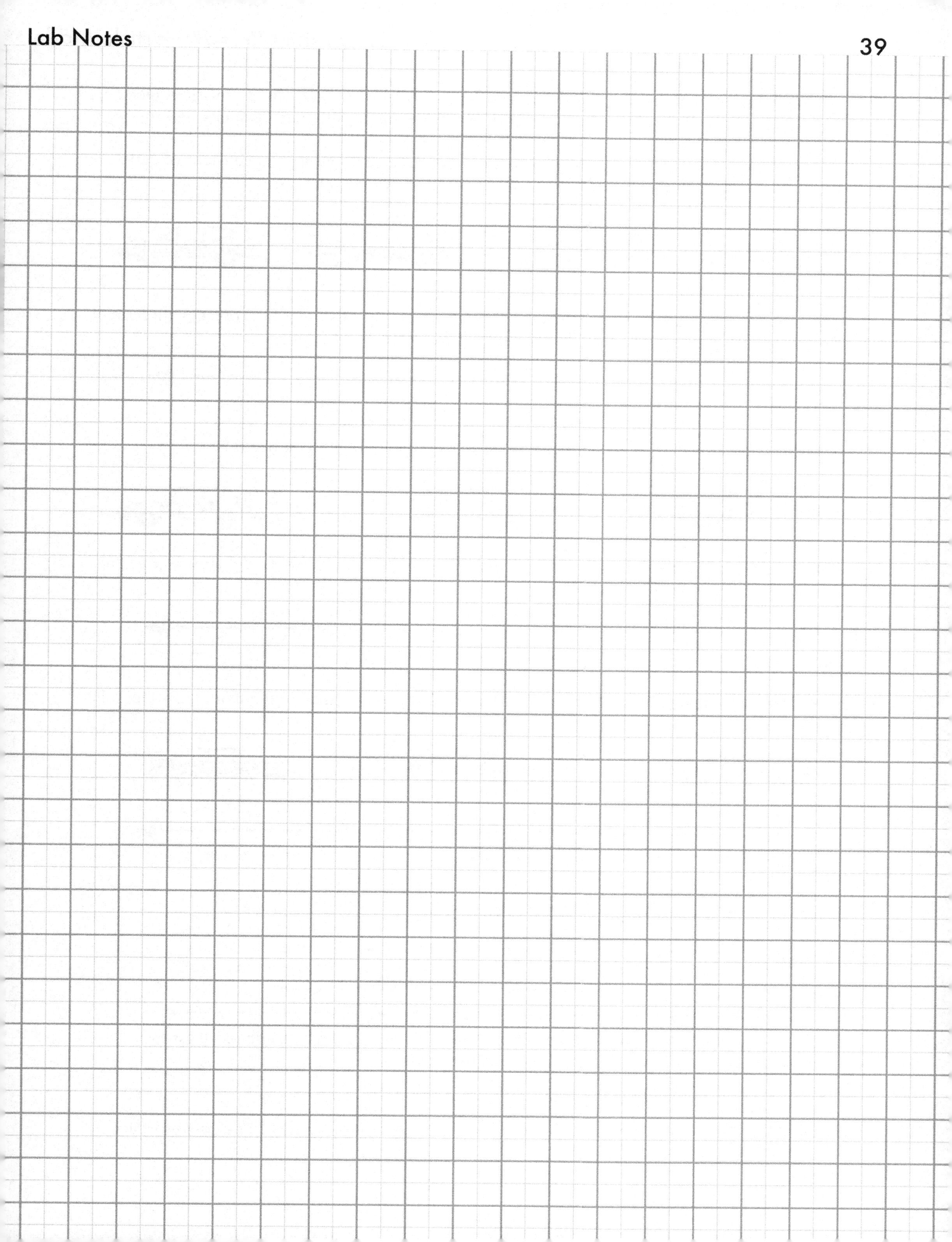

Reading: Motion Maps

A motion map represents the position, velocity, and acceleration of an object at various clock readings. (At this stage of the class, you will be representing position and velocity only.)

Suppose that you took a stroboscopic picture of a car moving to the right at constant velocity where each image revealed the position of the car at one-second intervals.

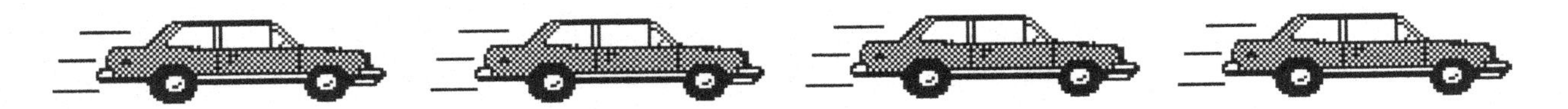

This is the motion map that represents the car. We model the position of the object with a small point. At each position, the object's velocity is represented by a vector.

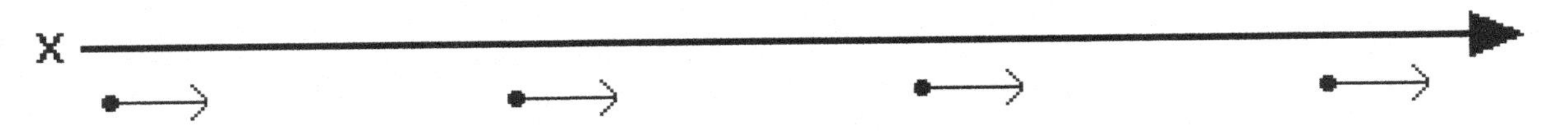

If the car were traveling at greater velocity, the strobe photo might look like this:

The corresponding motion map has the points spaced farther apart, and the velocity vectors are longer, implying that the car is moving faster.

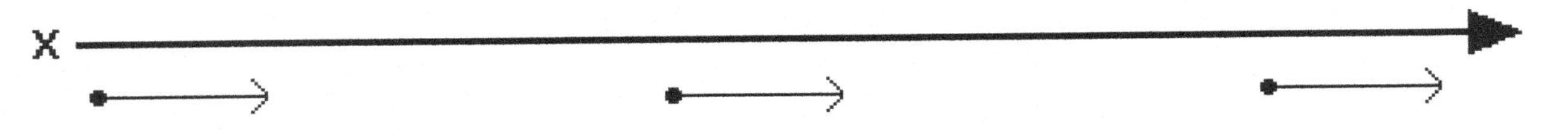

If the car were moving to the left at constant velocity, the photo and motion map might look like this:

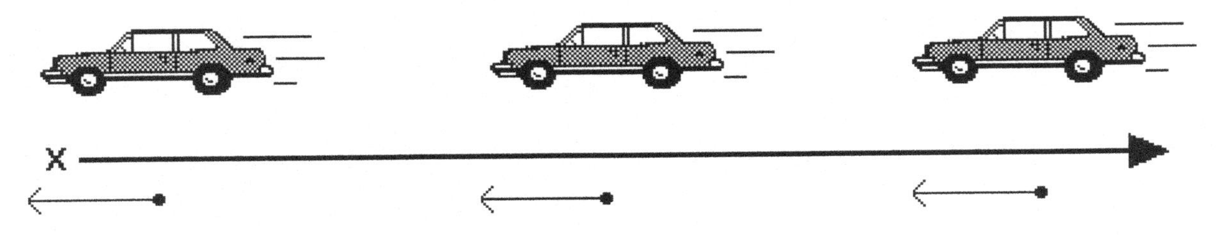

More complicated motion can be represented as well.

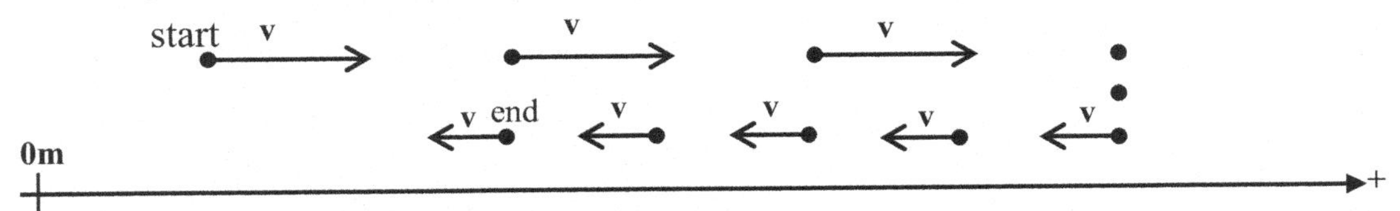

Here, an object moves to the right at constant velocity, stops and remains in place for two seconds, then moves to the left at a slower constant velocity.

Reading: Motion Maps

Consider the interpretation of the motion map below. At time t = 0, cyclist A starts moving to the right at constant velocity, at some position to the right of the origin.

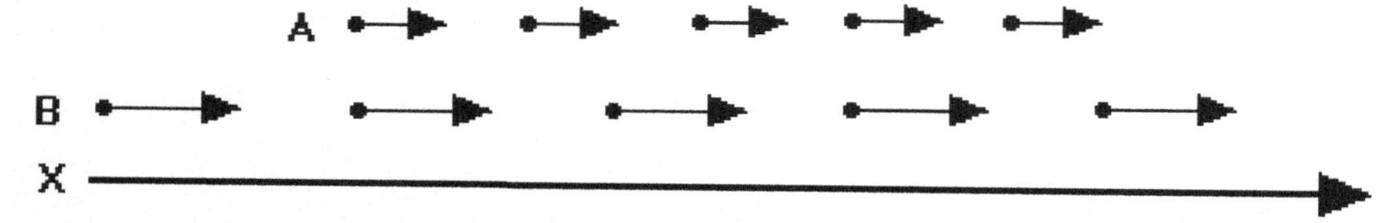

Cyclist B starts at the origin and travels to the right at a constant, though greater velocity. At t = 3 s, B overtakes A (i.e., both have the same position, but B is moving faster).

A graphical representation of the behavior of cyclists A and B would like this:

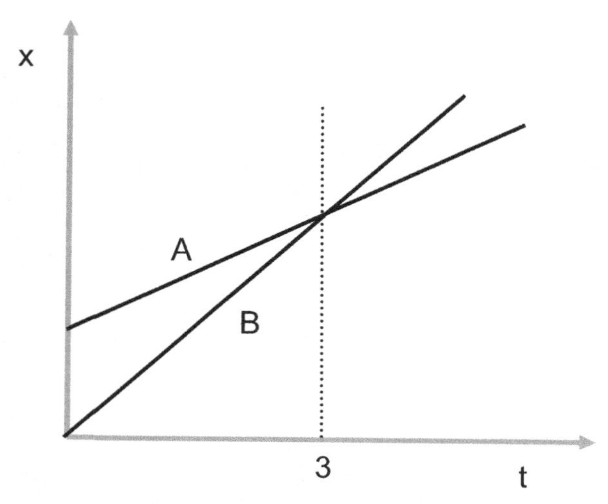

You could also represent the behavior algebraically as follows:

$x = v_A t + x_0$, for A
$x = v_B t$, for B

where $v_B > v_A$

Throughout this semester, you will be representing the behavior of objects in motion in multiple ways: diagrammatically (motion maps), graphically and algebraically.

Hints on drawing your own motion maps:

1. Draw dots indicating the position of the object at equal time intervals, i.e. each second.
2. Attach arrows to the dots indicating the direction of motion. Make the arrow length half of the space between the dots to make your motion map easy to read.
3. When an object is stopped for several time intervals, draw multiple dots at the same position.
4. Make sure your sequence of arrows has a logical flow so that the motion is clearly communicated.

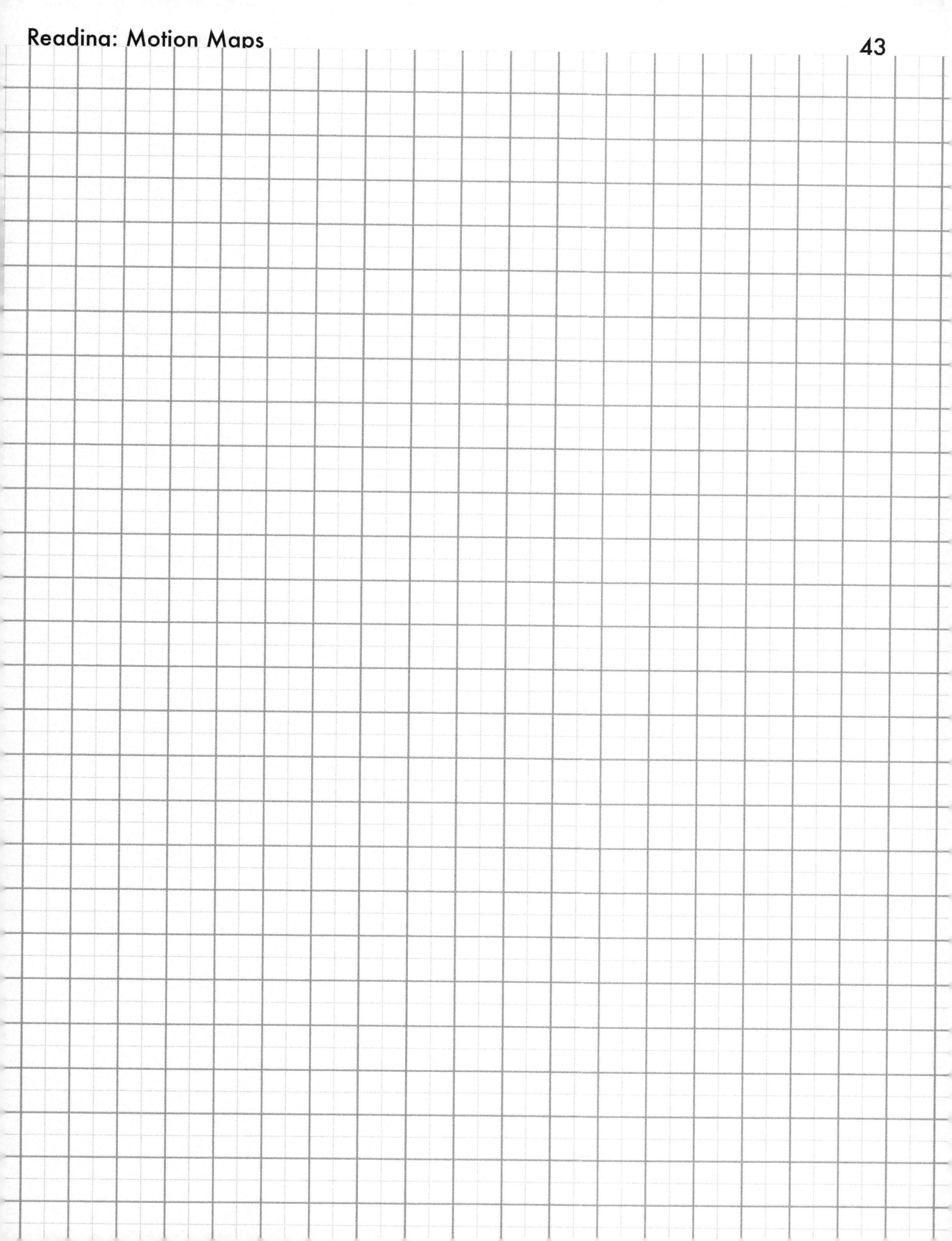

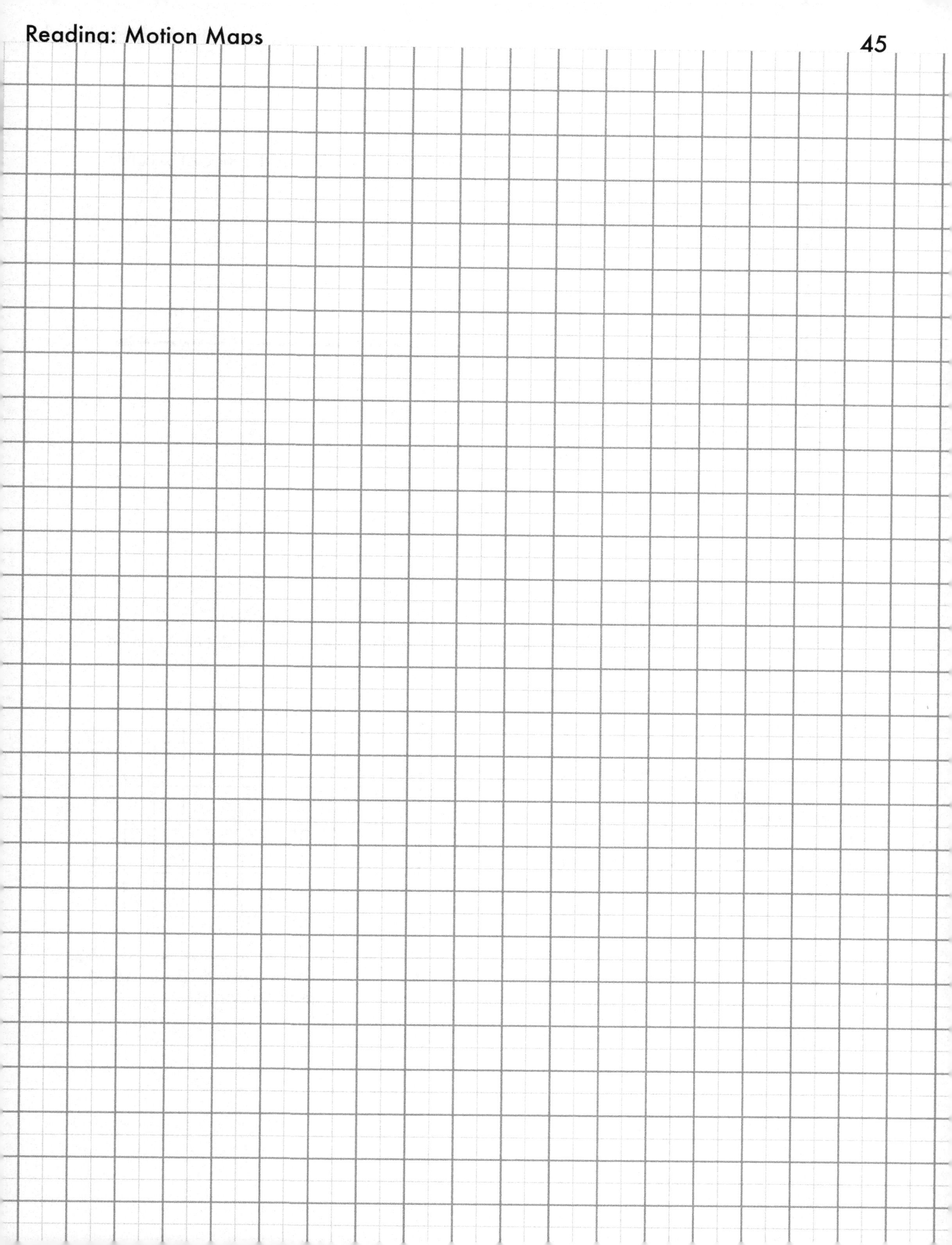

Worksheet 1: Motion Maps and Position vs. Time Graphs

1. Given the following position vs. time graph, draw a motion map with one dot for each second.

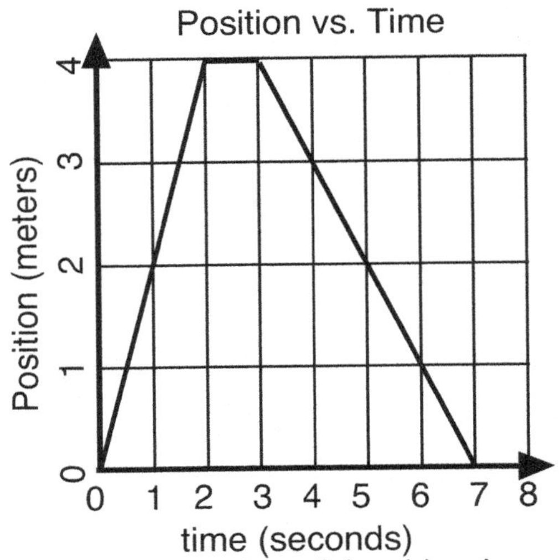

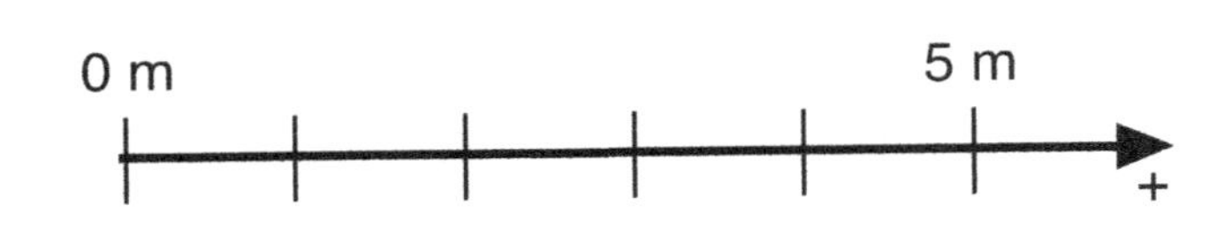

Describe the motion of the object in words:

. Given the following motion map, where positions have been recorded with one dot each second, draw a position vs. time graph.

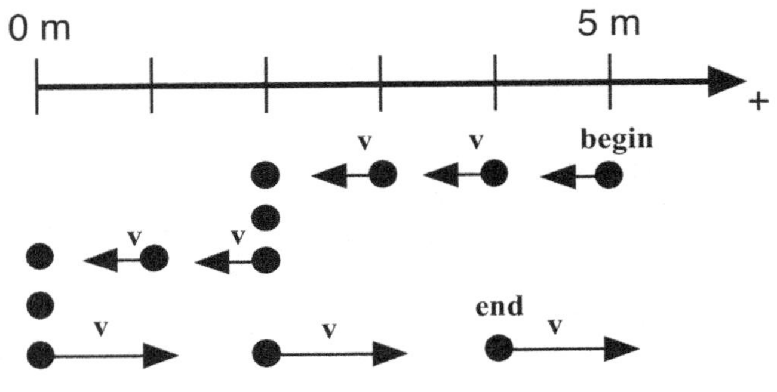

Describe the motion of the object in words:

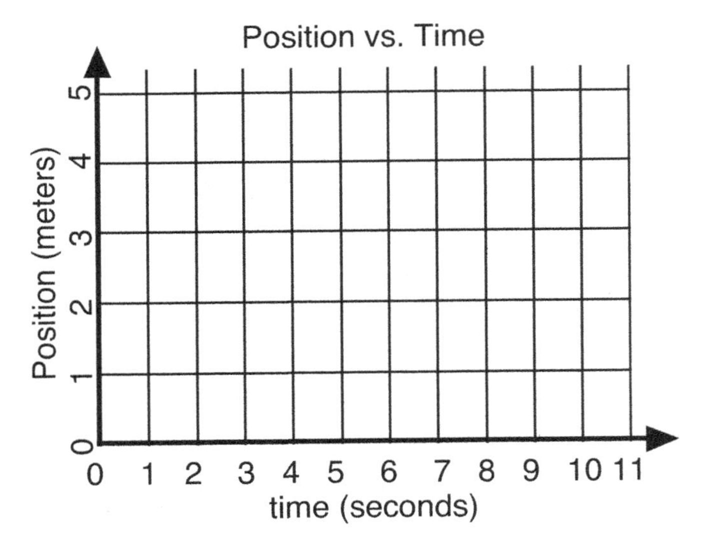

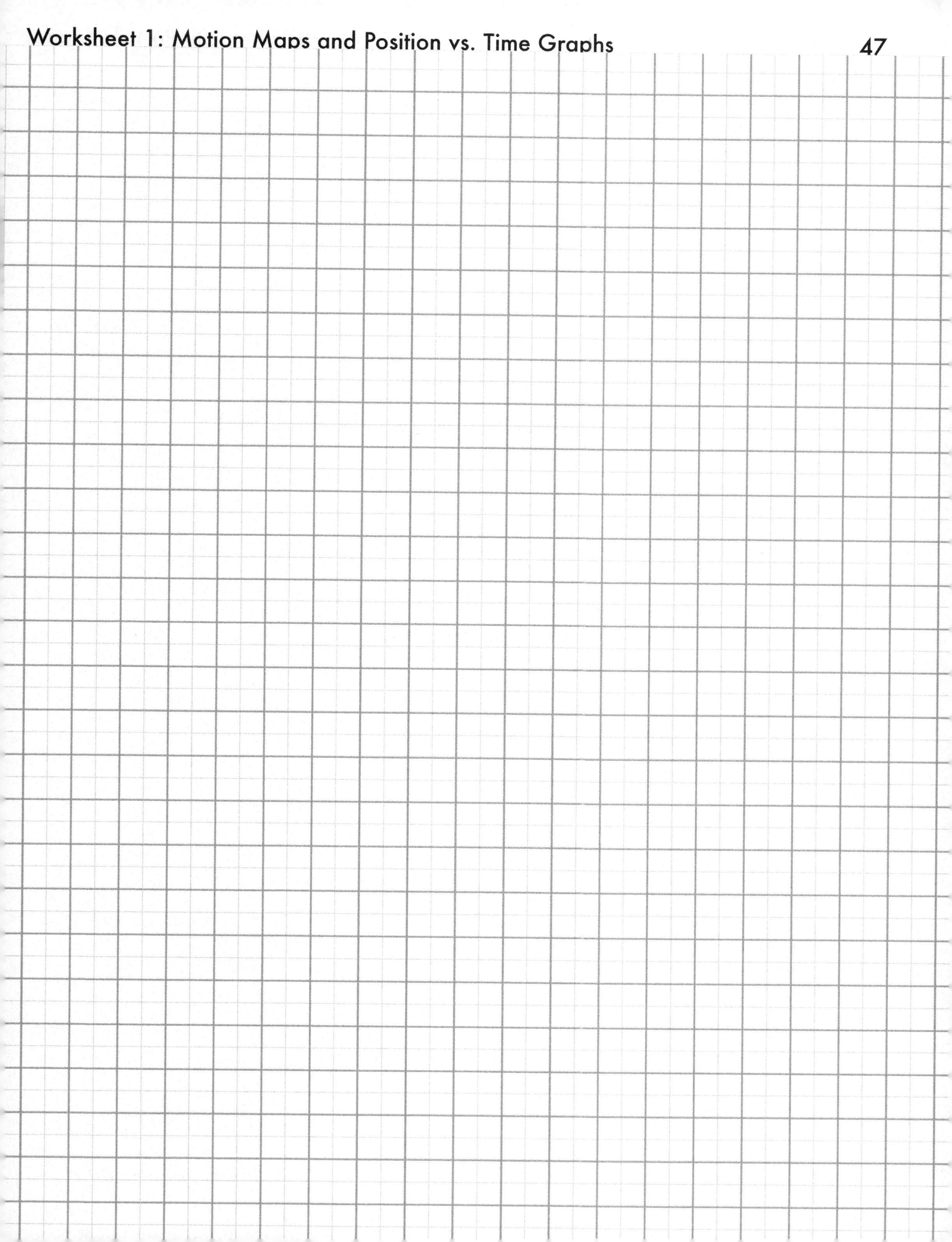

3. Consider the position vs. time graph below for cyclists A and B.

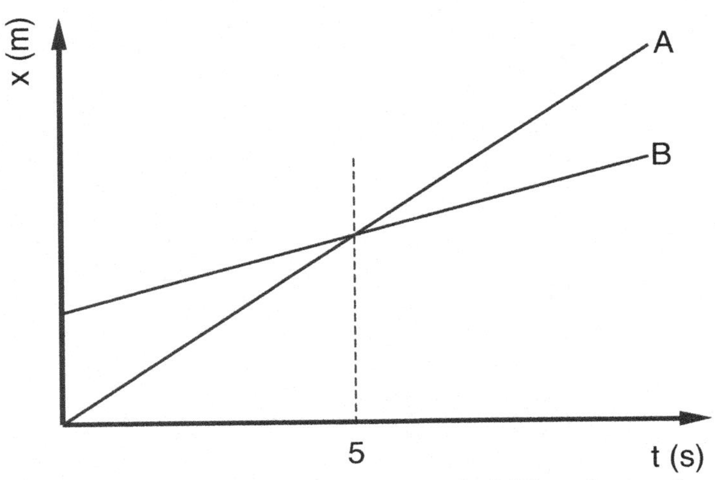

a. Do the cyclists start at the same point? How do you know? If not, which is ahead?

b. At t= 7s, which cyclist is ahead? How do you know?

c. Which cyclist is traveling faster at 3s? How do you know?

d. Are their velocities equal at any time? How do you know?

e. What is happening at the intersection of lines A and B?

f. Draw a motion map for cyclists A and B.

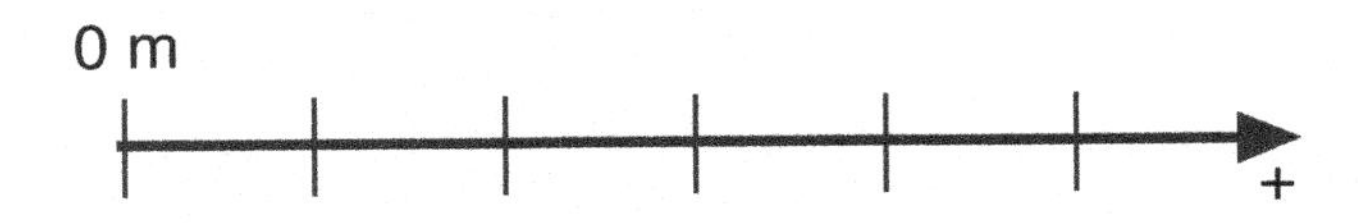

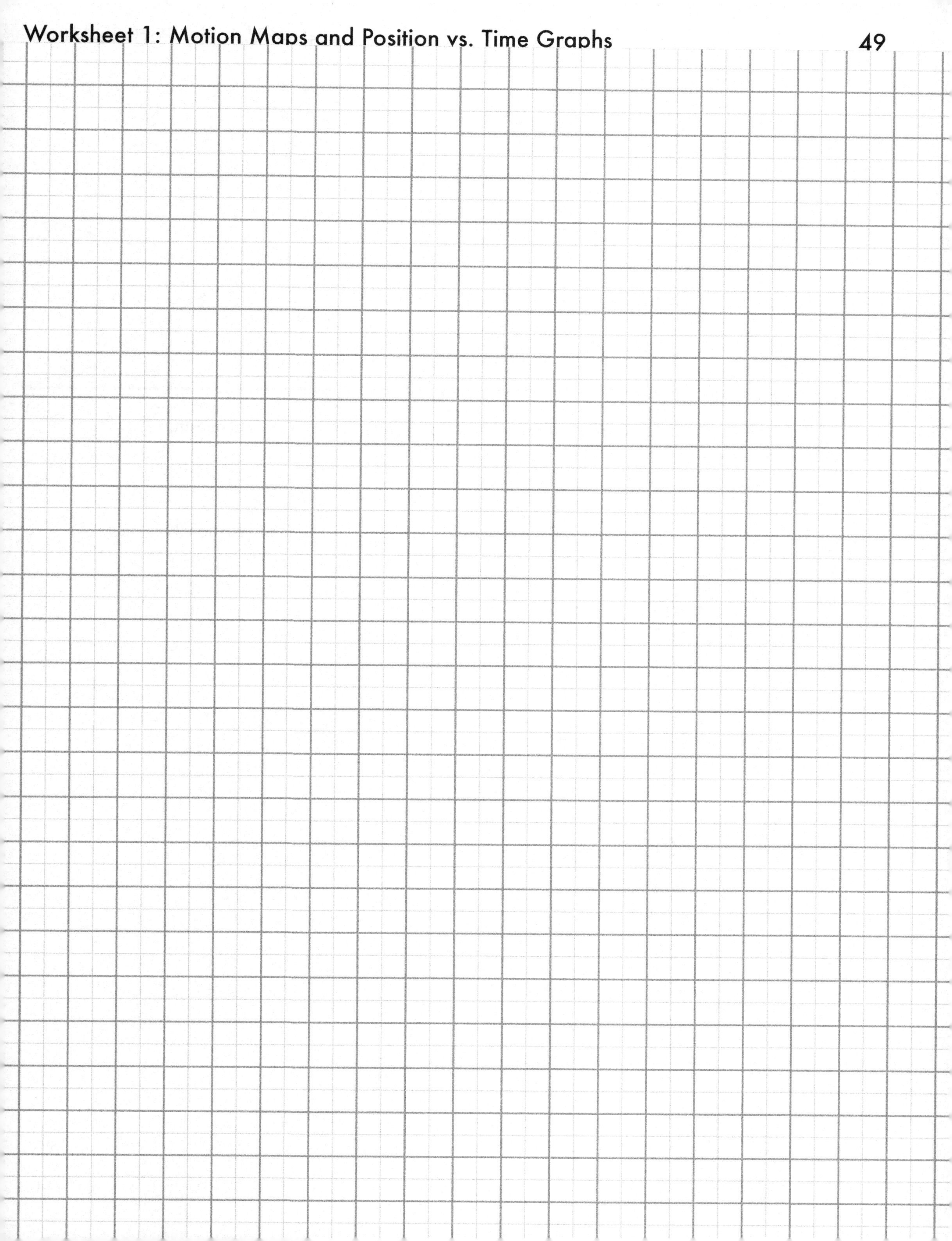

4. Consider the new position vs. time graph below for cyclists A and B.

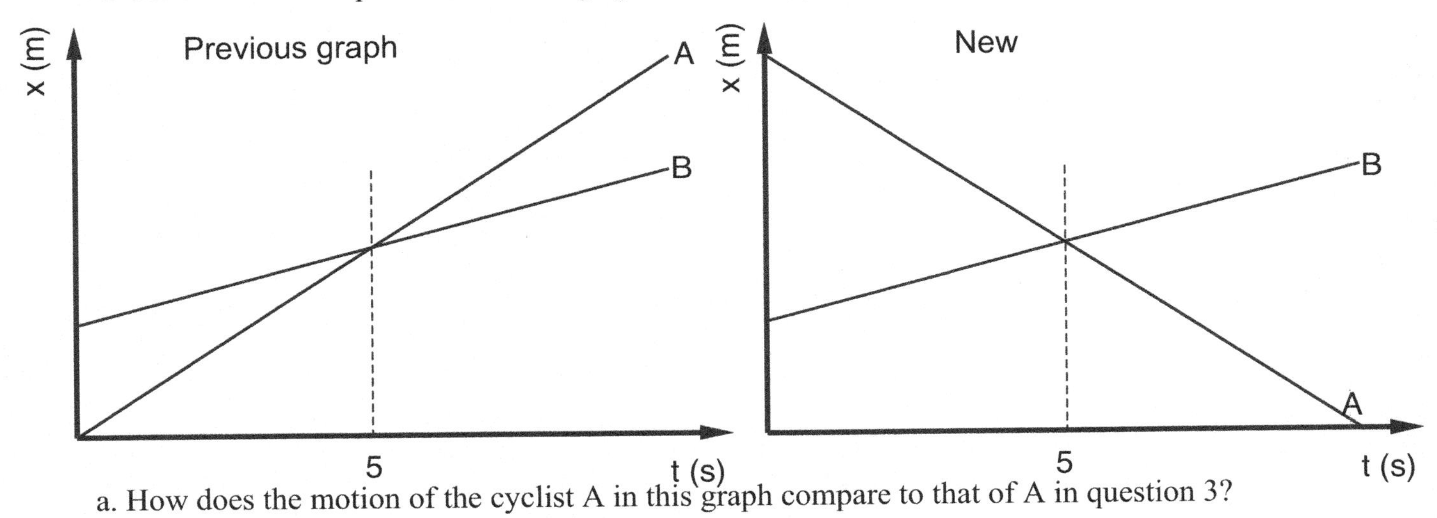

a. How does the motion of the cyclist A in this graph compare to that of A in question 3?

b. How does the motion of cyclist B in this graph compare to that of B in question 3?

c. Which cyclist has the greater speed? How do you know?

d. Describe what is happening at the intersection of lines A and B.

e. Which cyclist has traveled further during the first 5 seconds? How do you know?

f. Draw a motion map for cyclists A and B.

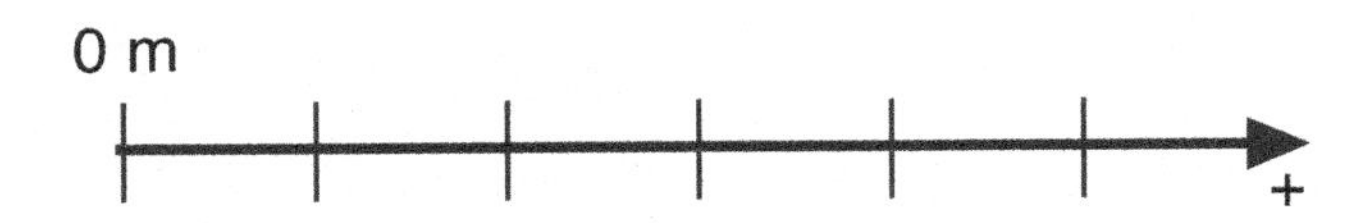

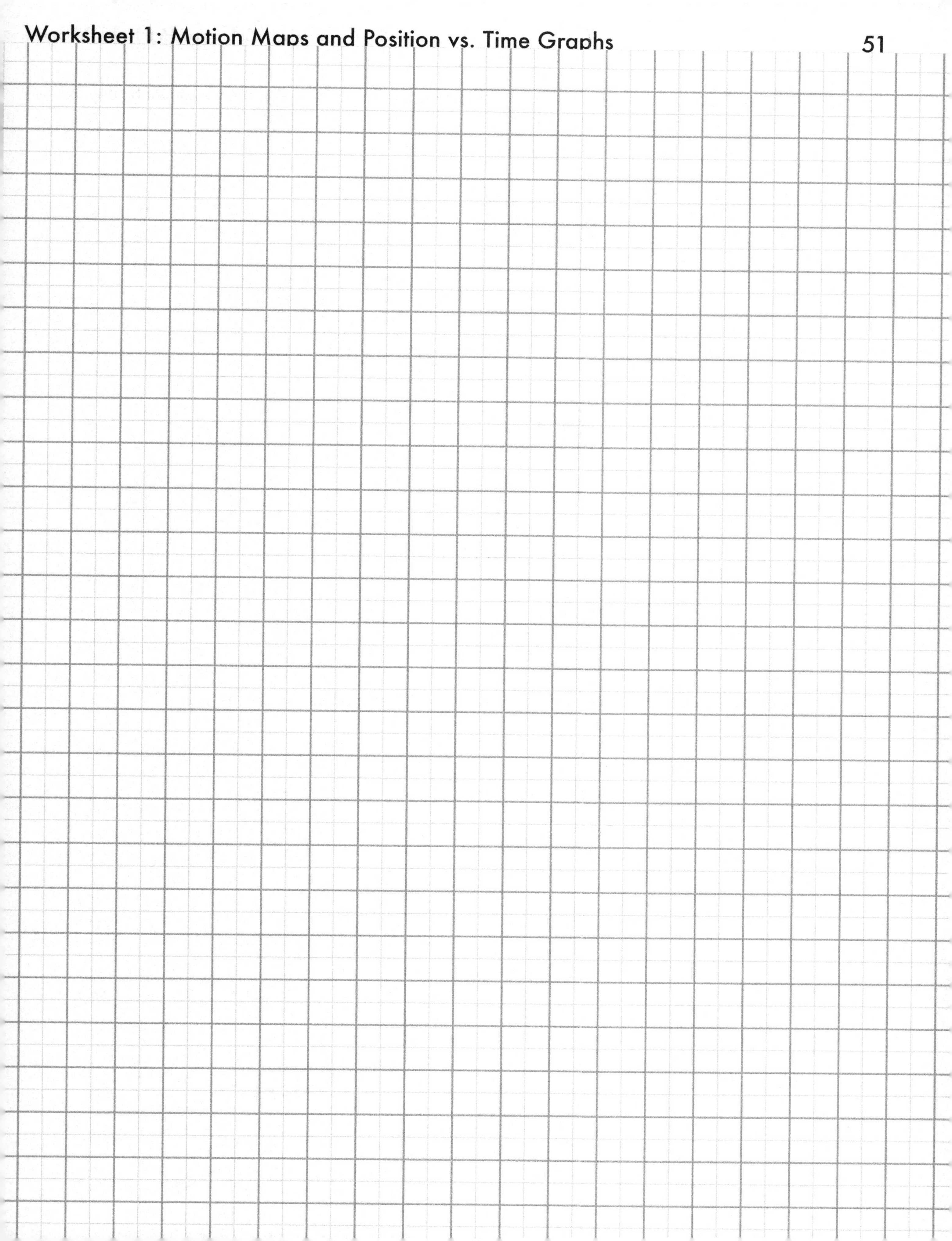

5. An overhead snapshot of Dorothy and Toto walking along the yellow brick road is shown below.

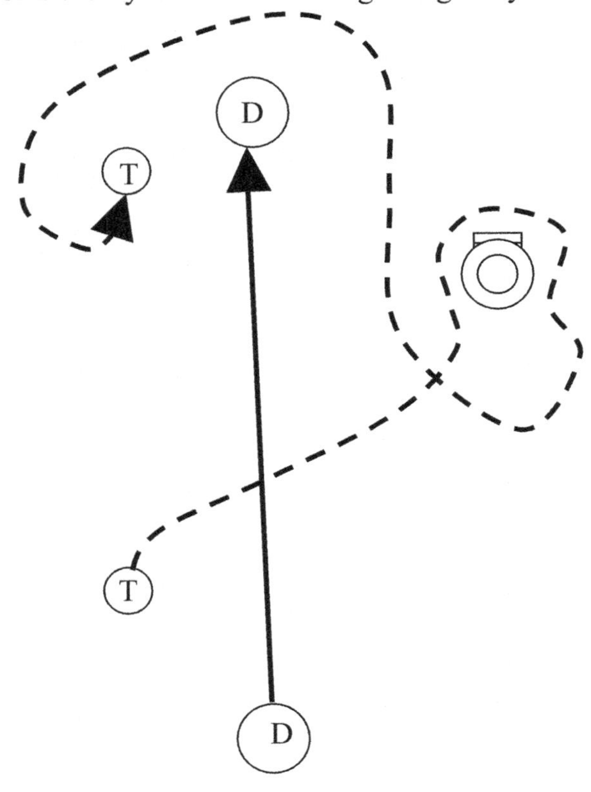

a. From start to finish, who travels farther? Justify your answer.

b. Develop two different definitions for measuring "how far" something travels.

Worksheet 2: Motion Maps and Velocity vs. Time Graphs

Sketch **velocity vs. time** graphs and **motion maps** corresponding to the following descriptions of the motion of an object.

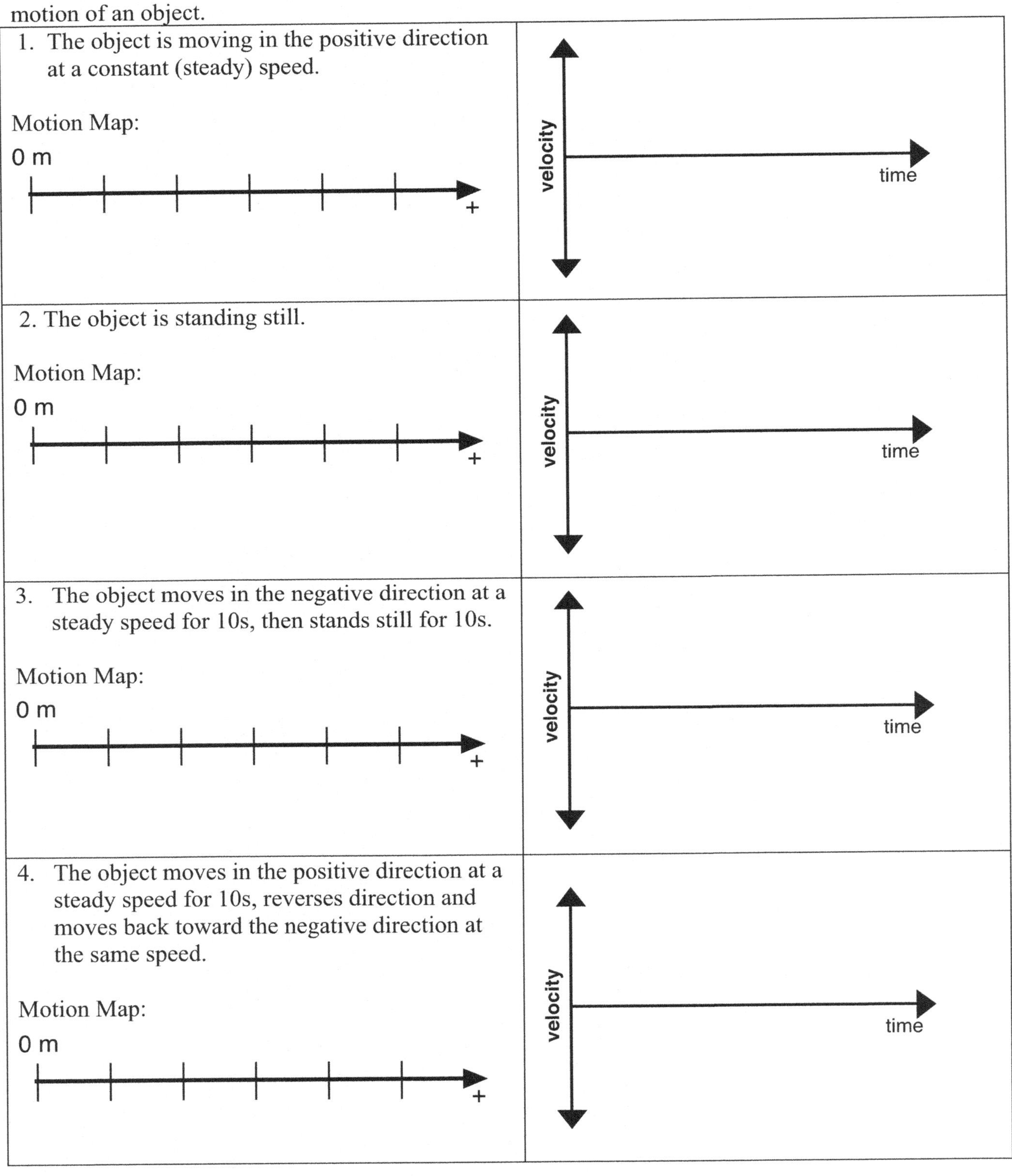

1. The object is moving in the positive direction at a constant (steady) speed.

   Motion Map:

2. The object is standing still.

   Motion Map:

3. The object moves in the negative direction at a steady speed for 10s, then stands still for 10s.

   Motion Map:

4. The object moves in the positive direction at a steady speed for 10s, reverses direction and moves back toward the negative direction at the same speed.

   Motion Map:

Draw the velocity vs time graphs for an object whose motion produced the position vs time graphs shown below at left.

5.

6.

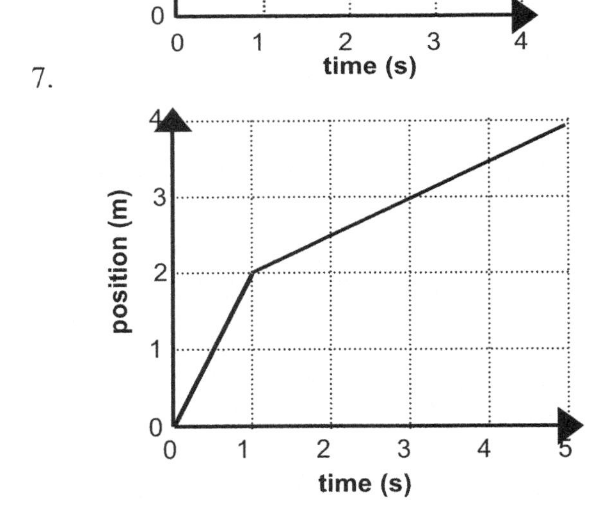

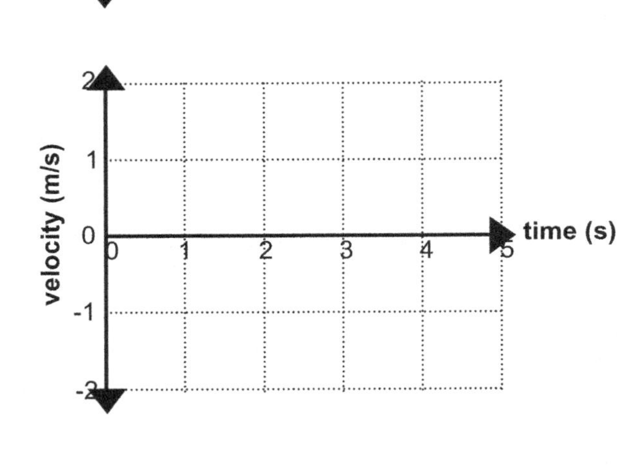

7.

8. For many graphs, both the **slope** of the line and the **area** between the line and the horizontal axis have physical meanings.

a. What does the slope of a position time graph tell you about the motion of an object?

b. Looking at the velocity time graphs, determine the units for a square of area on the graph.

Worksheet 3: Position vs. Time Graphs

1. Robin, rollerskating down a marked sidewalk, was observed at the following positions at the times listed below:

t (s)	x (m)
0.0	10.0
1.0	12.0
2.0	14.0
5.0	20.0
8.0	26.0
10.0	30.0

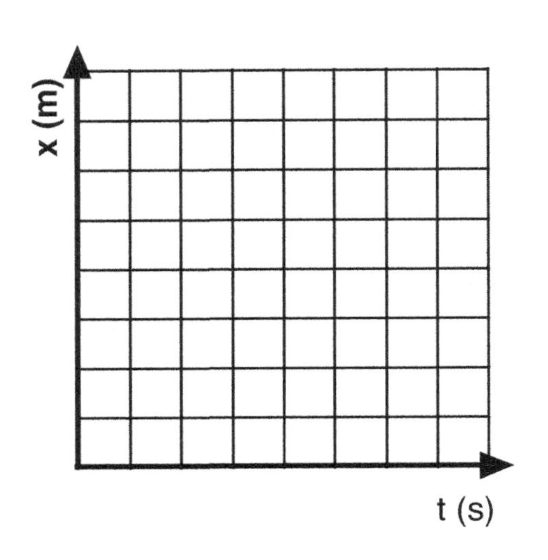

a. Plot a position vs. time graph for the skater.

b. Explain how you can use the graph to determine how far he was from the origin at t = 6.0s.

c. Write a mathematical expression that describes the skater's motion.

d. Was his speed constant over the entire interval? How do you know?

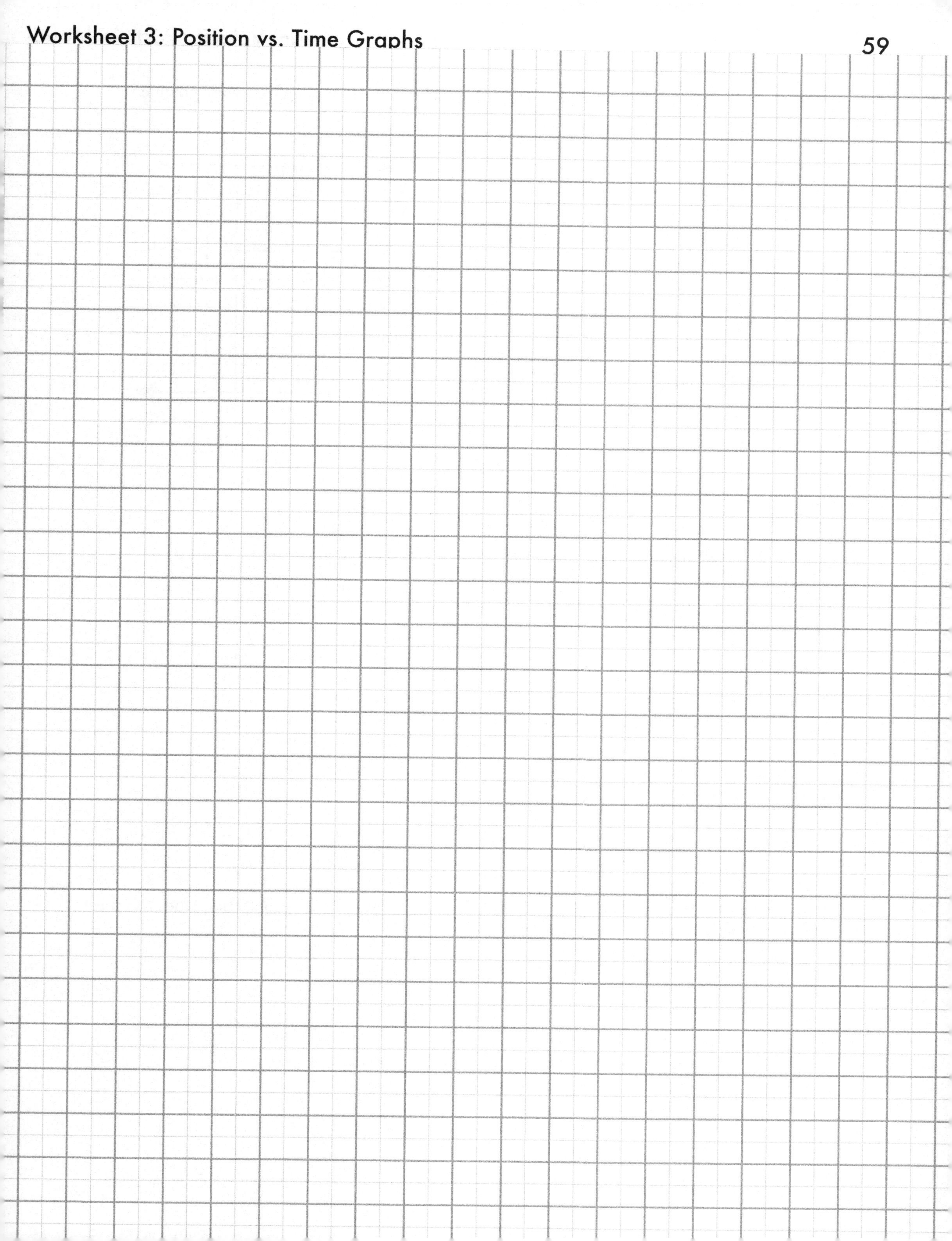

2. In a second trial, the timer started her watch a bit sooner. The following data were obtained:

t (s)	x (m)
0.0	4.0
2.0	10.0
4.0	16.0
6.0	22.0
8.0	28.0
10.0	34.0

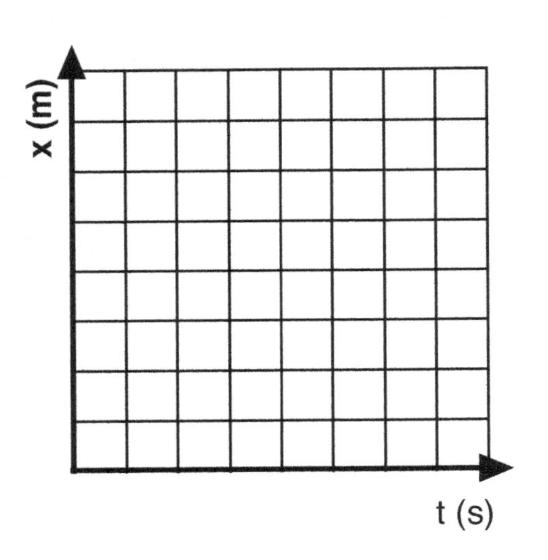

a. Plot the position vs. time graph for the skater.

b. How far from the origin was the skater at t = 5.0s? How do you know?

c. Was the skater's speed constant? If so, what was it?

d. In the first trial, the skater was further along at 2s than he was in the second trial. Does this mean that he was going faster? Explain your answer.

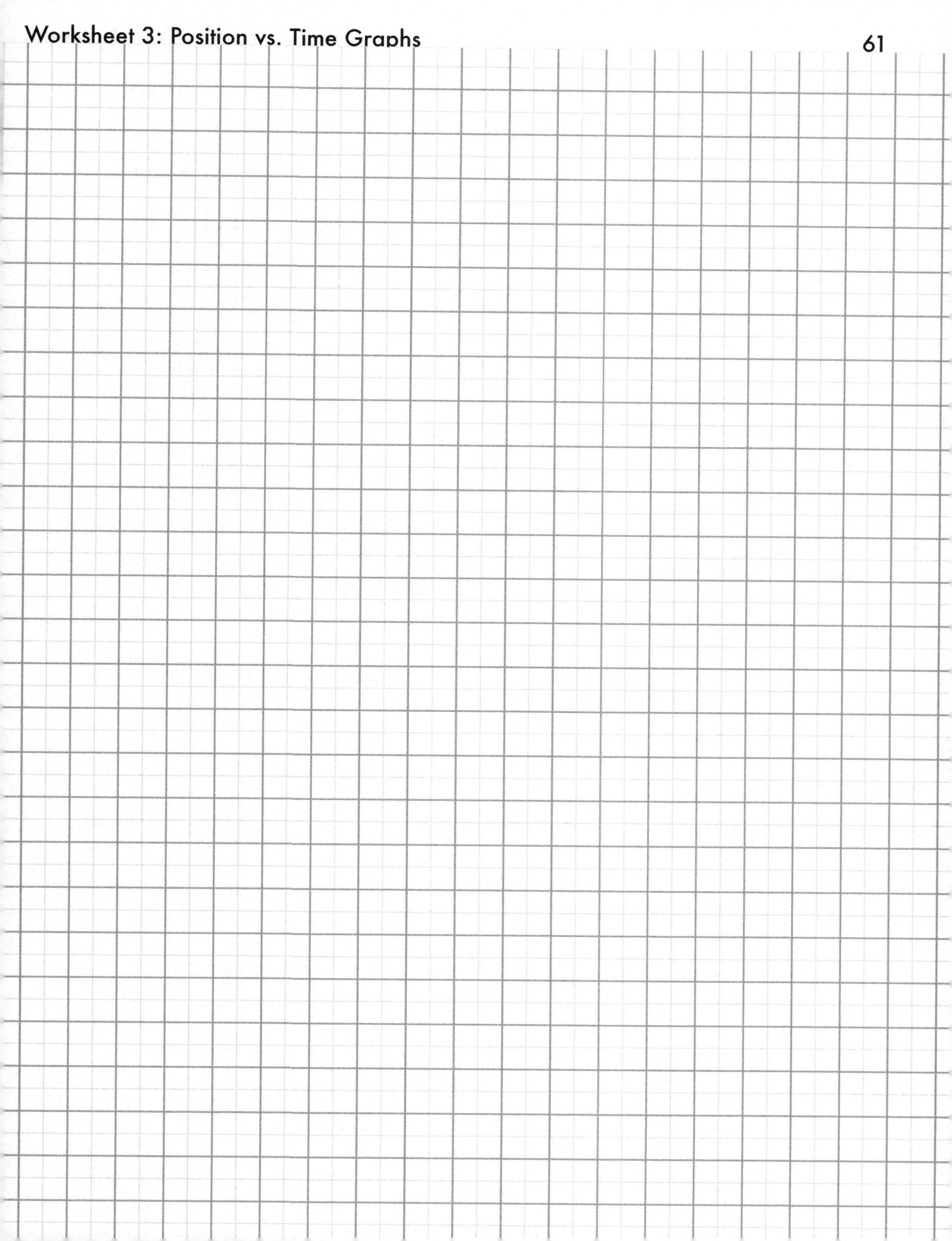

3. Suppose now that our skater was observed in a third trial. The following data were obtained:

t (s)	x (m)
0.0	0.0
2.0	2.0
4.0	4.0
6.0	4.0
8.0	3.0
10.0	2.0
12.0	2.0
14.0	5.0
16.0	8.0

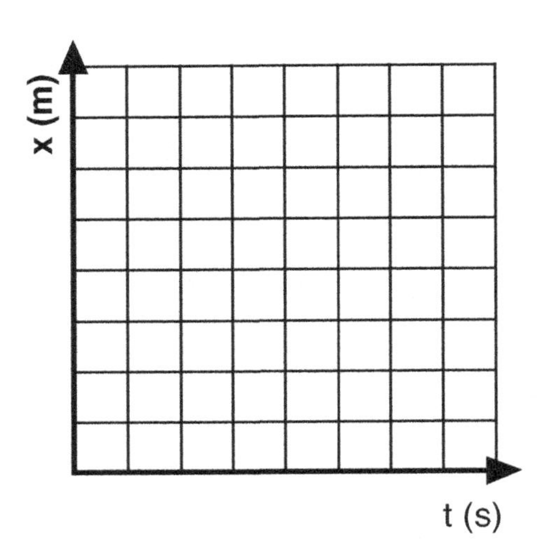

a. Plot the position vs. time graph for the skater.

b. What do you think is happening during the time interval: t = 4s to t = 6s? How do you know?

c. What do you think is happening during the time interval: t = 6s to t = 10s? How do you know?

d. Determine the skater's average **velocity** from t = 0s to t = 16s. (Average **velocity** is the displacement (final position minus initial position) divided by time elapsed.)

e. Determine the skater's average **speed** from t = 0s to t = 16s. (Average **speed** path length divided by time elapsed.)

4a. In what situation might average **speed** be a better measure of motion than average velocity?

4b. In what situation might average **velocity** be a better measure of motion than average speed?

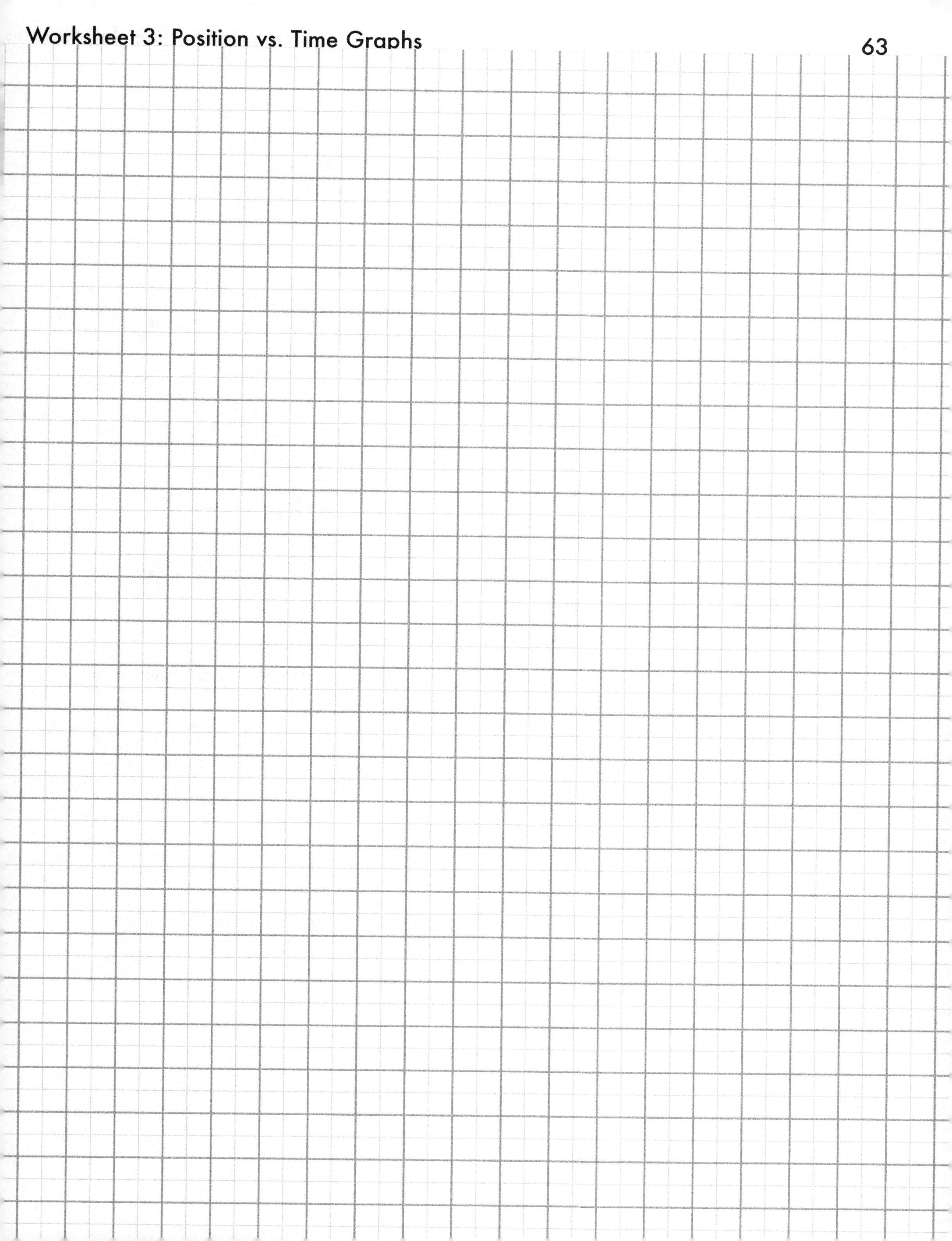

5. Rank the following:

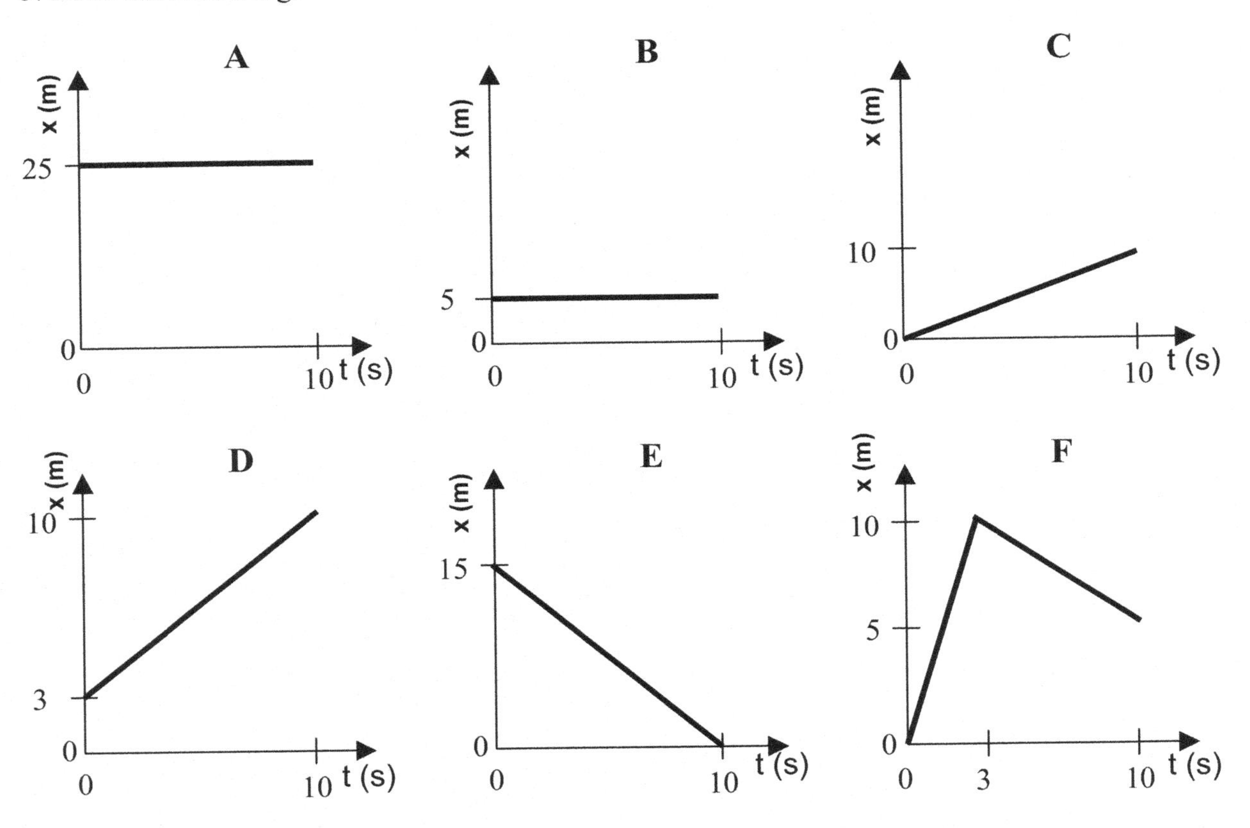

a. Rank the graphs according to which show the greatest **average velocity** from the beginning to the end of the motion. (Zero is greater than negative, and ties are possible.)

Most pos. v 1________ 2________ 3________ 4________ 5________ 6________ Most neg. v

Explain your reasoning for your ranking:

b. Rank the graphs according to which show the greatest **average speed** from the beginning to the end of the motion.

Greatest 1________ 2________ 3________ 4________ 5________ 6________ Least

Explain your reasoning for your ranking:

Worksheet 4: Velocity vs. Time Graphs and Displacement

1. This motion map shows the position of an object once every second. From the motion map, answer the following:

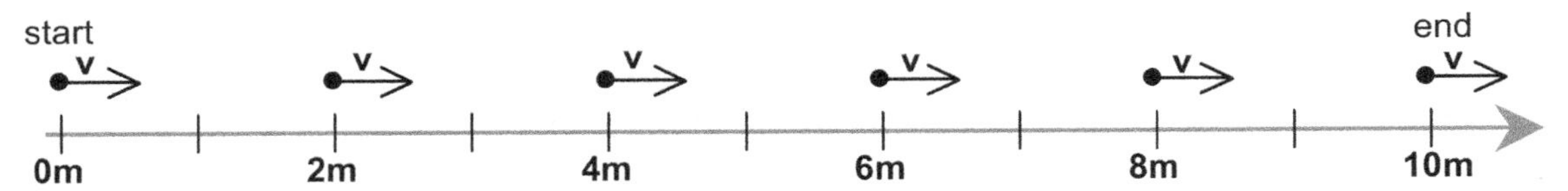

a. Describe the motion of the object.

b. Represent the motion with a quantitative **x** vs. **t** graph.

c. Represent the motion with a quantitative **v** vs. **t** graph.

d. Write a mathematical expression that represents the relationship between position and time.

e. From the position-time graph find the displacement from t = 1 s to t = 3 s.

f. Find the area under the velocity-time graph from t = 1 s to t = 3 s. What are the units of this area? Describe what this area represents.

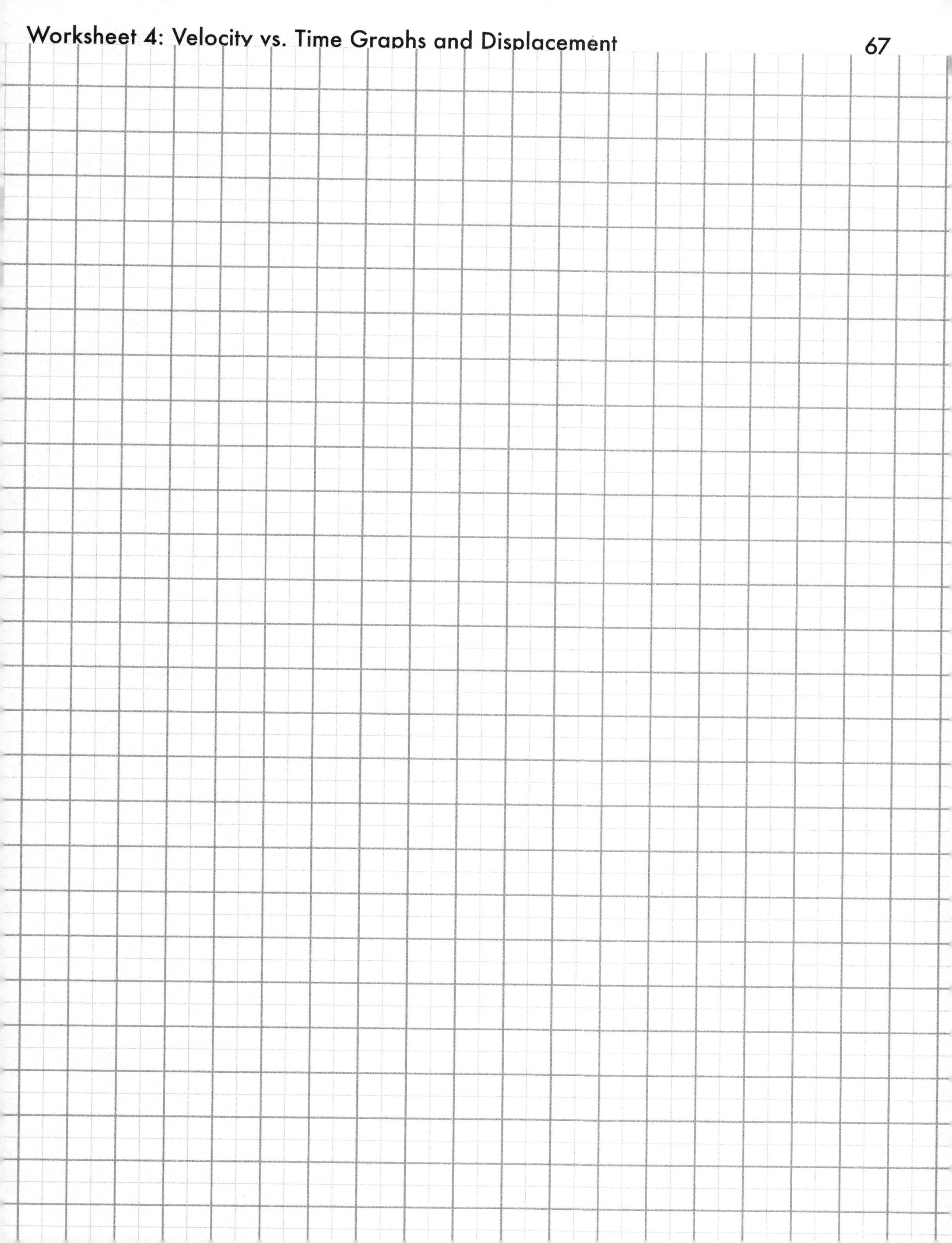

2. From the position vs. time data below, answer the following questions.

a. Construct a graph of position vs. time.

b. Construct a graph of velocity vs. time.

t (s)	x (m)
0	0
1	2
2	4
3	4
4	7
5	10
6	10
7	10
8	5
9	0

c. Draw a motion map for the object.

d. Determine the displacement from t = 3.0 s to 5.0 s using the velocity vs. time graph.

e. Determine the displacement from t = 7.0 s to 9.0 s using the velocity vs. time graph.

f. Determine the average **velocity** from t = 4 s to 8 s.

g. Determine the average **speed** from t = 4 s to 8 s.

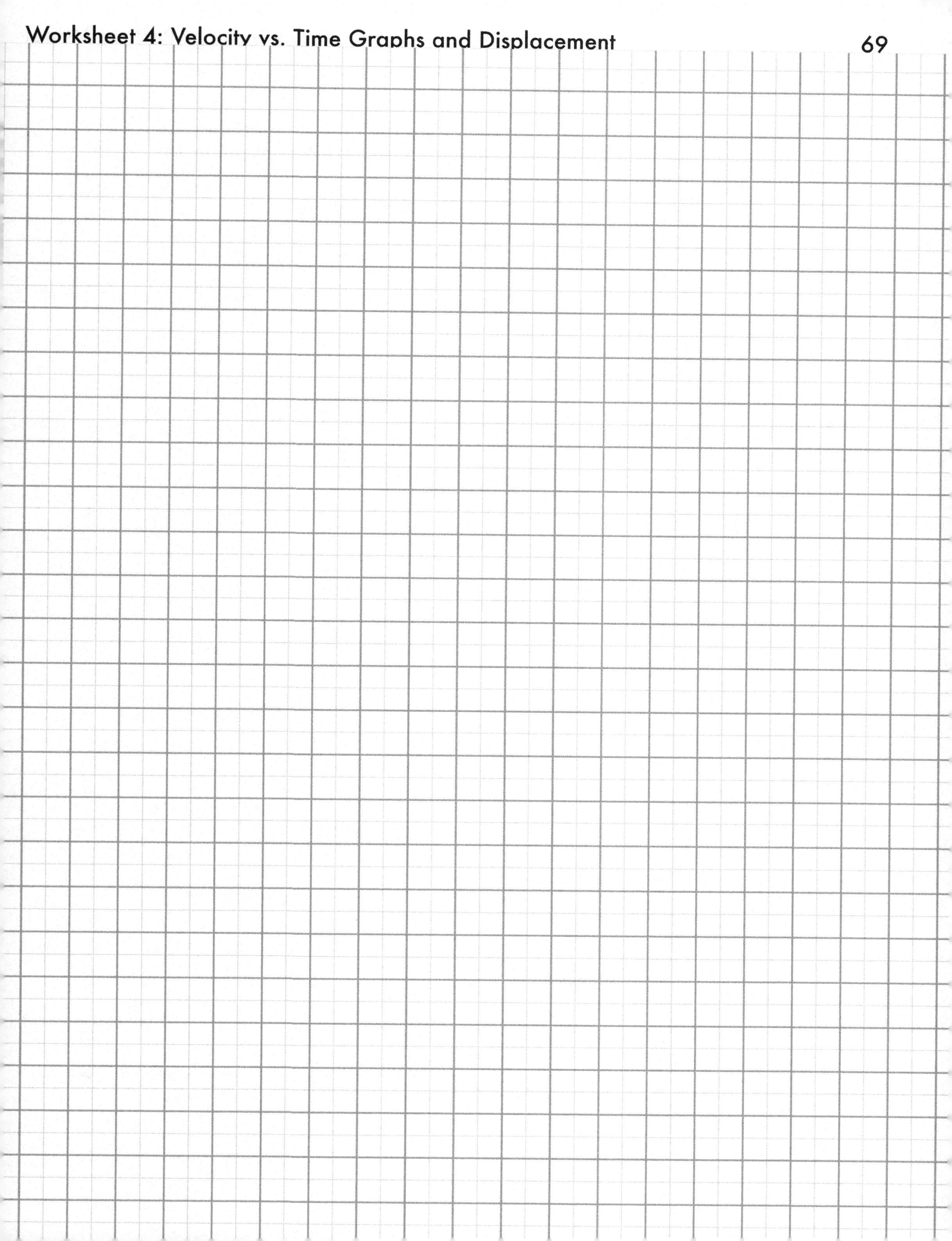

Worksheet 5: Multiple Representations of Motion

Given one motion representation, supply the other three missing motion representations.

1.

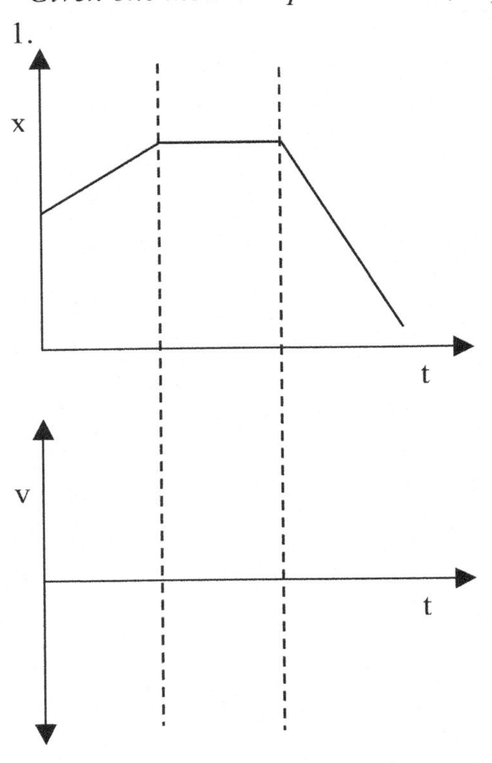

Written description:

Motion map:

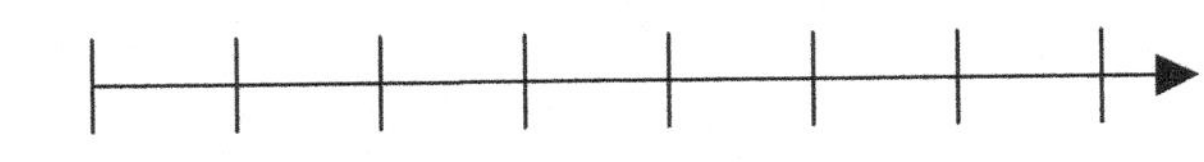

2.

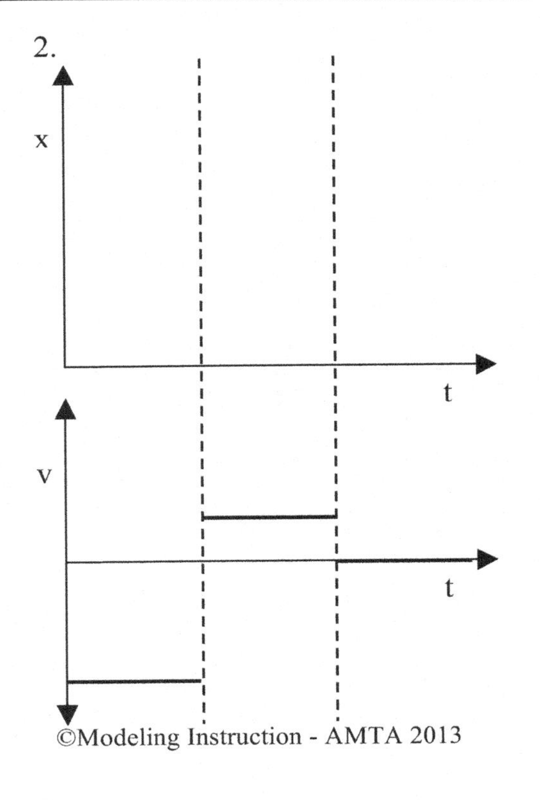

Written description:

Motion map:

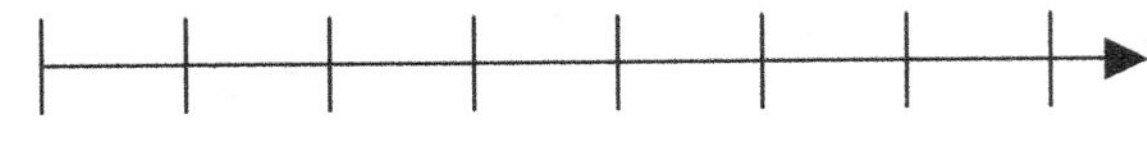

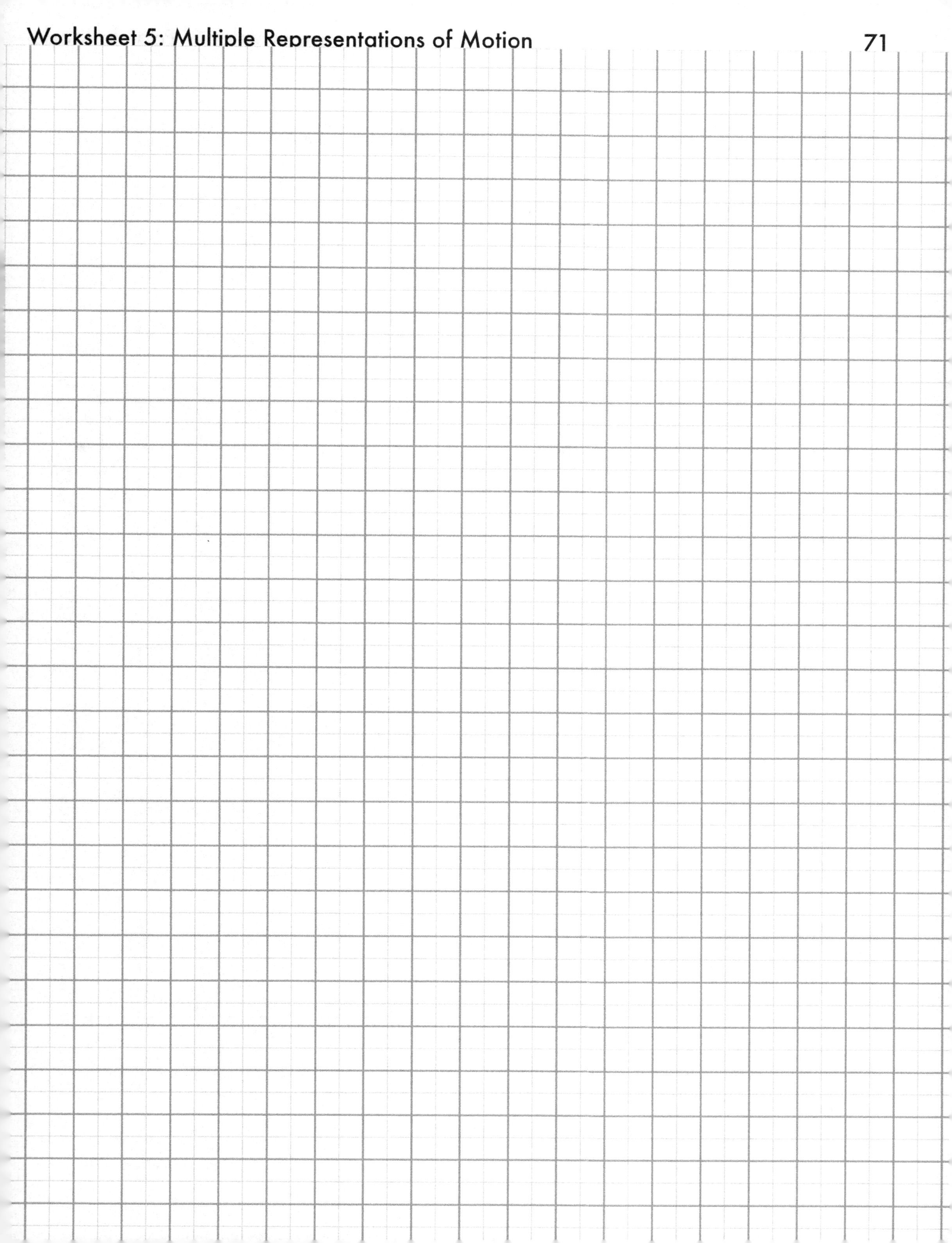

3.

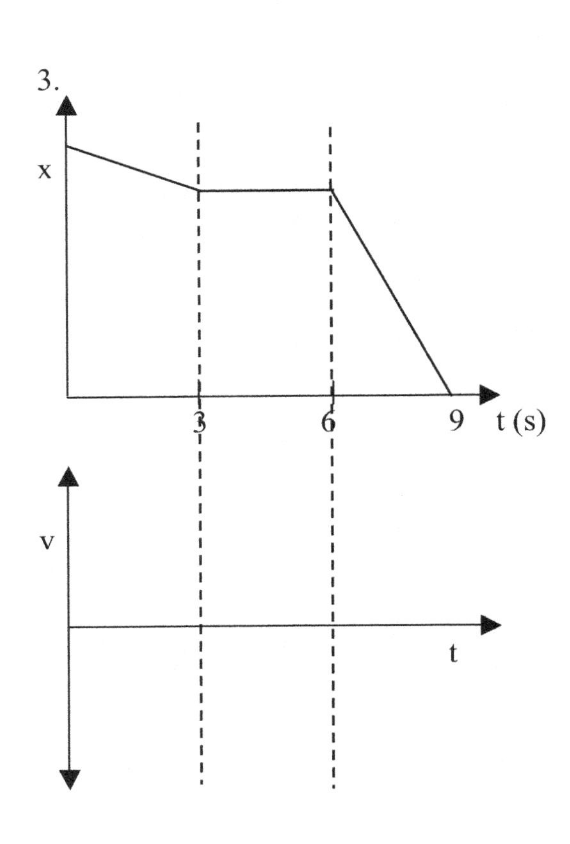

Written description:

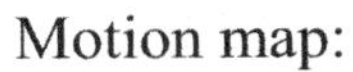
Motion map:

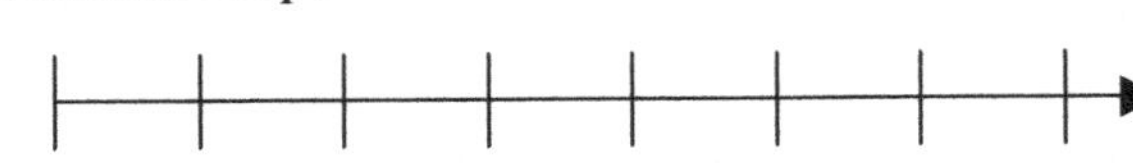

4.

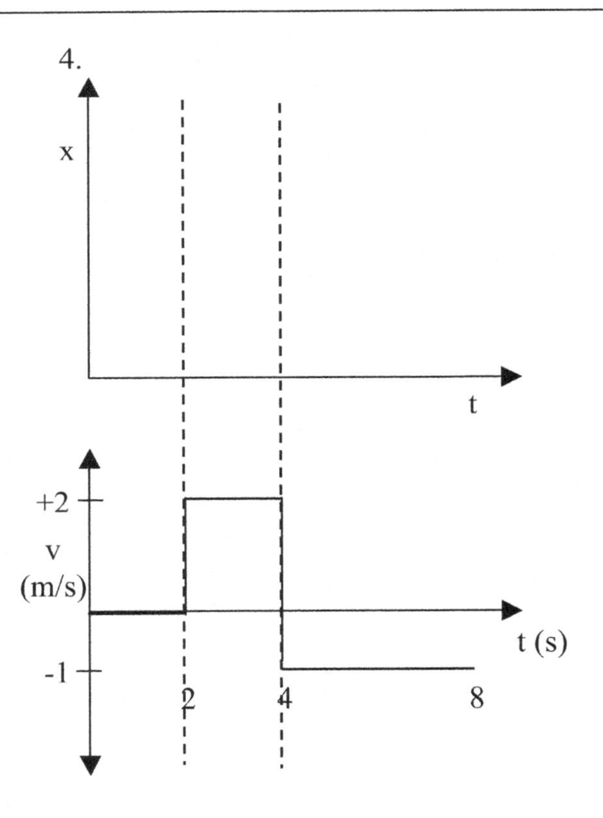

Written description:

Motion map:

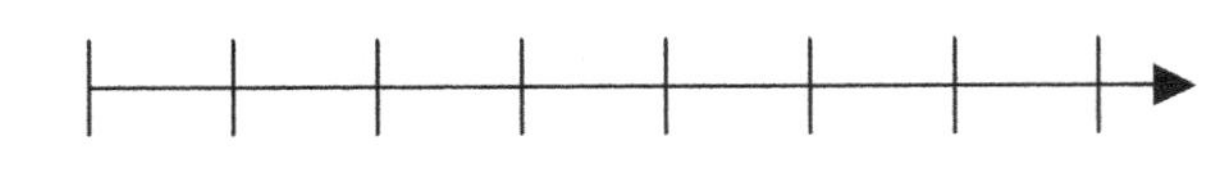

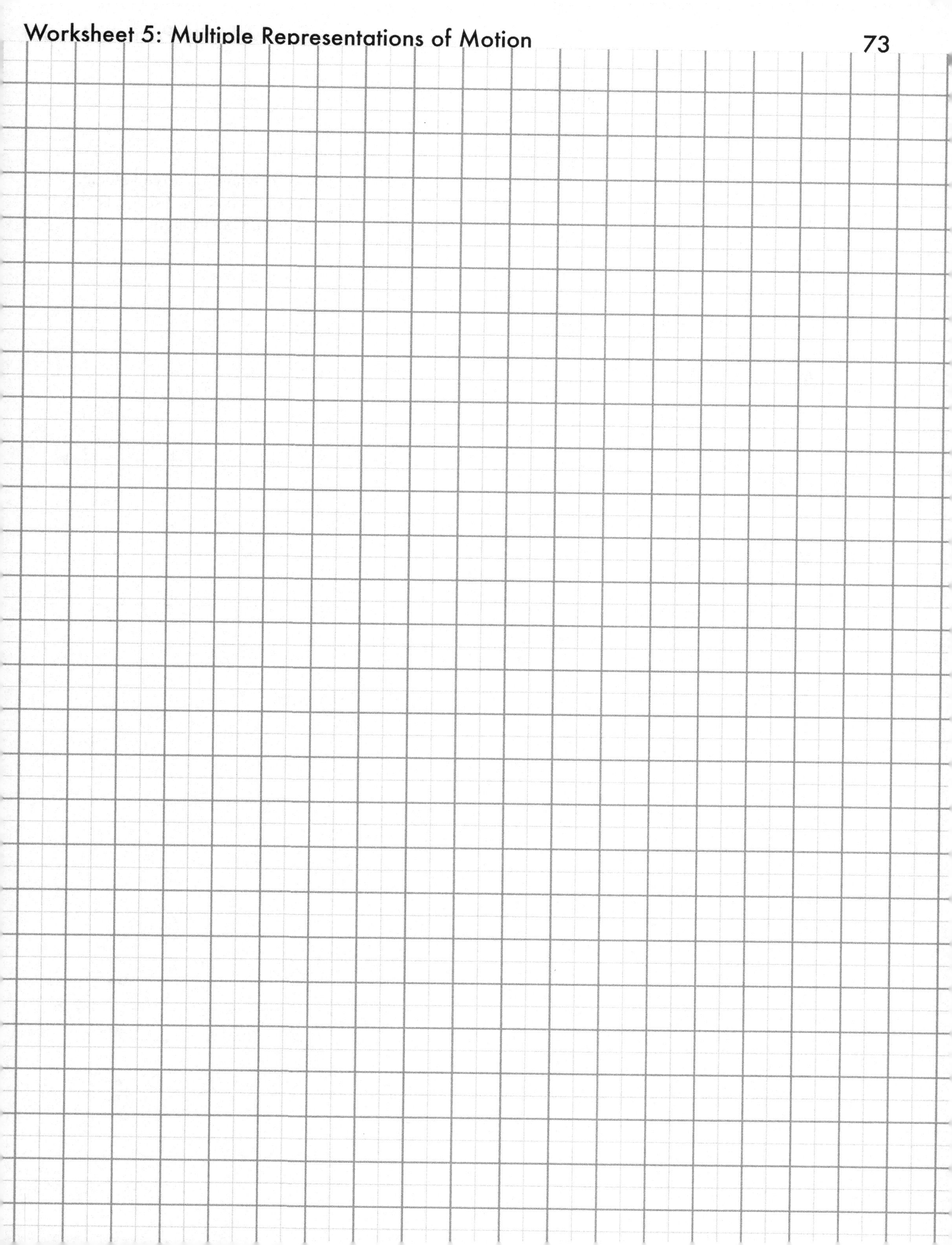

5.

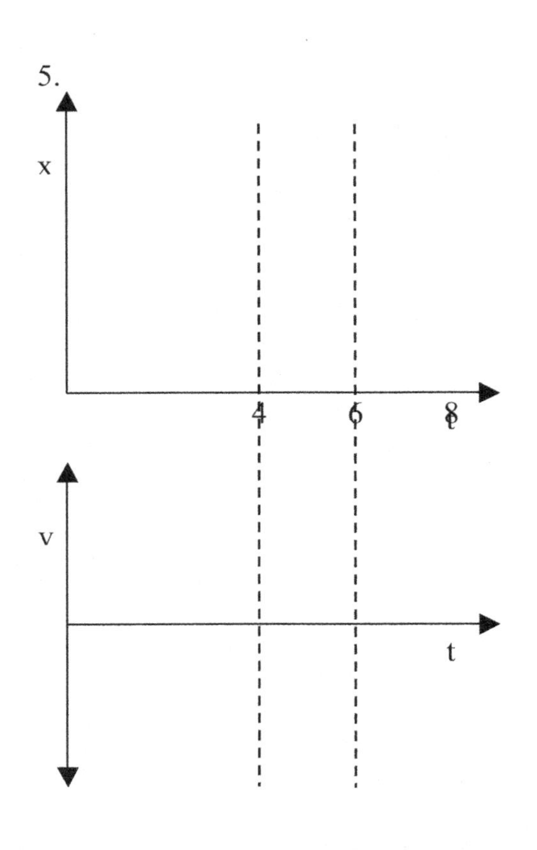

Written description:

Object moves with constant positive velocity for 4 seconds. Then, it stops for 2 seconds and returns to the initial position in 2 seconds.

Motion map:

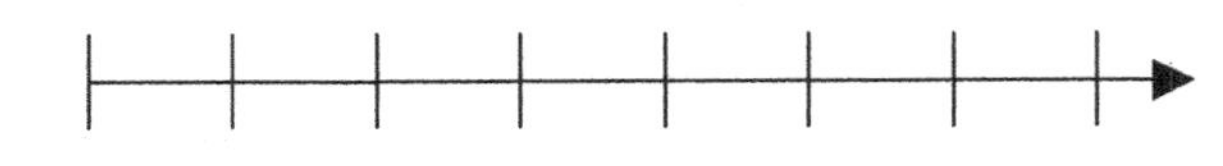

6.

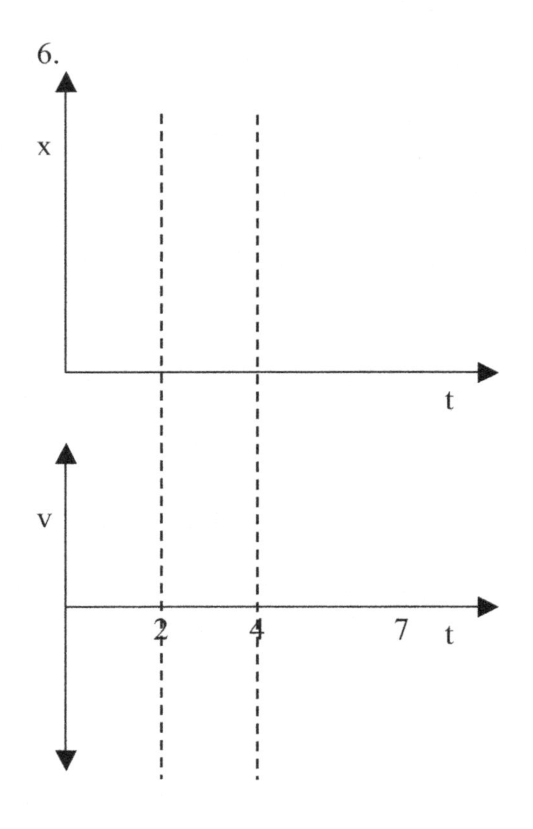

Written description:

Motion map: $\Delta t = 1$ s

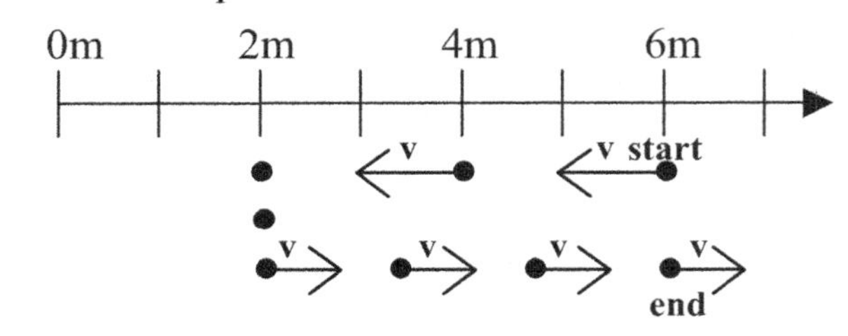

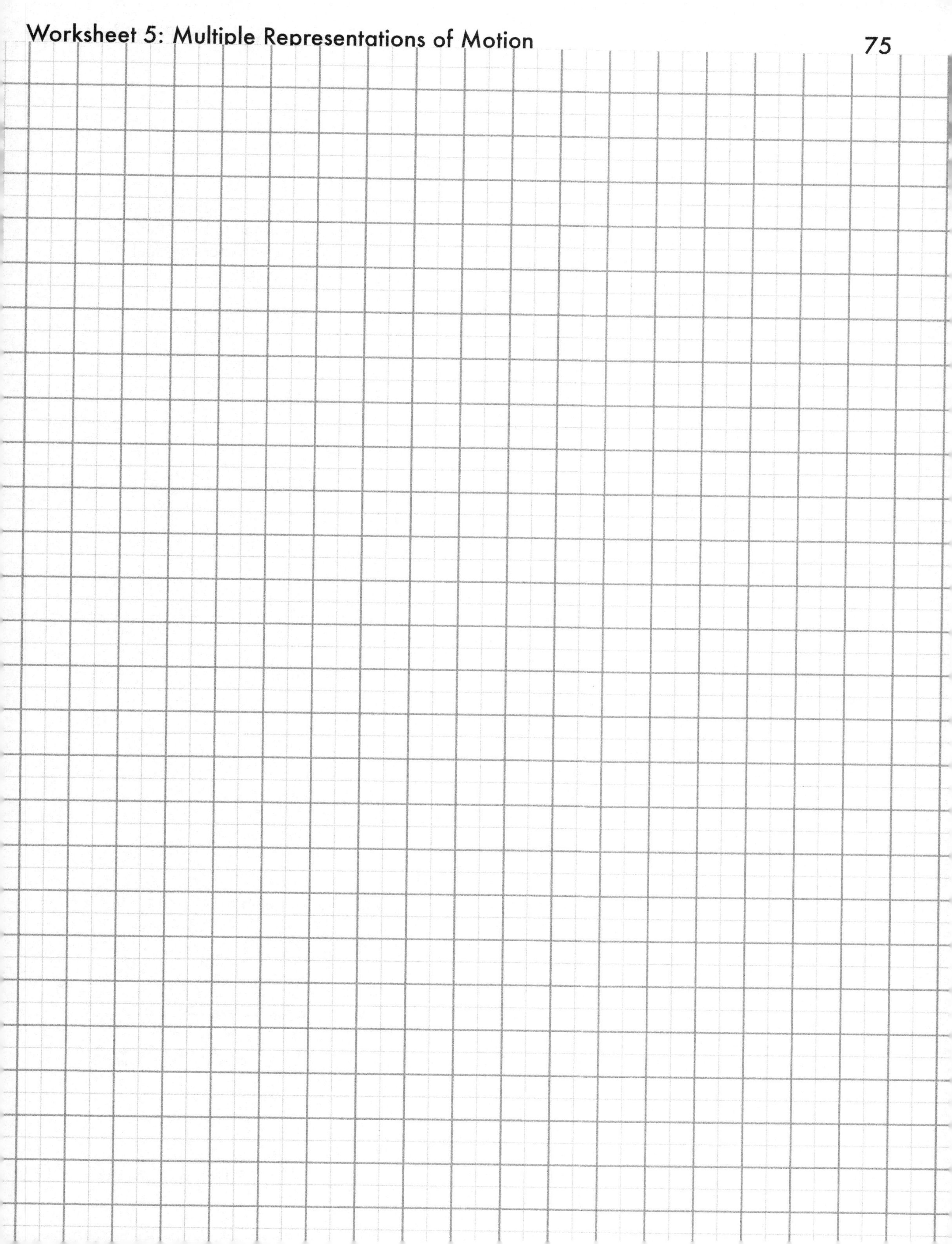

7.

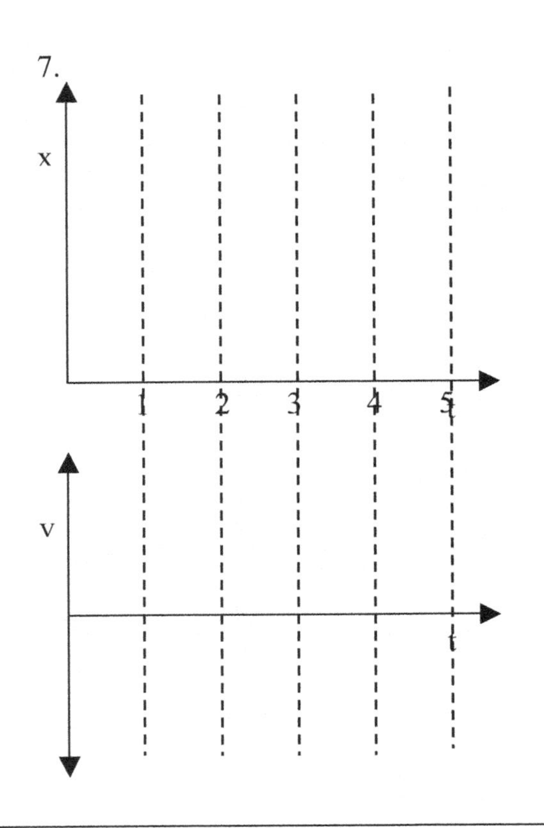

Written description:

Object A starts 10m to the right of the zero position and moves to the left at 2 m/s. Object B starts at the zero position and moves to the right at 3 m/s.

Motion map:

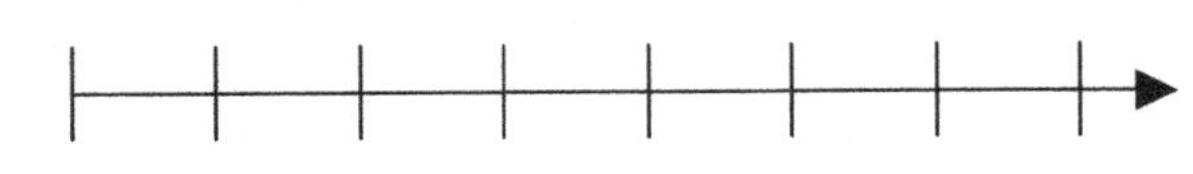

8.

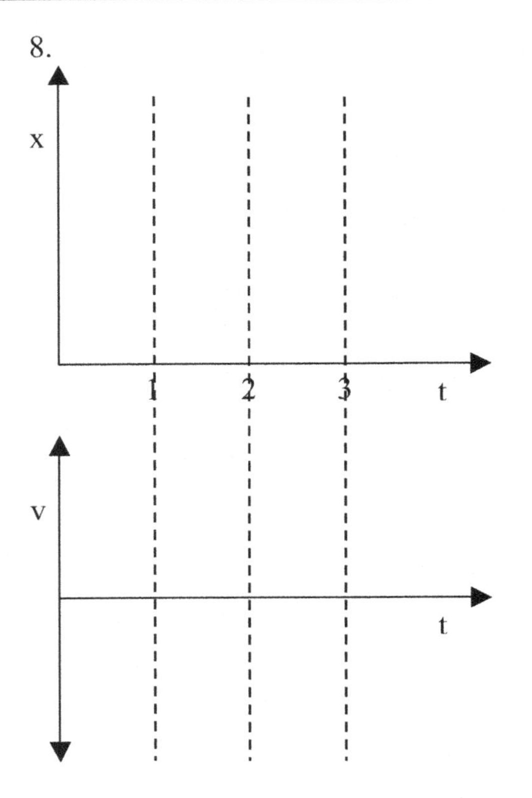

Written description:

*Both objects begin moving at t = 0.

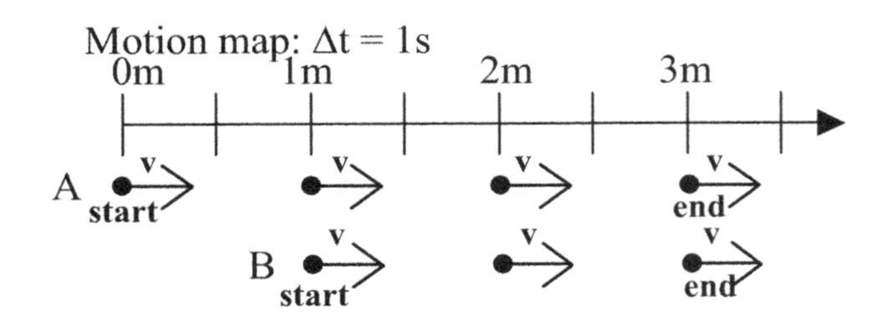

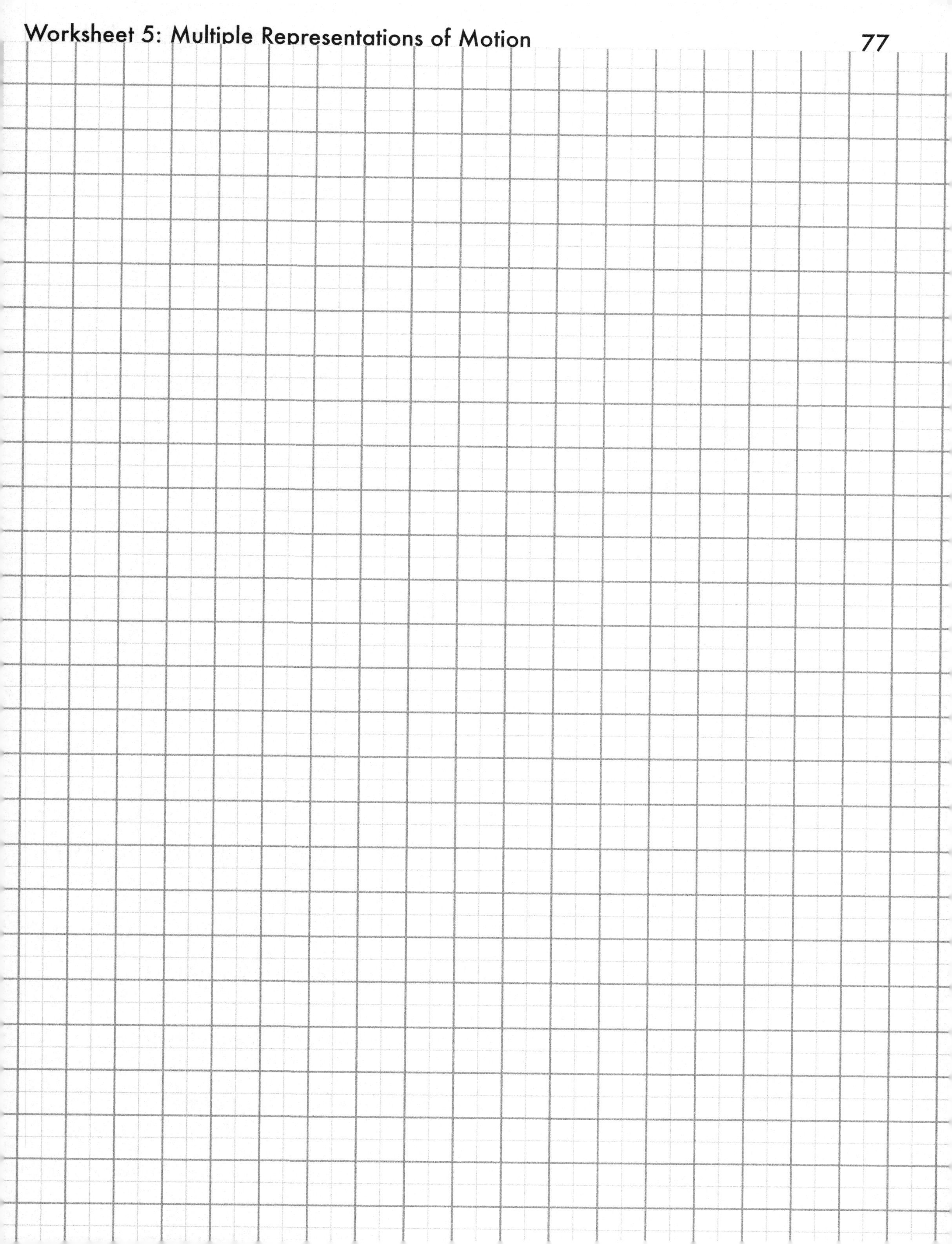

Review Problems

1. Consider the following position vs. time graph.

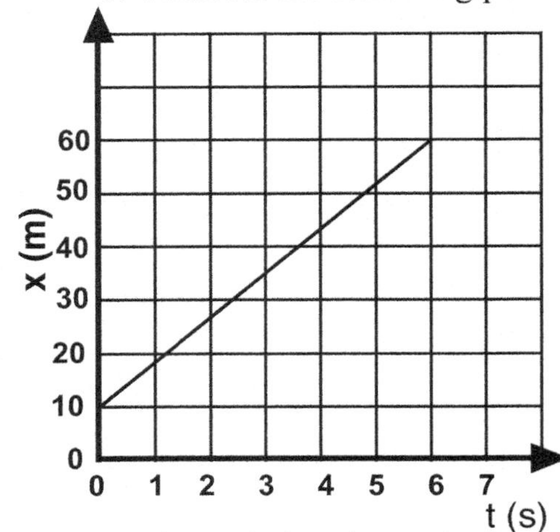

a. Determine the average velocity of the object.

b. Write a mathematical expression to describe the motion of the object.

2. Shown below is a velocity vs. time graph for an object.

a. Describe the motion of the object.

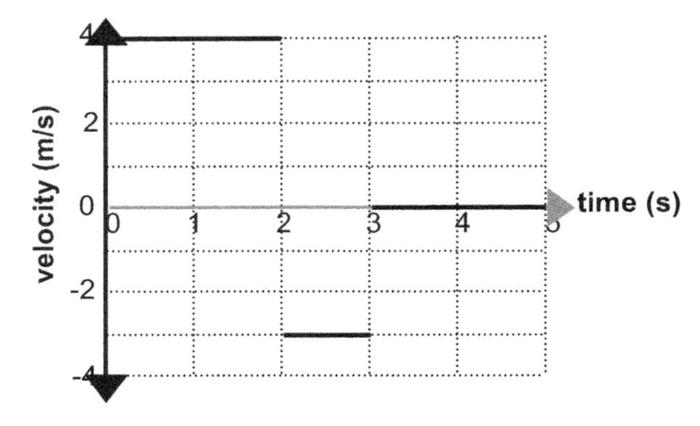

b. Draw a corresponding position vs. time graph. Number the axes. You may assume the object starts from zero position.

c. How far did the object travel in the interval t = 1 s to t = 2 s?

d. Find the displacement from t = 0 s to t = 5 s. Explain how you got your answer.

e. Find the average velocity from t = 0 s to t = 5 s. Explain how you got your answer.

f. Find the average speed from t = 0 s to t = 5 s. Explain how you got your answer.

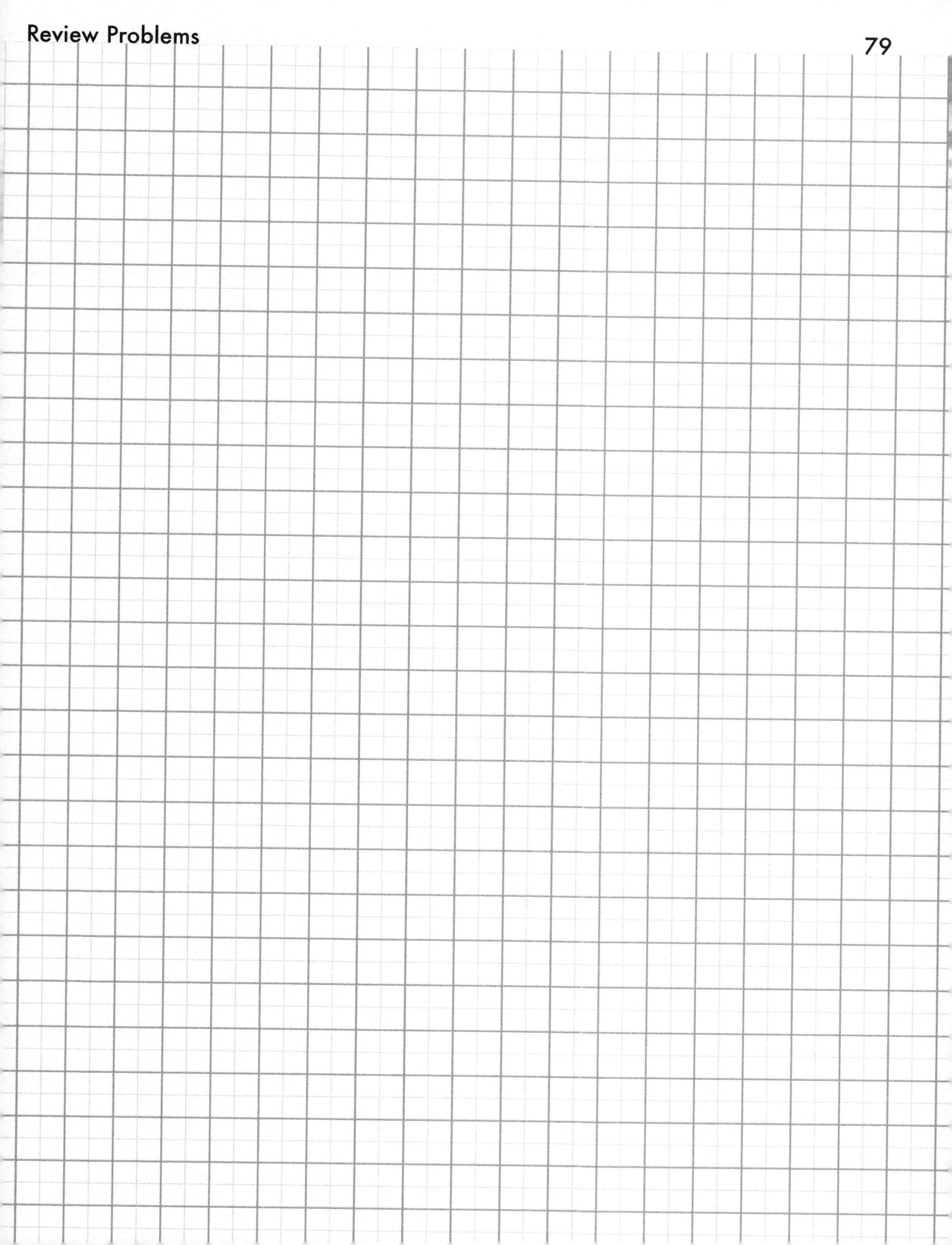

3. A bird travels toward zero position, then suddenly reverses direction.

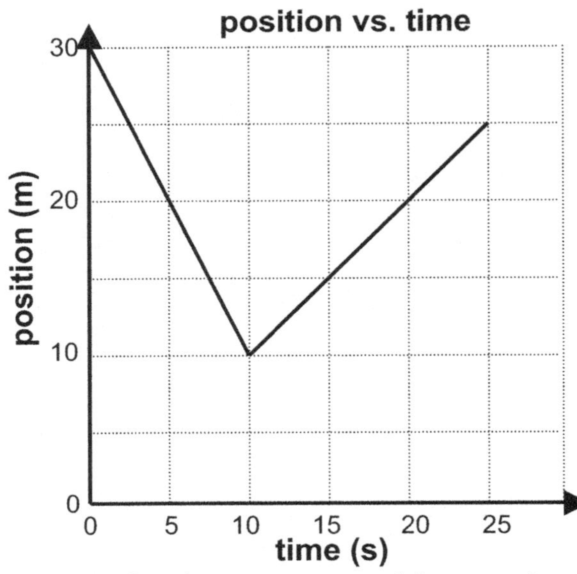

a. Find the average velocity from t = 0 s to t = 10 s.

b. Find the average velocity from t = 10 s to t = 20 s.

c. Determine the average speed from t = 0 s to t = 20 s.

d. Determine the average velocity from t = 0 s to t = 20 s.

e. Find the velocity at t = 5 seconds.

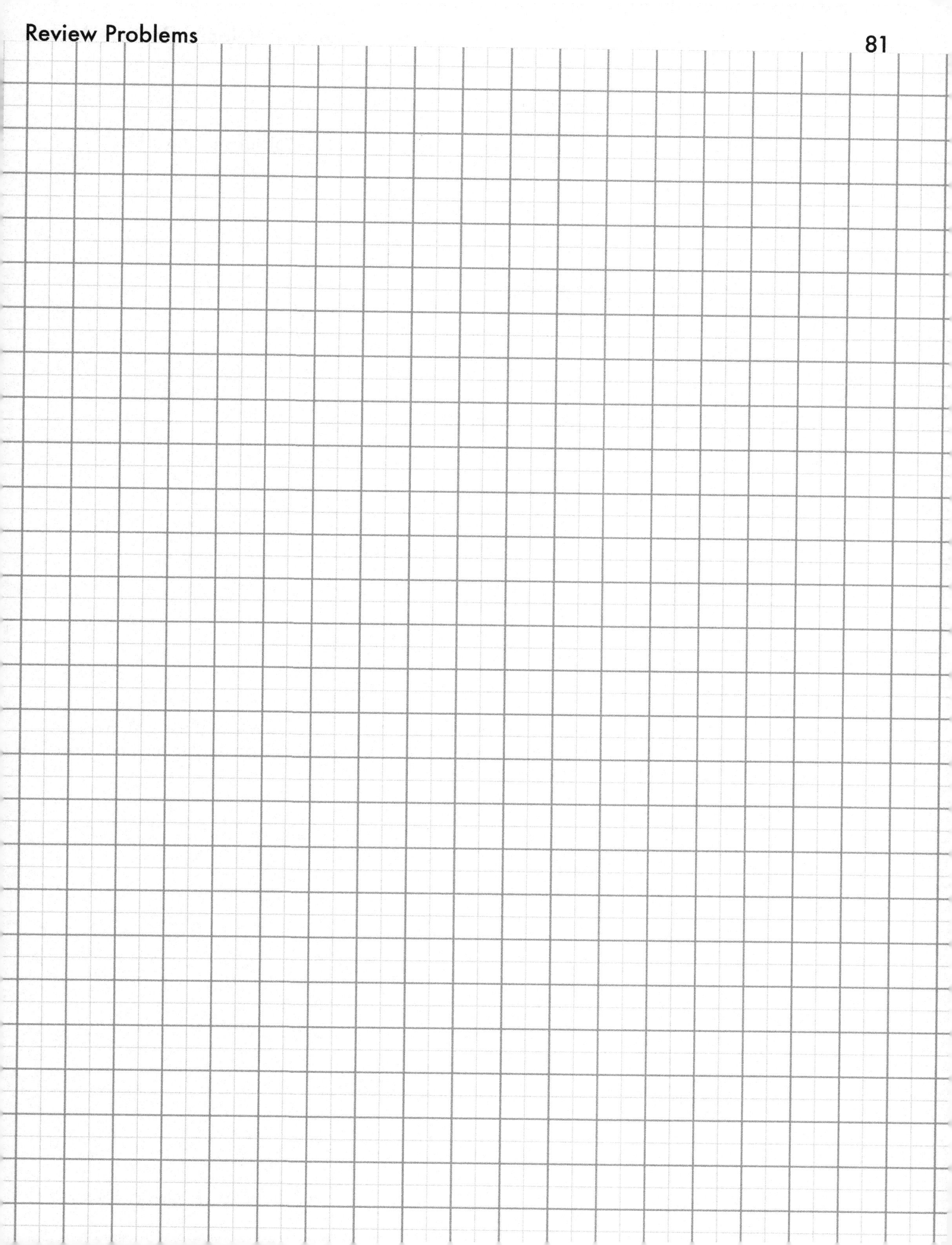

4. A basketball initially travels at 3 meters per second for 3 seconds:

a. Describe the motion of the ball after t = 3 seconds.

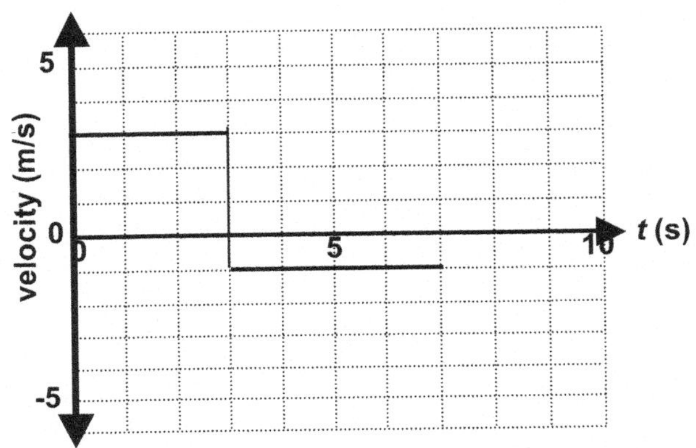

b. Draw a quantitative motion map that represents the motion of the object.

c. How far did the ball travel from t = 3 s to t = 7 s?

5. A racecar reaches a speed of 95 m/s after it is 450 meters past the starting line. If the car travels at a constant speed of 95 m/s for the next 12.5 s, how far will the car be from the starting line? Use the appropriate mathematical expression and show how units cancel.

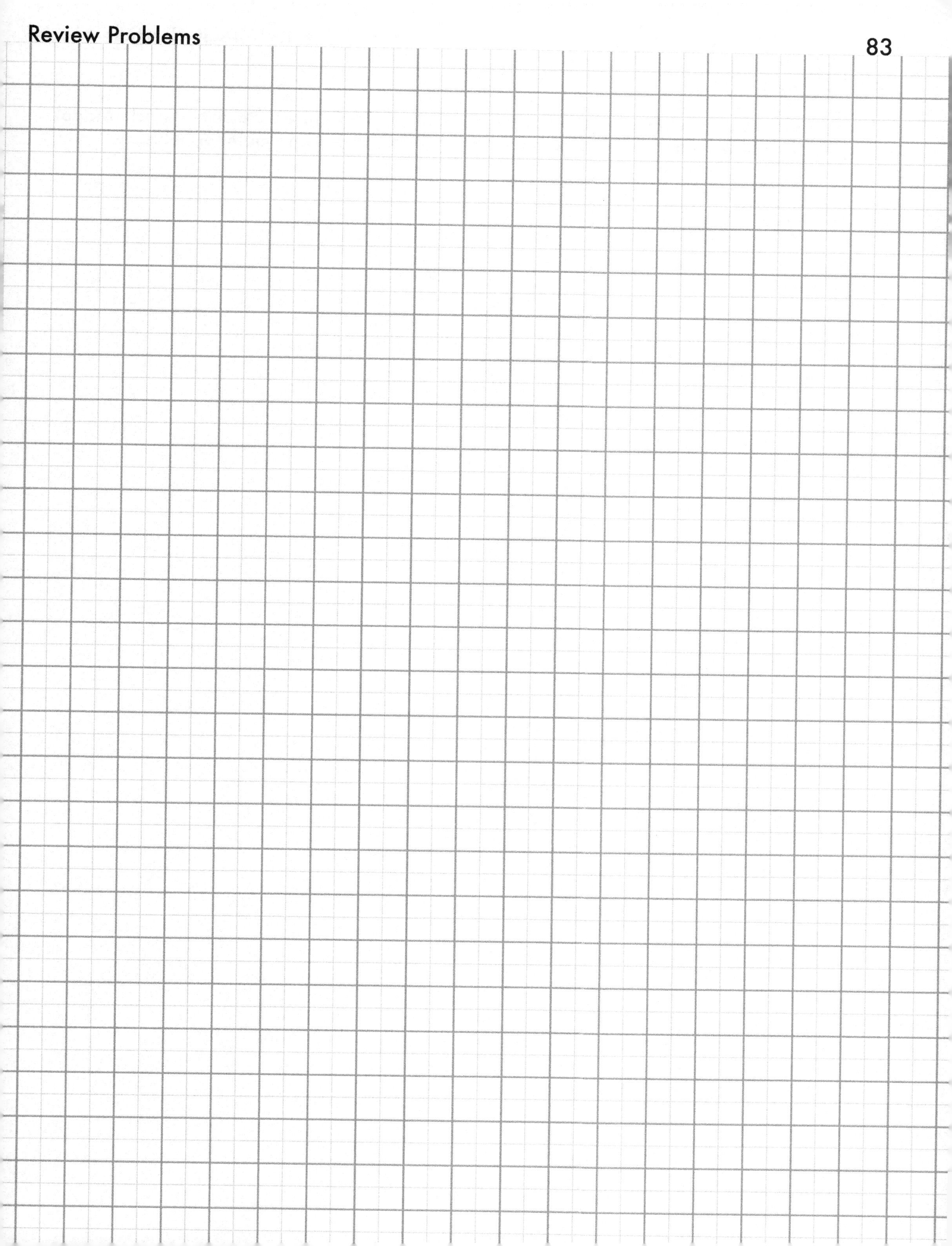

Model Summary

This is a place to summarize different representations of the Constant Velocity Particle Model. Representations include graphs, diagrams, motion maps, words and math formulas.

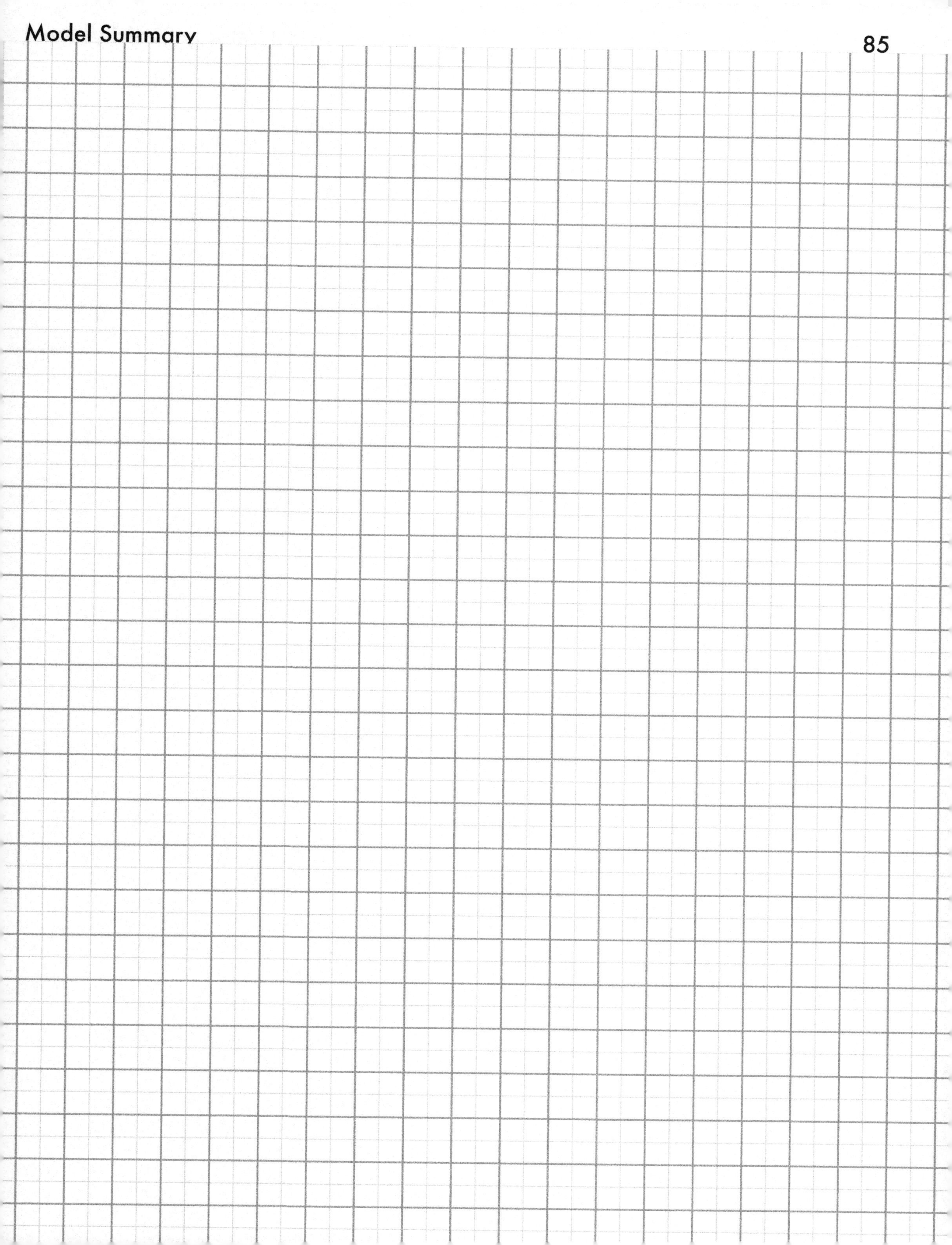

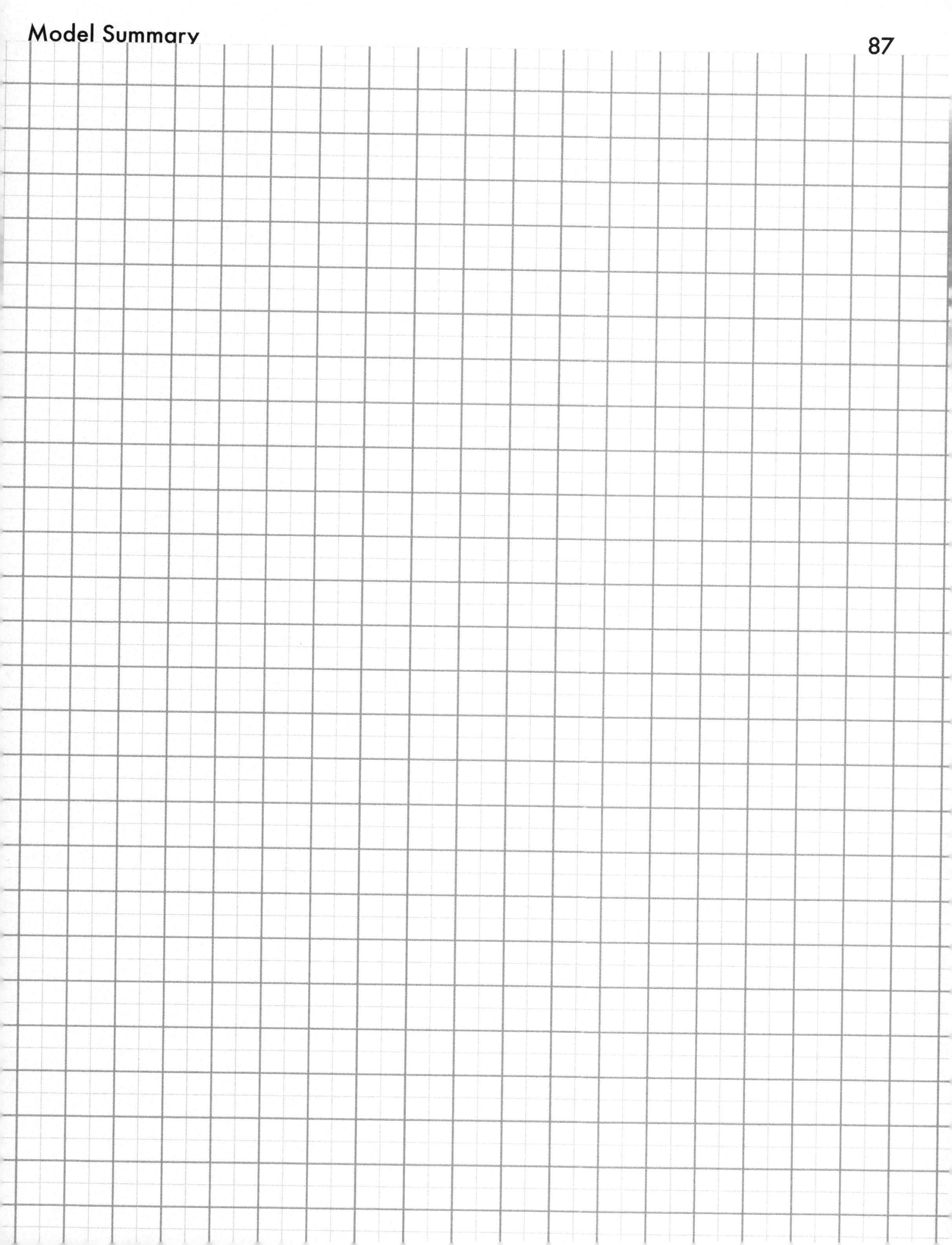

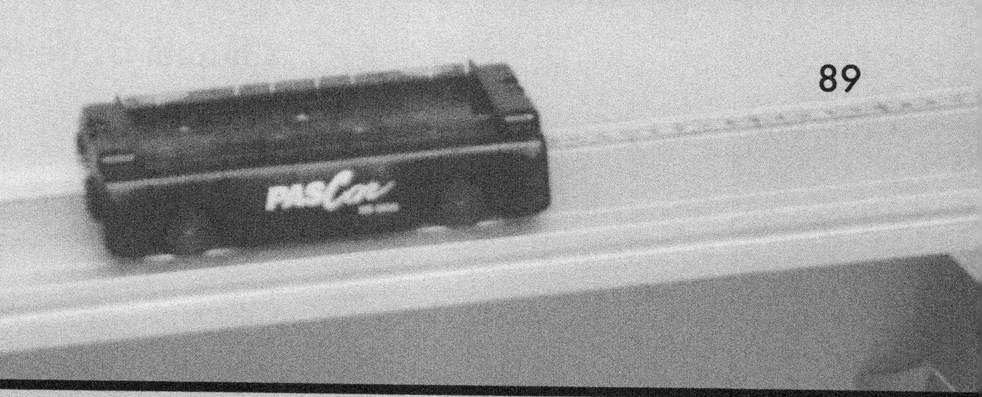

Chapter 3: Uniform Acceleration Particle Model

Chapter Sections

chapter 3 online help

Lab Notes

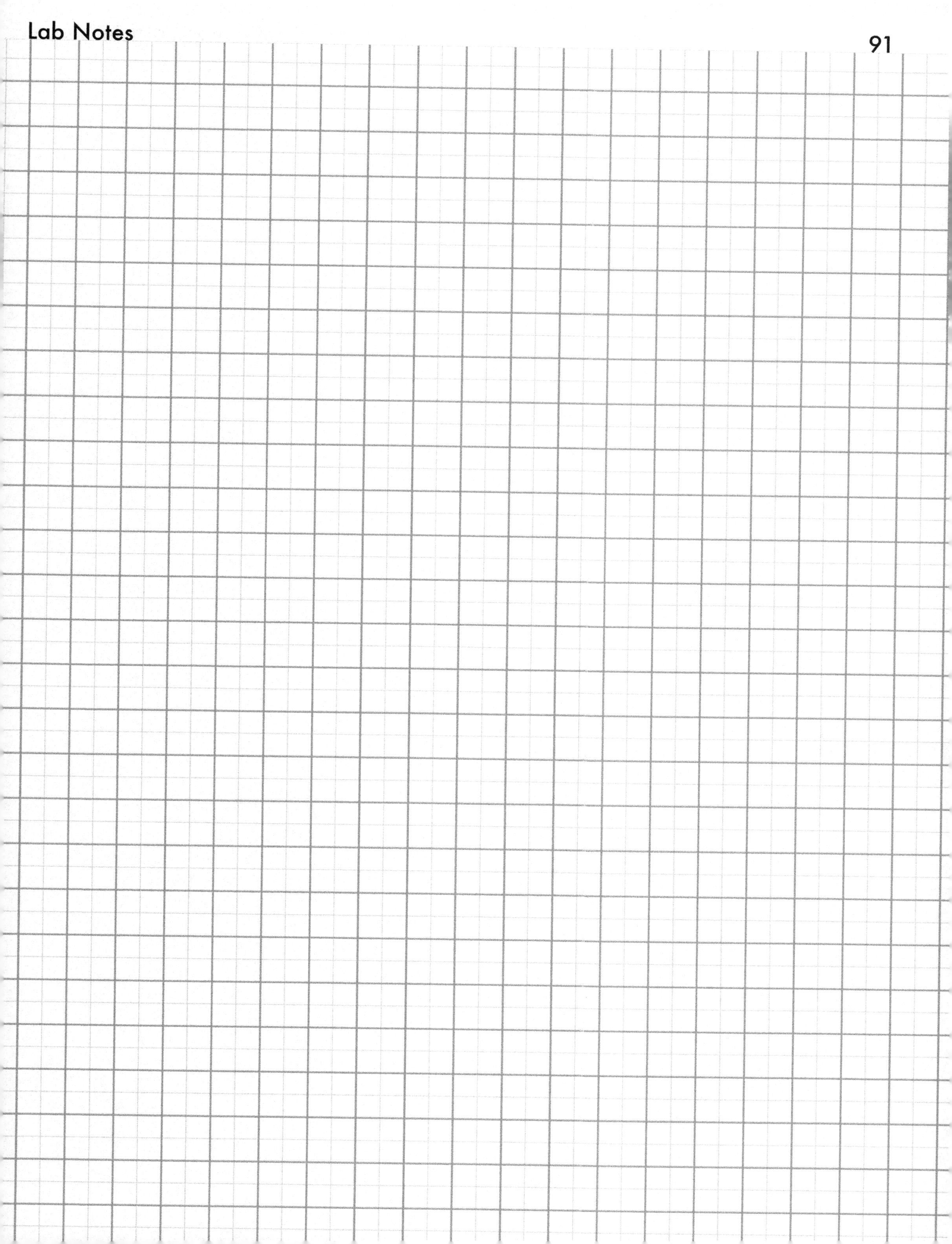

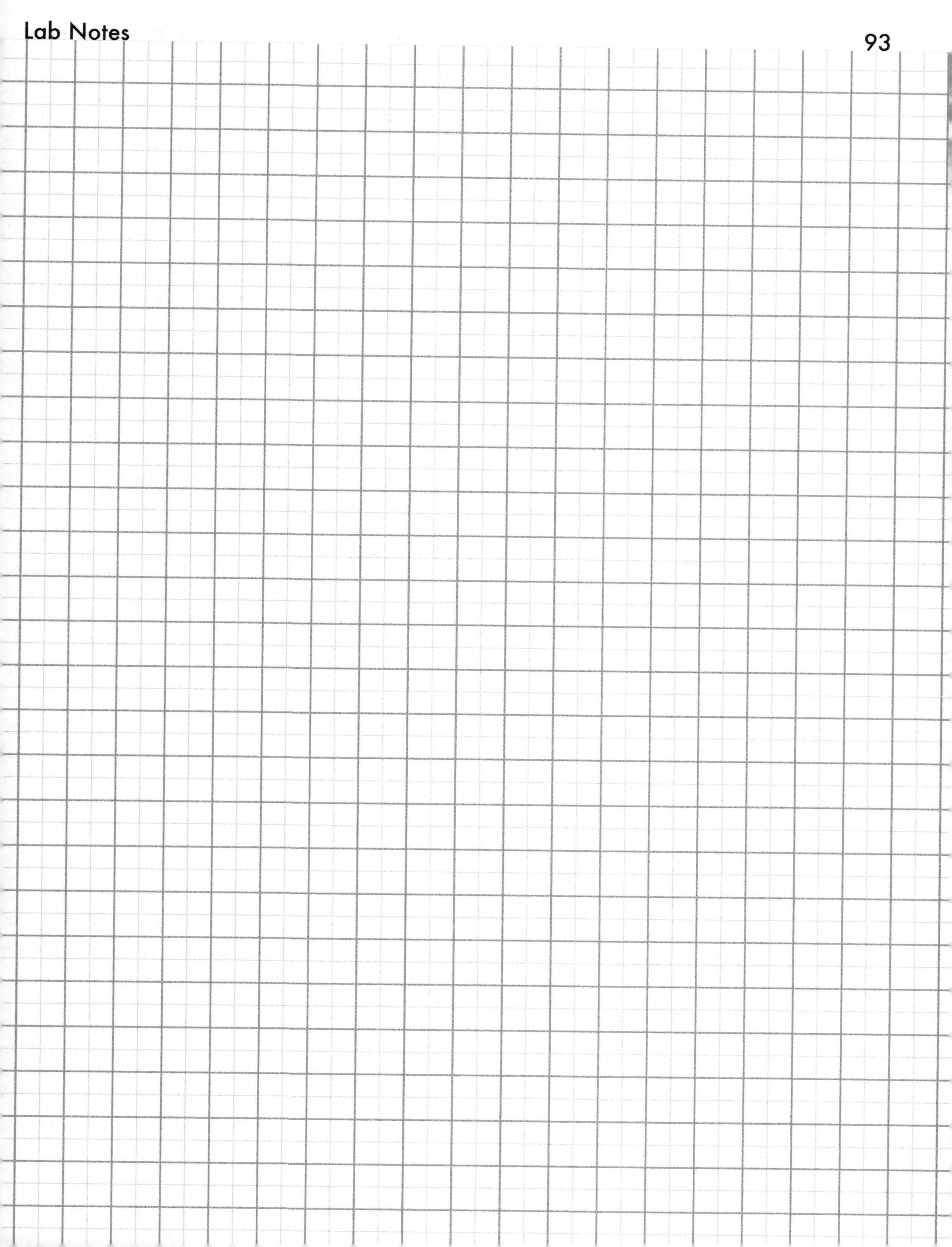

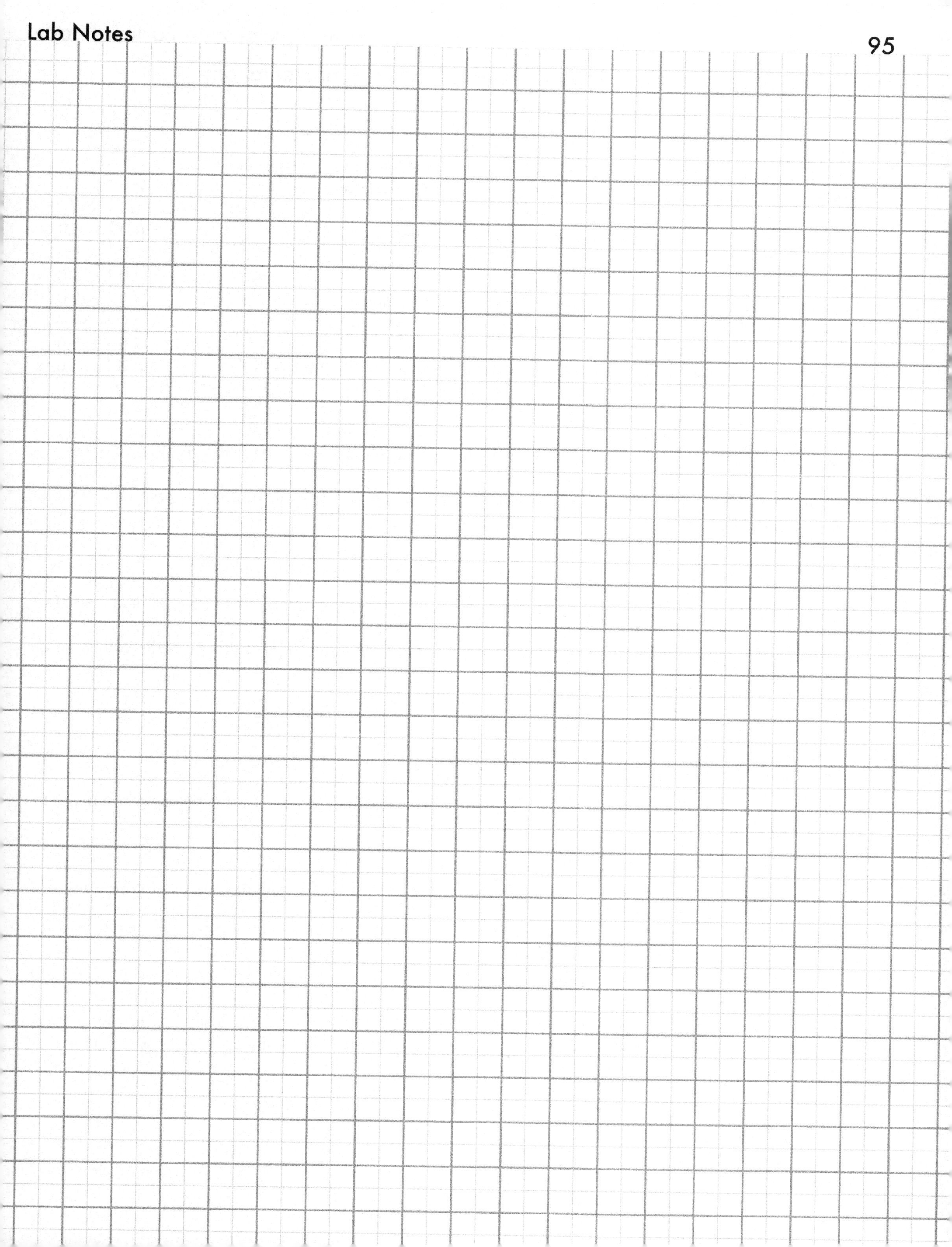

Worksheet 1: Development of Accelerated Motion Representations

t (s)	x (cm)
0.0	0.0
1.0	5.0
2.0	20.0
3.0	45.0
4.0	80.0
5.0	125.0
6.0	180.0

1. The data to the left are for a wheel rolling from rest down an incline. Using the position/time data given in the data table, plot the position vs. time graph.

2. What is the significance of the slope of a position vs. time graph?

3. What is happening to the slope of your position vs. time graph as time goes on?

4. Explain what your answers to questions 2 and 3 tell you about the motion of the wheel.

5. On the position vs. time graph, draw a line which connects the point at $t = 0$ to the point at $t = 6.0$ s.

6. Calculate the slope of this line in the space below. Explain what the slope of this line tells you about the motion of the wheel.

7. On the position vs. time graph, draw a line which connects the point at t = 2.0 s to the point at t = 4.0 s.

8. Calculate the slope of this line in the space below. Explain what the slope of this line tells you about the motion of the wheel.

9. On the position vs. time graph, draw a line tangent to the graph at t = 3.0 s.

10. Calculate the slope of this line in the space below. Explain what the slope of this line tells you about the motion of the wheel.

11. Compare the slopes you have calculated in questions 6, 8, and 10. Explain the results of your comparison.

12. Consider an object accelerates uniformly. If you were to calculate the average speed of the object for a given interval of time, would the object ever be traveling with an instantaneous speed equal to that average speed? If so when? Explain!

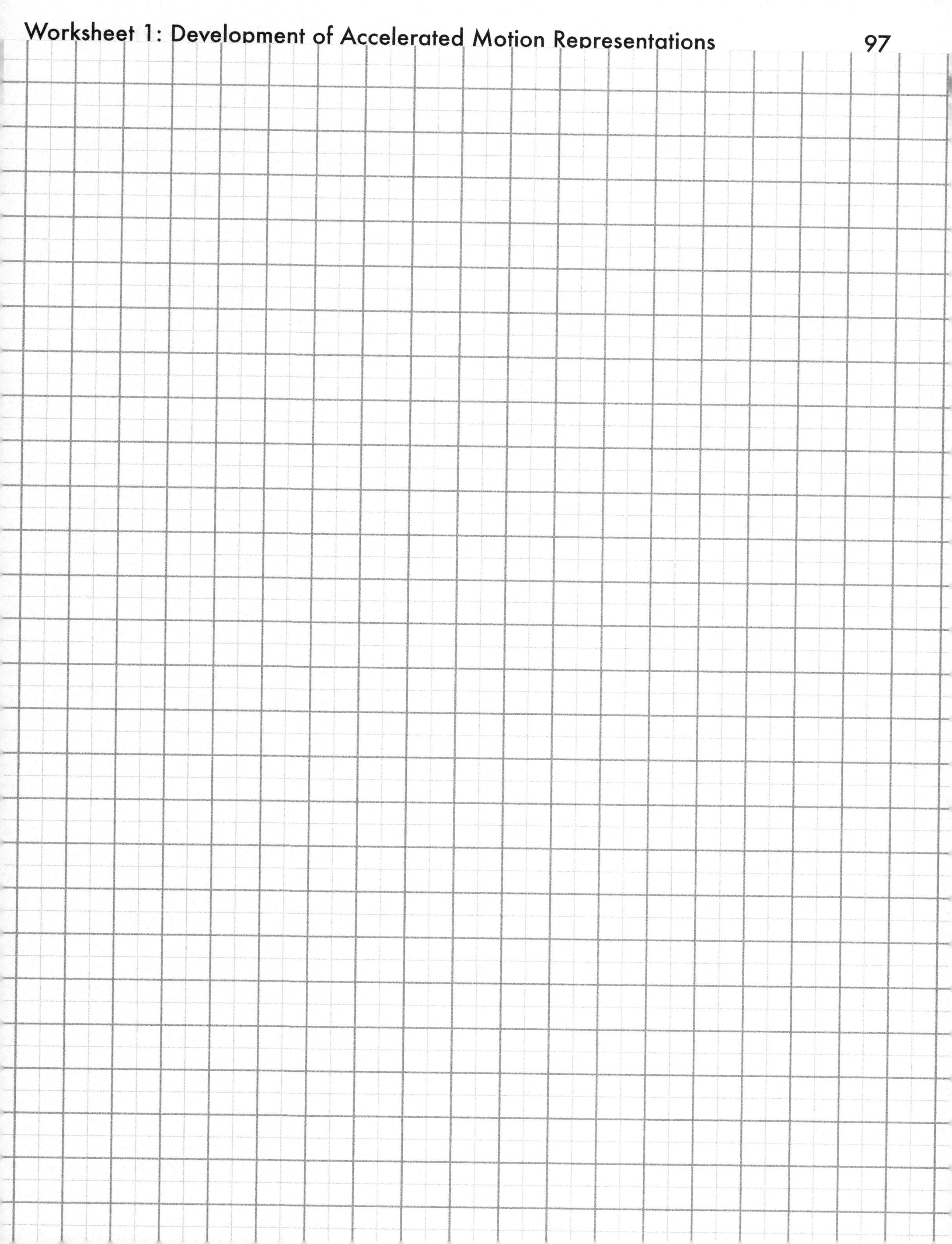

13 Use the position vs. time data to complete the data tablebelow. Using the completed table, plot a velocity vs. time graph on the graph paper to the right. Perform a mathematical analysis of the resulting velocity vs. time graph in the space provided, to yield a mathematical model that describes the relationship between velocity and time for this wheel.

t	x	Δt	Δx	t_{mid}	$\bar{v}$
(s)	(cm)	(s)	(cm)	(s)	(cm/s)
0.0	0.0				
1.0	5.0				
2.0	20.0				
3.0	45.0				
4.0	80.0				
5.0	125.0				
6.0	180.0				

Mathematical Analysis:

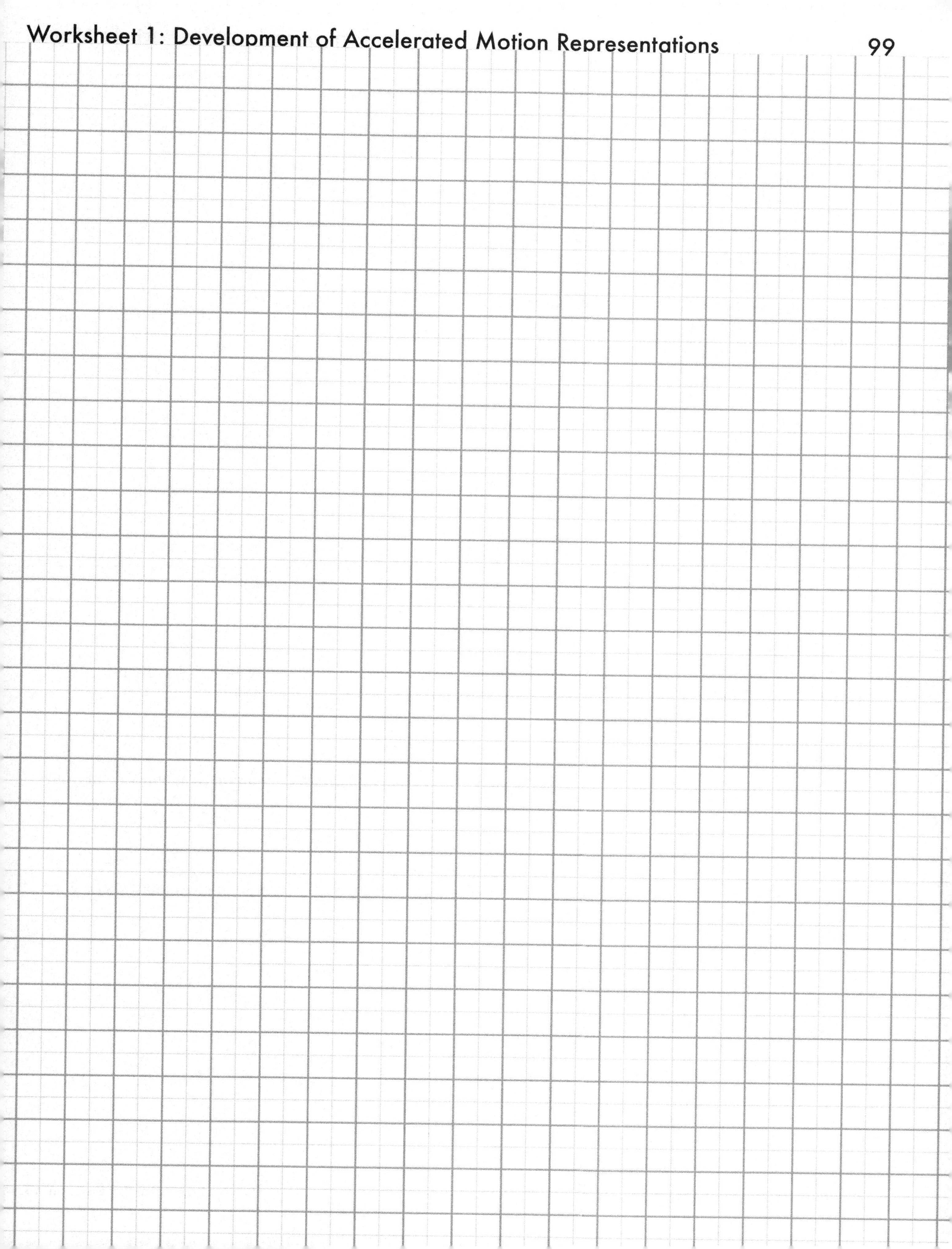

14. Based on the shape of your position vs. time graph for these data, it should be clear to you that further manipulation of the data is necessary in order to develop a mathematical model that describes the relationship between position and time. Complete the data table below and plot a graph of position vs. time^2. Why were you asked to square time and make this new plot? In the space provided, perform the mathematical analysis of the position vs. time^2 graph to develop the mathematical model that describes the relationship between position and time.

t	x	t^2
(s)	(cm)	(s^2)
0.0	0.0	
1.0	5.0	
2.0	20.0	
3.0	45.0	
4.0	80.0	
5.0	125.0	
6.0	180.0	

Mathematical Analysis:

15. What is the significance of the slope of your velocity vs. time graph? Explain!

16. Compare the slope of your velocity vs. time graph to the slope of your position vs. time^2 graph. What does this say about the significance of the slope of your position vs. time^2 graph.

17. Write the equation that relates velocity and time for the wheel using the mathematical analysis of your velocity vs. time graph.

18. Write the equation that relates position and time for the wheel using the mathematical analysis of your position vs. time^2 graph.

19. What does the area under a velocity vs. time graph tell you?

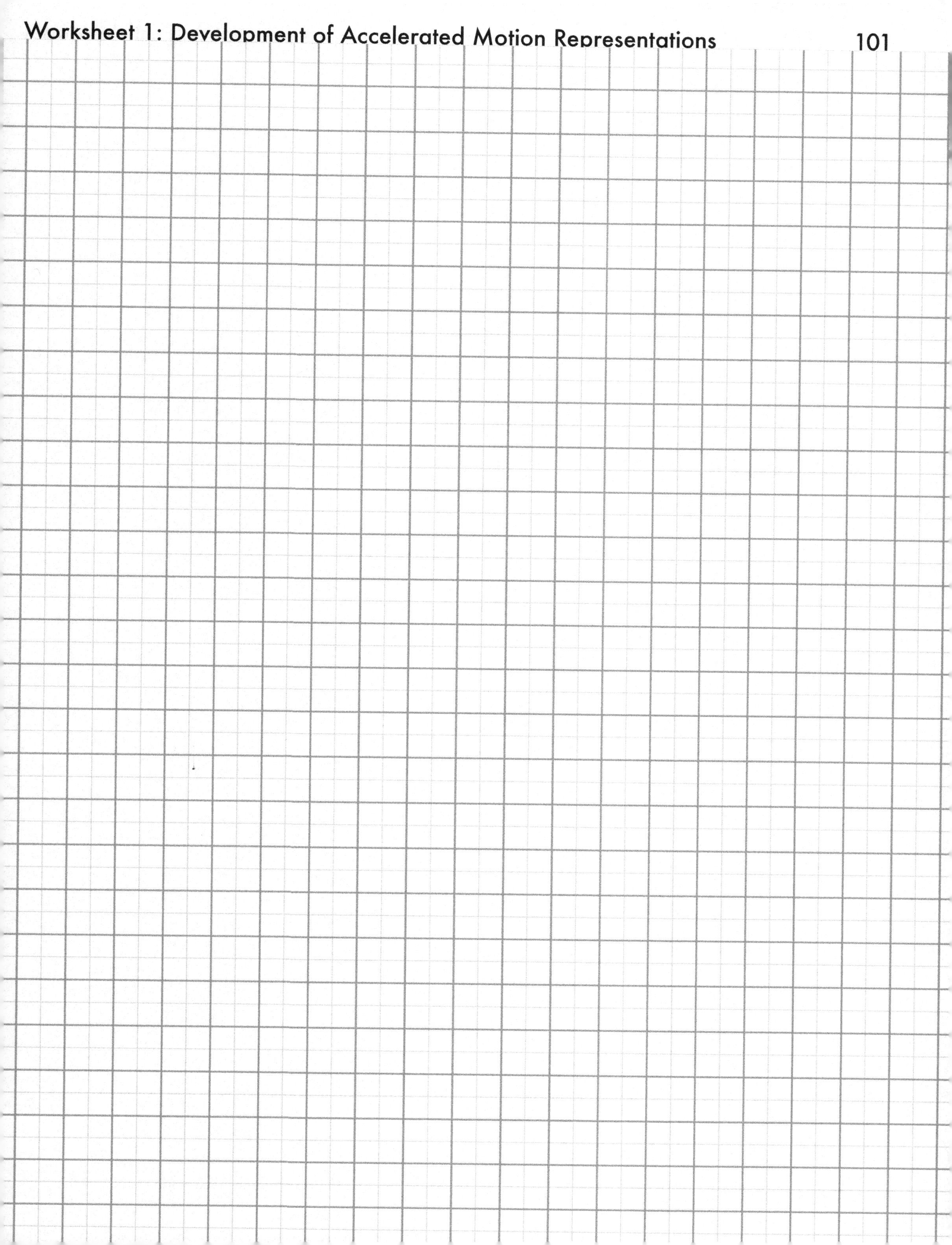

Worksheet 2: Accelerated Motion Representations

1. Draw a motion map along the ramp for the motion of the ball as it rolls down the ramp from rest.

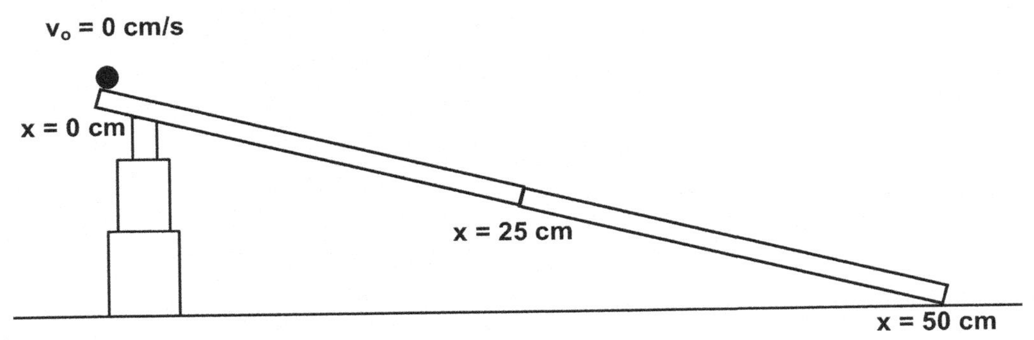

Draw graphs corresponding to the motion of the ball in **problem 1**.

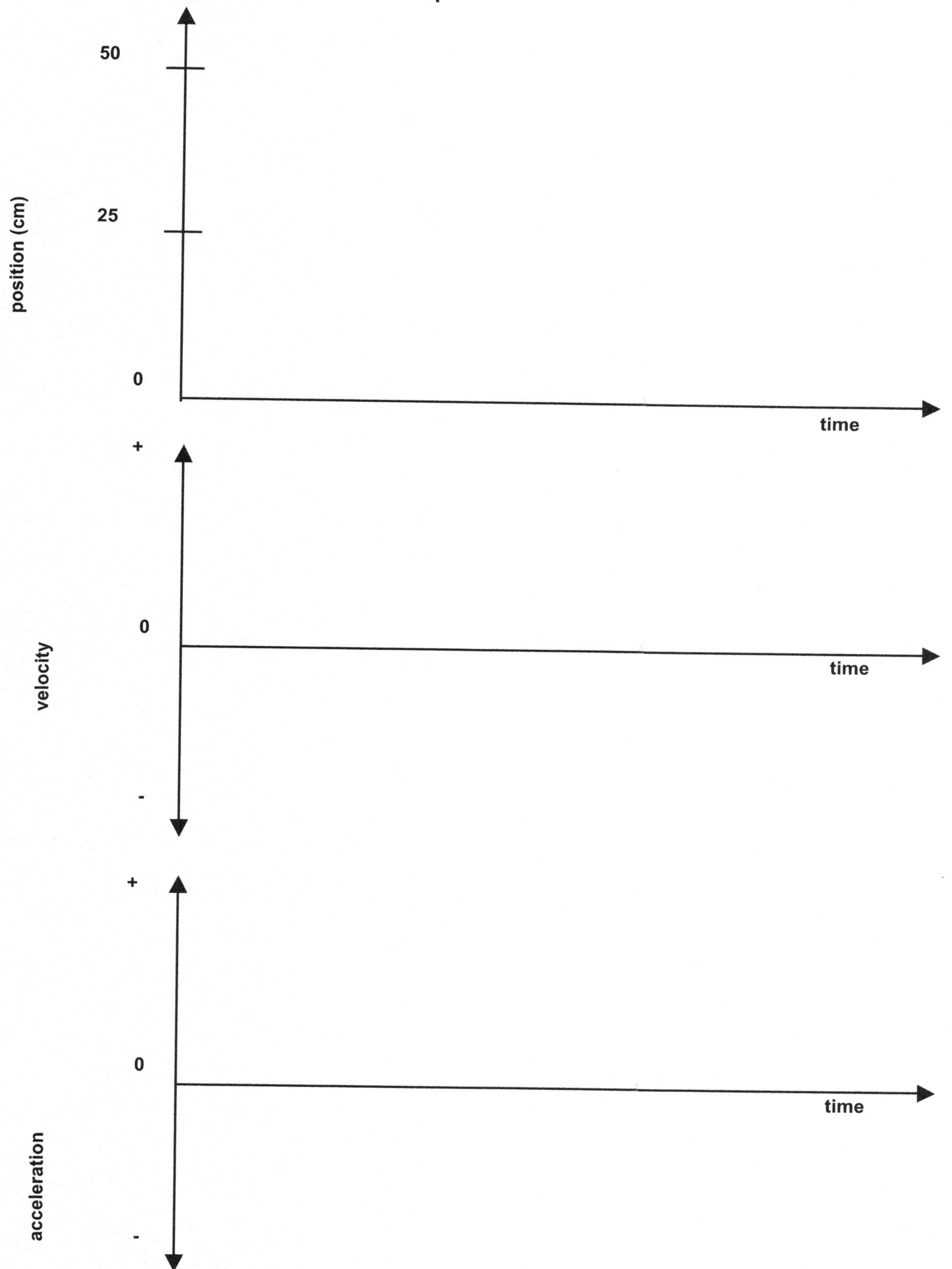
50
25
0
position (cm)
time
+
0
-
velocity
time
+
0
-
acceleration
time

2. Draw a motion map along the ramp for the motion of the ball as it rolls up the ramp and across the level section.

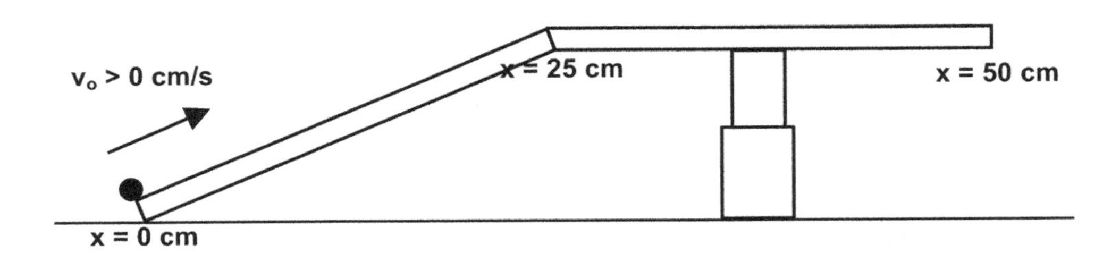

Draw graphs corresponding to the motion of the ball in **problem 2**.

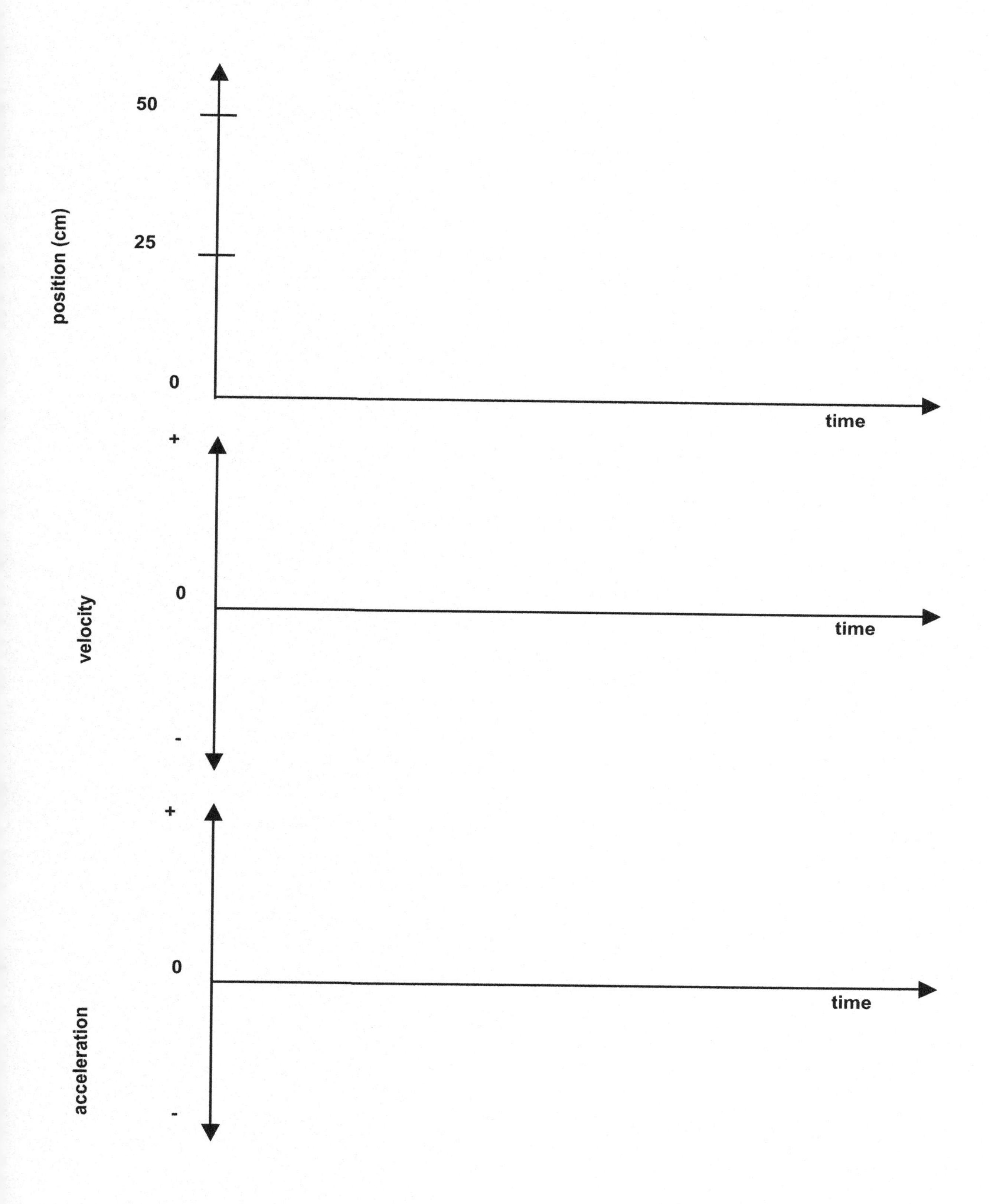
50
25
position (cm)
0
time
+
0
velocity
time
-
+
0
time
acceleration
-

3. Draw a motion map along the ramp for the motion of the ball as it rolls down the ramps from rest.

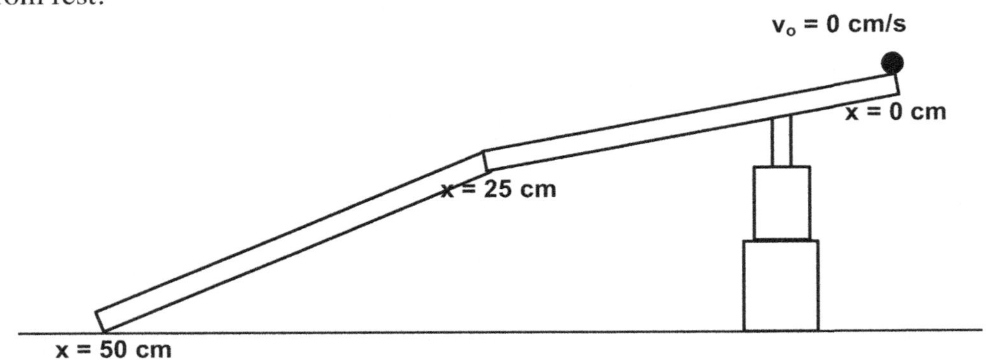

Draw graphs corresponding to the motion of the ball in **problem 3**.

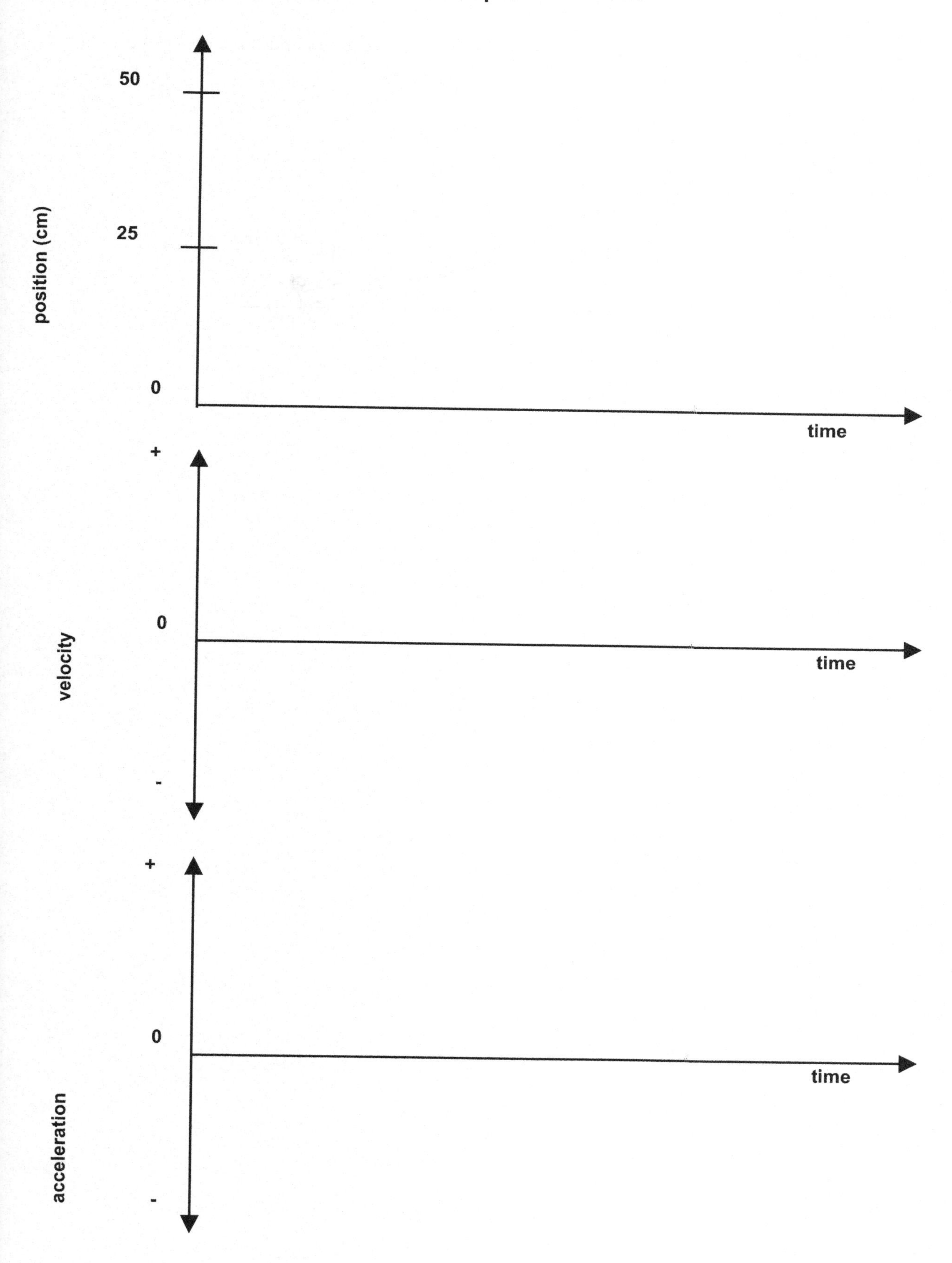
position (cm)
50
25
0
time
velocity
+
0
-
time
acceleration
+
0
-
time

4. Draw a motion map along the ramp for the motion of the ball as it rolls up and back down the ramp.

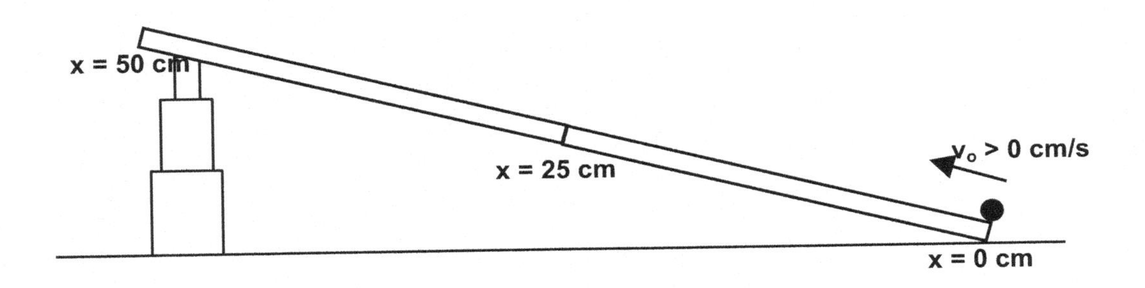

Draw graphs corresponding to the motion of the ball in **problem 4**.

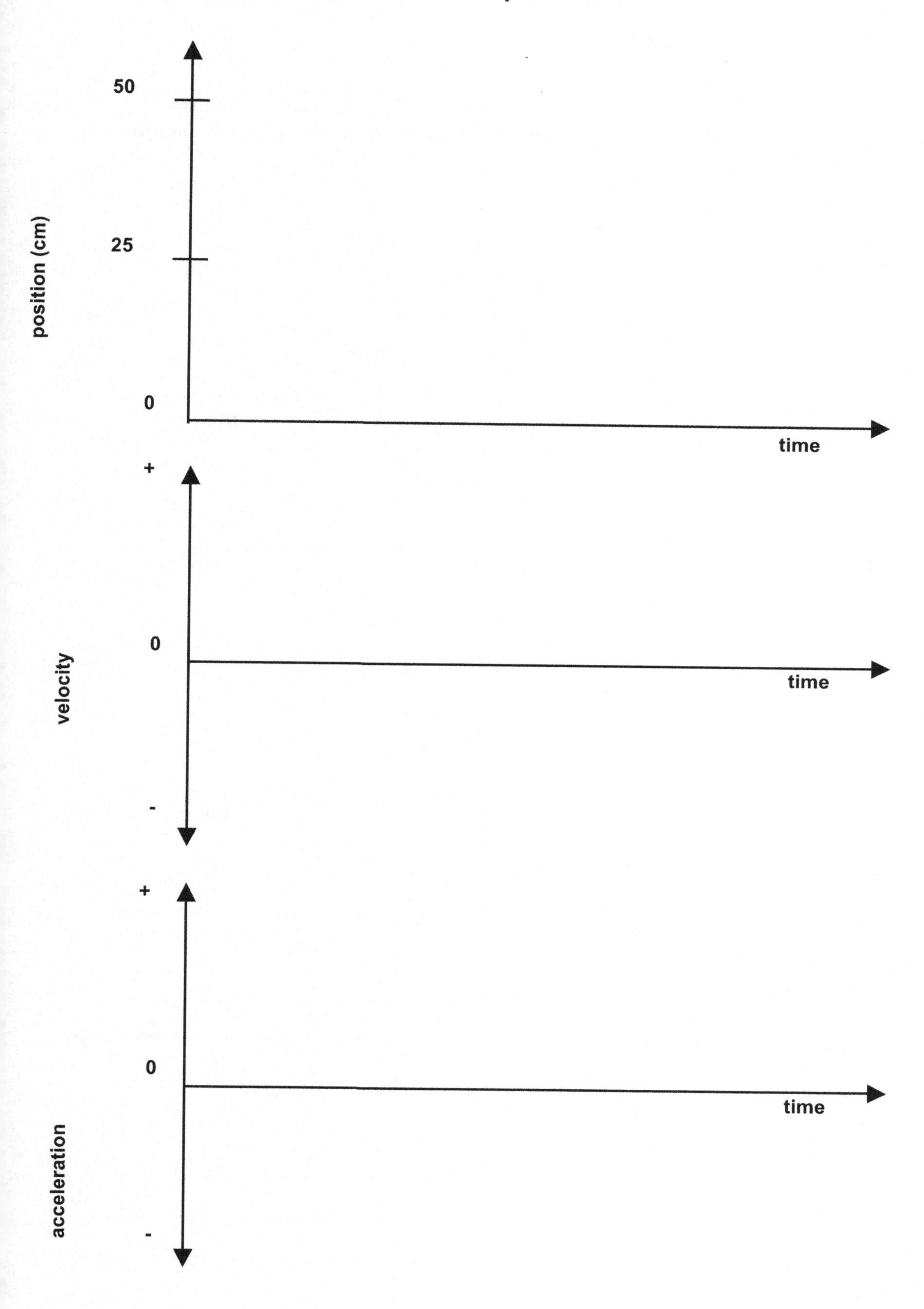

50
25
0
position (cm)
time
+
0
velocity
-
time
+
0
acceleration
-
time

Worksheet 3: Stacks of Kinematic Graphs

Given the following position vs time graphs, construct the corresponding velocity vs time and acceleration vs time graphs, create velocity and acceleration motion maps and describe the motion. If you see a dashed line in a graph it tells you the motion changes at that time.

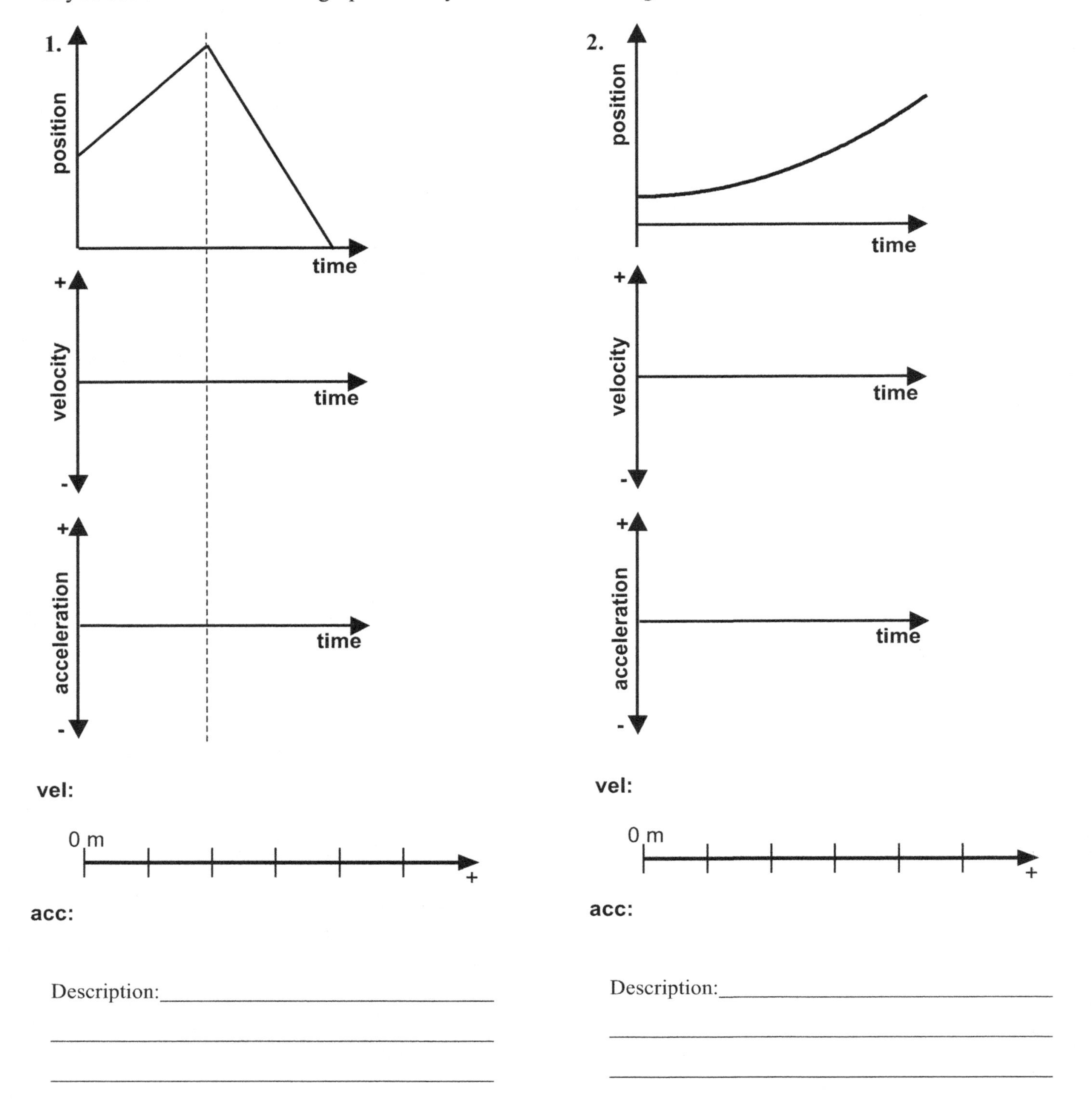

Description:______________________________

Description:______________________________

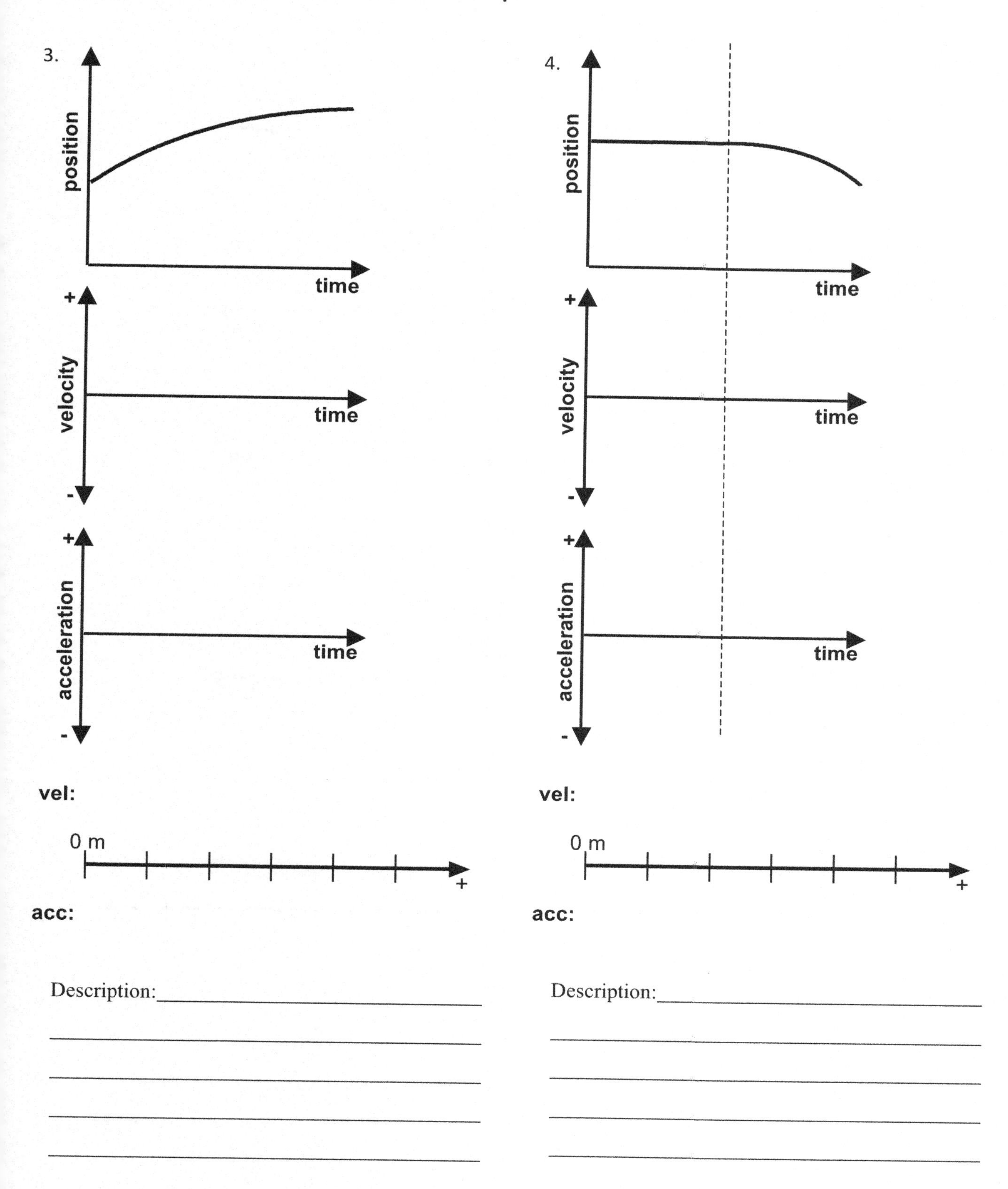
3.
position
time
+
velocity
time
-
+
acceleration
time
-
vel:
0 m
+
acc:
Description:
4.
position
time
+
velocity
time
-
+
acceleration
time
-
vel:
0 m
+
acc:
Description:

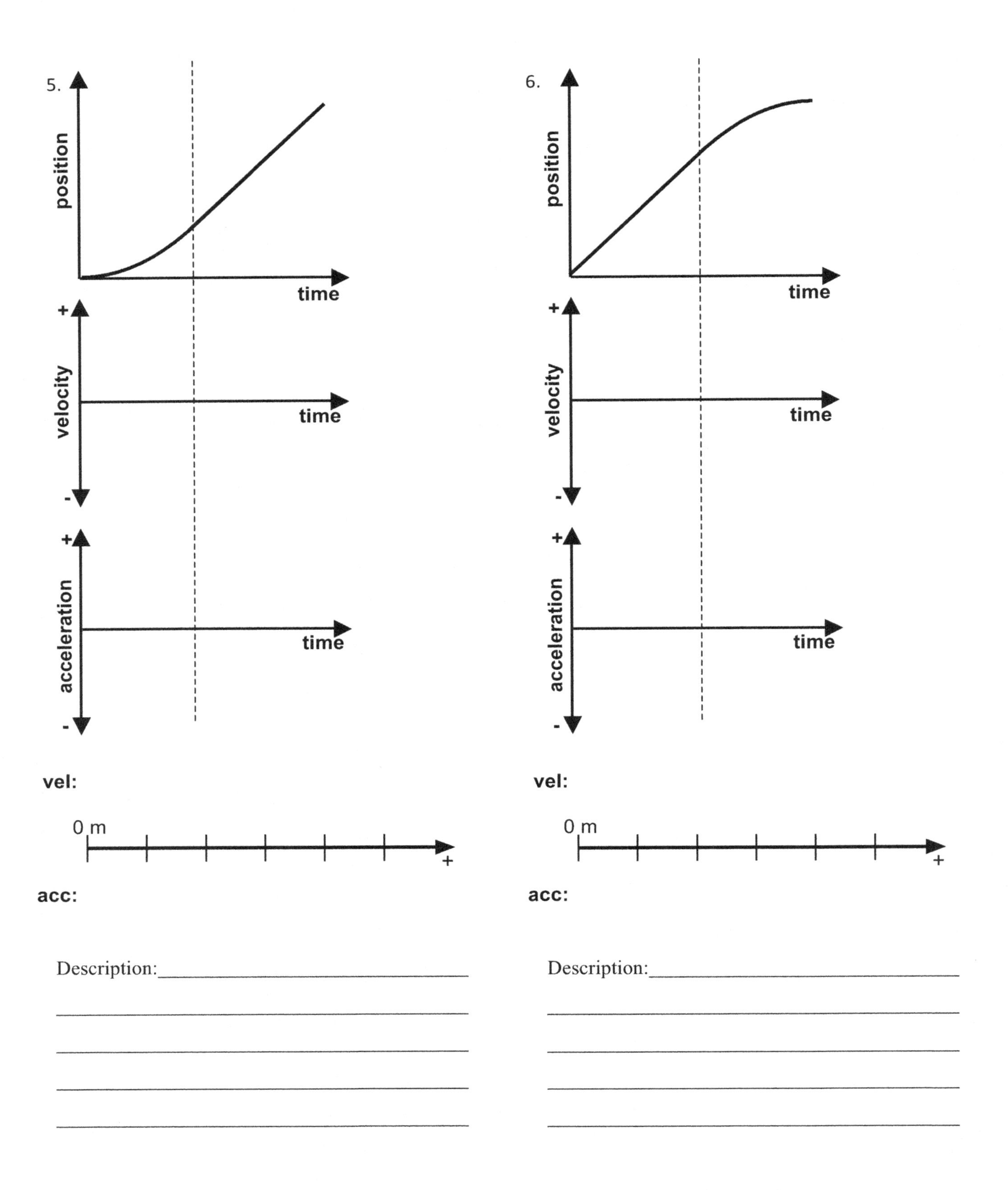

Description:____

____

____

____

____

Description:____

____

____

____

____

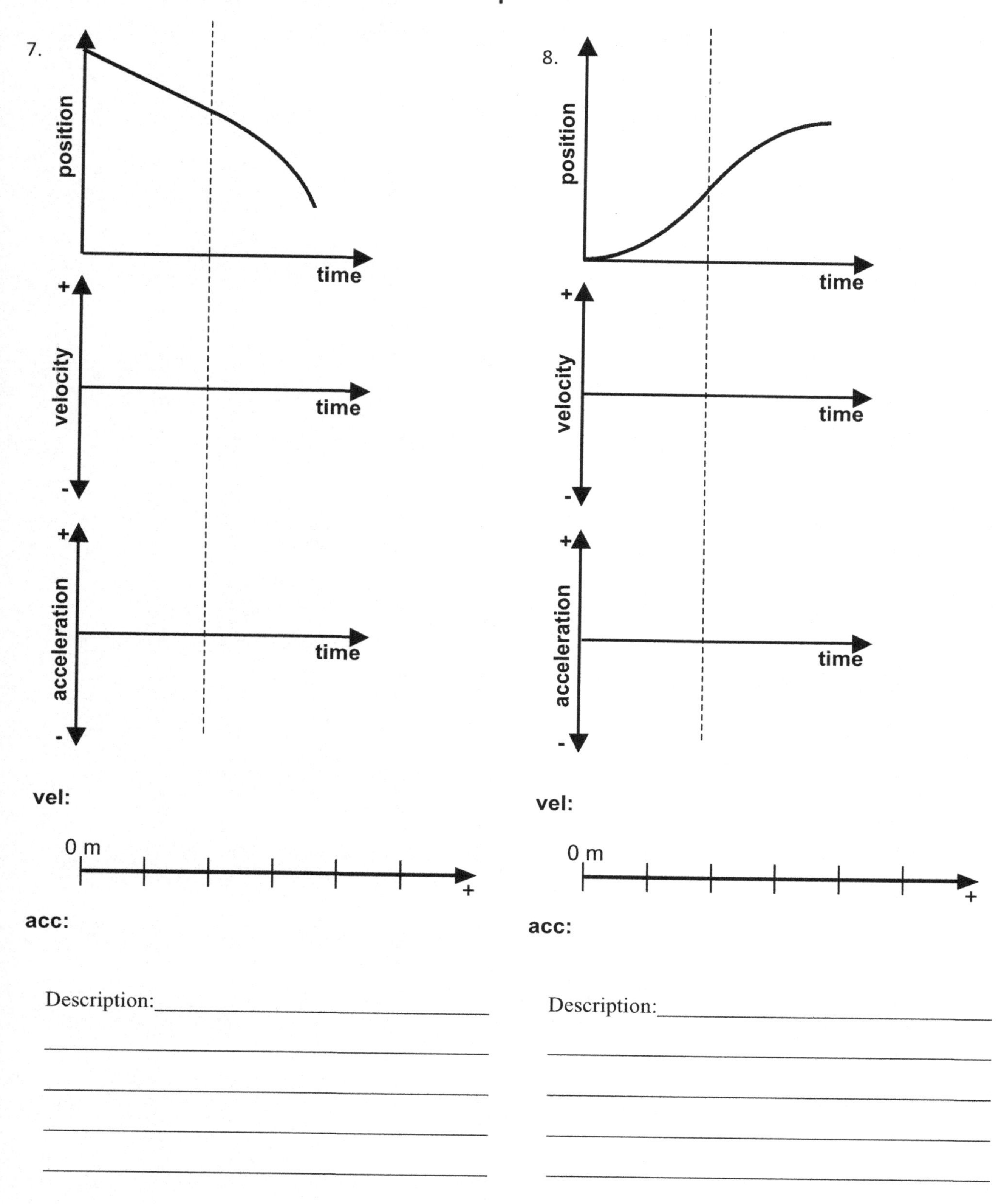
7.
position
time
velocity
time
acceleration
time
vel:
0 m
acc:
Description:
8.
position
time
velocity
time
acceleration
time
vel:
0 m
acc:
Description:

Worksheet 4: Interpreting Graphs of Accelerated Motion

Object A:

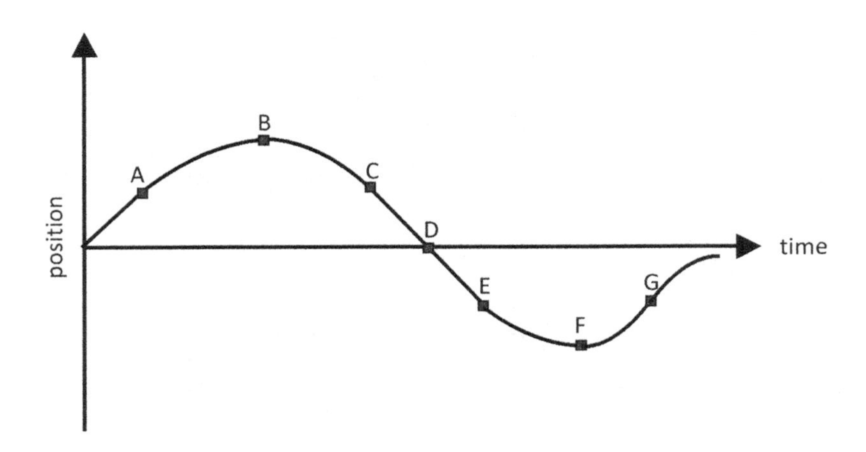

a. Where on the graph above is the object moving most slowly? How do you know?

b. Between which points is the object speeding up? How do you know?

c. Between which points is the object slowing down? How do you know?

d. Where on the graph above is the object changing direction? How do you know?

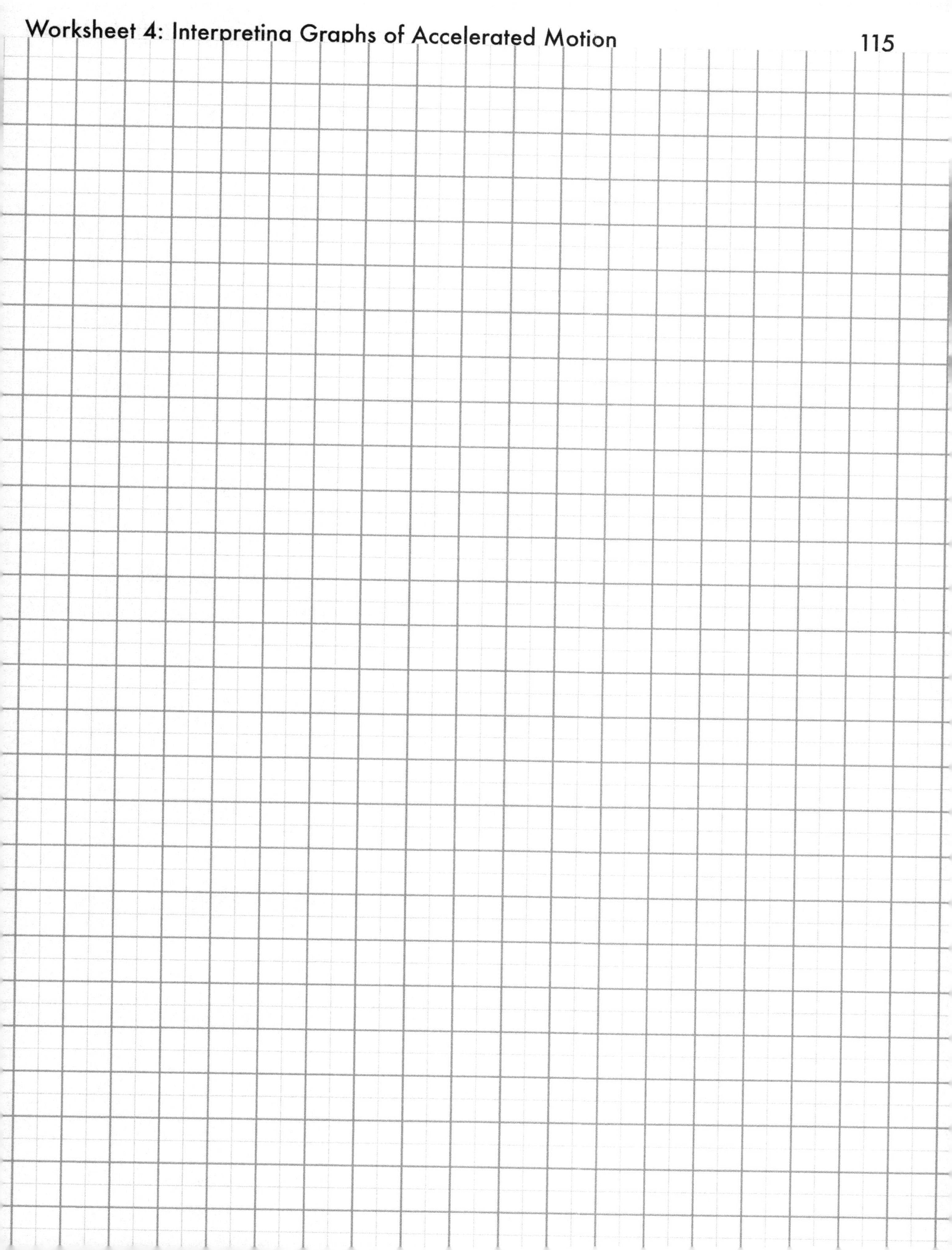

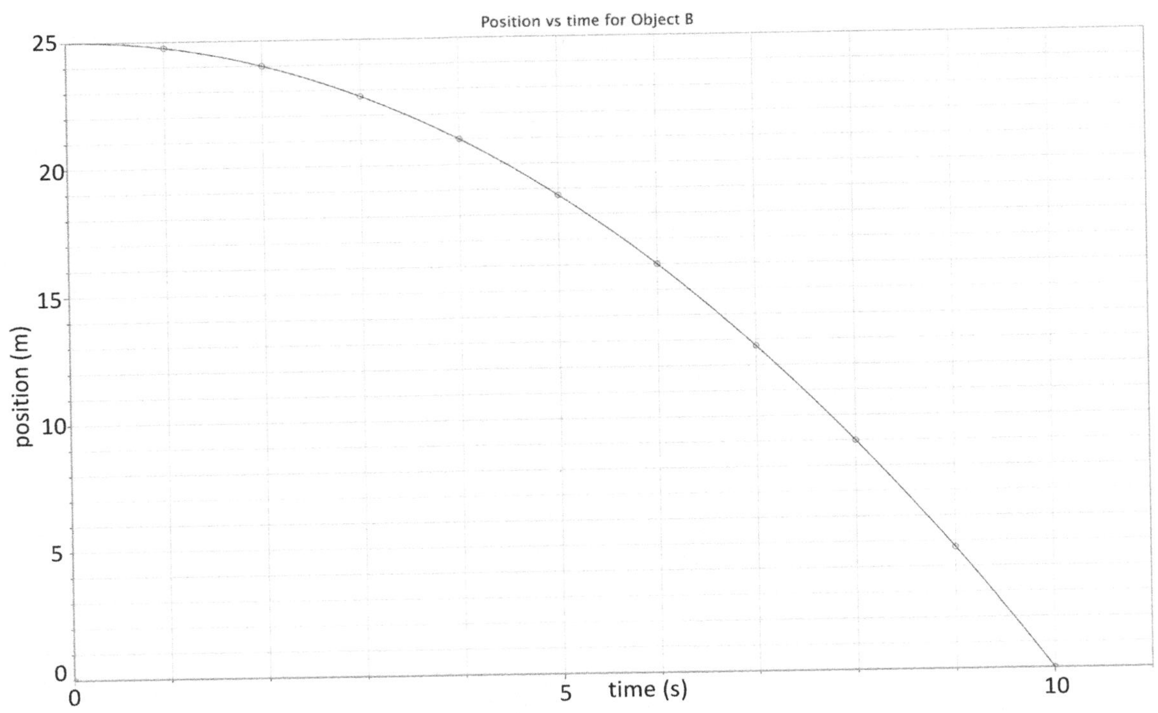

a. Give a written description of the motion.

b. Represent object B's motion with a motion map. Include both velocity and acceleration vectors.

vel:

0m

\+

acc:

c. Find the **displacement** from t = 2.0 s to t = 8.0s.

d. Find the **average velocity** from t = 2.0 s to t = 8.0s.

e. Find the **instantaneous velocity** at t = 2.0 s and t = 8.0s by finding slopes of tangents.

f. Determine the **average acceleration** from t = 2.0 s to t = 8.0s.

g. What is the **instantaneous velocity** at t = 5.0 s? Explain.

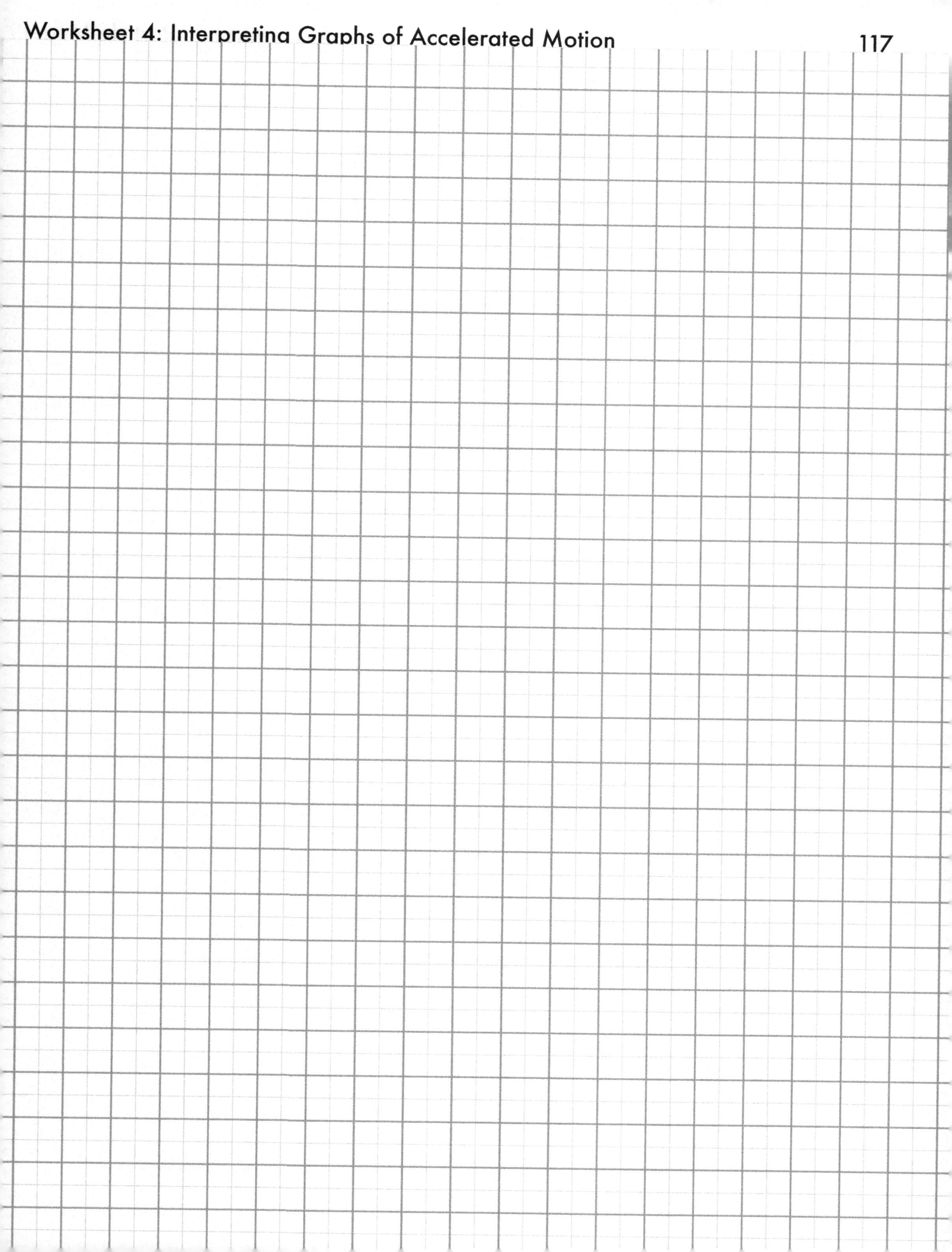

Object C:

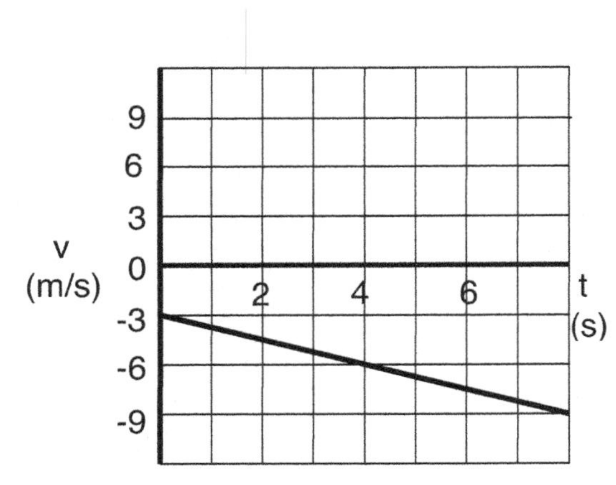

a. Give a written description of the motion.

b. Sketch a motion map. Be sure to include both velocity and acceleration vectors.

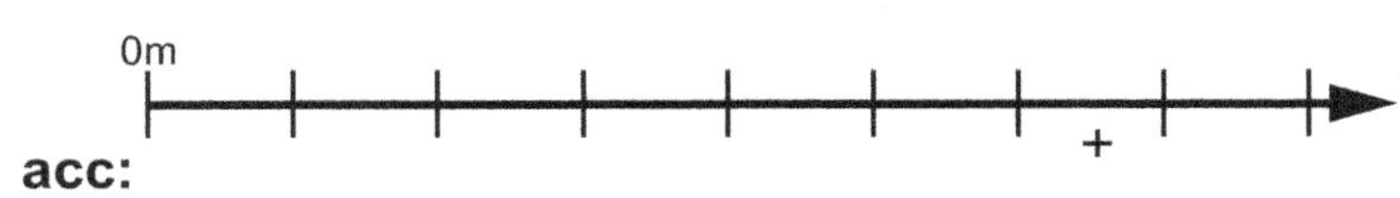

c. Determine the displacement from t = 0s to t = 4 s.

d. Determine the displacement from t = 4 s to t = 8 s.

e. Determine the average acceleration of the object's motion.

f. Sketch a possible x-t graph for the motion of the object.
Explain why your graph is only one of many possible graphs.

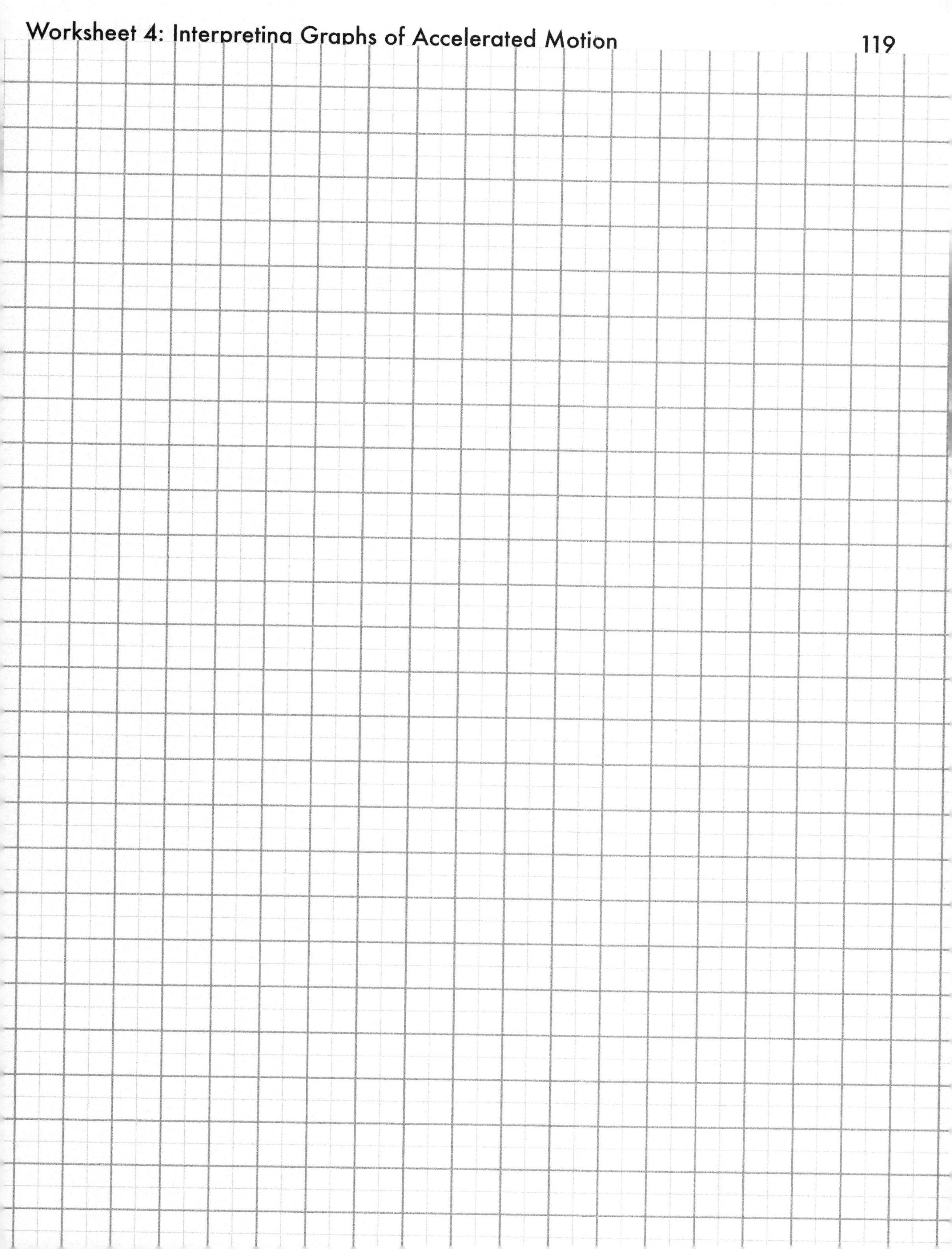

Object D:

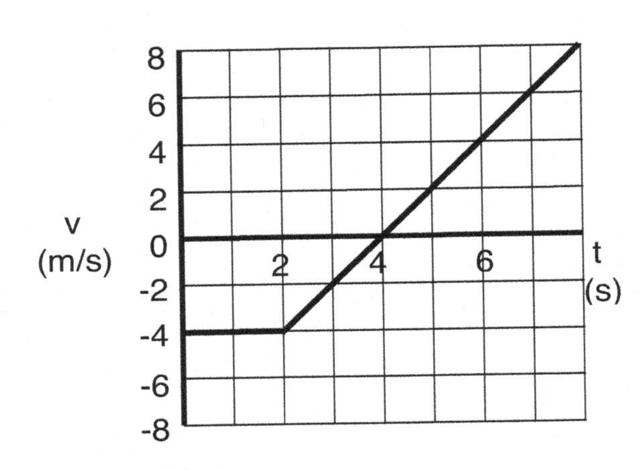

a. Give a written description of the motion.

b. Sketch a motion map. Be sure to include both velocity and acceleration vectors.

vel:

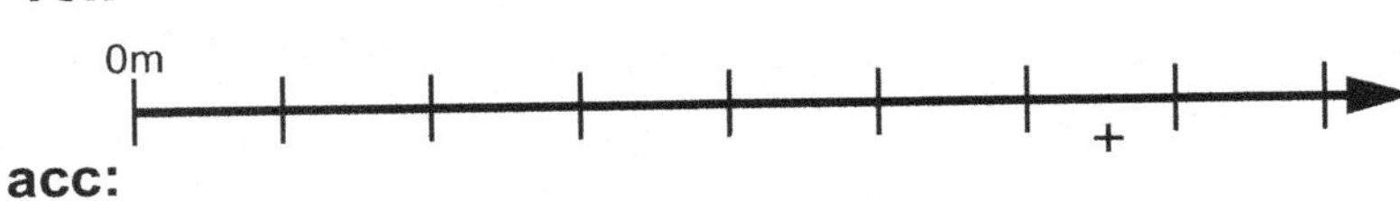

acc:

c. Determine the displacement from t = 0 s to t = 4 s.

d. Determine the displacement from t = 4 s to t = 8 s.

e. Determine the displacement from t = 2 s to t = 6 s.

f. Determine the object's acceleration at t = 4 s.

g. Sketch a possible x-t graph for the motion of the object.
Explain why your graph is only one of many possible graphs.

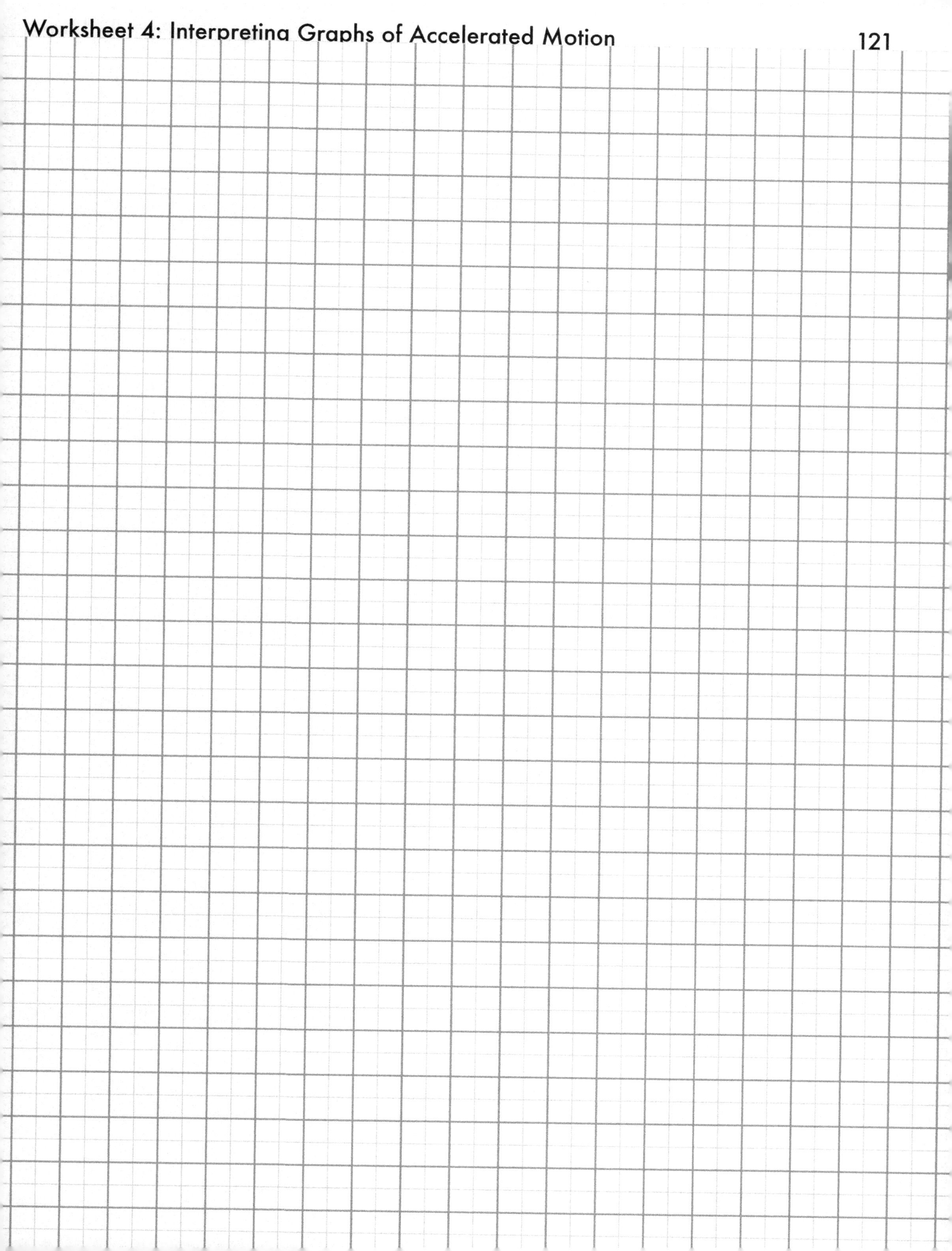

Worksheet 5: Quantitative Acceleration Problems

1. A poorly tuned car accelerates from rest to a speed of 28 m/s in 20 s.
   a. Make a well-labeled diagram of the situation.
   b. Make a well-labeled graphical representation of the situation.
   c. List given quantities and quantities to find as you determine:
      i. What is the average acceleration of the car?
      ii. How far does it travel in this time?

2. At t = 0 s a car has a speed of 30 m/s. After 6 s, its speed is 15 m/s.
   a. Make a well-labeled diagram of the situation.
   b. Make a well-labeled graphical representation of the situation.
   c. List given quantities and quantities to find as you determine:
      i. What is the average acceleration of the car?
      ii. How far does it travel in this time?

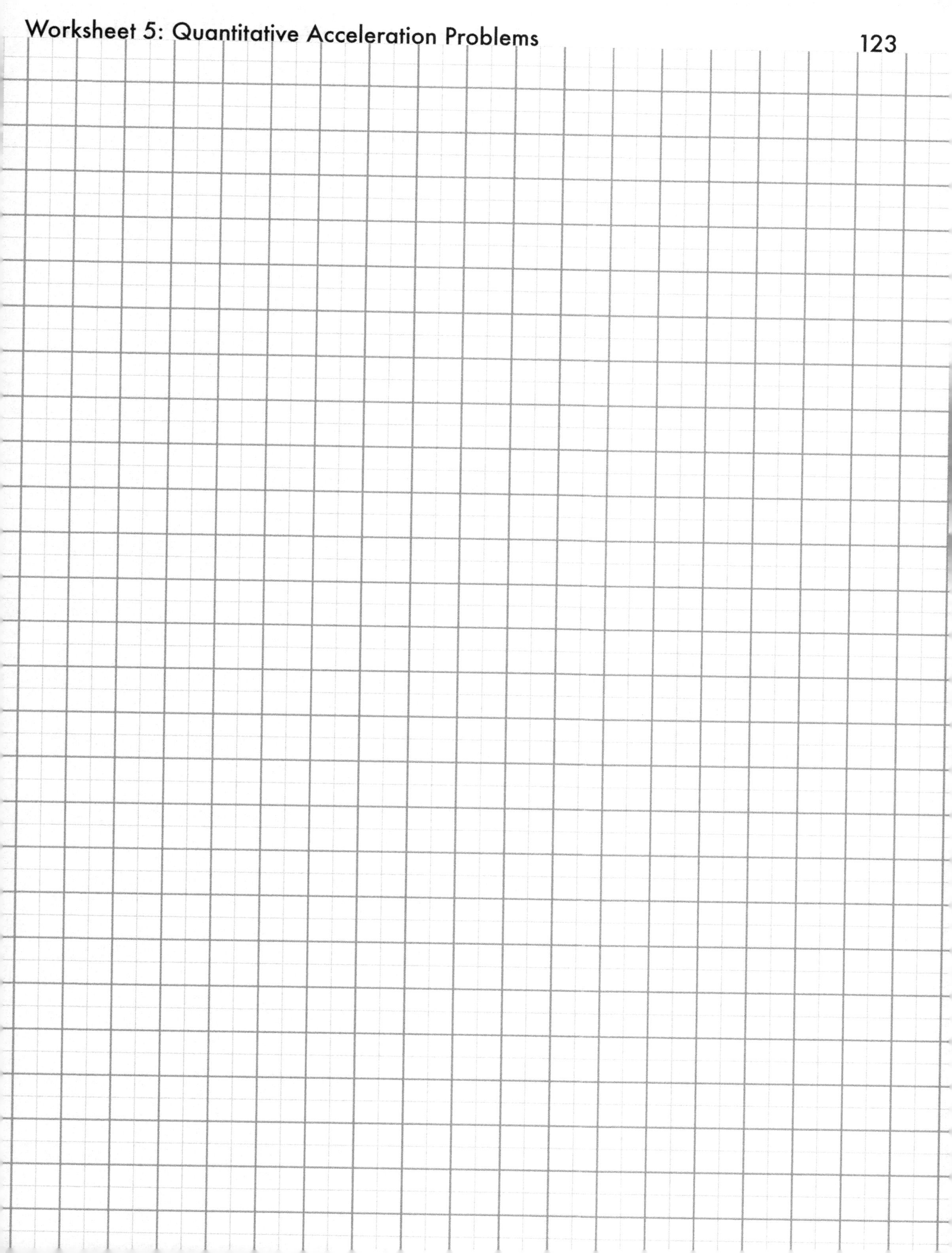

3. A student drops a rock from the top of a 30 meter tall building.
   a. Make a well-labeled diagram of the situation.
   b. Make a well-labeled graphical representation of the situation.
   c. List given quantities and quantities to find as you determine how fast the rock will be traveling just before impact.

4. A bus initially moving at 20 m/s slows by 4 m/s each second.
   a. Make a well-labeled diagram of the situation.
   b. Make a well-labeled graphical representation of the situation.
   c. List given quantities and quantities to find as you determine:
      i. How much time does it take the bus to stop?
      ii. How far does it travel while braking?

5. A car whose initial speed is 30 m/s slows uniformly to 10 m/s in 5 seconds.
   a. Make a well-labeled diagram of the situation.
   b. Make a well-labeled graphical representation of the situation.
   c. List given quantities and quantities to find.
      i. Determine the acceleration of the car.
      ii. Determine the distance the car travels in the 3rd second (from t = 2s to t = 3s).

6. A dog runs down his driveway with an initial speed of 5 m/s for 8 s, then uniformly increases his speed to 10 m/s in 5 s.
   a. Make a well-labeled diagram of the situation.
   b. Make a well-labeled graphical representation of the situation.
   c. List given quantities and quantities to find as you determine:
      i. What was the dog's acceleration during the 2nd part of the motion?
      ii. How long is the driveway?

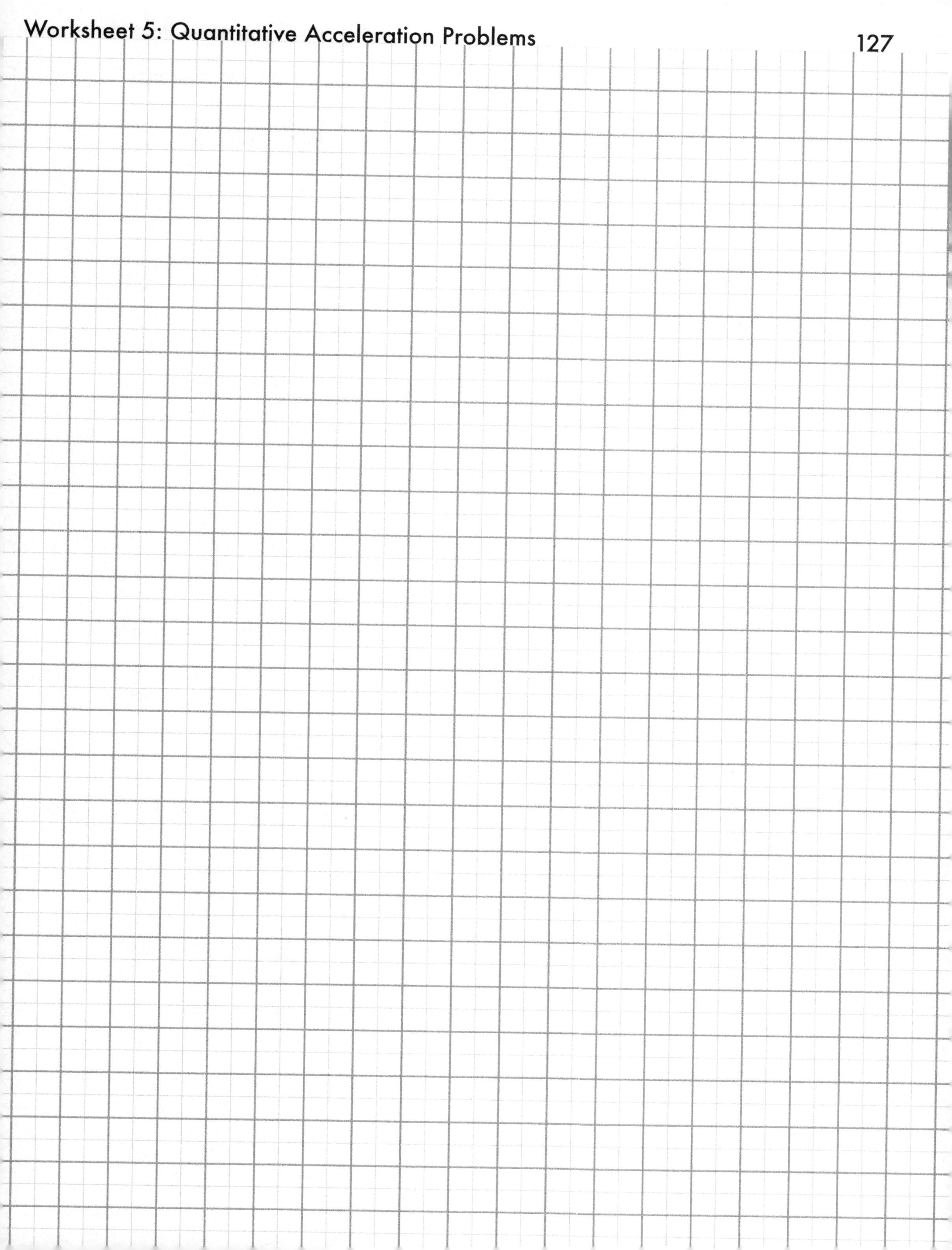

7. A physics student skis down a slope, with a constant acceleration of 2.0 m/s^2 for 15 seconds.
   a. Make a well-labeled diagram of the situation.
   b. Make a well-labeled graphical representation of the situation.
   c. List given quantities and quantities to find as you determine the length of the slope.

8. A mountain goat starts a rock slide and the rocks crash down the slope 100 m in five seconds.
   a. Make a well-labeled diagram of the situation.
   b. Make a well-labeled graphical representation of the situation.
   c. List given quantities and quantities to find as you determine the acceleration of the rocks.

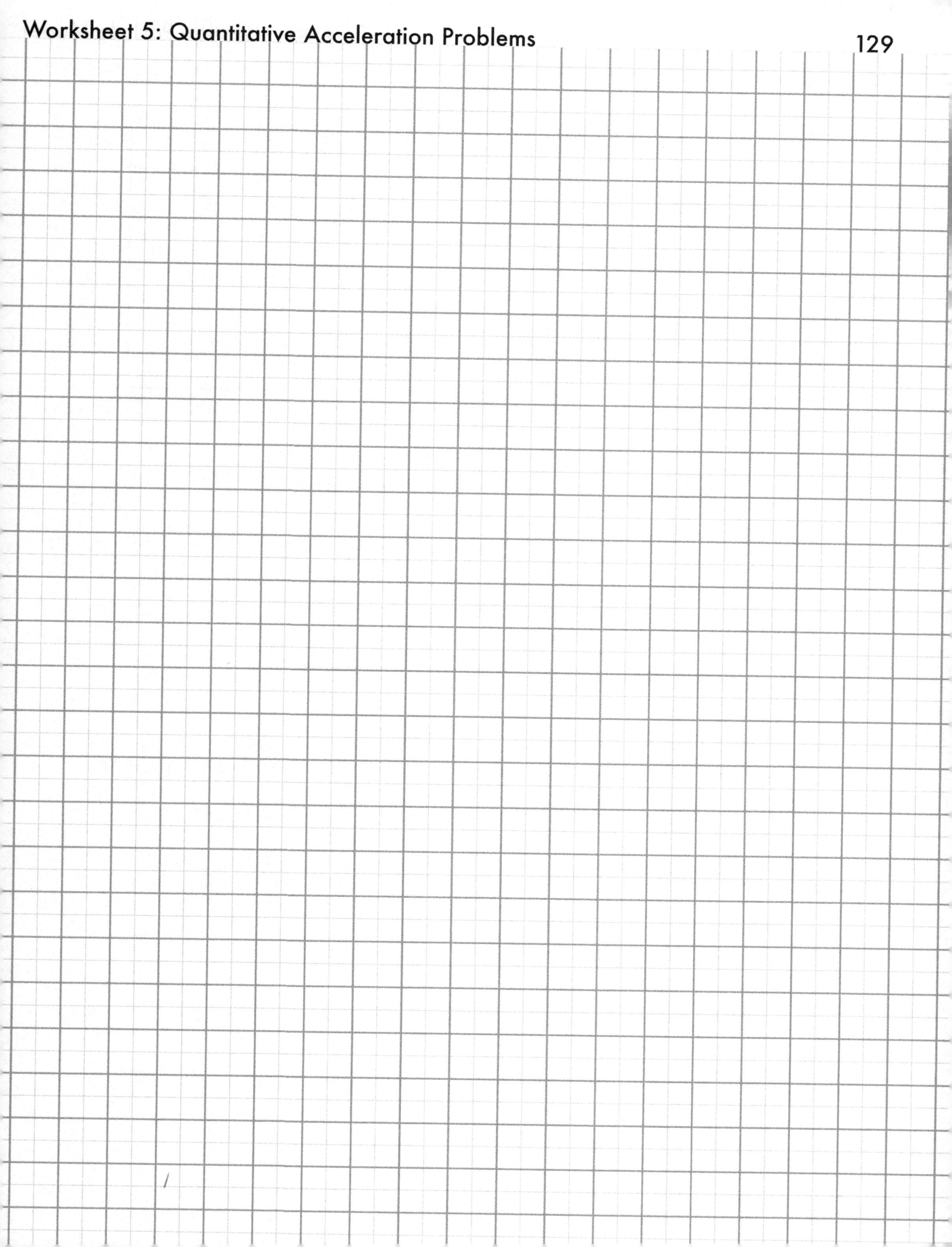

Review Problems

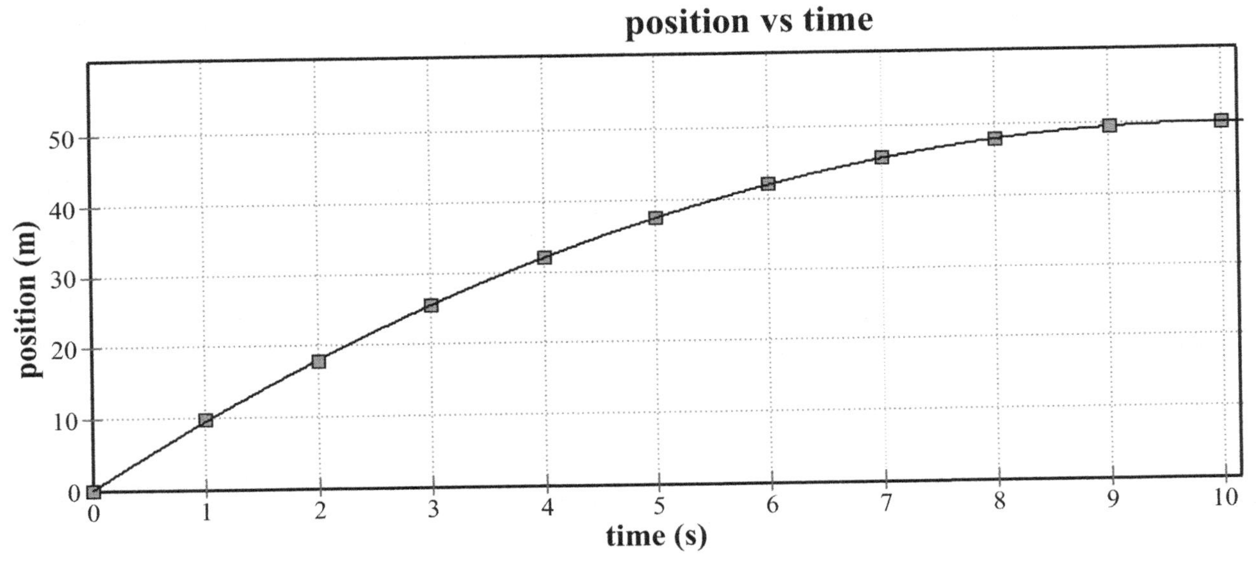

1. Use the graph above to answer the following questions:
   a. Give a written description to describe the motion of this object.

   b. Draw the motion map for the object. Include velocity and acceleration vectors.

vel:

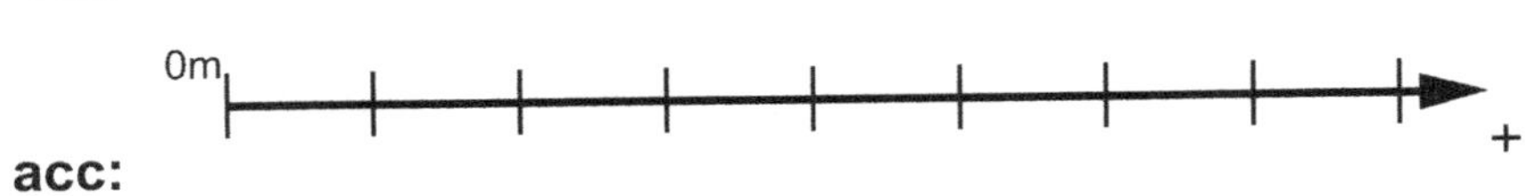

acc:

   c. Determine the instantaneous velocity of the object at **t** = 2 s and explain how you did it.

   d. Assume the initial velocity was 10 m/s, determine the acceleration of the object.

   e. Sketch a corresponding velocity time graph for the graph above.

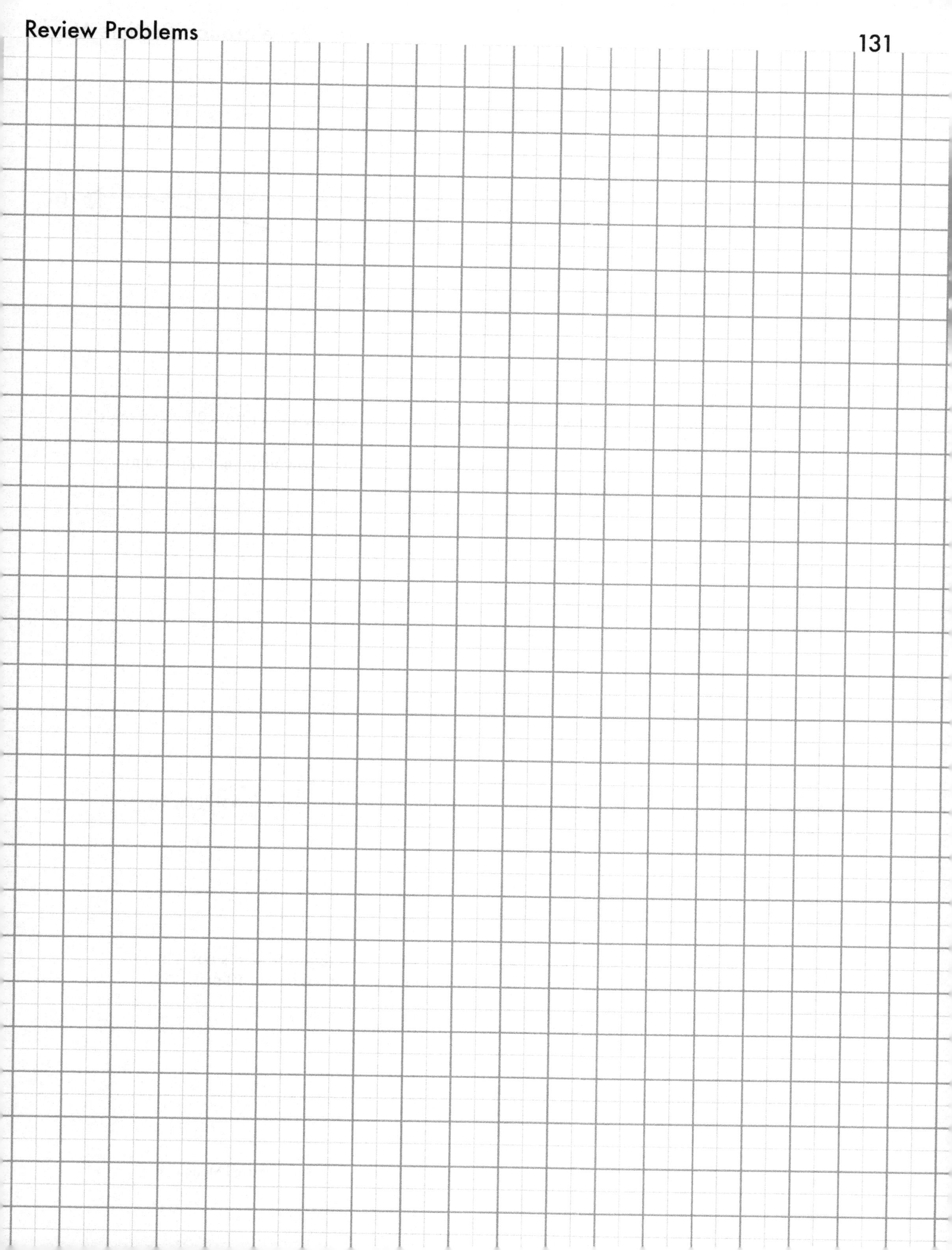

2. Use the graph to answer the following questions.

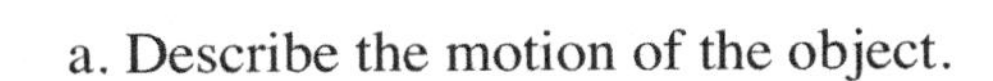

a. Describe the motion of the object.

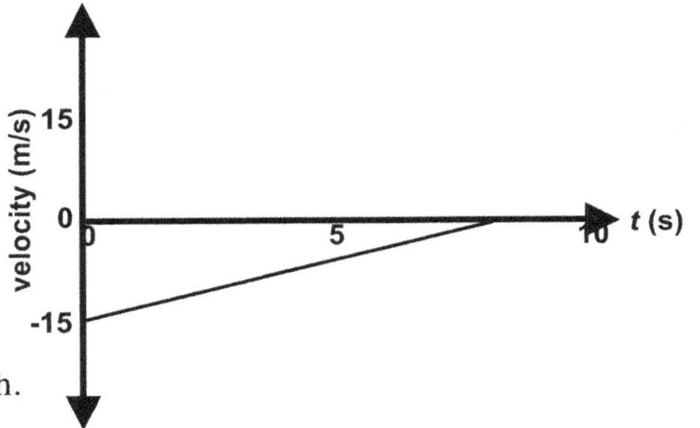

b. Determine the acceleration of the object from the graph.

c. Shade the portion of the graph that represents the displacement of the object from 2 to 6 seconds.

d. Calculate the velocity of the object at 2 seconds and at 6 seconds. (No you are not allowed to just take the values off the graph.)

e. Calculate the object's displacement from 2 to 6 seconds.

3. A car, initially at rest, accelerates at a constant rate of 4.0 m/s^2 for 6 s. How fast will the car be traveling at **t** = 6 s?

4. A tailback initially running at a velocity of 5.0 m/s becomes very tired and slows down at a uniform rate of 0.25 m/s^2. How fast will he be running after going an additional 10 meters?

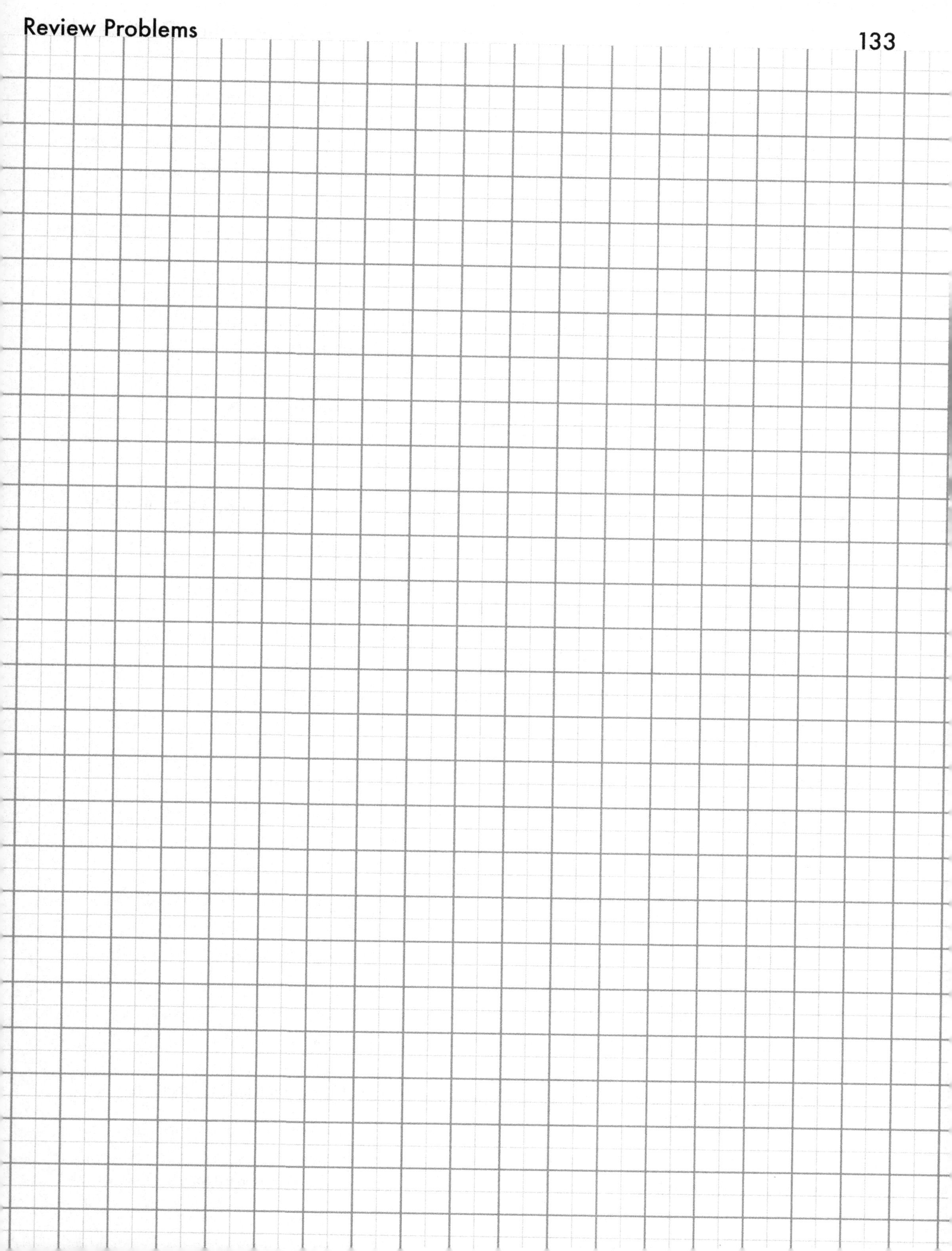

5. Draw a motion map along the ramp for the motion of the ball when released from rest.

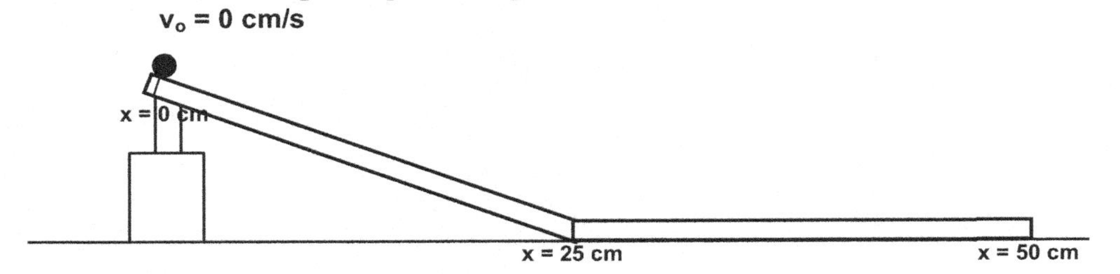

6. Draw a motion map along the ramp for the motion of the ball when released from rest.

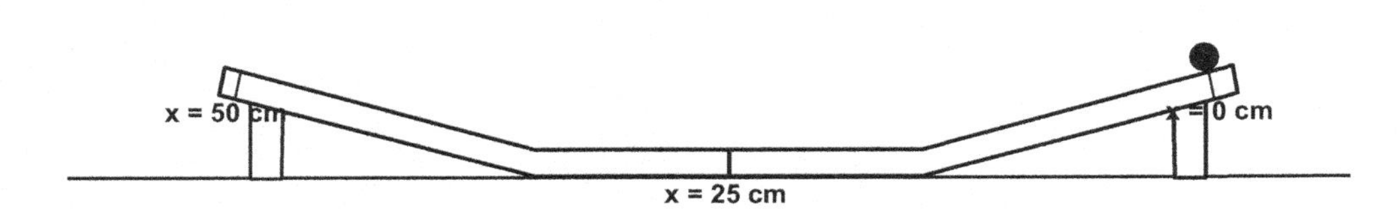

7. Using the graph compare the following quantities for objects A and B. **Is A > B, A < B, or A = B.**

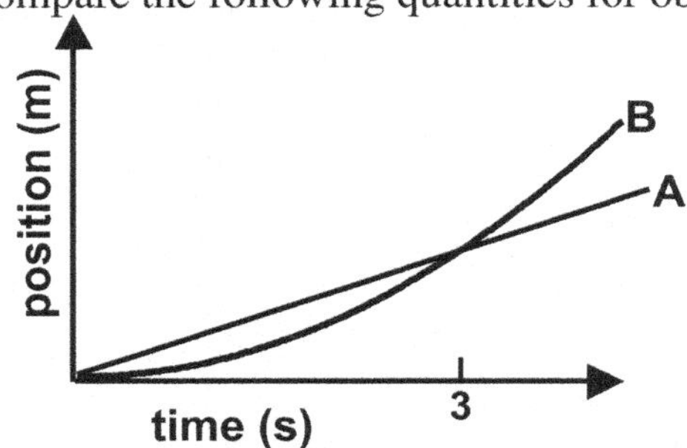

a. **Displacement** from 0 to 3 s ___________ How do you know?

b. **Displacement** from 0 to 1.5 s ___________ How do you know?

c. **Displacement** from 1.5 to 3 s ___________ How do you know?

d. **Average** velocity from 0 to 3 s ___________ How do you know?

e. **Average** velocity from 0 to 1.5 s ___________ How do you know?

f. **Average** velocity from 1.5 to 3 s ___________ How do you know?

g. **Instantaneous** velocity at 3 s ___________ How do you know?

h. **Instantaneous** velocity at 0 s ___________ How do you know?

i. If the motion of B is uniformly accelerated, at what time will both graphs have exactly the same slope? Explain.

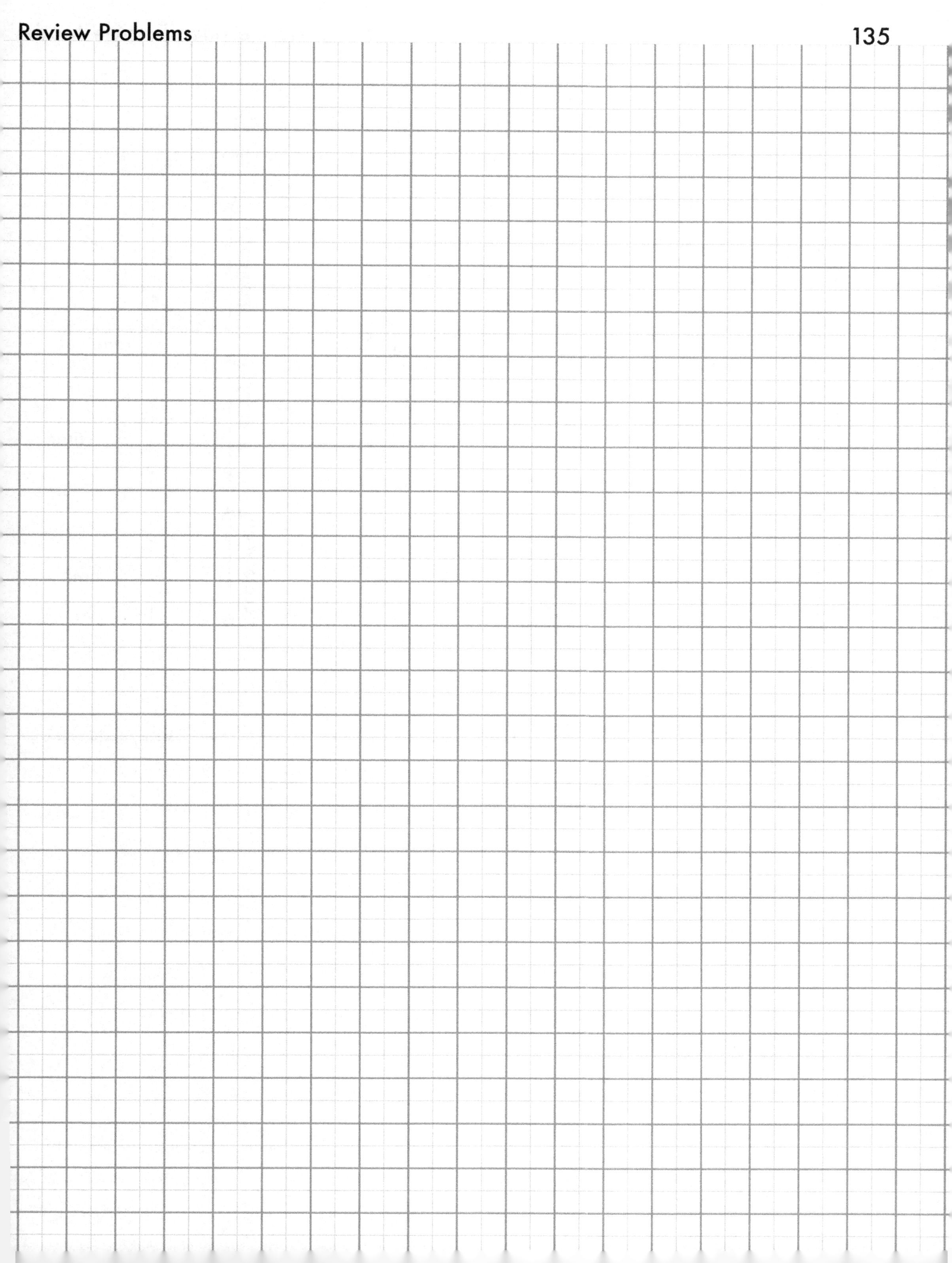

8. For each of the position vs time graphs shown below, draw the corresponding **v** vs **t**, **a** vs **t** , and motion map.

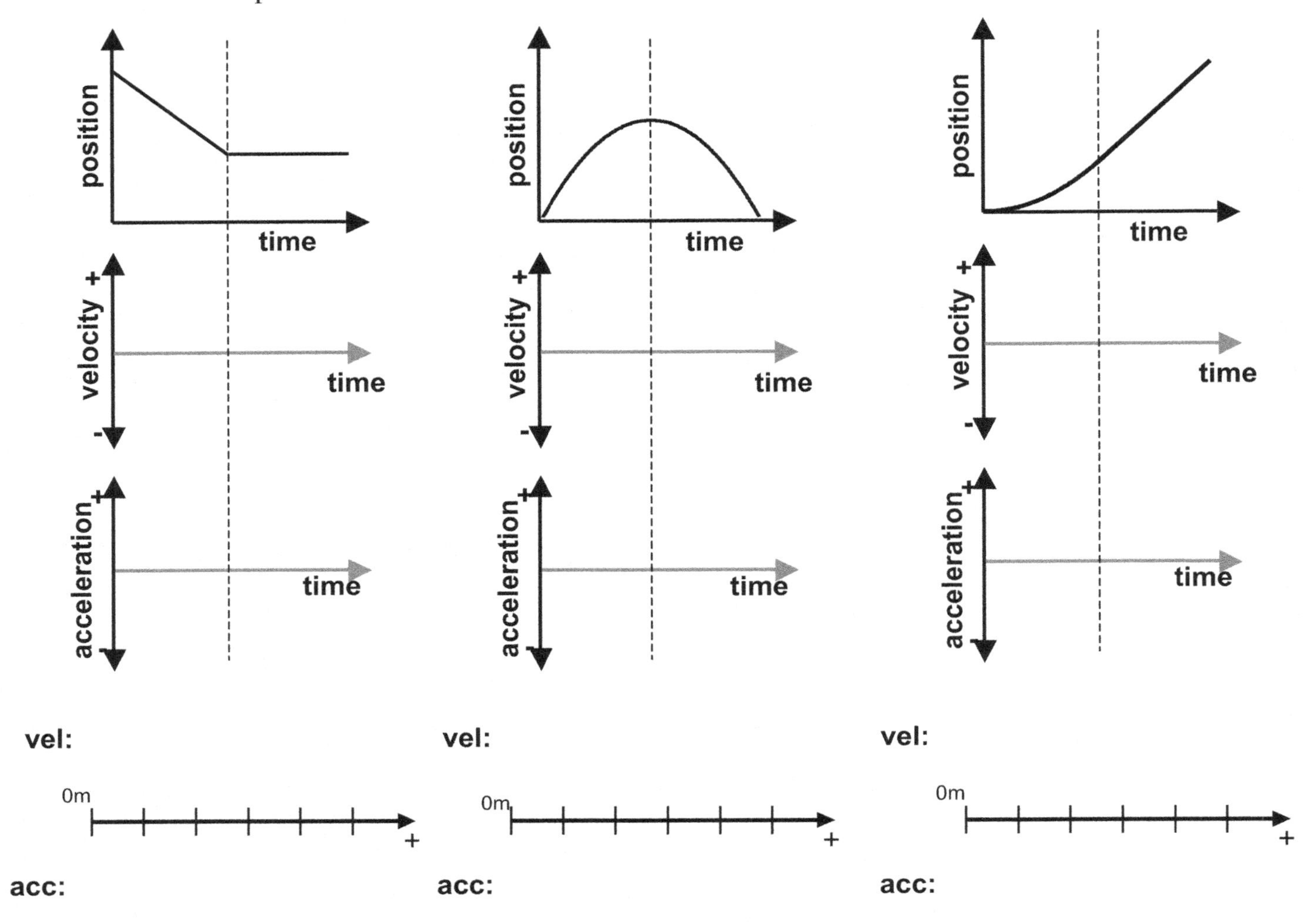

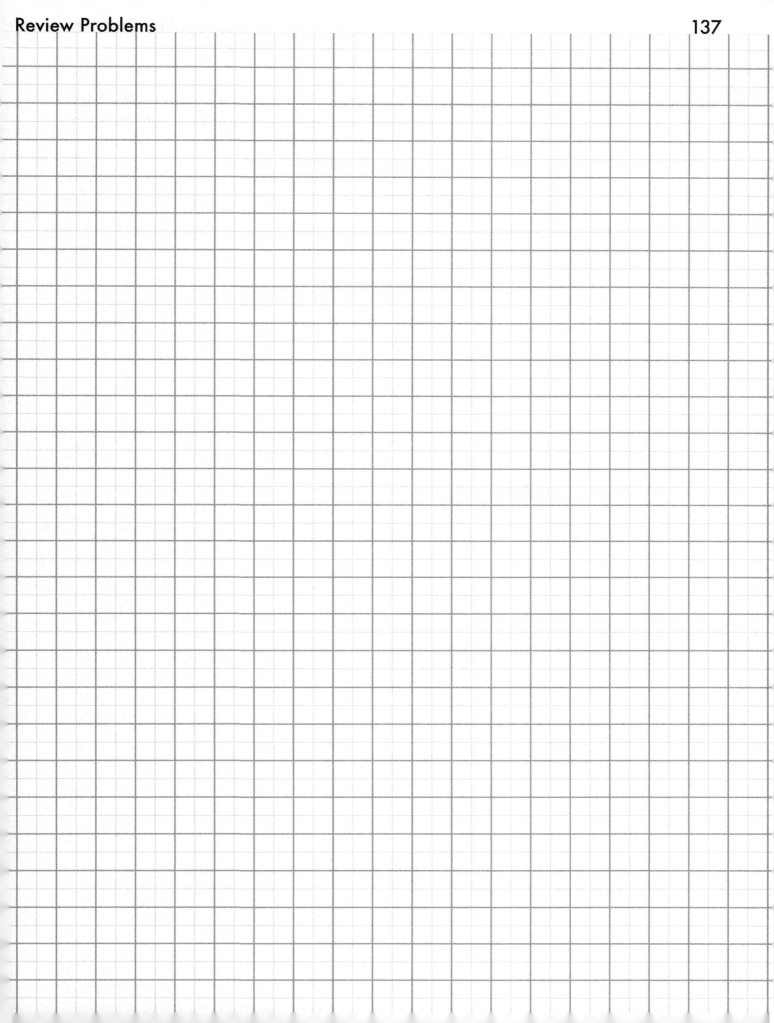

Model Summary

This is a place to summarize different representations of the Uniform Acceleration Particle Model. Representations include graphs, diagrams, motion maps, words and math formulas.

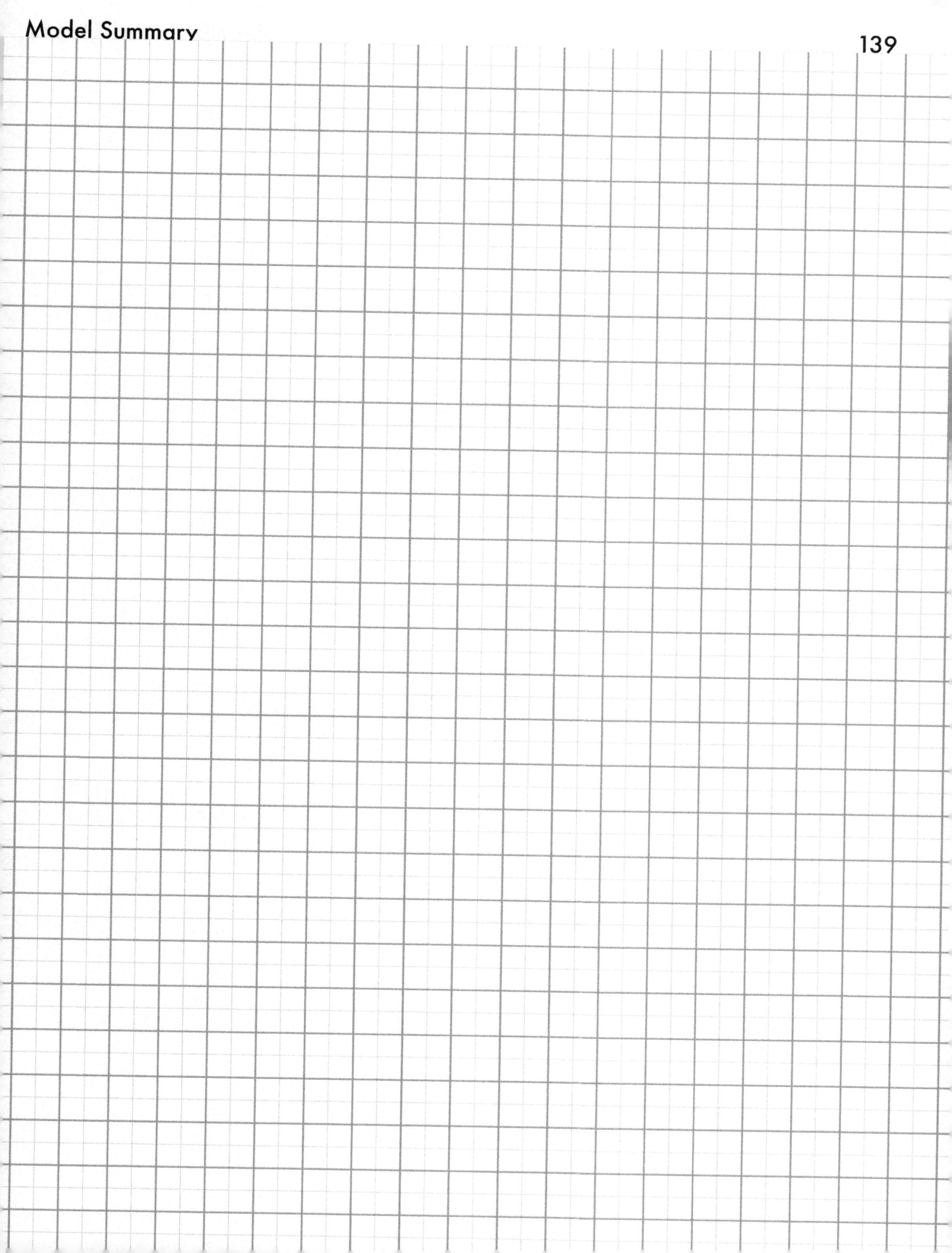

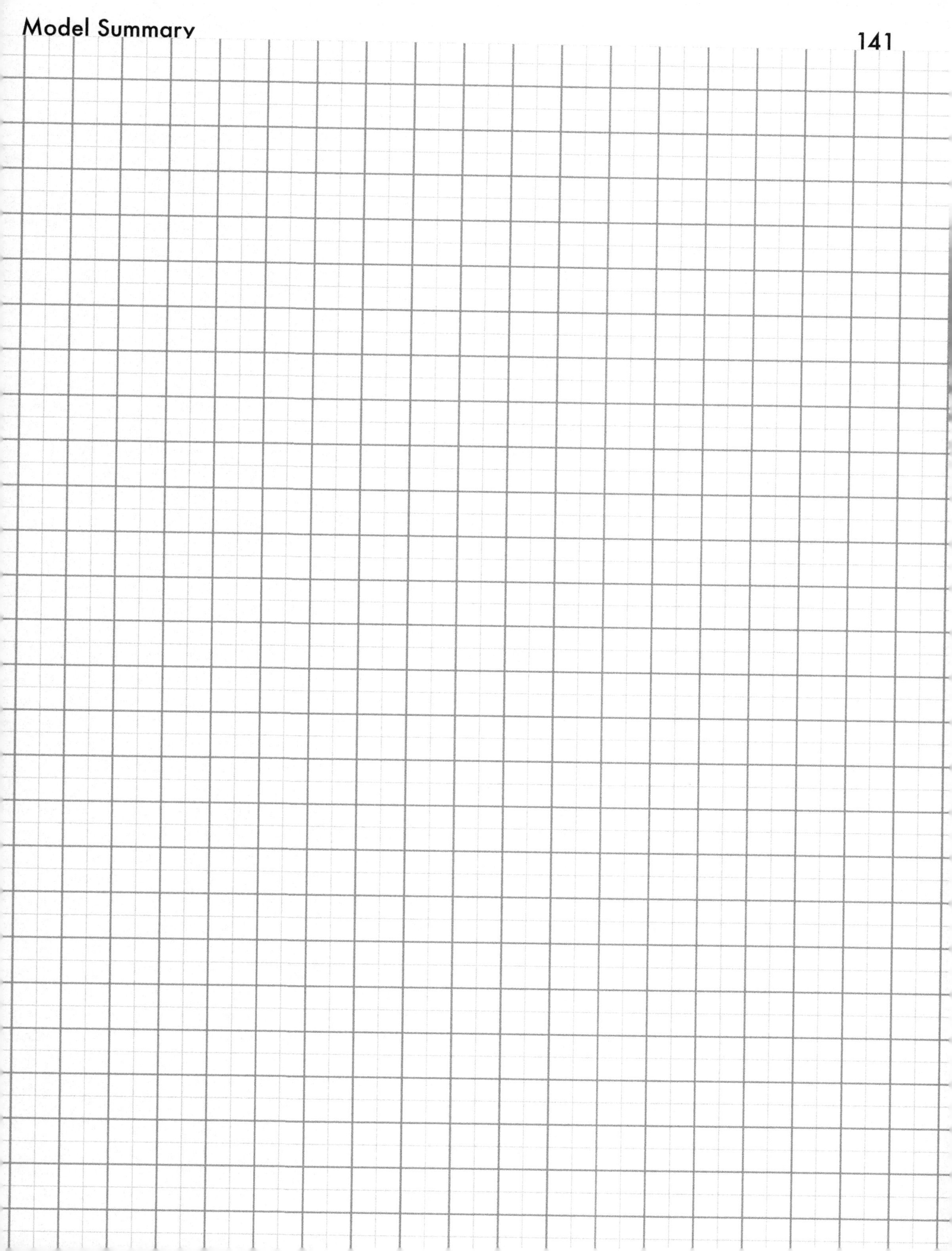

Chapter 4: Free Particle Model

Chapter Sections

chapter 4 online help

Lab Notes

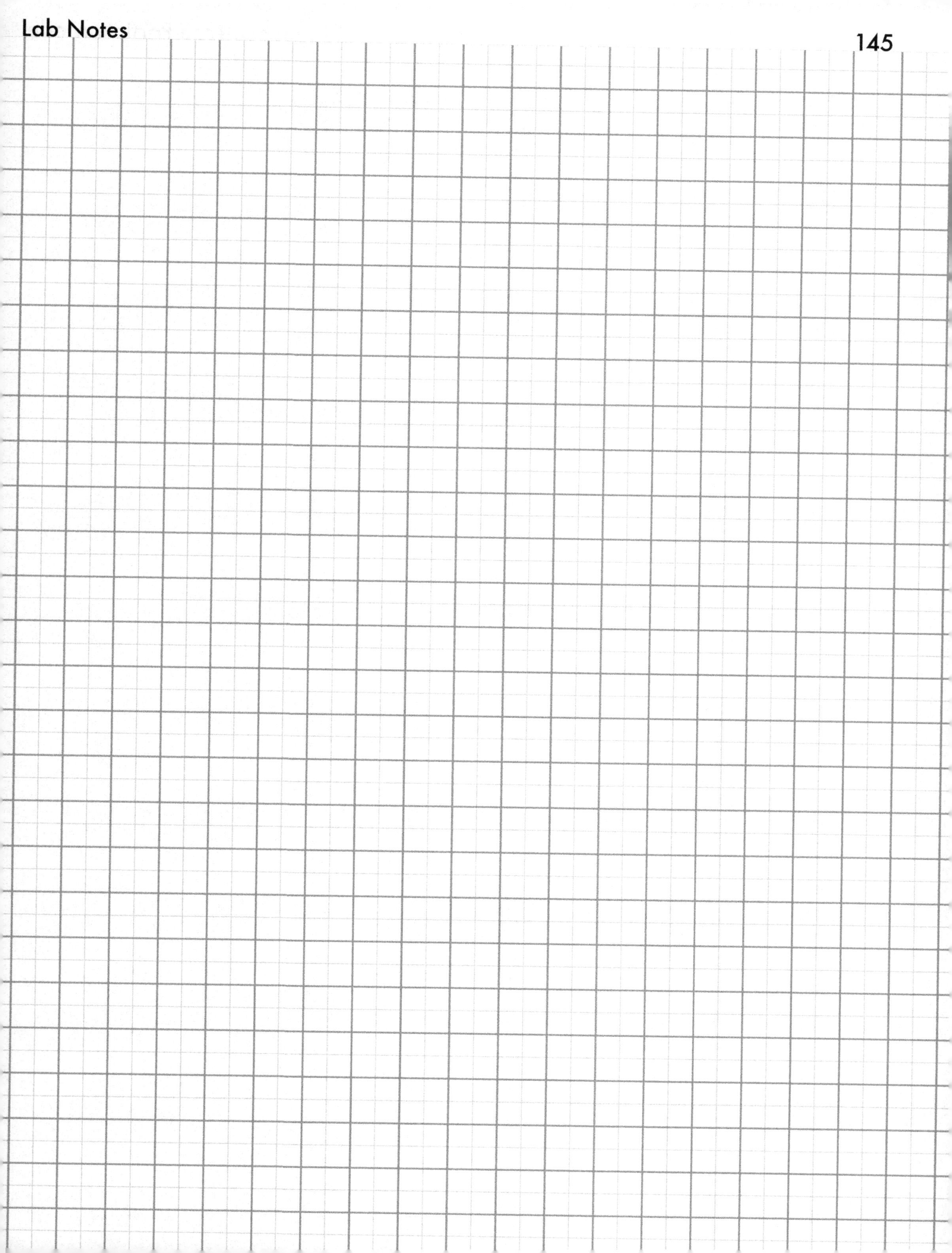

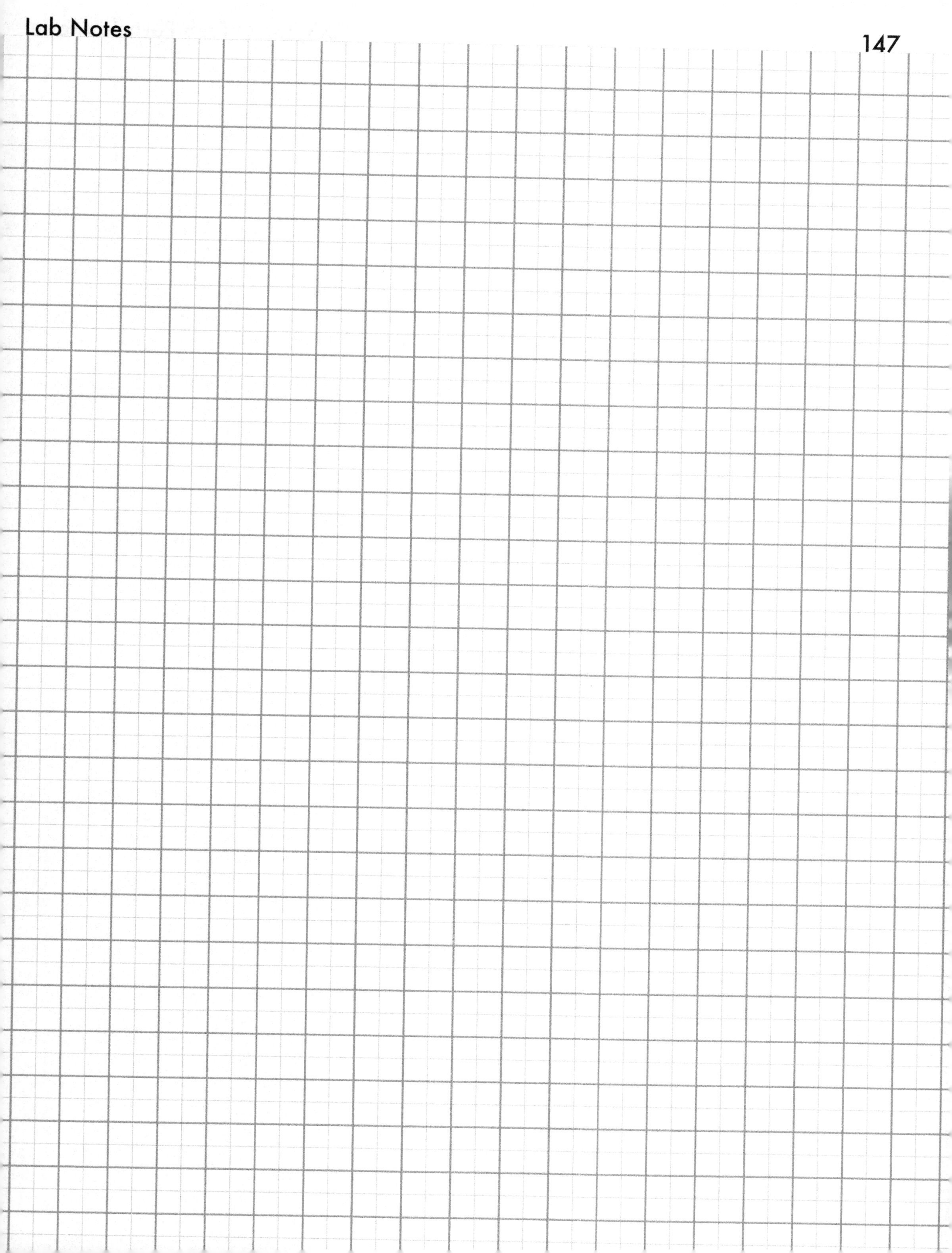

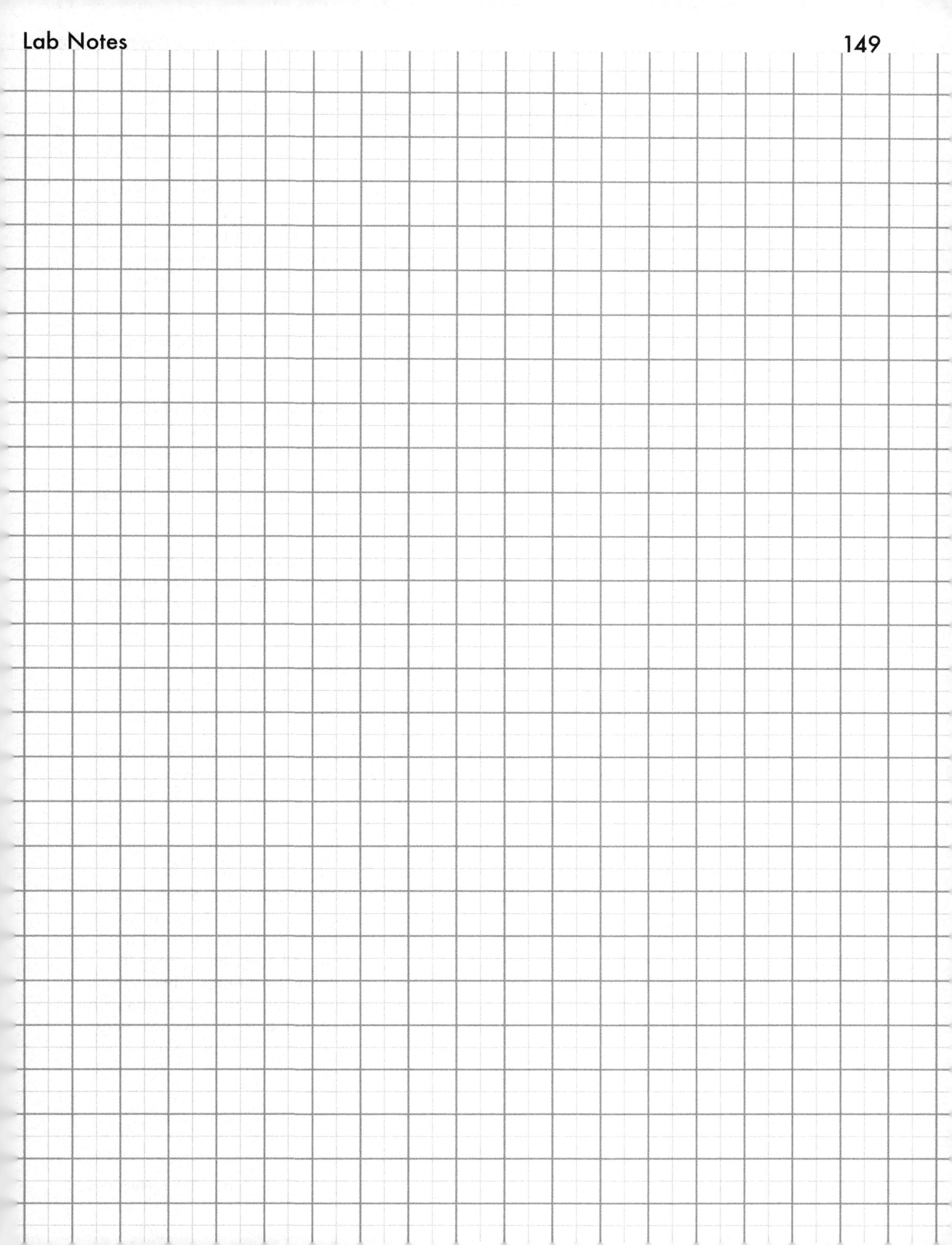

Readings: Forces and Force Diagrams

Forces can intuitively be thought of as pushes and pulls. For example, you exert a force (a push or a pull) on a door to open it. Gravity exerts a force on you (a pull) which holds you to the surface of the earth. Friction with the surface of a hill exerts a force on your car that keeps it from sliding when parked. Note that in every situation, forces are an interaction between two objects--you can't touch without being touched. The door also pushes back on your hand, the earth is also gravitationally attracted to you, and the car exerts a frictional force on the road.

There are many types of forces between objects that are differentiated by the way in which two objects interact. Here are some of the ones we will use in class:

> When two surfaces touch each other, forces perpendicular to the surfaces are called **normal** forces (here "normal" is a mathematical term meaning perpendicular) and forces parallel to the surfaces in contact are **frictional**. The Friction force that allows us to step forward or keeps car wheels from spinning can be called **traction**. When we touch things a combination of both normal and frictional forces are present. For simplicity, we can call a combination force a **push** or a **pull**.
>
> Extended or linked materials such as a string or chain exert **tension** forces on an object. When an object interacts with a fluid, such as water or air, propelling forces are called **thrust**, resistive forces are called **drag**, floating forces are called **buoyant**, and steering (or Bernoulli's) forces are called **lift**.
>
> When two objects interact without touching, they exert forces through a force field. Earth, for example, exerts a **gravitational** force on the Moon even though the Earth and Moon do not touch. Other non-contact forces include **electric** and **magnetic** forces.

When we label forces, we want to indicate the type of interaction between the objects, what object the force is acting on and what object the force is by. Therefore, we will use the following notation:

$$\mathbf{F}_{\text{kind, on victim, by agent}}$$

For example, the gravitational force on you would be written: $\mathbf{F}_{\text{gravity, on you, by earth}}$.
The analysis of a problem in dynamics usually involves the selection and analysis of the relevant forces acting on some object under consideration. An important first step in this analysis process is to carefully select the object of interest that will be the focus of our analysis. For purposes of this analysis, we will refer to the object under consideration as the **system,** and everything else in the environment that might in any significant way affect the system as the **surroundings**. This analysis process can often times be greatly simplified by utilizing a technique of constructing **force diagrams** to assist you in selecting the relevant forces and appropriately representing these forces with **vector** notations.

In general, we will follow the following steps when creating force diagrams.

1. Sketch the system and its surroundings.
2. Enclose the system within a system boundary.
3. Shrink the system to a point at the center of coordinate axes with one axis parallel to the direction of motion.
4. Represent all relevant forces (across the system boundary) with a labeled vector.
5. Indicate which forces (if any) are equal in magnitude to other forces.

Consider the analysis of forces acting on a log as a tractor pulls it at a constant speed. The analysis proceeds as follows:

Step 1. Sketch a diagram of the system and its surroundings.

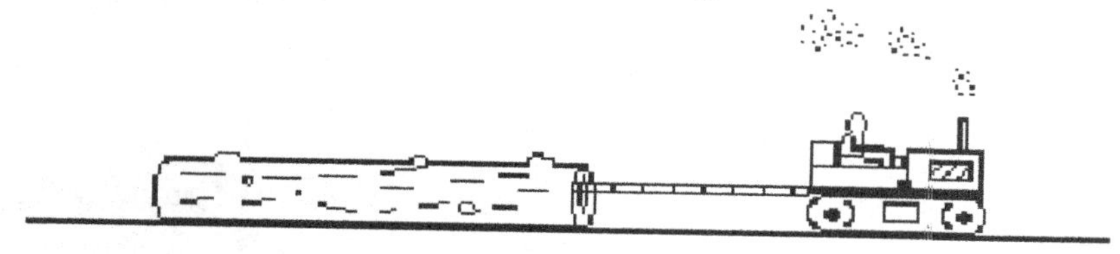

Step 2. In order to assist in the identification of the relevant forces acting on the system, enclose the system (log) within a closed boundary line.

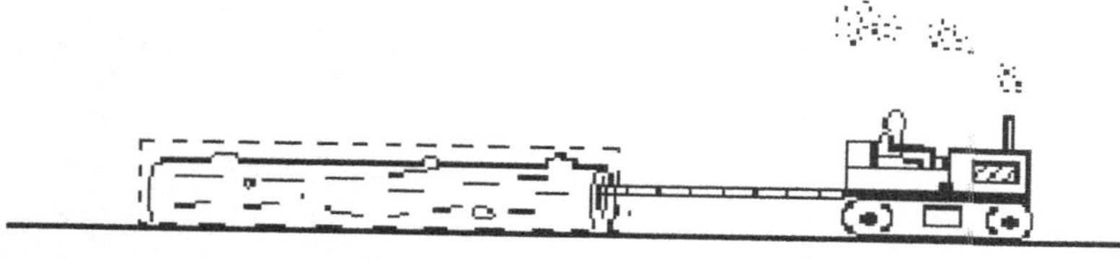

A broken line was used for emphasis in this sample problem; however, the line need not be broken.

Step 3. Since the shape of the object is unimportant, shrink it to a point. Place it at the intersection of a set of coordinate axes with one of the *axes parallel to the direction of motion* as shown in figure 4.

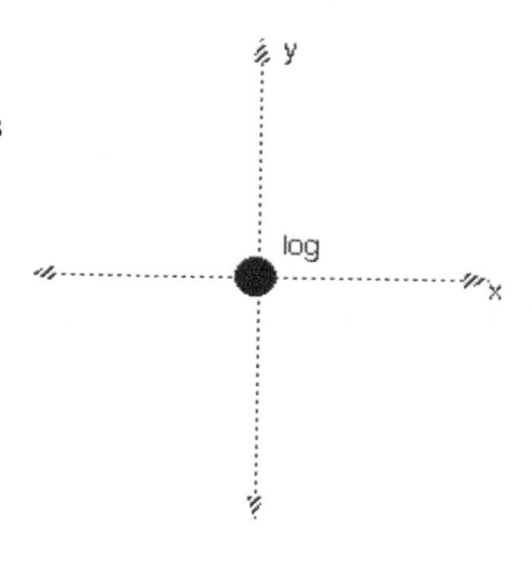

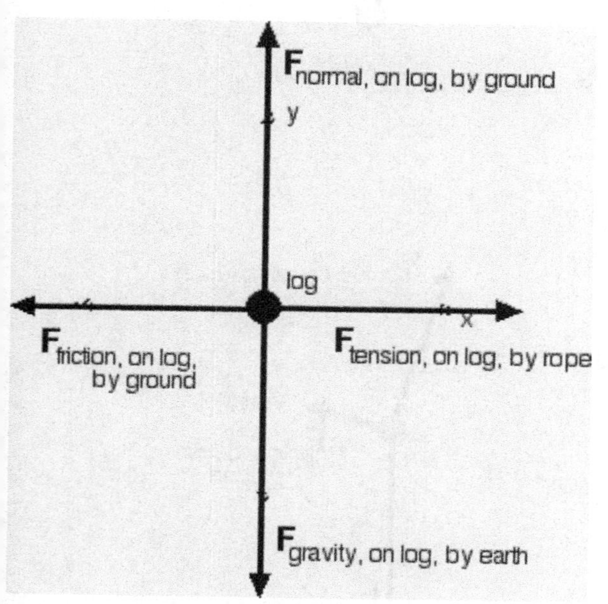

Step 4. Proceed around the system boundary line and identify all points at which there is contact between the system (log) and its surroundings. Construct qualitative vectors (indicate directions and **relative** magnitudes) to represent these forces.

Step 5: Indicate which forces (if any) are equal in magnitude to other forces. The problem states that the tractor pulls the log at constant velocity, so we know that the net force has to be zero. In other words, the forces up must equal the forces down, and the forces left must equal the forces right. In the diagram below these equalities have been marked with hashes like those used to indicate congruences in geometry.

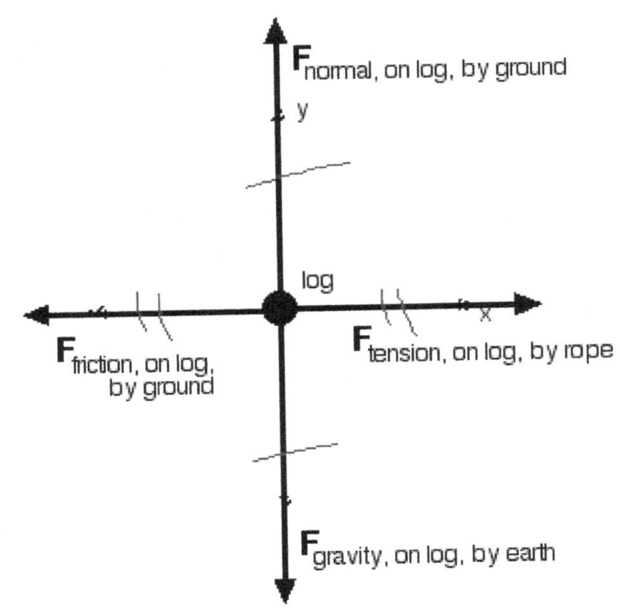

Let us now look at a more complicated example: A car parked on a hill.

Step 1. Sketch the system and its surroundings.

Step 2. Enclose the system within a system boundary.

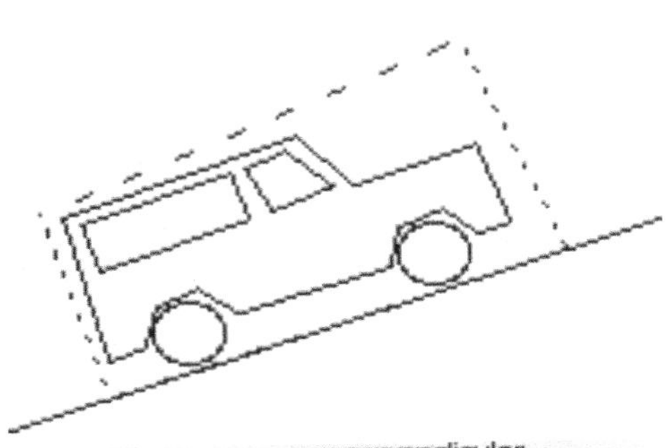

Step 3. Shrink the system to a point at the center of coordinate axes with one axis parallel to the direction of motion. Although the car isn't moving, if it did, it would slide down the hill. Therefore, the coordinate axes have been aligned parallel and perpendicular to the hill. Although it may seem strange, rotating the coordinate axis will make the rest of the analysis easier.

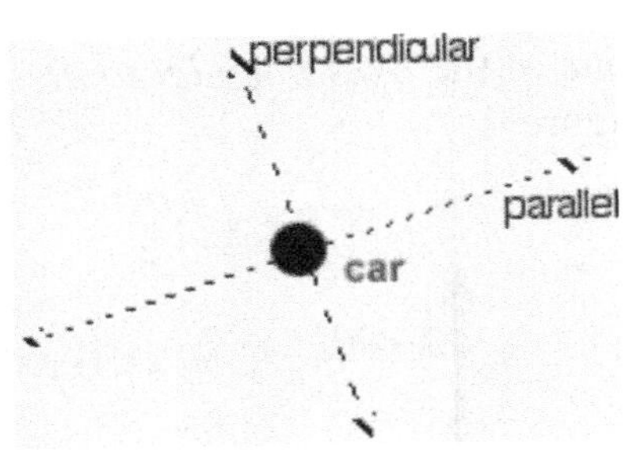

Step 4. Represent all relevant forces (across the system boundary) with a labeled vector. Gravity always points toward the center of the earth (down). The normal force is perpendicular to the road/tire surface and the friction force is parallel to the road/tire surface. Friction exerts a force up the hill to resist the tendency of the car to slide down the hill due to gravity.

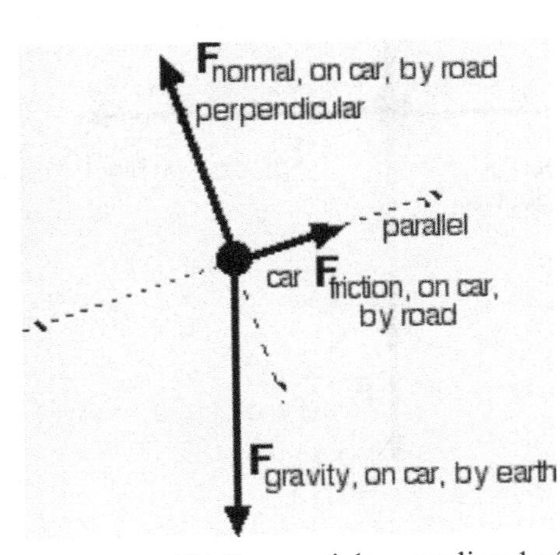

Step 5. Indicate which forces (if any) are equal in magnitude to other forces. Here's where the parallel/perpendicular coordinate axis helps. Since the car is motionless, the forces must be balanced along each coordinate axis. Gravity isn't along either coordinate axis, but we can represent gravity with two **component vectors**. F_g parallel is how much of the gravitational force tends to pull the car along the slope and F_g perpendicular is how much of the gravitational force tends to pull the car to the road. For the forces to be balanced, F_g parallel must be equal in size to $F_{friction}$ and F_g perpendicular must be equal in size to Fnormal, as indicated by the hash marks. Note that no hash marks are placed on F_g since we have replaced it with its equivalent component vectors.

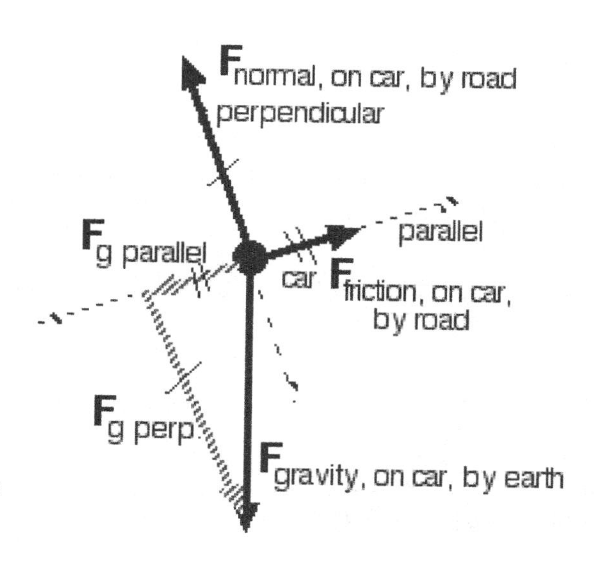

Hints . . .

1. Seeing the components in the previous problem is often difficult for students. It may be helpful to physically rotate your paper so that the parallel/perpendicular components become aligned left/right and up/down. The result is a force diagram that looks like the one on the right.

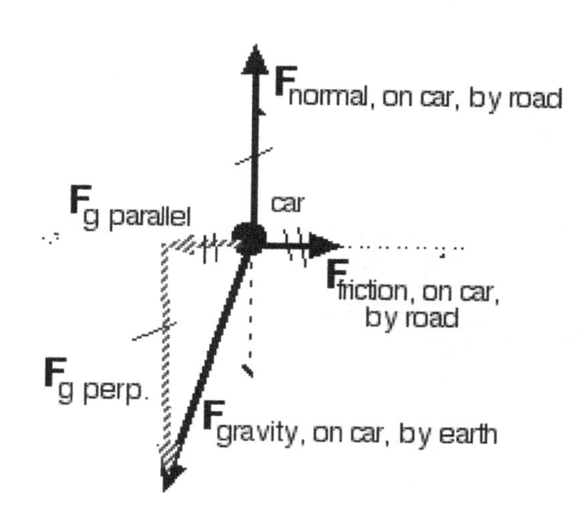

2. Here's a very different looking situation, but the analysis is very similar. In fact, turning the previous force diagram 180 degrees results in the force diagram shown. Realizing that all force diagrams have many similarities can be a relief. You don't need to memorize a bunch of different approaches to be able to draw a wide variety of force diagrams.

A rock climber on a cliff:

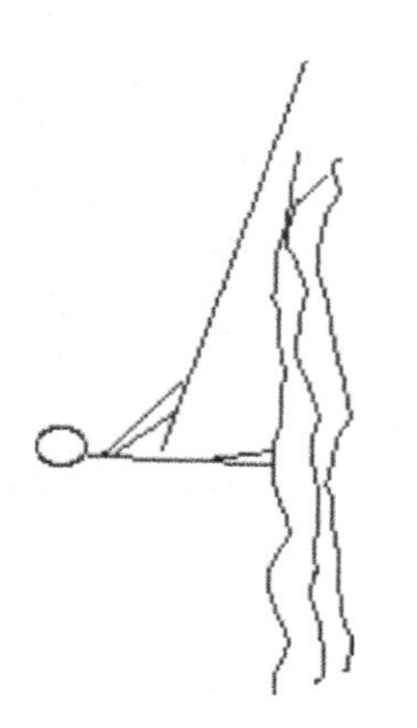

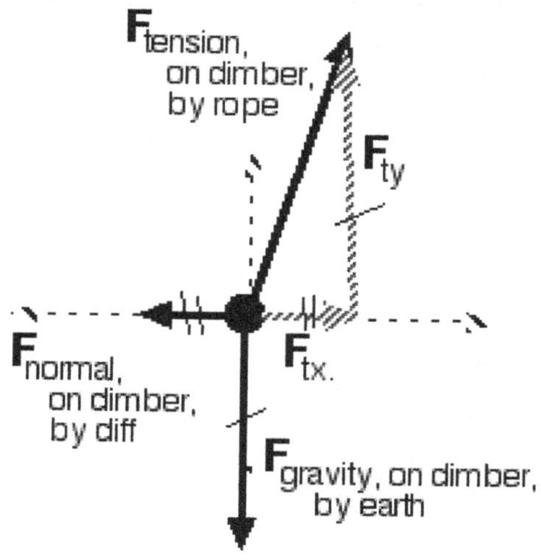

Worksheet 1a: Force Diagrams

In each of the following situations, represent the object with a particle. Sketch all the forces acting upon the object, making the length of each vector represent the magnitude of the force. Also use congruency marks to indicate which vectors are equal in magnitude.

1. Draw a force diagram for the motionless cat on a rug. Label the forces and use equality marks on the force vectors.

2. Draw a force diagram for the skater, moving at constant speed across frictionless ice. Label the forces and use equality marks on the force vectors.

3. Draw a force diagram for the softball player who is slowing as she slides into the base. Label the forces and use equality marks on the force vectors.

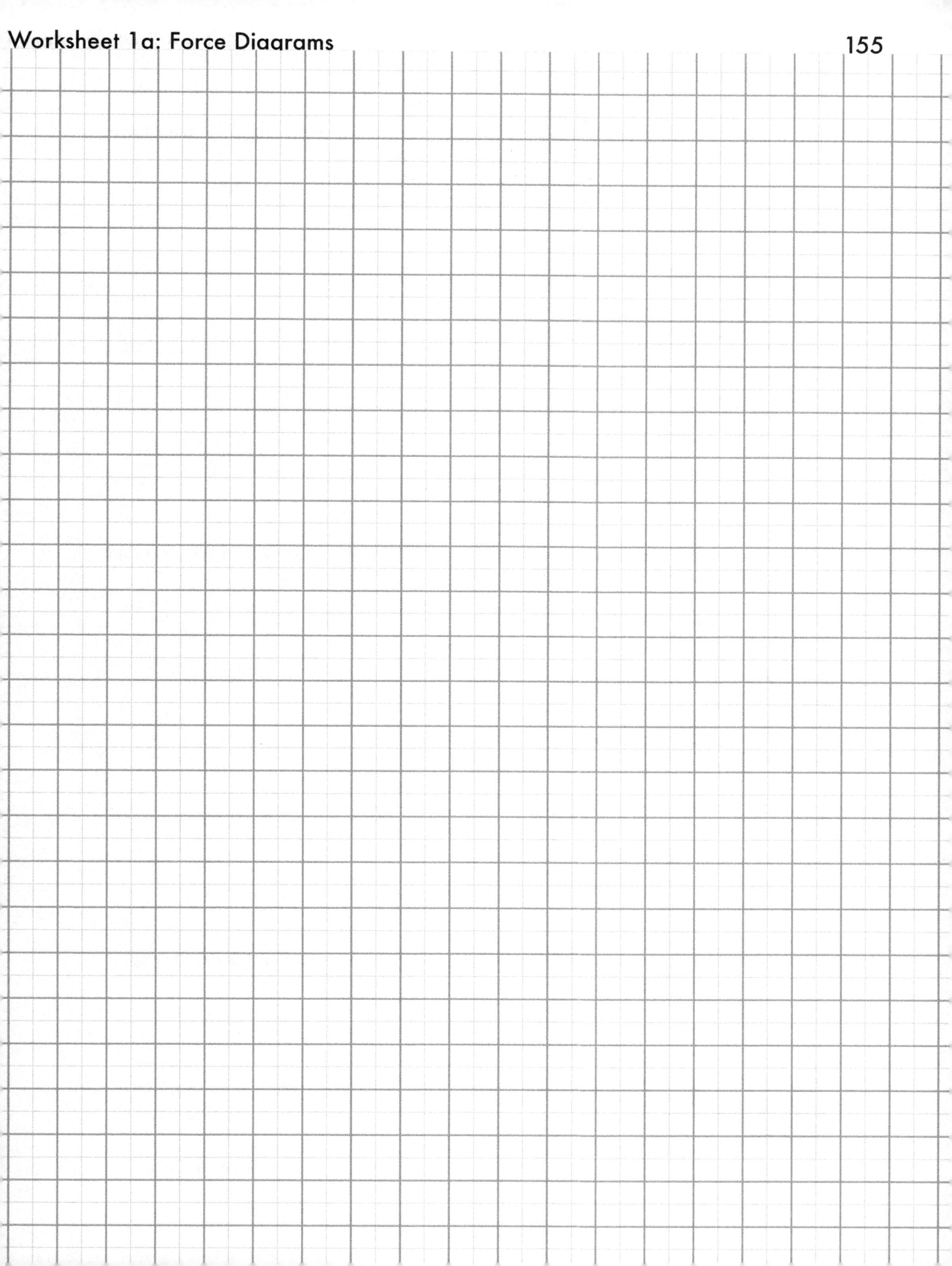

4. Draw a force diagram for a chandelier that is suspended from the ceiling by a chain. Label the forces and use equality marks on the force vectors.

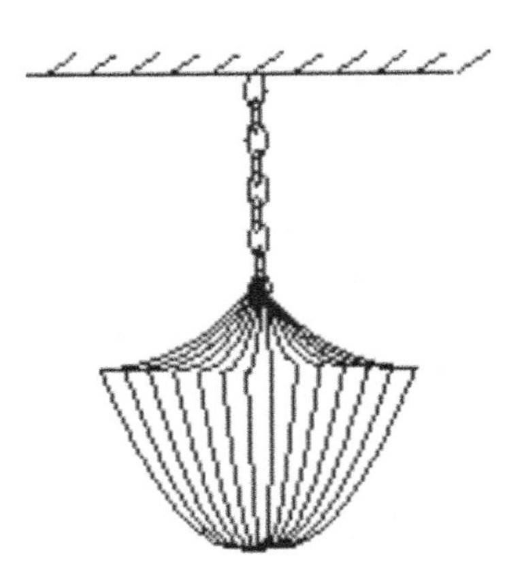

5. Draw a force diagram for the bucket of water that is being raised from the well at constant speed. Label the forces and use equality marks on the force vectors.

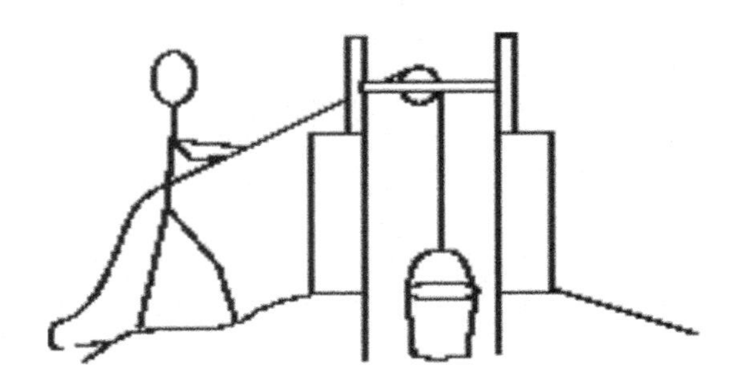

6. Draw a force diagram for a skydiver who has just left the plane and is still speeding up. Label the forces and use equality marks on the force vectors.

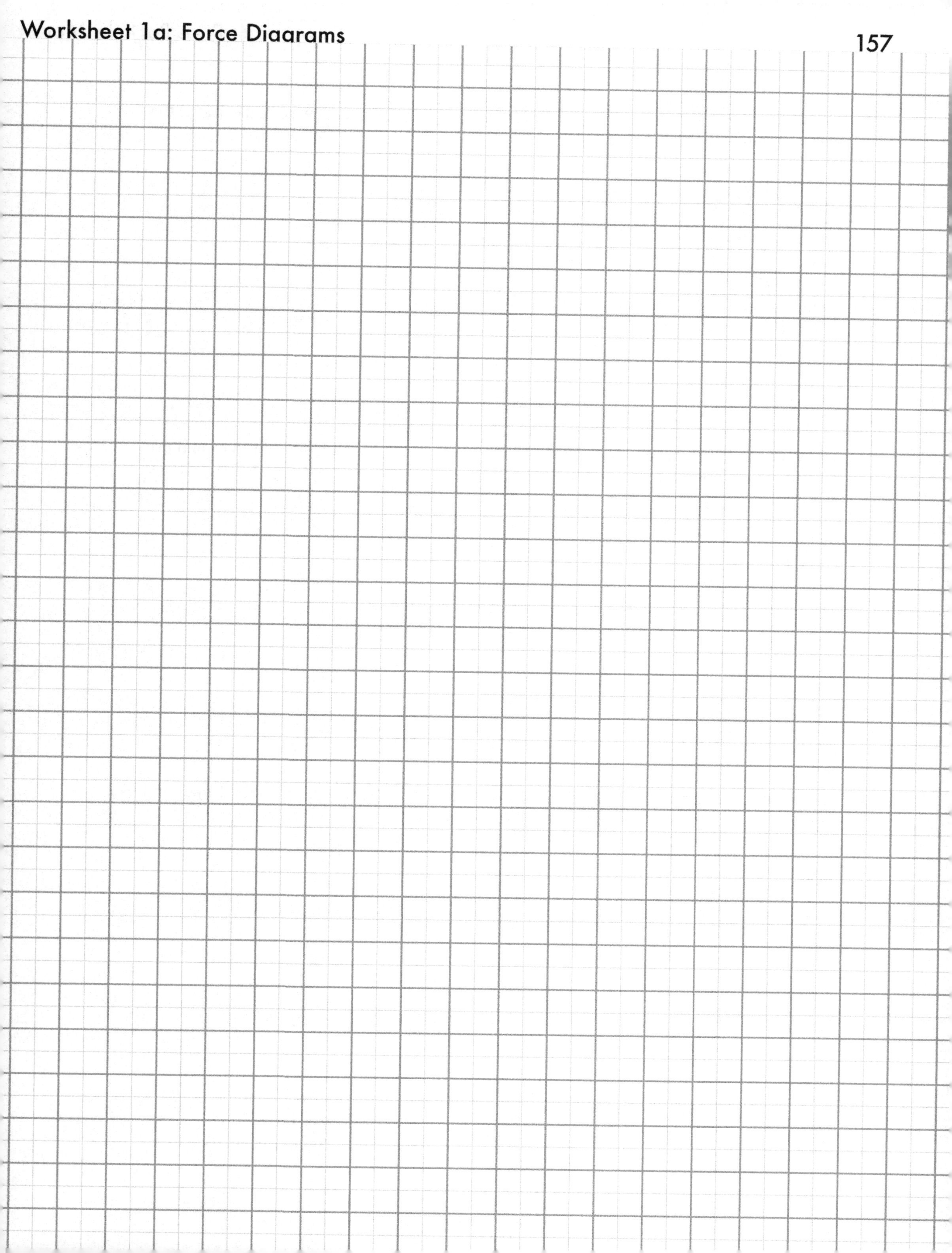

7. Draw a force diagram for a skydiver who is descending at a constant velocity. Label the forces and use equality marks on the force vectors.

8. Draw a force diagram for a ball rising in a parabolic trajectory. Label the forces and use equality marks on the force vectors.

9. Draw a force diagram for a ball at the top of a parabolic trajectory. Label the forces and use equality marks on the force vectors.

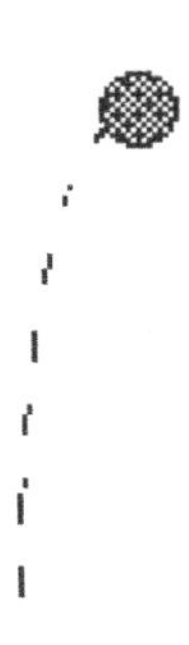

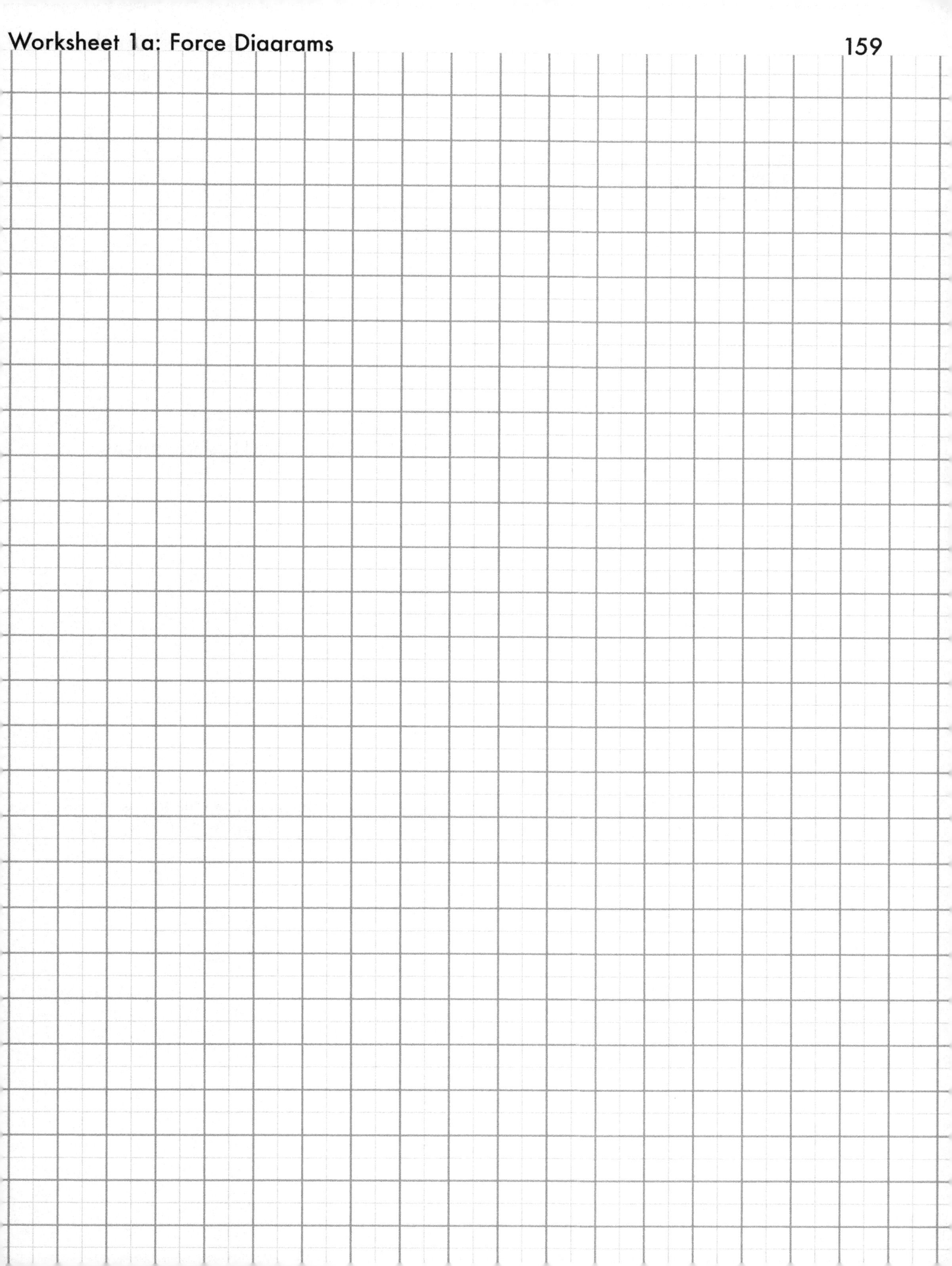

10. Draw a force diagram for a cork floating in water. Label the forces and use equality marks on the force vectors.

11. Draw a force diagram for an airplane in straight and level flight. Label the forces and use equality marks on the force vectors.

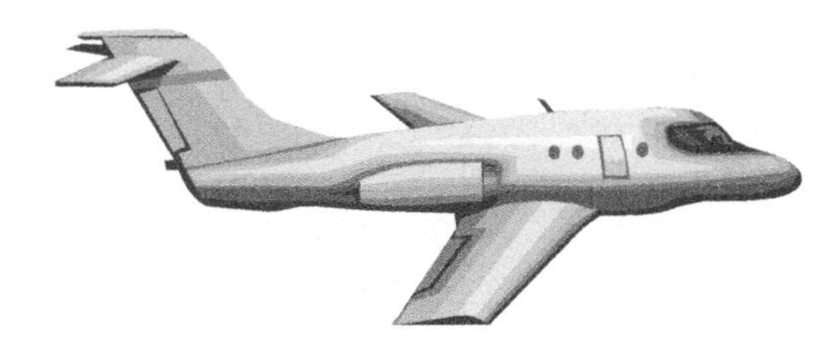

12. Draw a force diagram for a nail that has been picked up by a magnet. Label the forces and use equality marks on the force vectors.

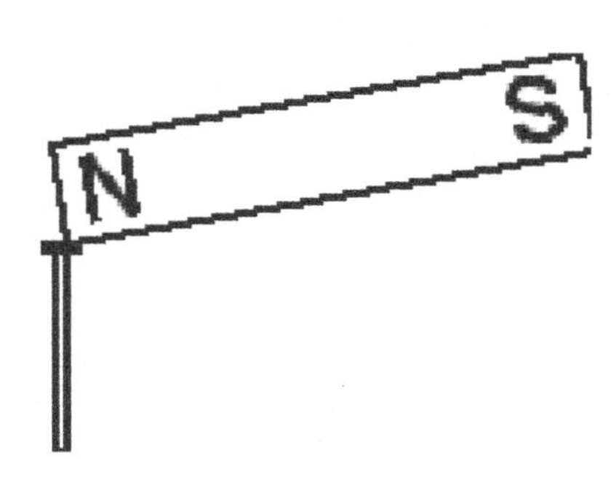

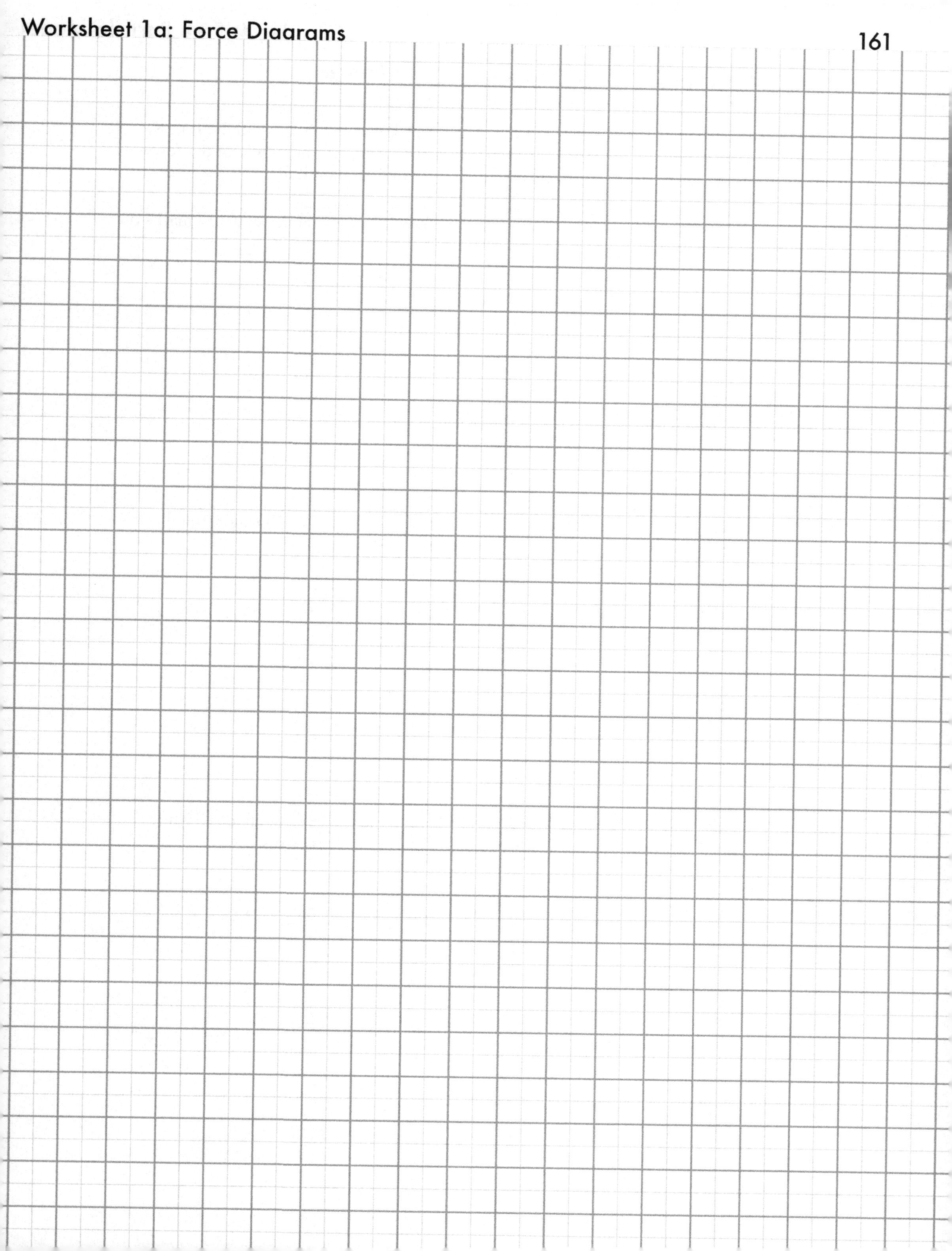

Worksheet 1b: Force Diagrams and Component Forces

In each of the following situations, represent the object with a particle. Sketch all the forces acting upon the object, making the length of each vector represent the magnitude of the force. Also use congruency marks to indicate which vectors are equal in magnitude.

1. Draw a force diagram for the water-skier. Label the force vectors and use equality marks on the vectors.

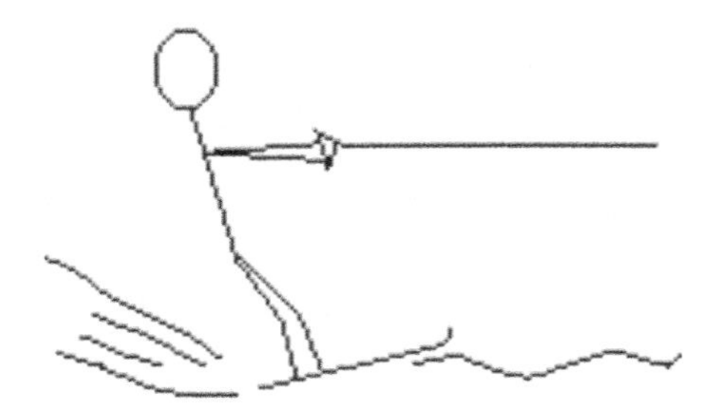

2. Draw a force diagram for the sled and kids. Note that the pull on the sled is at an angle. Label the force vectors and use equality marks on the vectors.

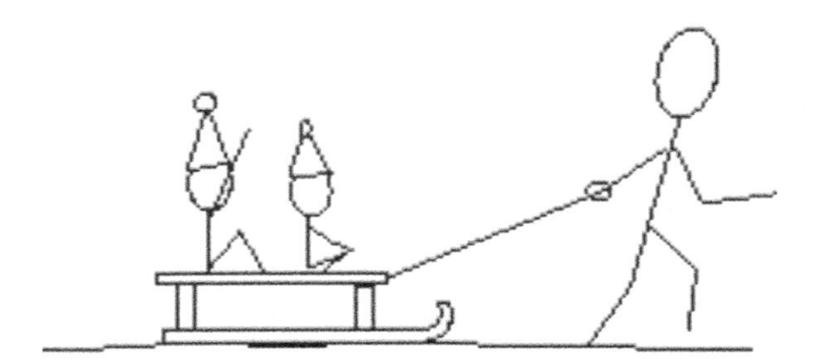

3. Draw a force diagram for the table. The dancer is leaning on the table at an angle while stretching. Label the force vectors and use equality marks on the vectors.

4. Draw a force diagram for the person hanging onto the rope bridge. Label the force vectors and use equality marks on the vectors.

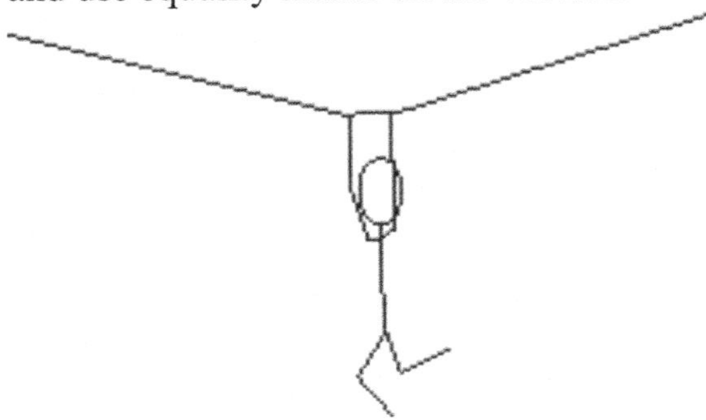

5. Draw a force diagram for a squirrel sitting still on a roof. Label the force vectors and use equality marks on the vectors.

6. Draw a force diagram for the skier who slides with negligible friction. (That means you can ignore the friction force.) Label the force vectors and use equality marks on the vectors.

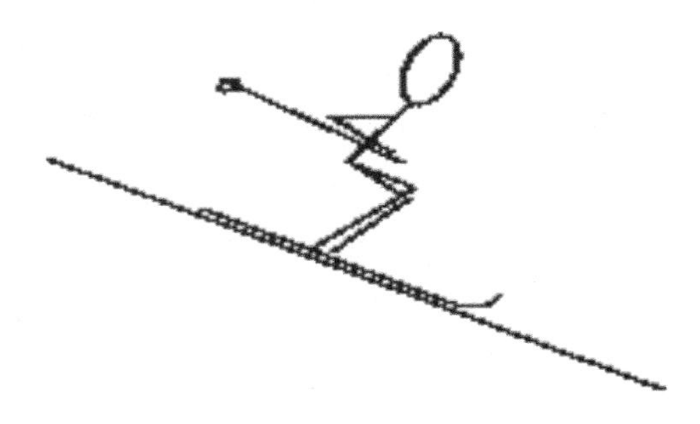

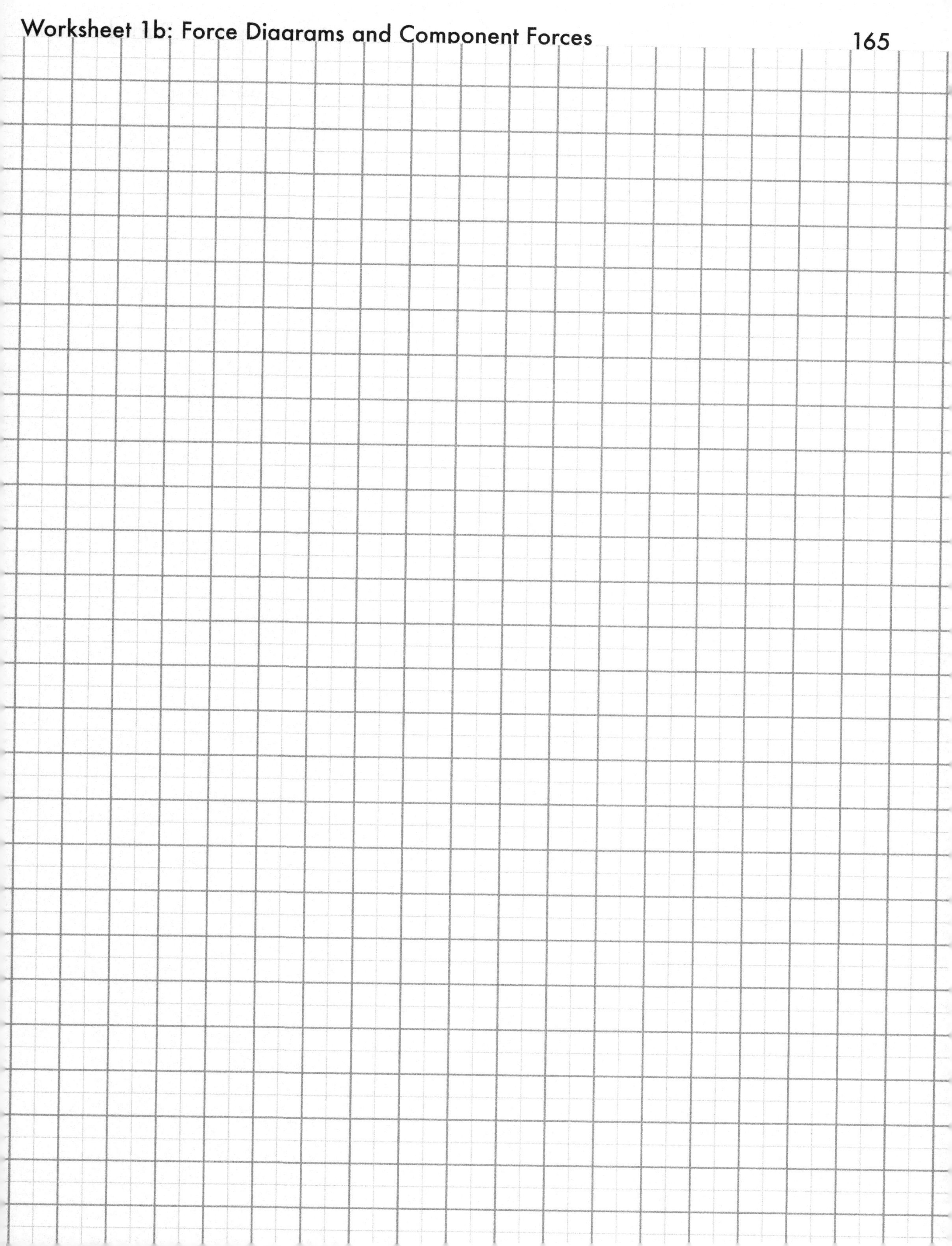

7. Draw a force diagram for the child on the swing who is being pulled back before being released. Label the force vectors and use equality marks on the vectors.

8. Draw a force diagram for the climber who has stopped to rest. Label the force vectors and use equality marks on the vectors.

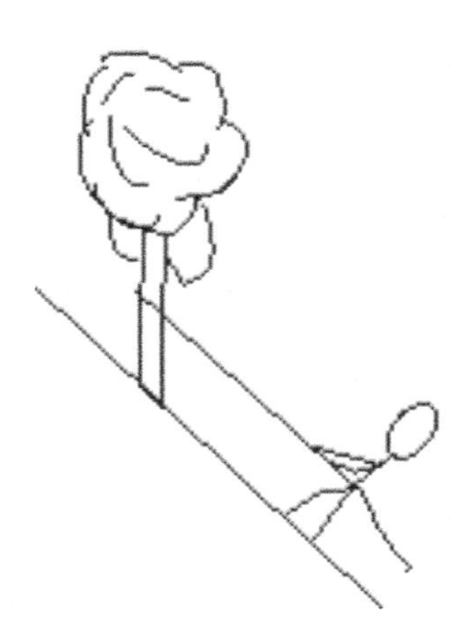

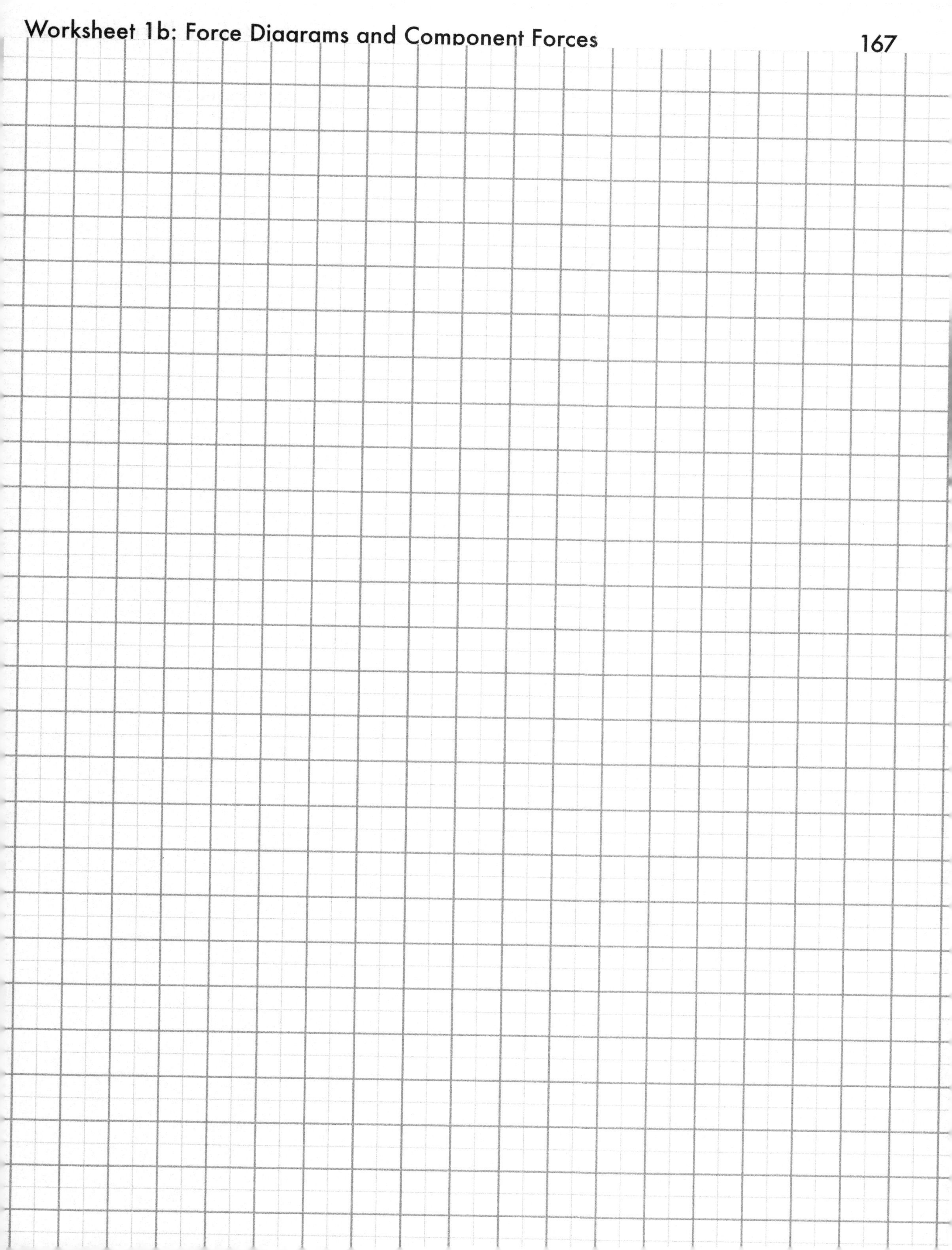

9. Draw a force diagram for the magazine on a magazine rack. Label the force vectors and use equality marks on the vectors.

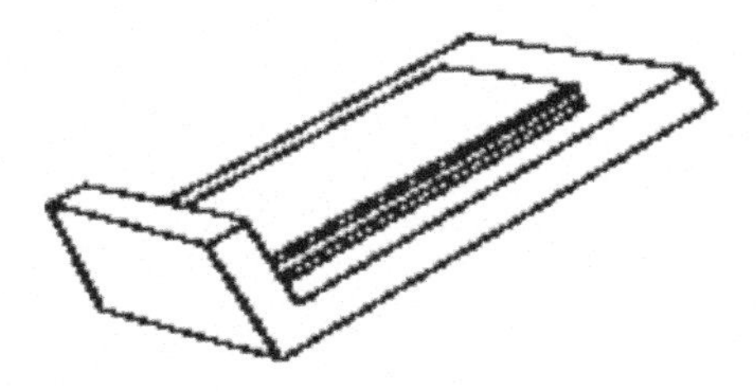

10. Draw a force diagram for the person:
    a) when stepping off
    b) when the stepping foot strikes the ground.

Label the force vectors and use equality marks on the vectors.

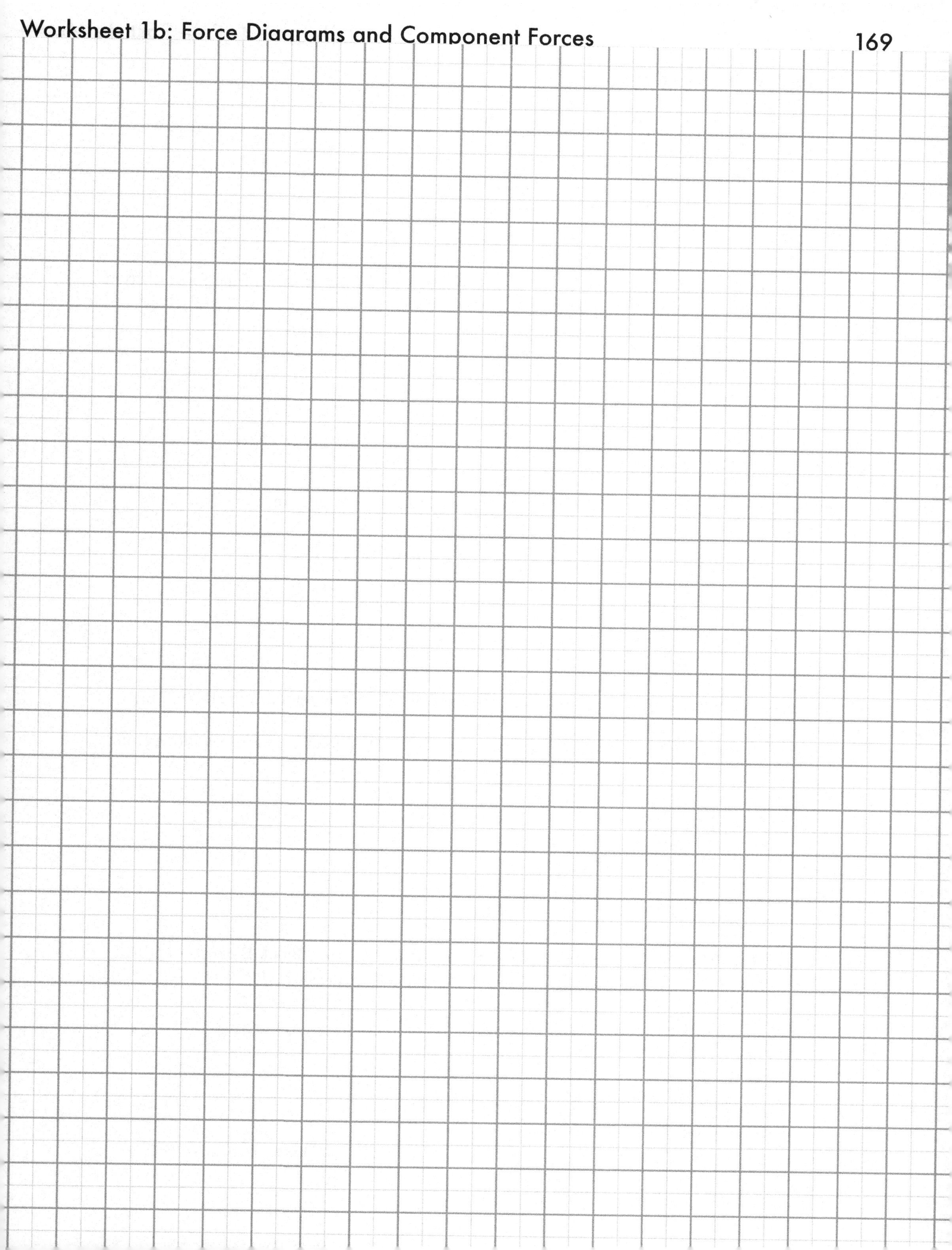

Worksheet 2: Interactions

1. Explain what a normal force is and give an example.

2. Can an inanimate object (such as a table) exert a force? Can the magnitude of the force exerted by an inanimate object change? Explain and give an example.

3. If the acceleration of an object is zero, are no forces acting on it? Explain.

4. How does the force block A exerts on block B compare to the force block B exerts on block A?

Draw and label a quantitative force diagram for each block, using equality marks on the vectors.

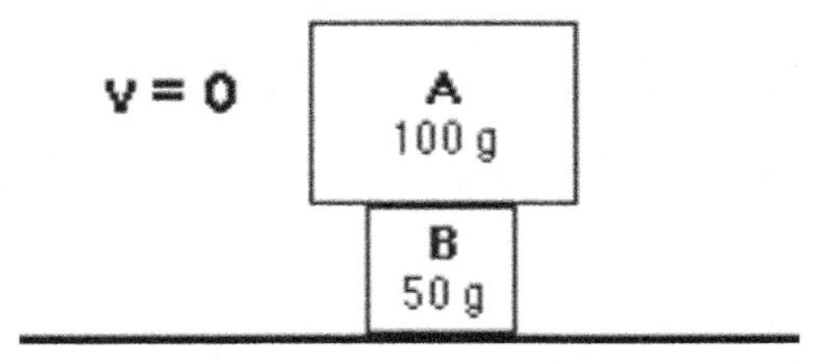

5. How does the force block A exerts on block B compare to the force block B exerts on block A? Draw and label a force diagram for each block, using equality marks on the vectors.

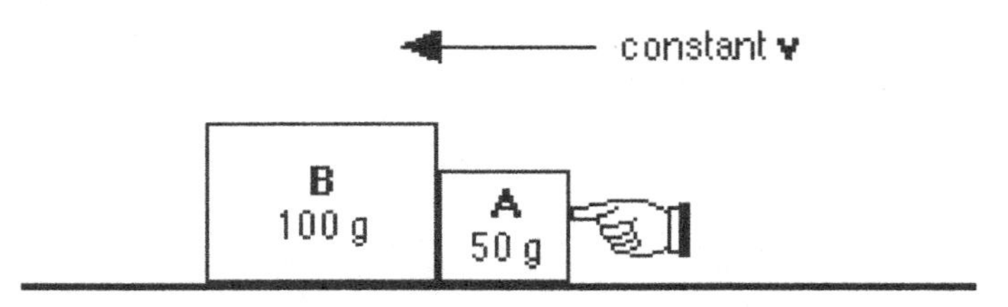

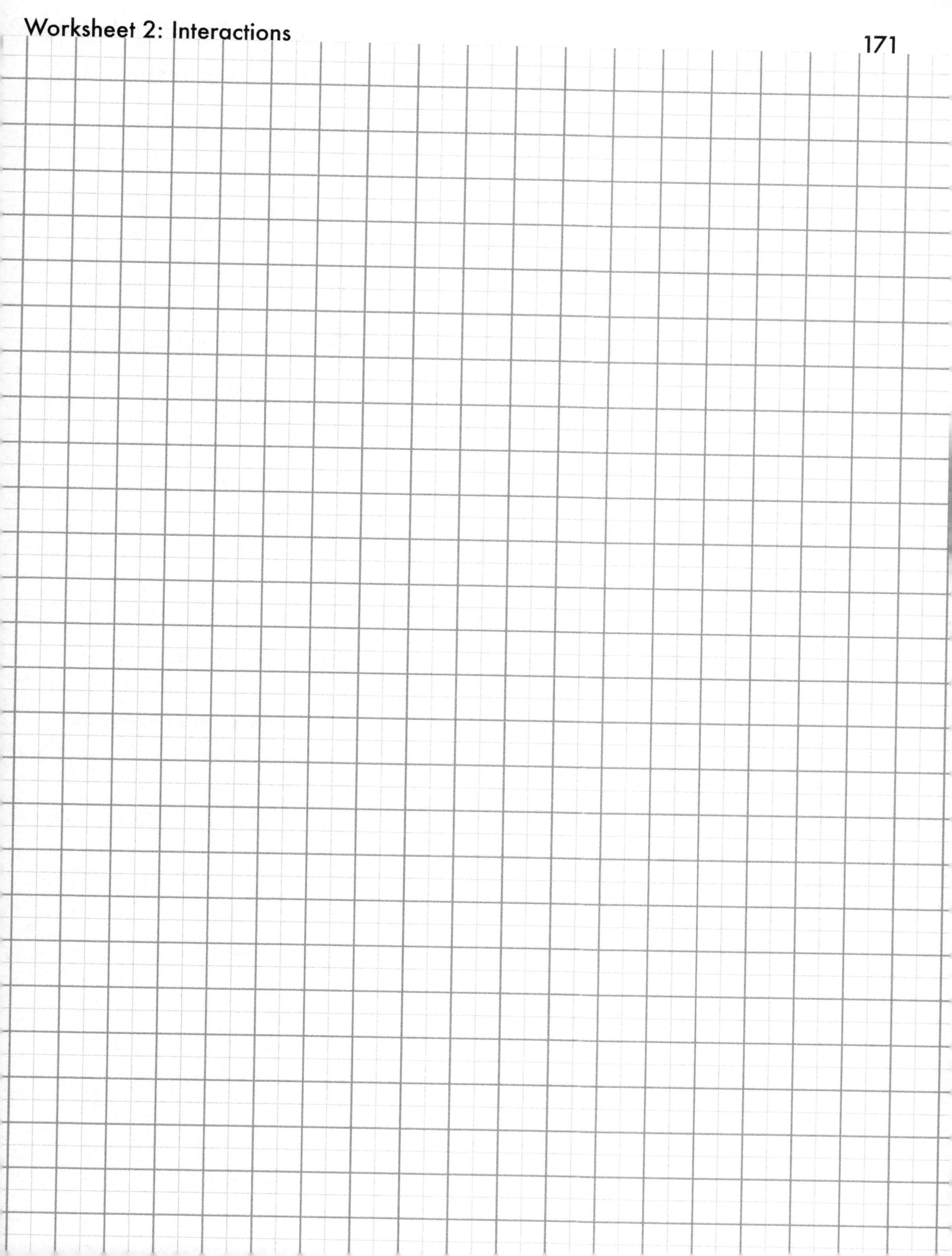

6. How does the force block A exerts on block B compare to the force block B exerts on block A?

Draw and label a force diagram for each block, using equality marks on the vectors.

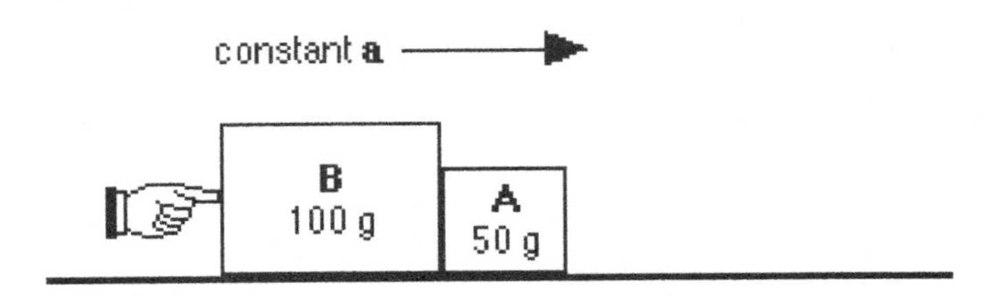

7. How does the force block A exerts on block B compare to the force block B exerts on block A?

Draw and label a force diagram for each block, using equality marks on the vectors.

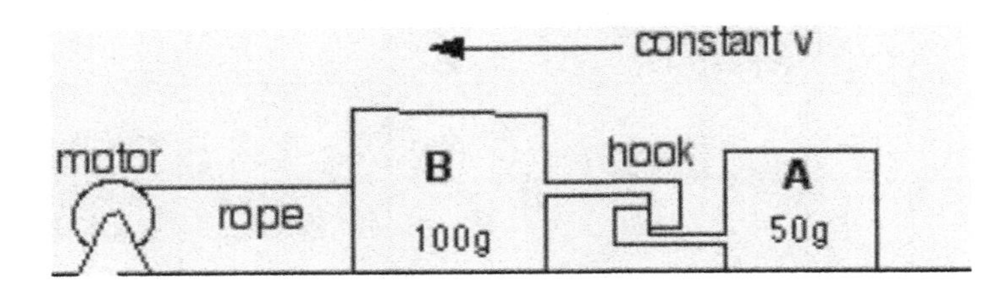

8. How does the force the magnet exerts on the refrigerator compare to the force the refrigerator exerts on the magnet?

Draw and label a force diagram for the magnet and the refrigerator, using equality marks on the vectors.

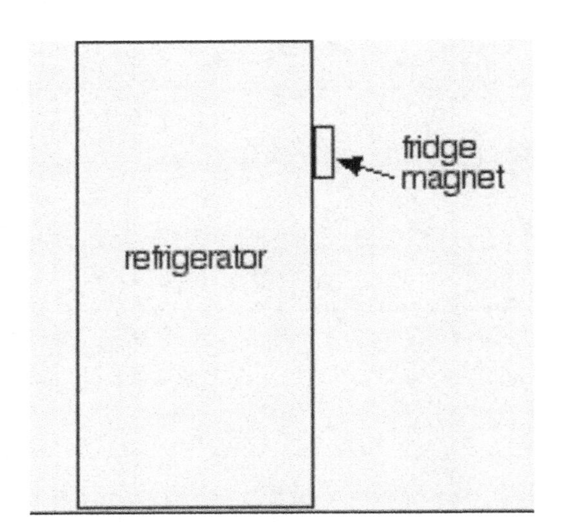

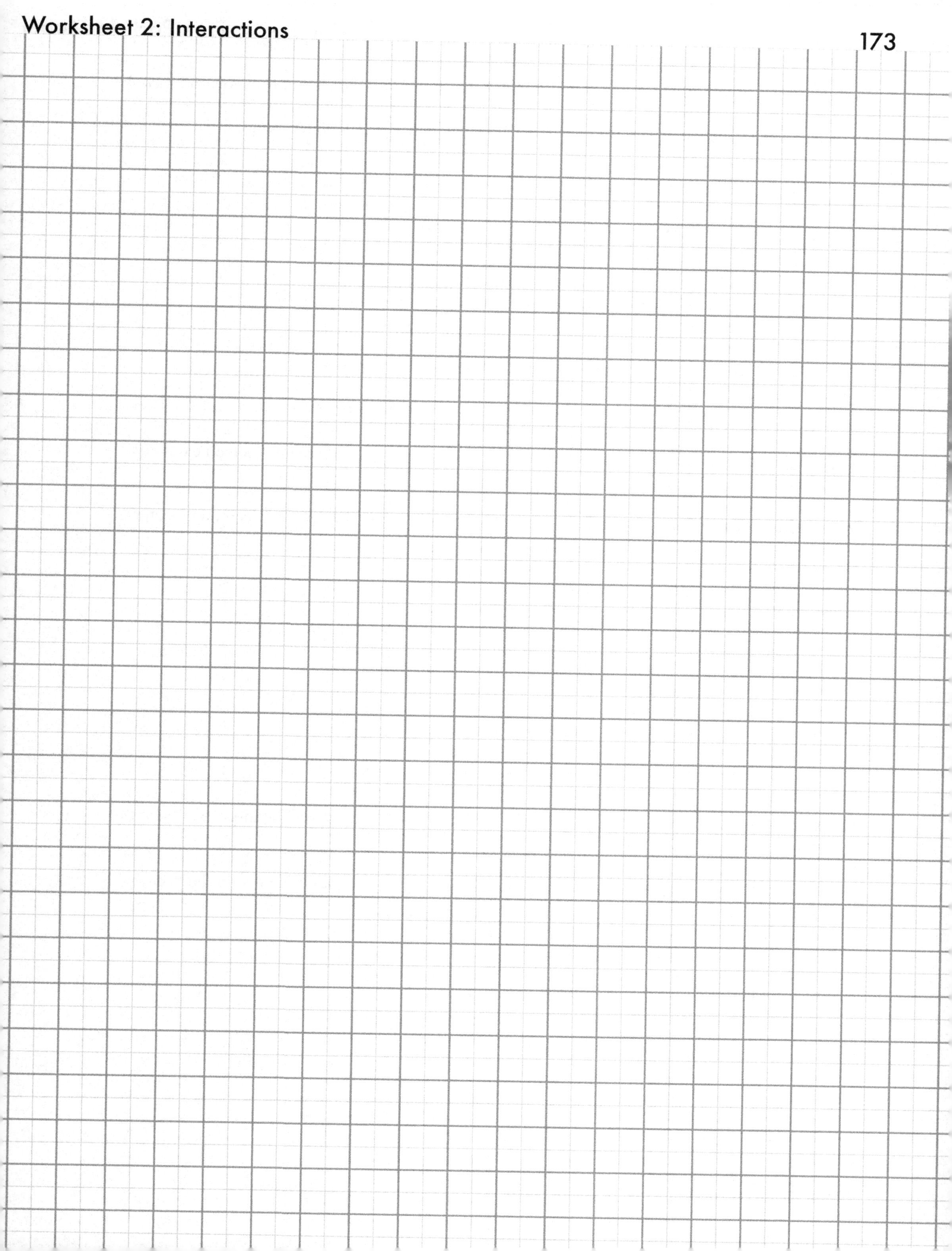

9. How does the force block A exerts on block B compare to the force block B exerts on block A?

Draw and label a force diagram for each block, using equality marks on the vectors.

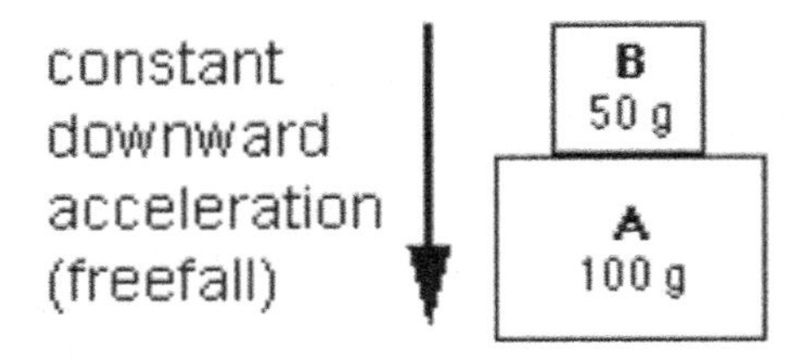

10. How does the force the earth exerts on the person compare to the force the person exerts on the earth?

Draw and label force diagrams for the earth and the person, using equality marks on the vectors.

11. How does the force the earth exerts on the moon compare to the force the moon exerts on the earth?

Draw and label force diagrams for the earth and the moon, using equality marks on the vectors.

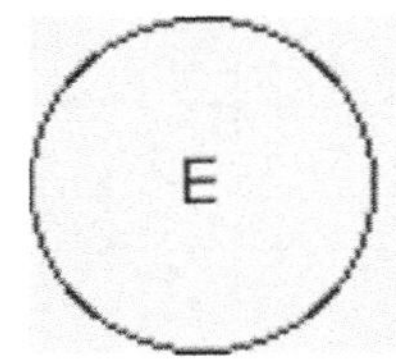

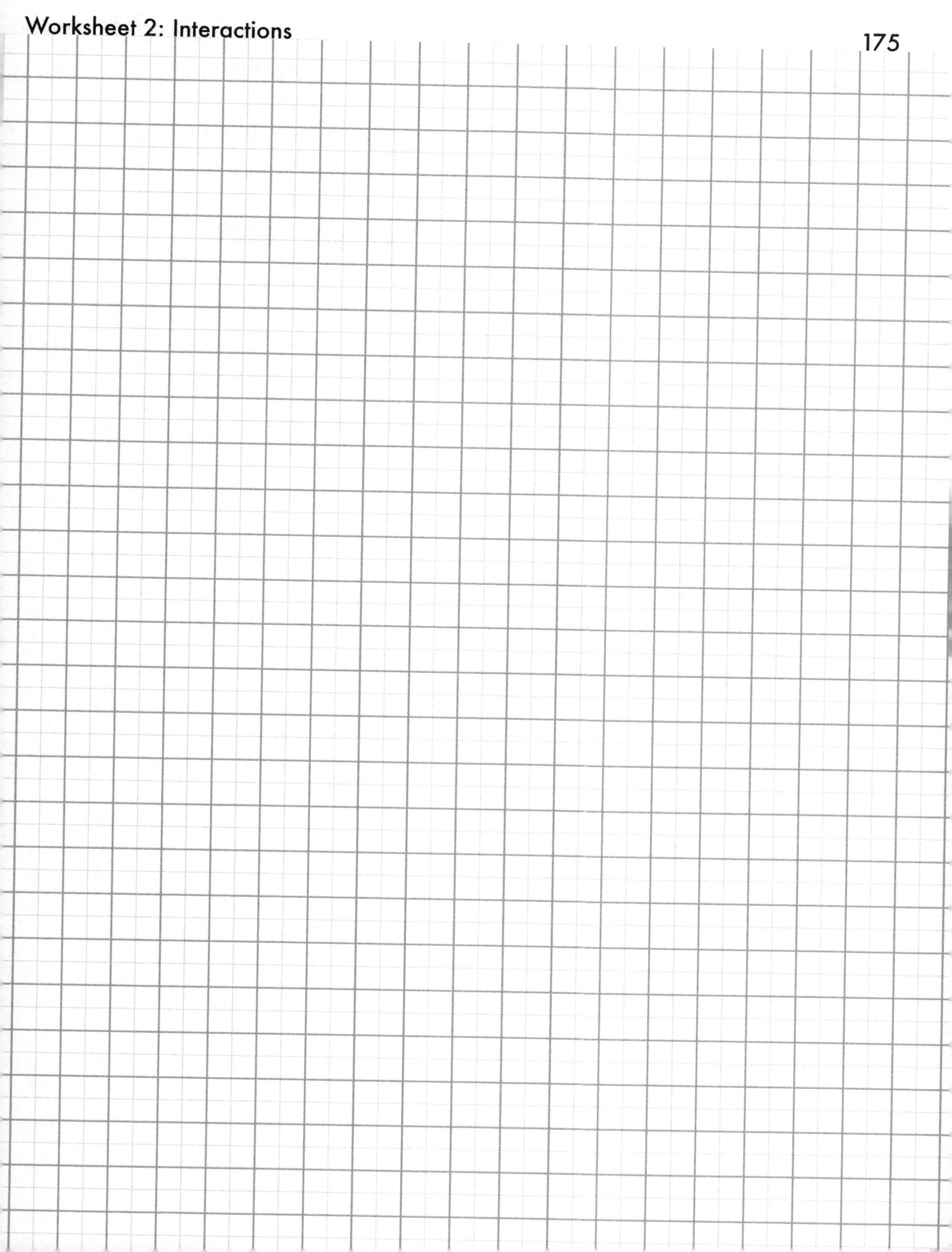

Worksheet 3: Quantitative Force Analysis & Vector Components

1. Determine the tension in each cable below. Draw a force diagram for the system before solving the problem.
   Case A - ball suspended on one cable Case B - ball suspended by two cables

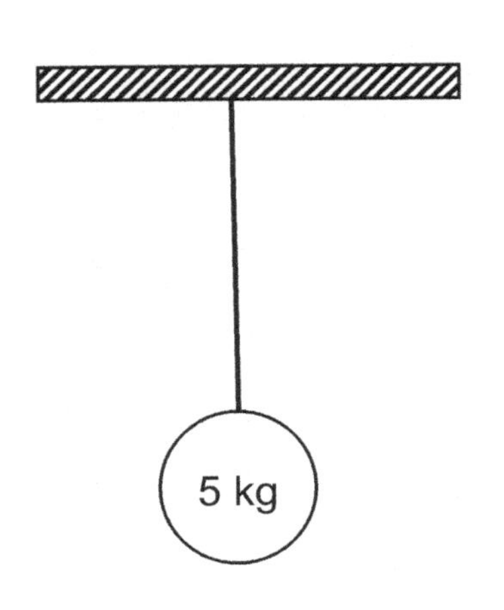

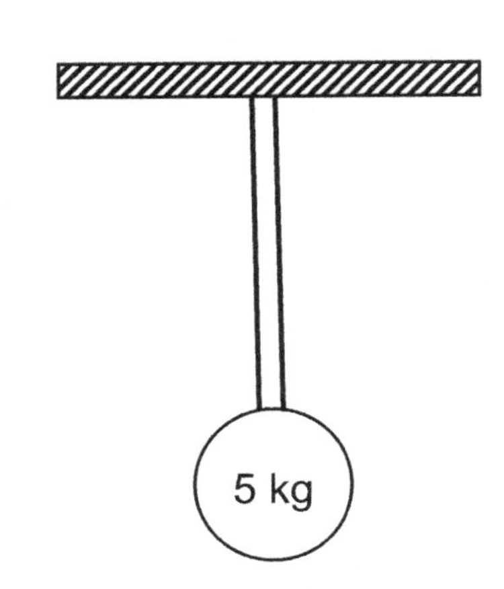

2. Determine tension in each cable.

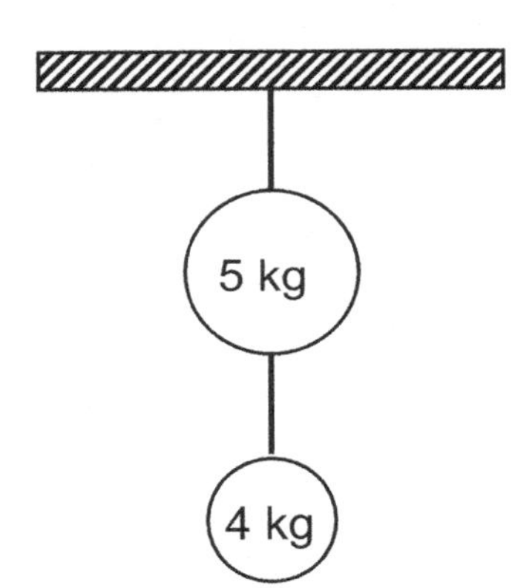

3. Find the horizontal and vertical components of the tension in the fishing line. Show your work.

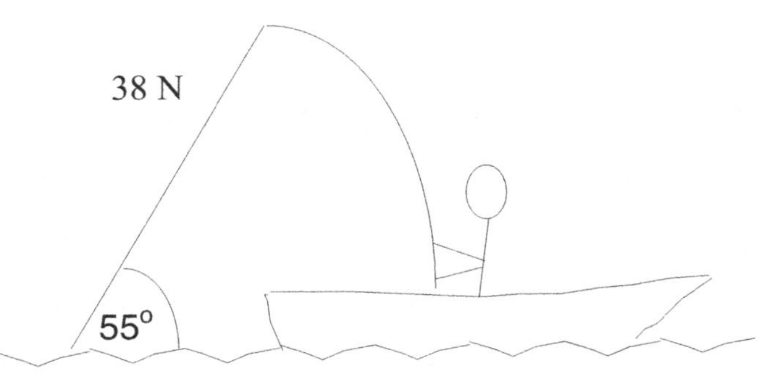

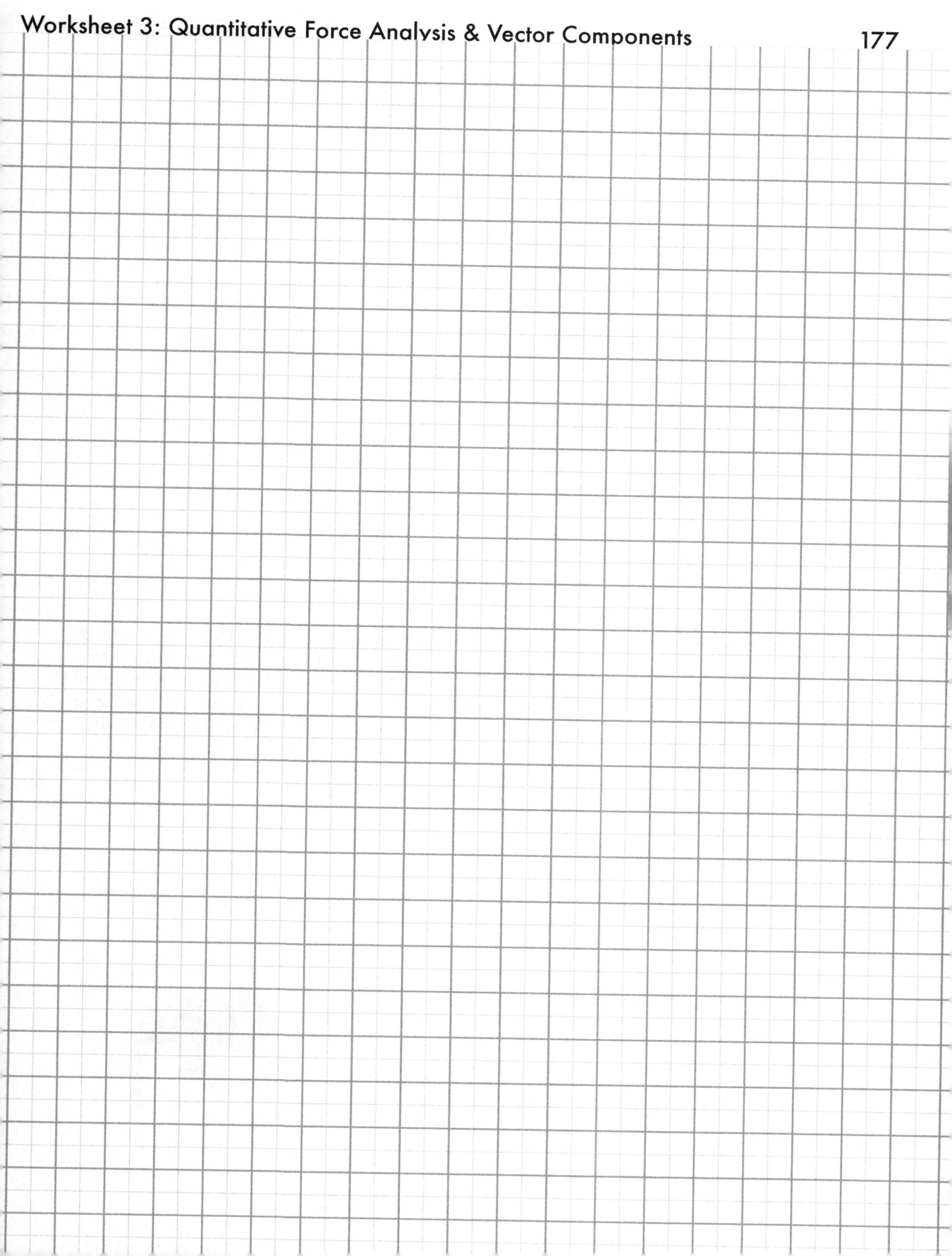

4. A suspension bridge cable is connected to its anchor at a 20° angle. Draw a force diagram for the anchor, and then find the vertical and horizontal component forces on the anchor by the cable.

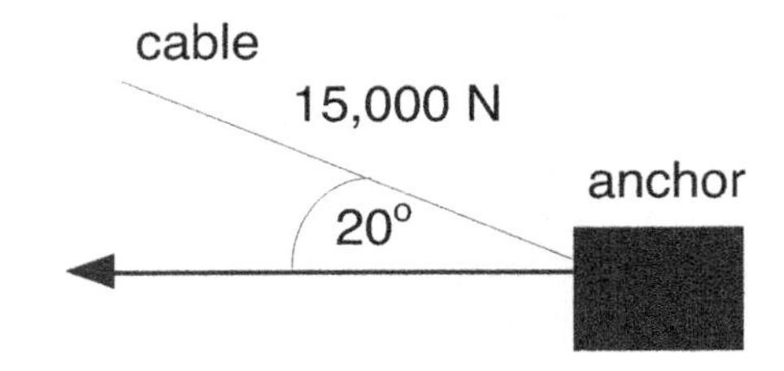

A real suspension bridge anchor

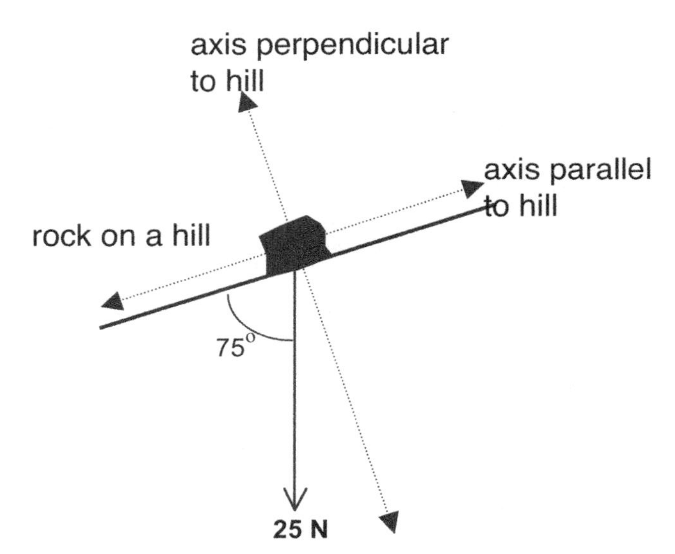

5. A rock sits on a hill. Draw a force diagram for the rock that allows you to determine how much of the rock's weight is parallel to the hill, (that would tend to make it slide down the hill) and how much of the rock's weight is perpendicular to the hill (that tends to hold the rock in contact with the hill.)

6. A 2000 kg elephant stands on a ramp. Draw a force diagram to determine the components of the elephant's weight parallel and perpendicular to the ramp.

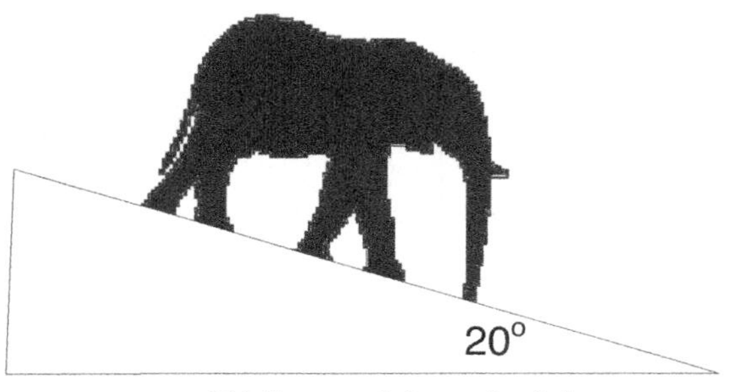

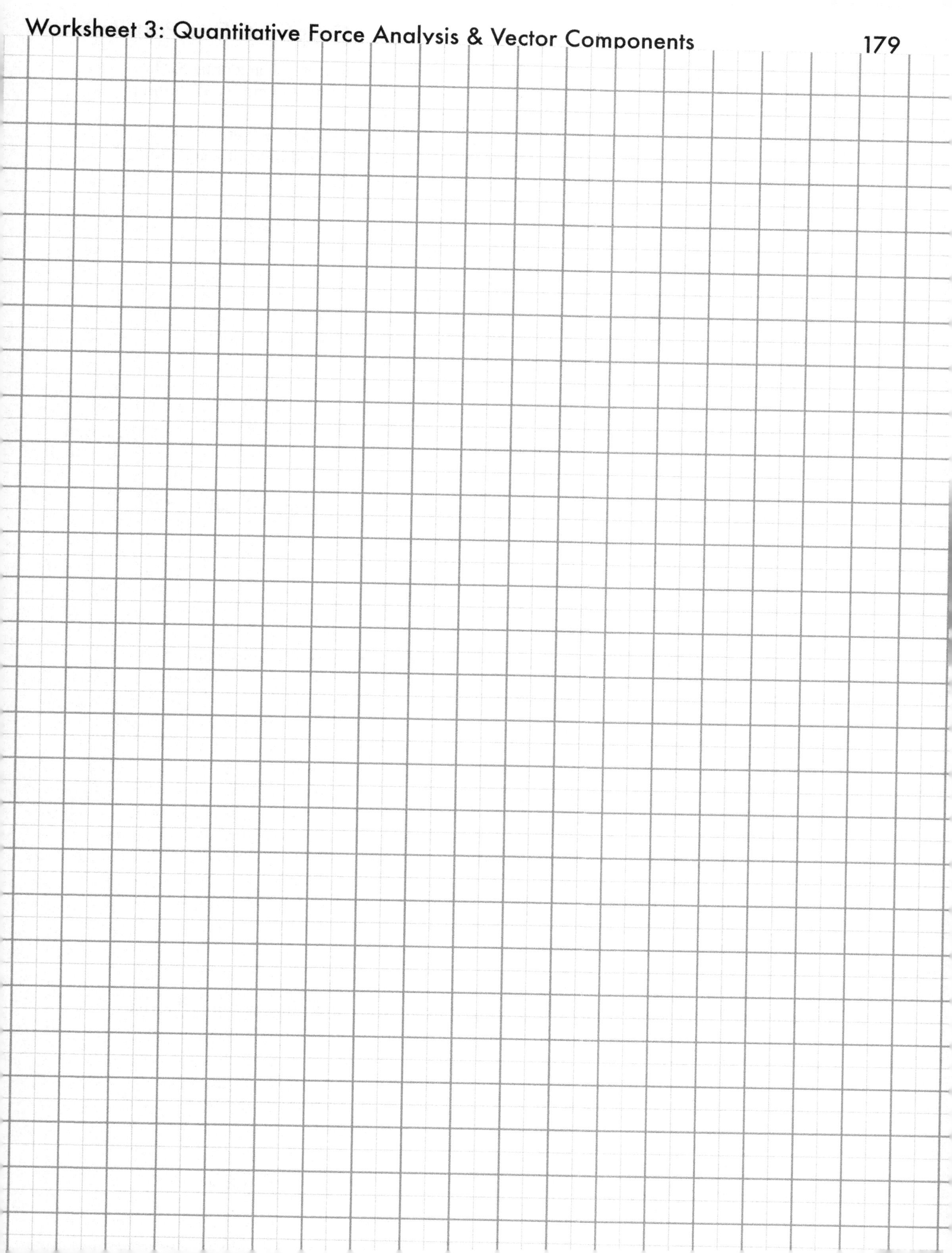

7. Tarzan prepares to swing and much to his dismay, gets his loincloth stuck on a branch. He's left hanging with the vine pulling upward at a 40-degree angle and his loincloth pulling him horizontally to the right.

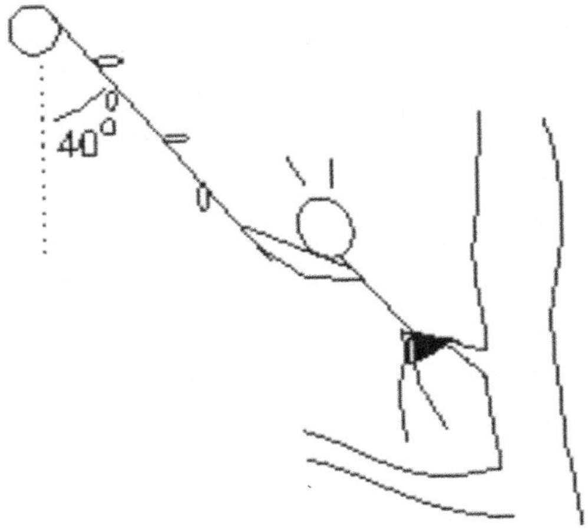

a. Draw a force diagram for Tarzan. Be sure to break angled forces into components and indicate which forces are equal with equality marks.

40°

b. Write an equation for the vertical forces on Tarzan. (Look at your equality marks.)

c. Write an equation for the horizontal forces on Tarzan. (Look at your equality marks.)

d. Tarzan's mass is 75 kg. Calculate his weight.

e. Use the appropriate equation for the forces on Tarzan to determine the tension in the vine.

f. Determine the tension in his loincloth.

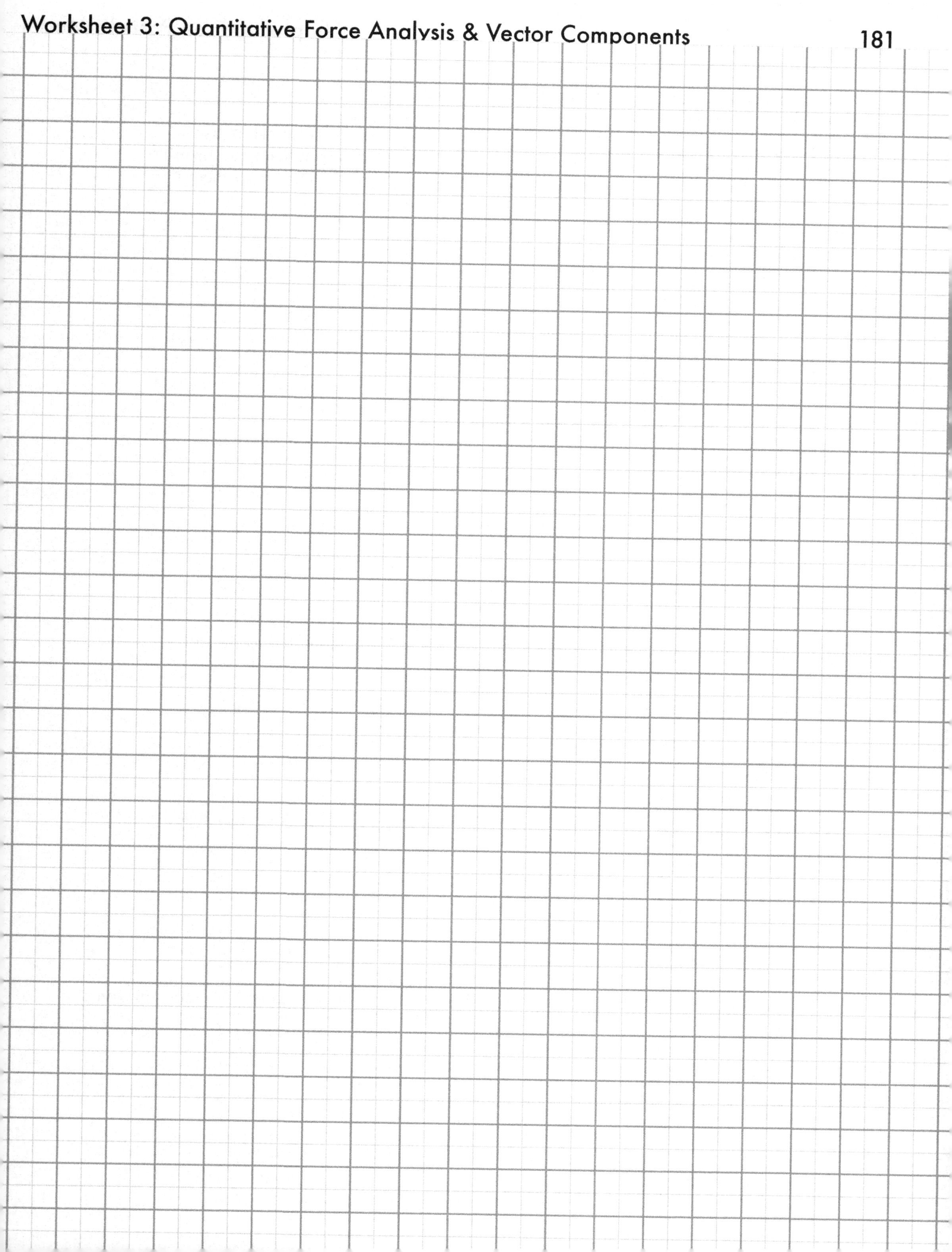

8. A 90 kg skier takes to the slopes and reaches a constant velocity.

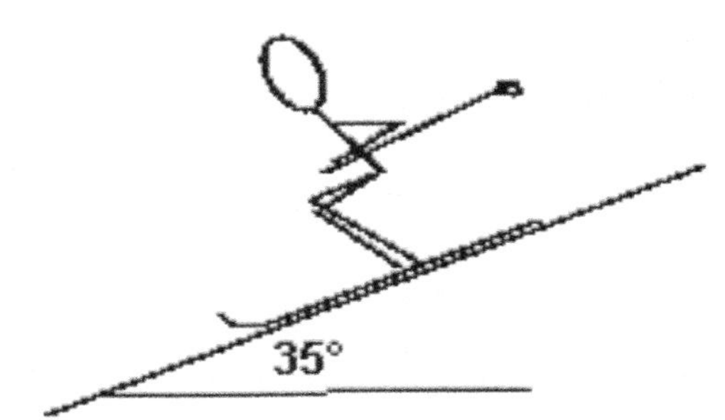

a. Draw a force diagram for the skier. (Hint: use a coordinate axis parallel and perpendicular to the hill's surface as in questions 5 and 6 on this worksheet.)

b. Determine the skier's weight.

c. Determine the component of the skier's weight that must be supported by the hill.

d. Determine the component of the skier's weight that pulls the skier down the slope.

e. What is the total force of friction and air resistance acting upon the skier? Explain how you know.

Worksheet 4: Force Diagrams & Statics

For each of the problems below, carefully draw a force diagram of the system before attempting to solve the problem.

1a. Volcanologists need a lava sample from an active lava pool below a plateau inside the volcano. After one end of a rope is anchored to the rock, another scientist hikes around the plateau rim so that the rope, and an attached cable, hangs over the lava pool. The cable is dipped into the lava pool and then the lava that congeals on the cable is retrieved. (This was done at Mt. Nyiragongo in Africa.)

When the cable with the lava sample has a weight of 125 N, how large is the tension in the rope? (Hint: make your force diagram for the junction of the cable and the rope, and don't worry about the fact that the rope has weight too.)

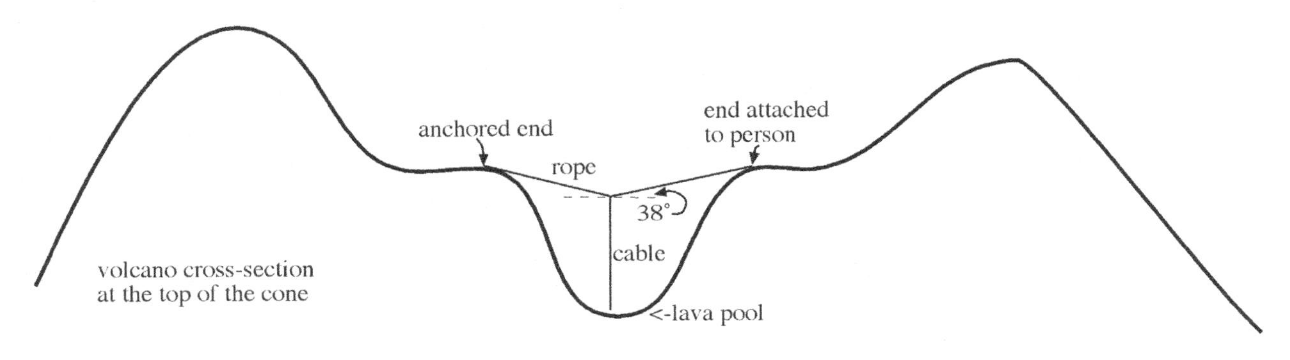

1b. The actual apparatus has a pulley in the middle of the rope. The cable parallels one side of the rope, goes over the pulley and down to the lava pool. The reason for this is that simply tightening the rope can't lift the lava sample out. Here's why: calculate how much tension would be needed in the rope to decrease the angle to 5°.

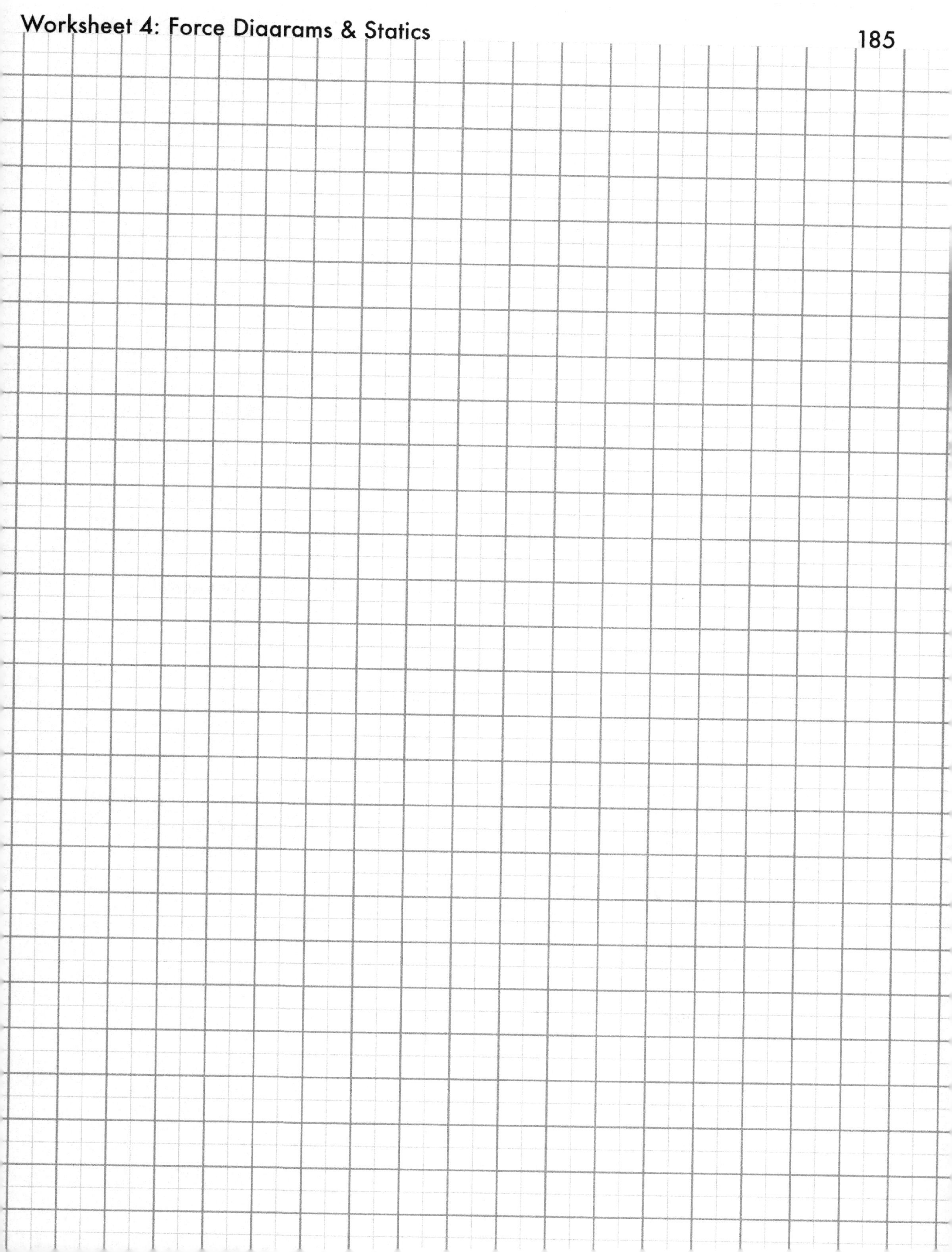

2. A man pulls a 50 kg box *at constant speed* across the floor. He applies a 200 N force at an angle of 30°.

Force diagram for the box:

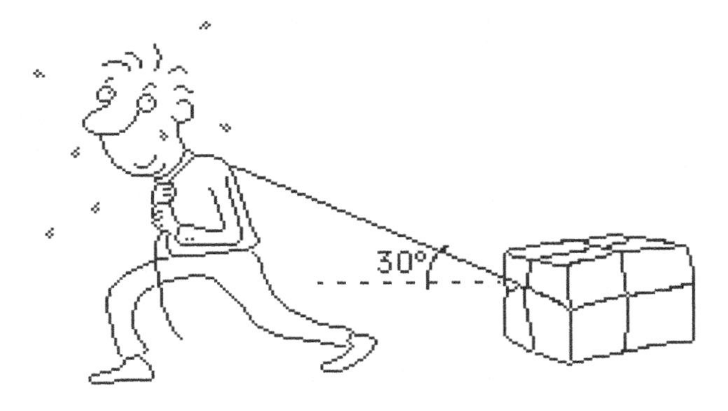

a. Write an equation for all the forces and components of force on the box in the vertical direction.

b. Calculate the size of the normal force on the box.

c. Write an equation for all the forces and components of force on the box in the horizontal direction.

d. Calculate the size of the frictional force opposing the motion of the box.

3. Determine the weight of the tram. The cable at left exerts a 30,000 N force. (The tram is attached to the cable so the tension in the left cable is not necessarily equal to the tension in the right cable.)

4. In the space at right, draw the force diagram for a bear climbing a hill at constant speed.

a. Write the equation that describes the forces that act parallel to the ramp.

b. Write the equation that describes the forces that act perpendicular to the ramp.

c. If the mass of the bear is 400 kg, determine the value of the normal force.

5. A 950 kg car is driven up a hill at constant velocity of 7 m/s, where 1200 N of friction and drag oppose its motion.

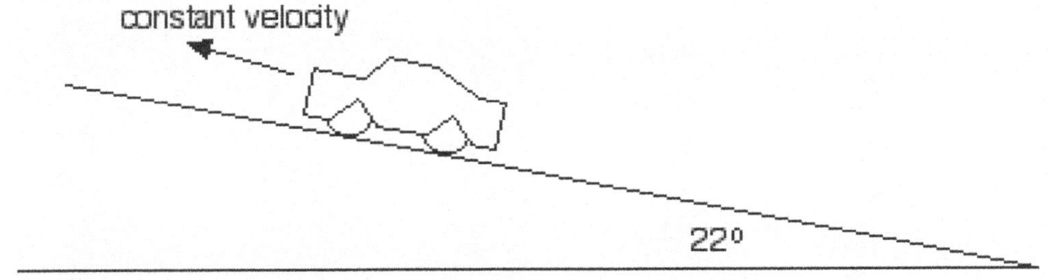

a. Draw a force diagram for the car.

b. What is the weight of the car?

c. Calculate the normal force on the car. Show your work.

d. Calculate the force on the car that allows it to go up the hill. Show your work.

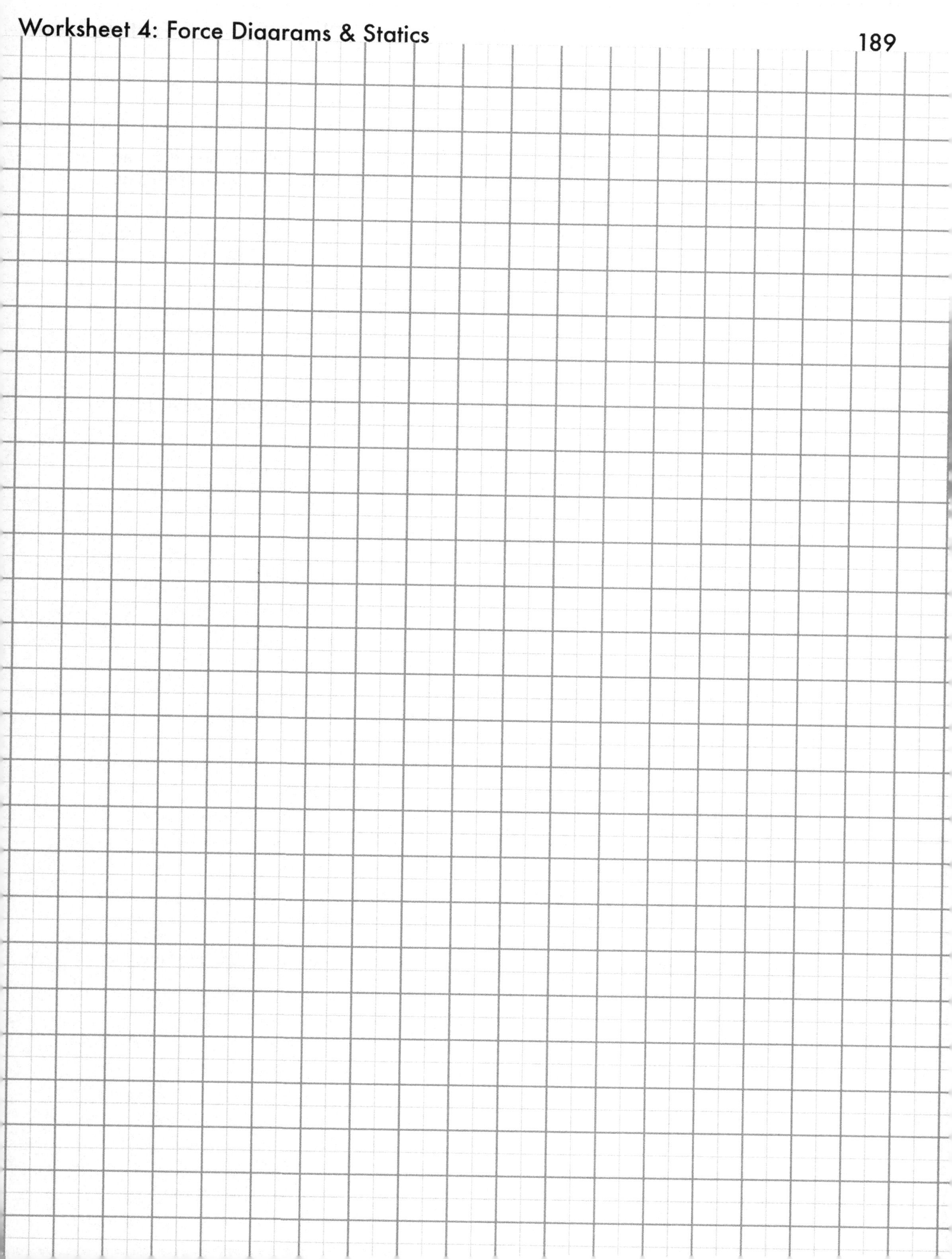

Review Problems

1. Consider a collision between a small car and a heavy truck. In such a collision, how does the size of the force exerted on the car by the truck compare with the size of the force exerted on the truck by the car? Explain your reasoning.

2. a. Draw a velocity-time graph for a ball thrown vertically into the air during its up-and-down motion.

   b. Draw a force diagram for the thrown ball when it reaches its highest point.

   c. At the highest point, is the velocity zero? Explain.

   d. At the highest point, is the acceleration zero? Explain.

   e. At the highest point, is the net force zero (i.e. are the forces balanced)? Explain how you know.

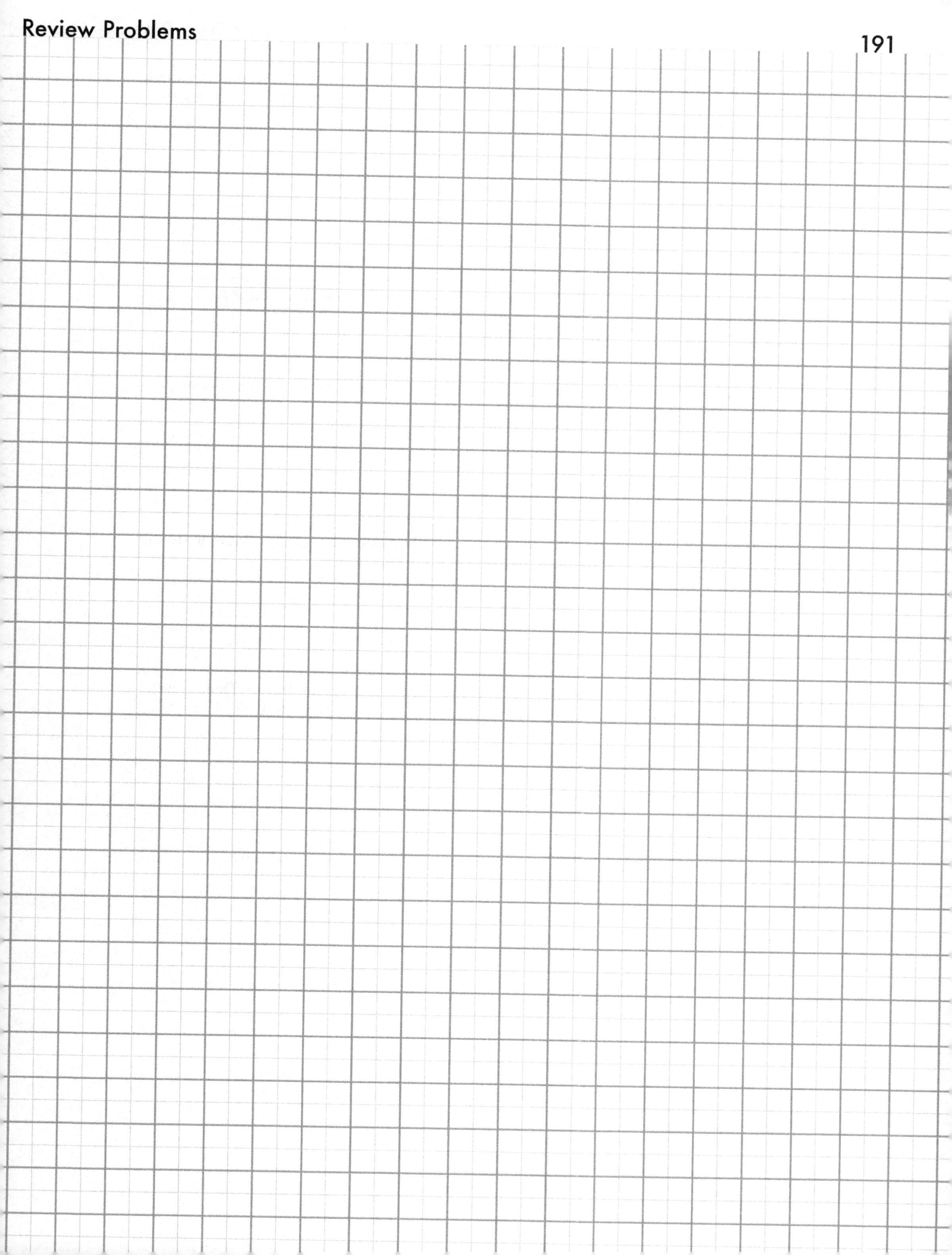

3. The figure below is a snapshot looking down on a bowling ball moving at constant velocity from left to right on a smooth, level floor. At the position shown, the ball is given a short, sharp hit in a direction perpendicular to the ball's initial motion.

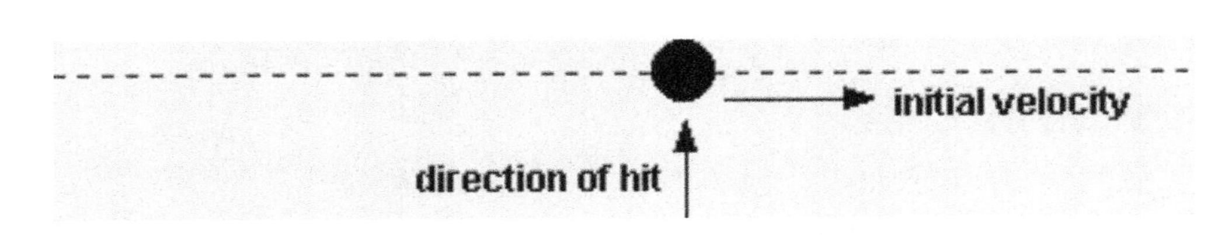

a. On the diagram, draw a path that the ball might follow after the hit. Explain your reasoning for the path you drew.

b. Immediately after the hit, will the speed of the ball be equal to, greater than, or smaller than the ball's velocity before the hit? Explain your reasoning.

c. How will the velocity of the ball behave as time goes by after the blow? That is, will either the magnitude or the direction of the velocity change? If so, how?

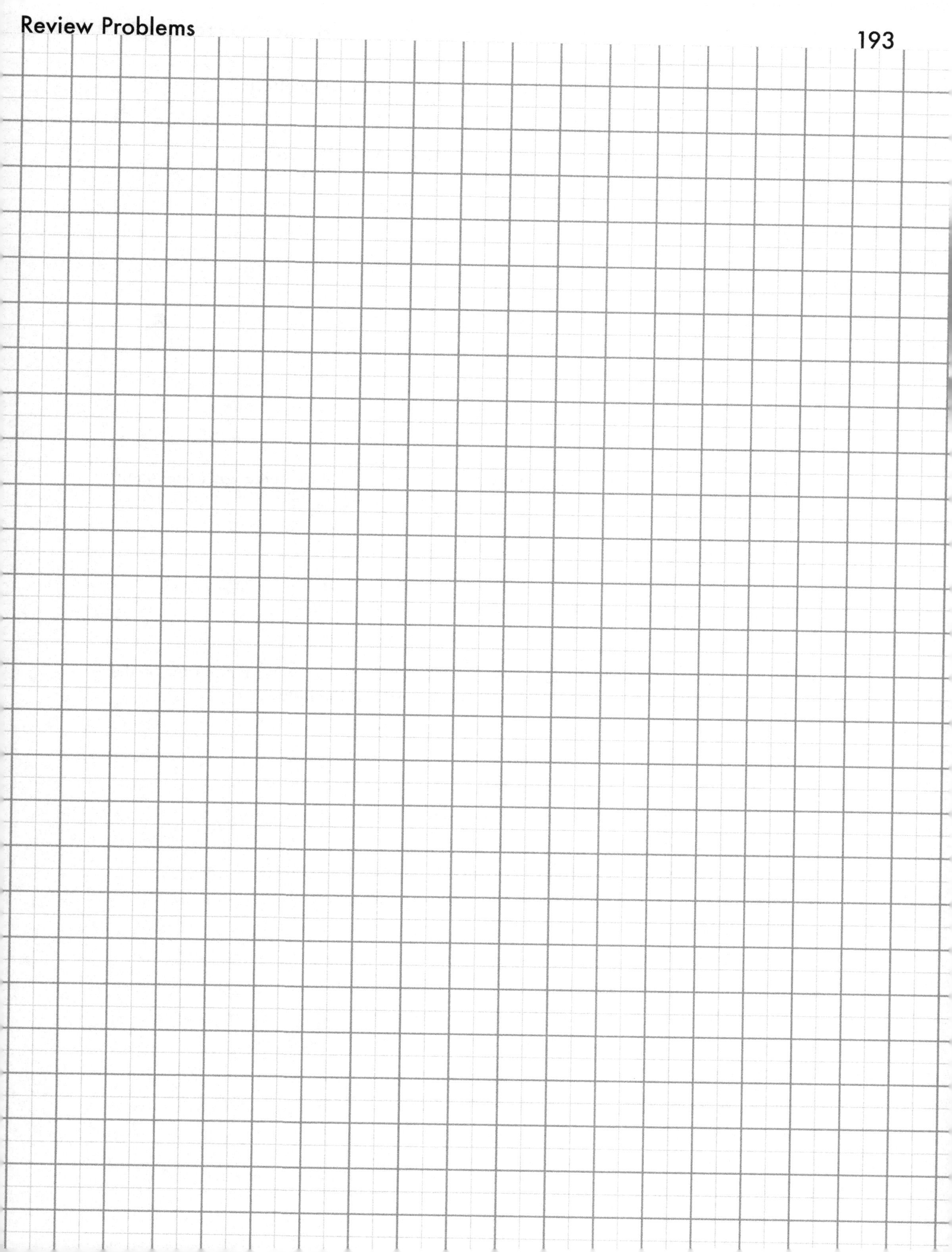

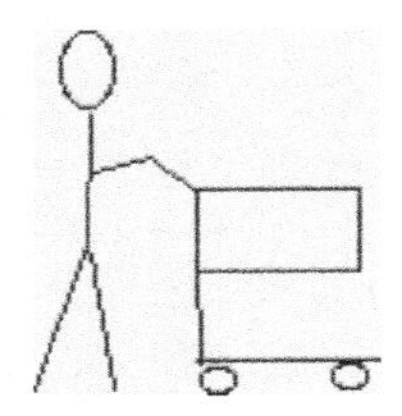

4. You push a grocery cart along a level floor in the presence of friction effects between the cart and the floor.

   a. Draw force diagrams for **you**, the **cart**, and the **floor/earth**. Fully label all vectors.

you floor/Earth cart

   b. While you are making the cart **speed up**, how does the size of the force you apply on the cart compare to the size of the force the cart exerts on you? Explain.

   c. While you are making the cart **speed up**, how does the size of the frictional force on the *cart* by the floor compare to the frictional force on *you* by the floor?

   d. Identify all of the Newton's Third Law pairs in your force diagrams.

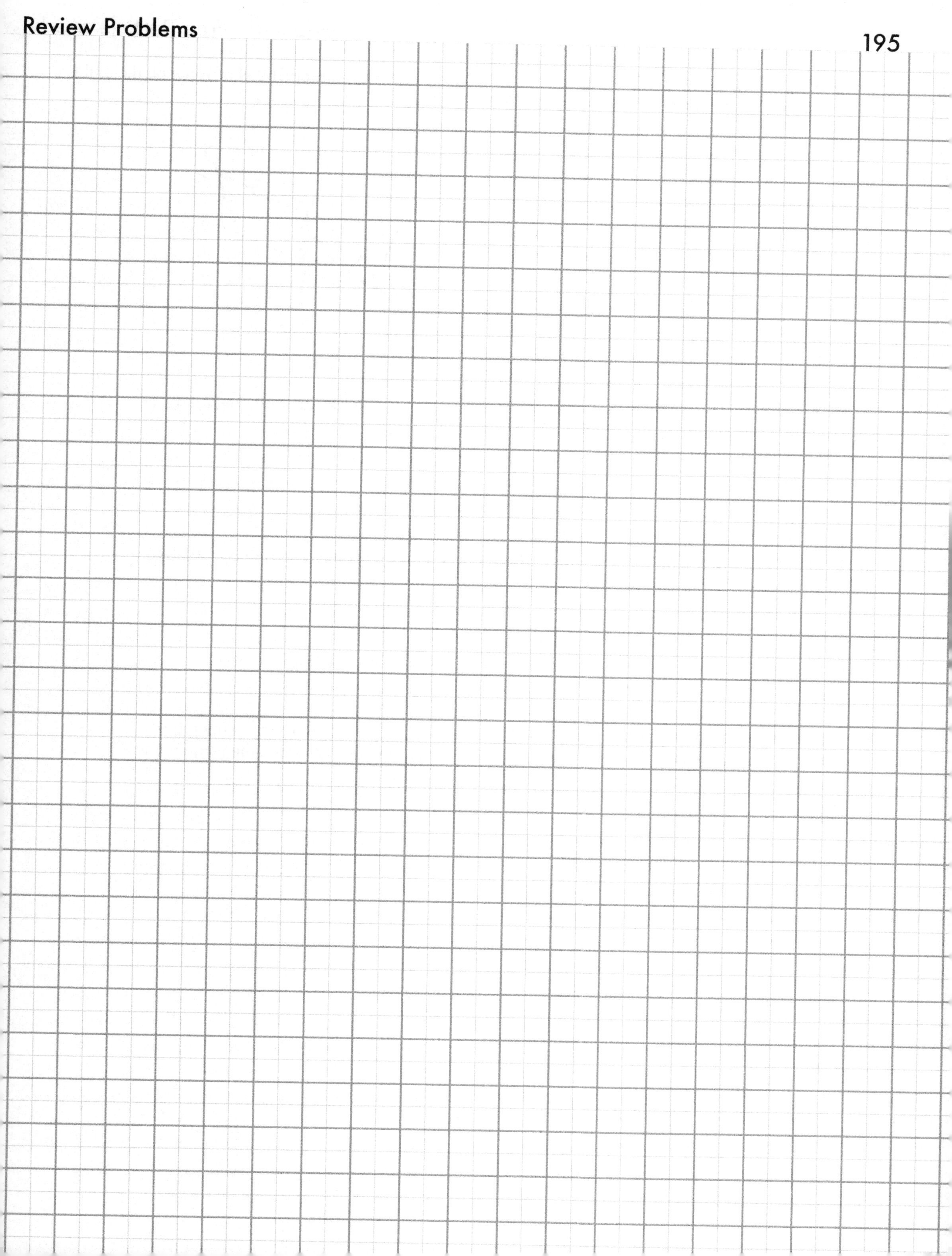

5. A 35 kg child pulls a 12 kg wagon up a hill at 0.6 m/s. The wagon exerts 60 N of force on the child.
   a. Draw a **quantitative** force diagram for the **wagon**.

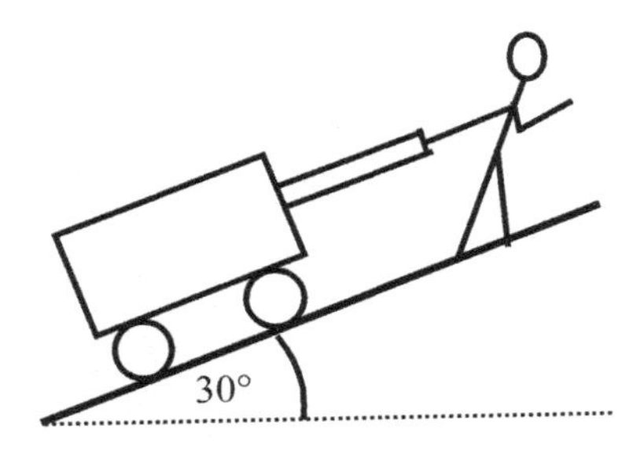

   b. Explain how you applied Newton's **first** law to make the force diagram quantitative.

   c. Explain how you applied Newton's **third** law to make the force diagram quantitative.

6. "The winning team in a tug of war contest is the team that puts more force on the rope." Is this a true statement? Explain your reasoning. If the statement is false, then explain how one team can win the contest.

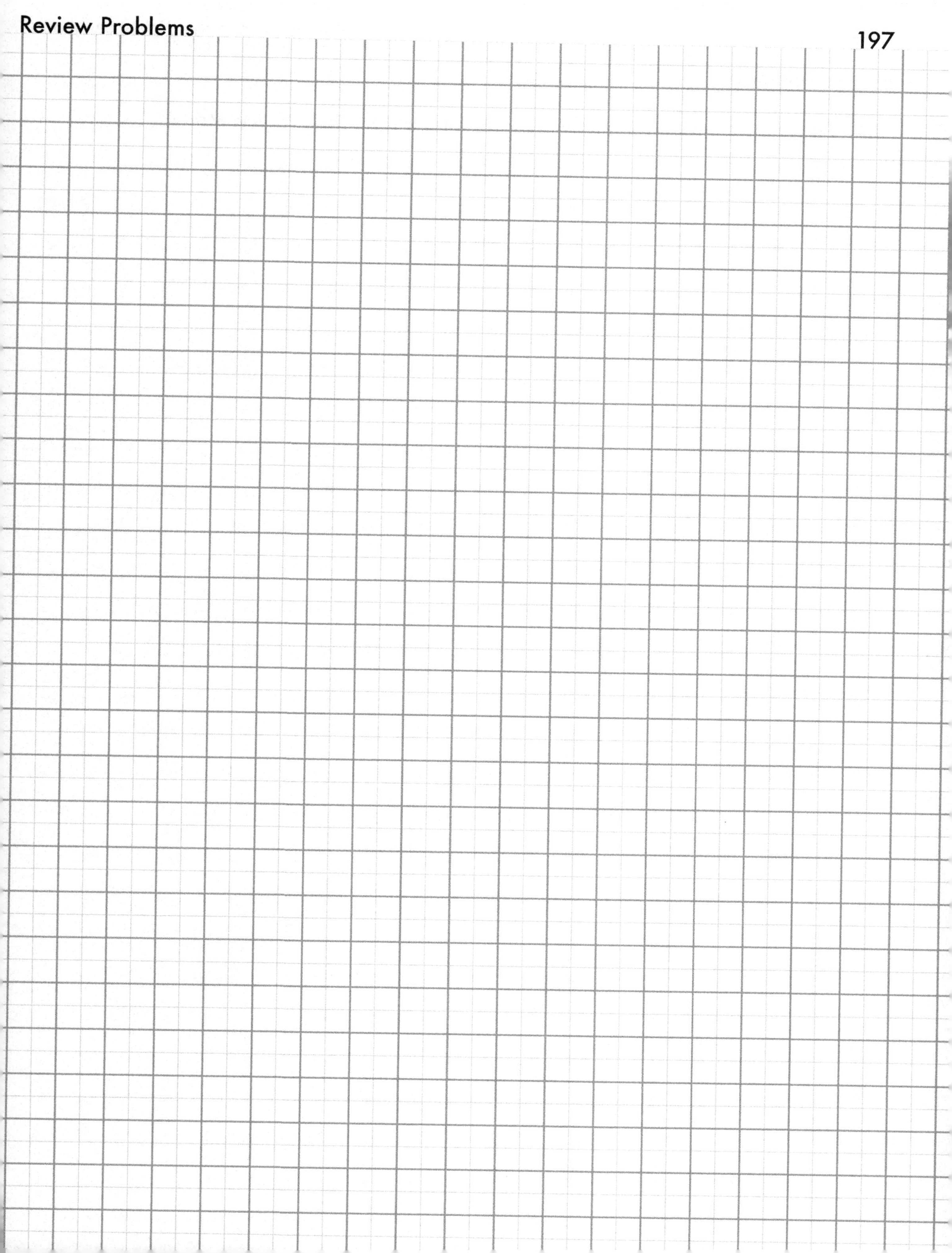

Model Summary

This is a place to summarize different representations of the Free Particle Model

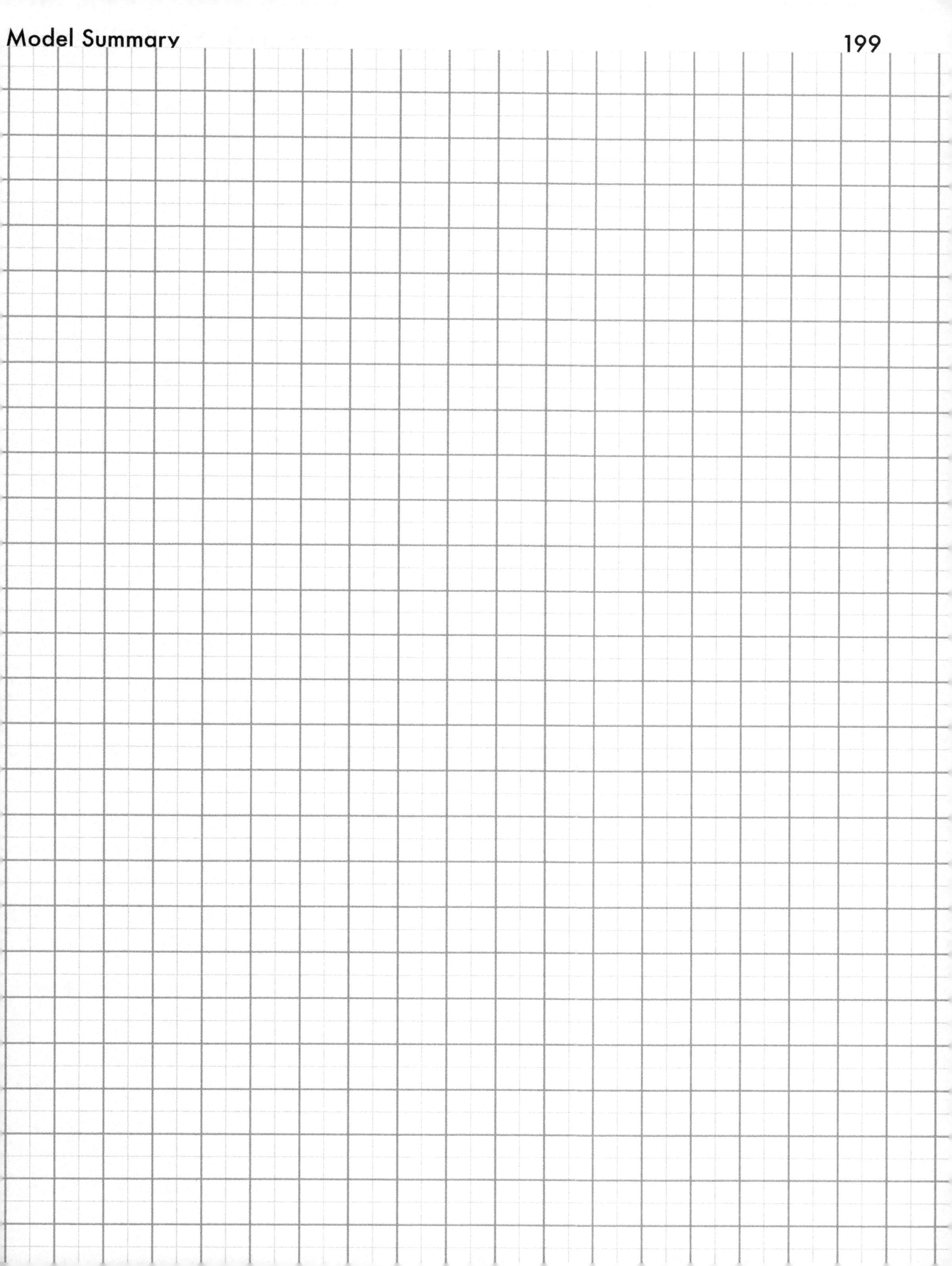

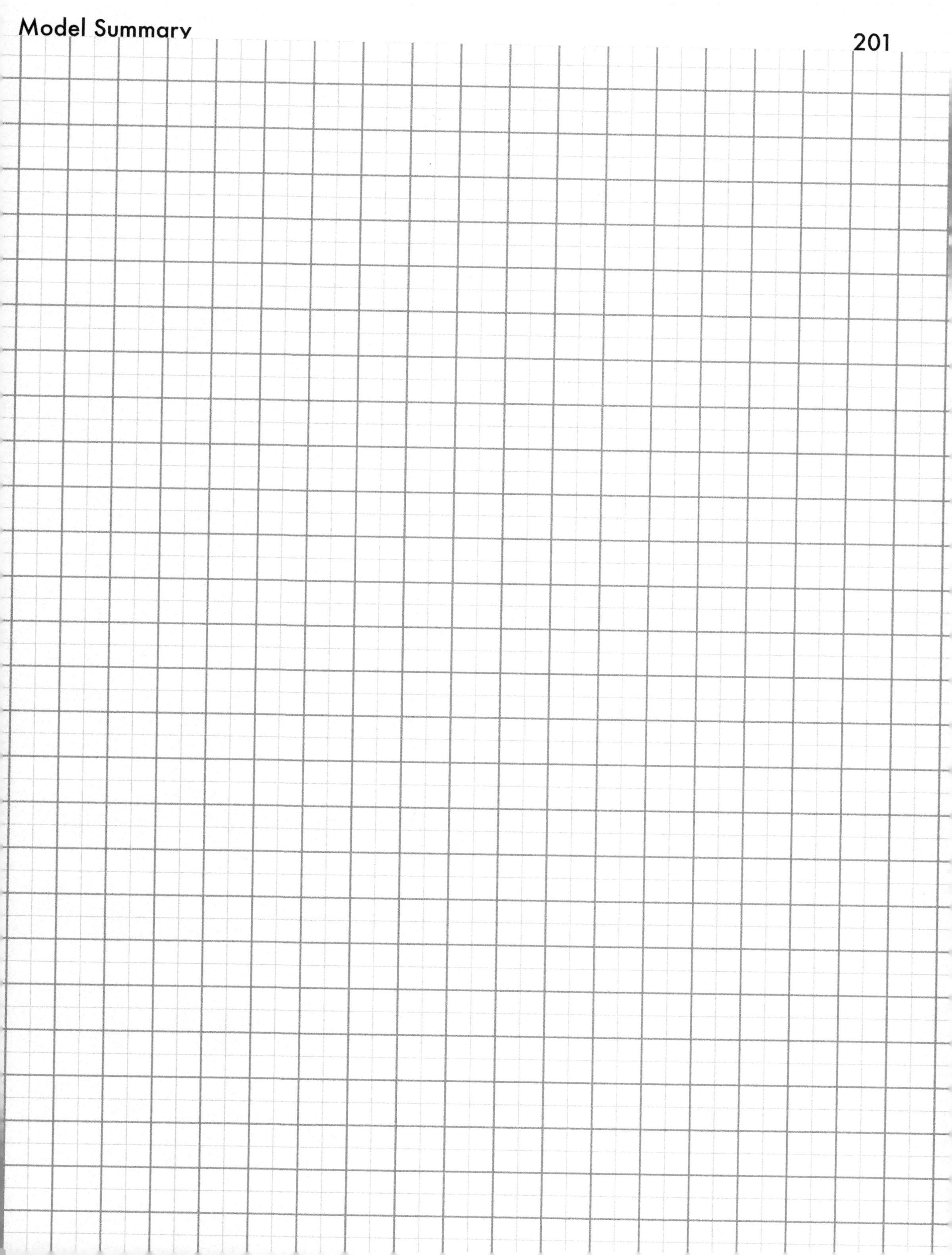

Chapter 5: Net Force Particle Model

Chapter Sections

chapter 5 online help

Lab Notes

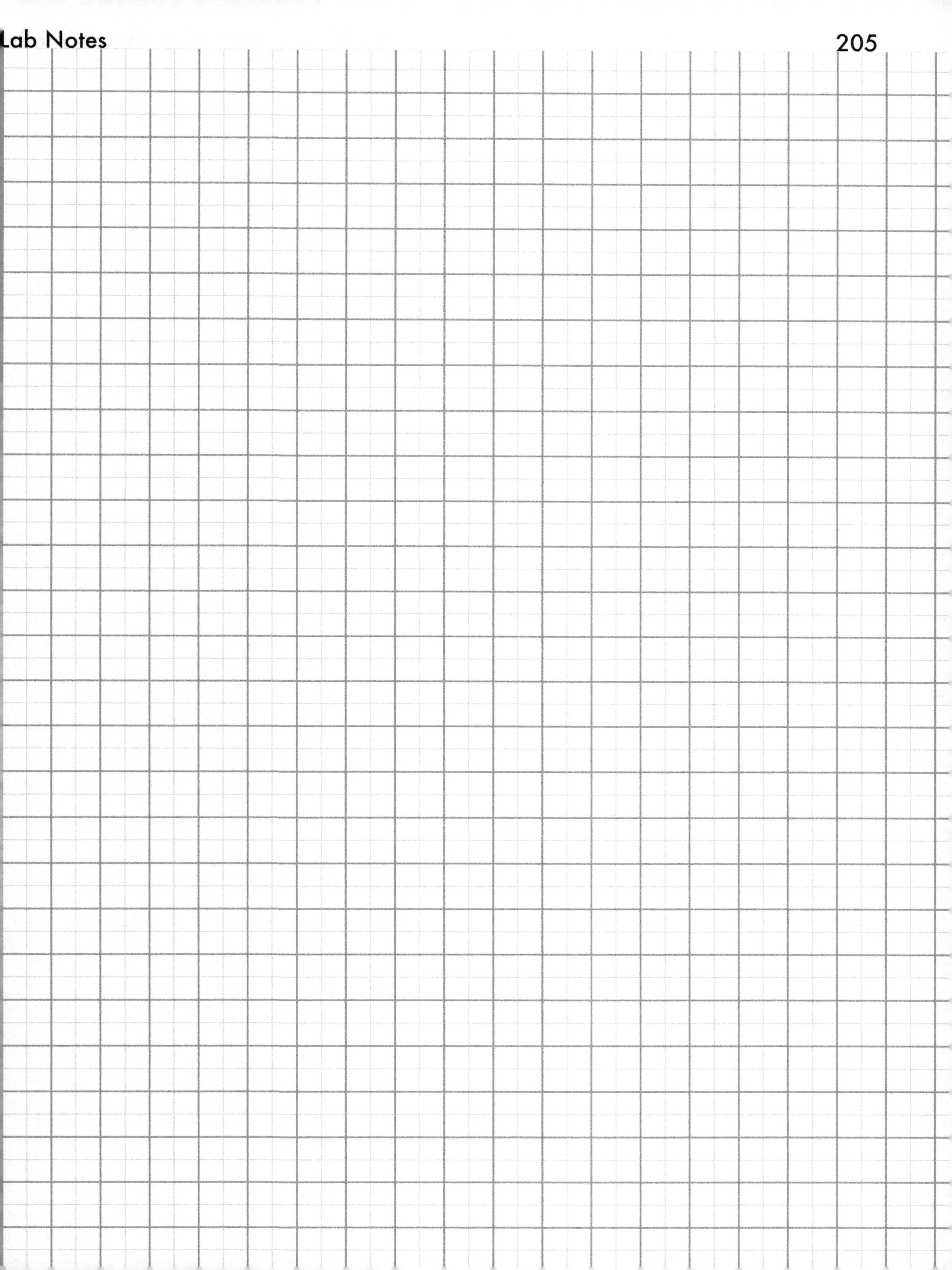

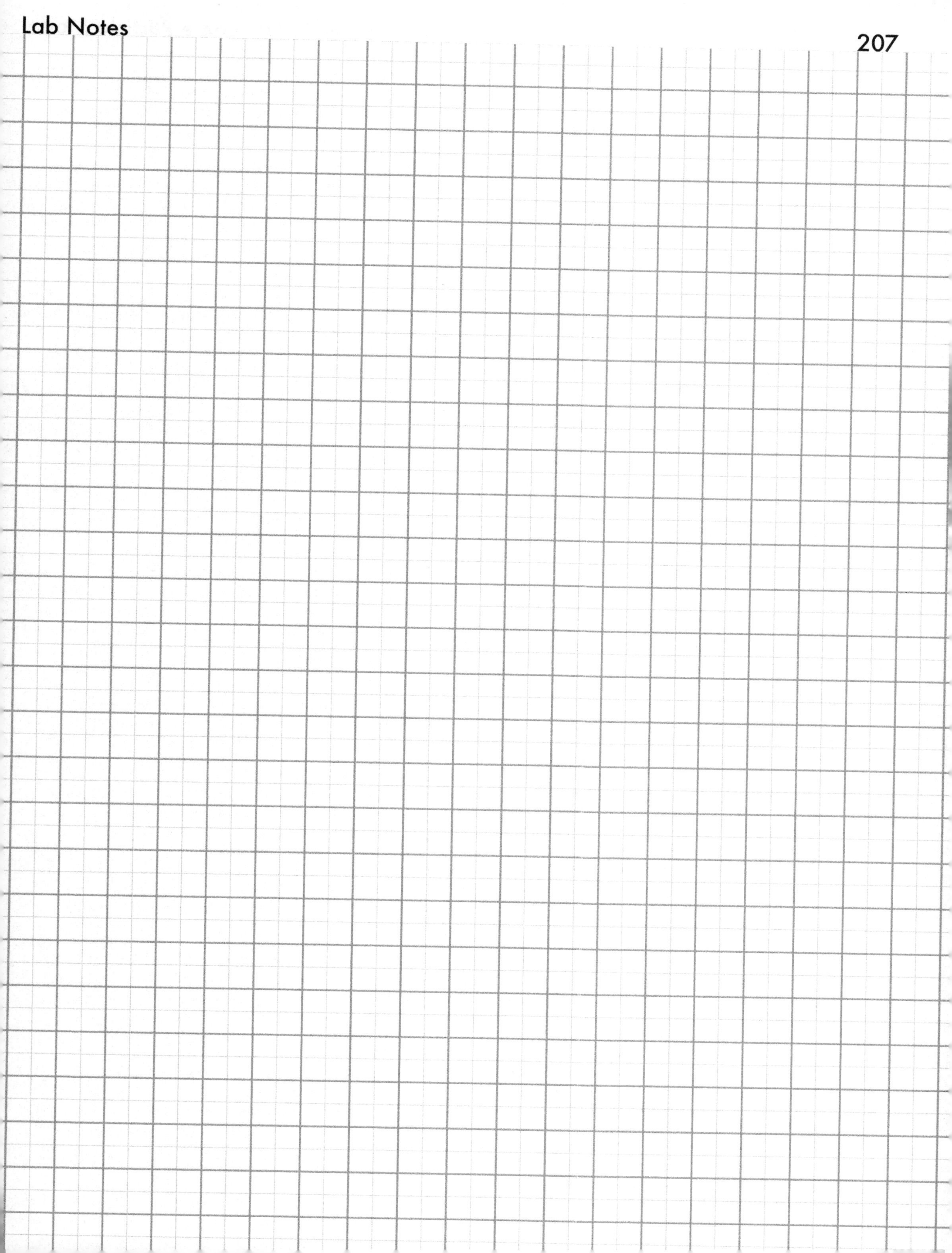

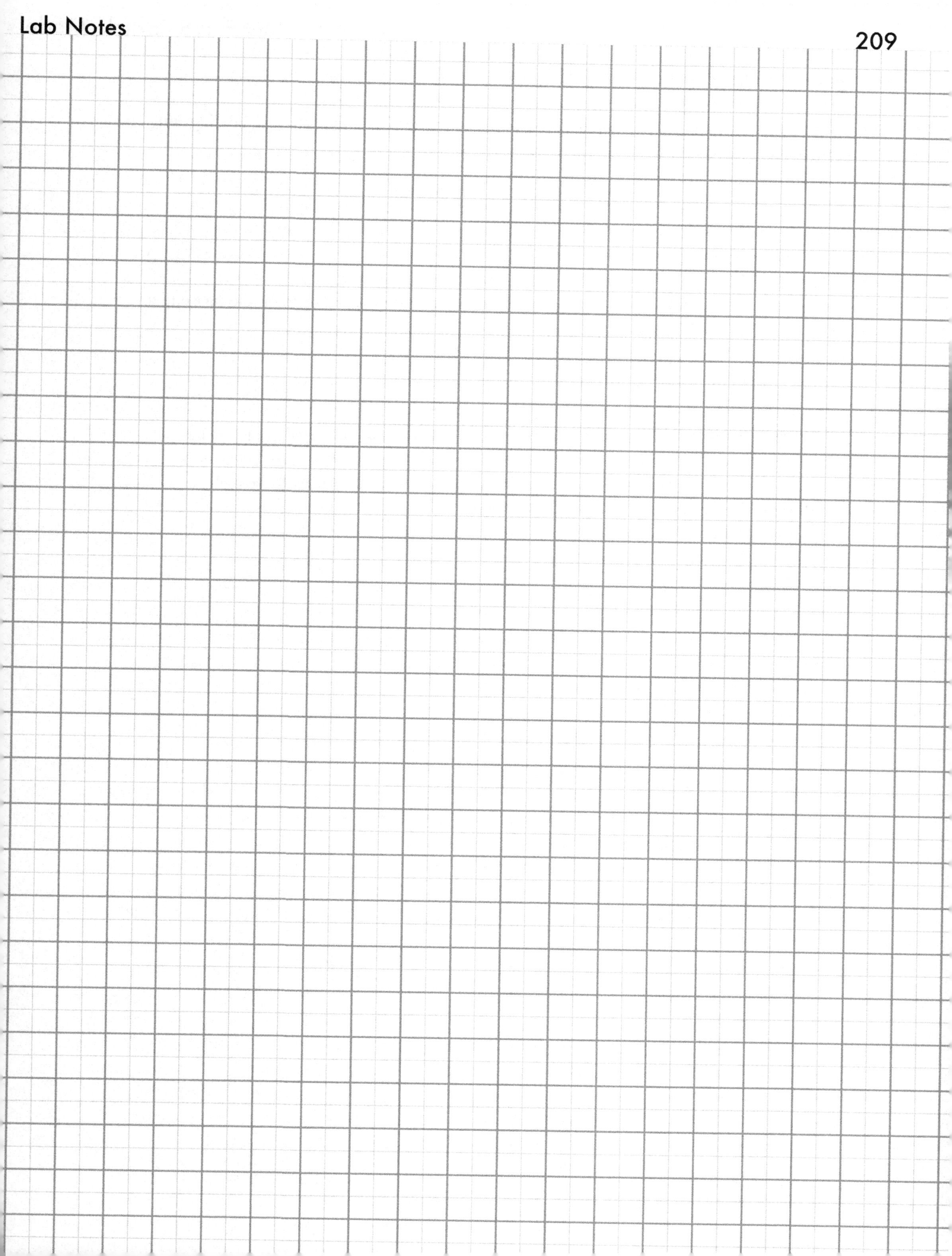

Worksheet 1: Force Diagram and Net Force

1. An elevator is moving up at a constant velocity of 2.5 m/s, as illustrated in the diagram below: The passenger has a mass of 85 kg.

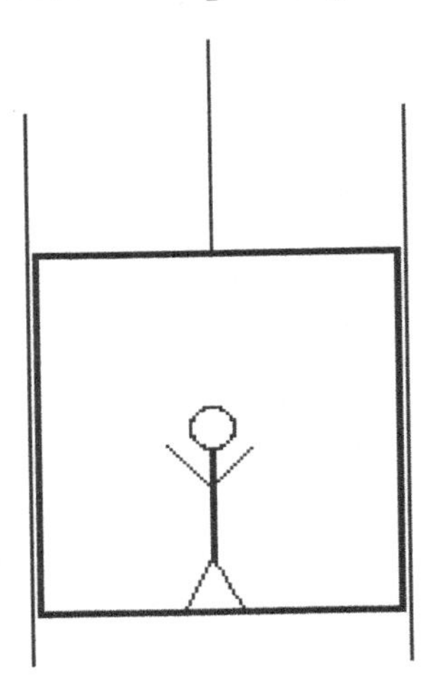

a. Construct a force diagram for the passenger.

b. Calculate the force the floor exerts on the passenger.

2. The elevator now accelerates upward at 2.0 m/s^2.

a. Construct a force diagram for the passenger.

b. Write an equation for the vertical forces on the passenger.

c. Calculate the force the floor exerts on the passenger.

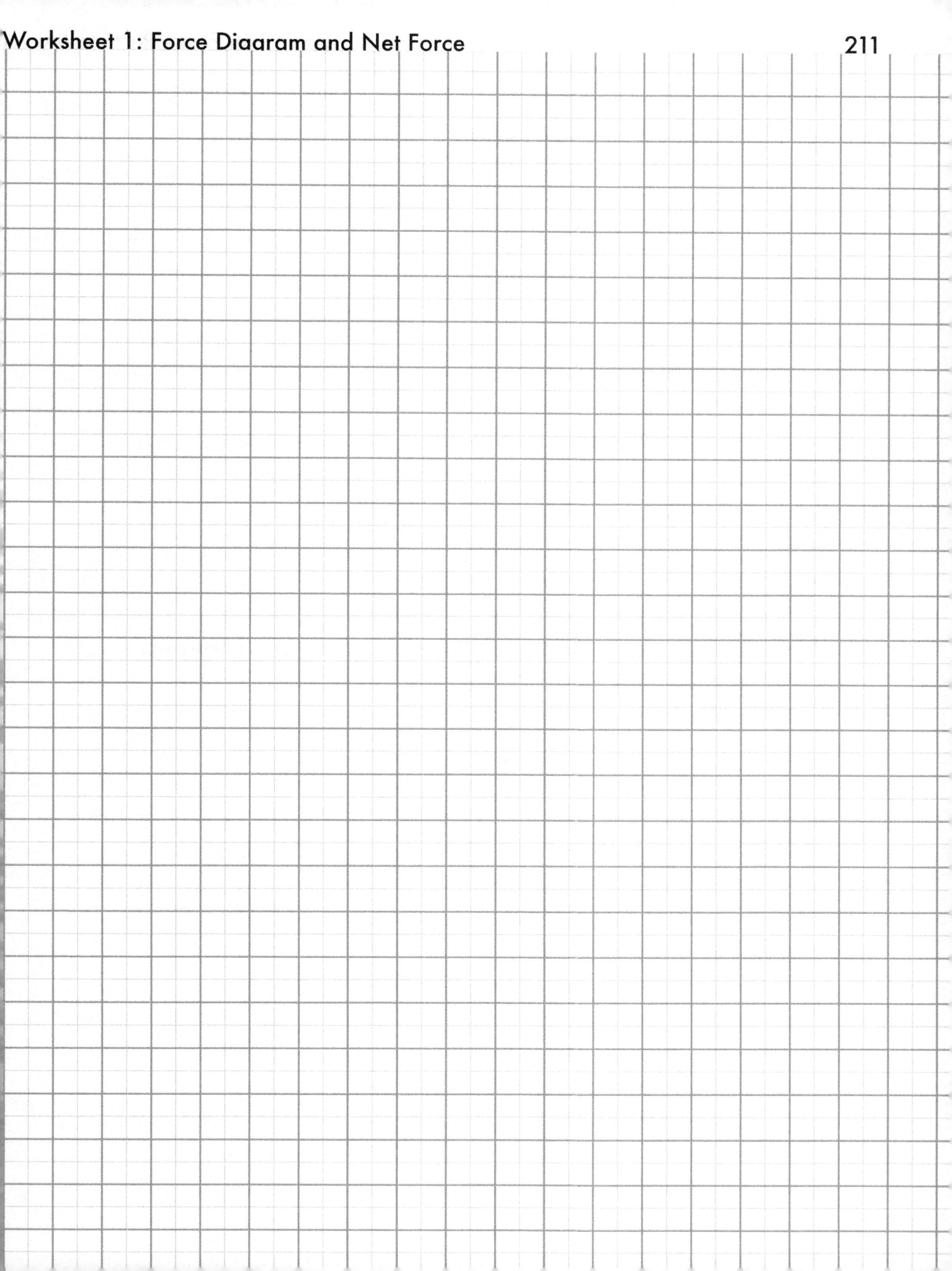

3. Upon reaching the top of the building, the elevator accelerates downward at 3.0 m/s^2.

   a. Construct a force diagram for the passenger.
   b. Write an equation for the vertical forces on the passenger.
   c. Calculate the force the floor exerts on the passenger.

4. While descending in the elevator, the cable suddenly breaks. How big is the force on the passenger by the floor? Explain your answer.

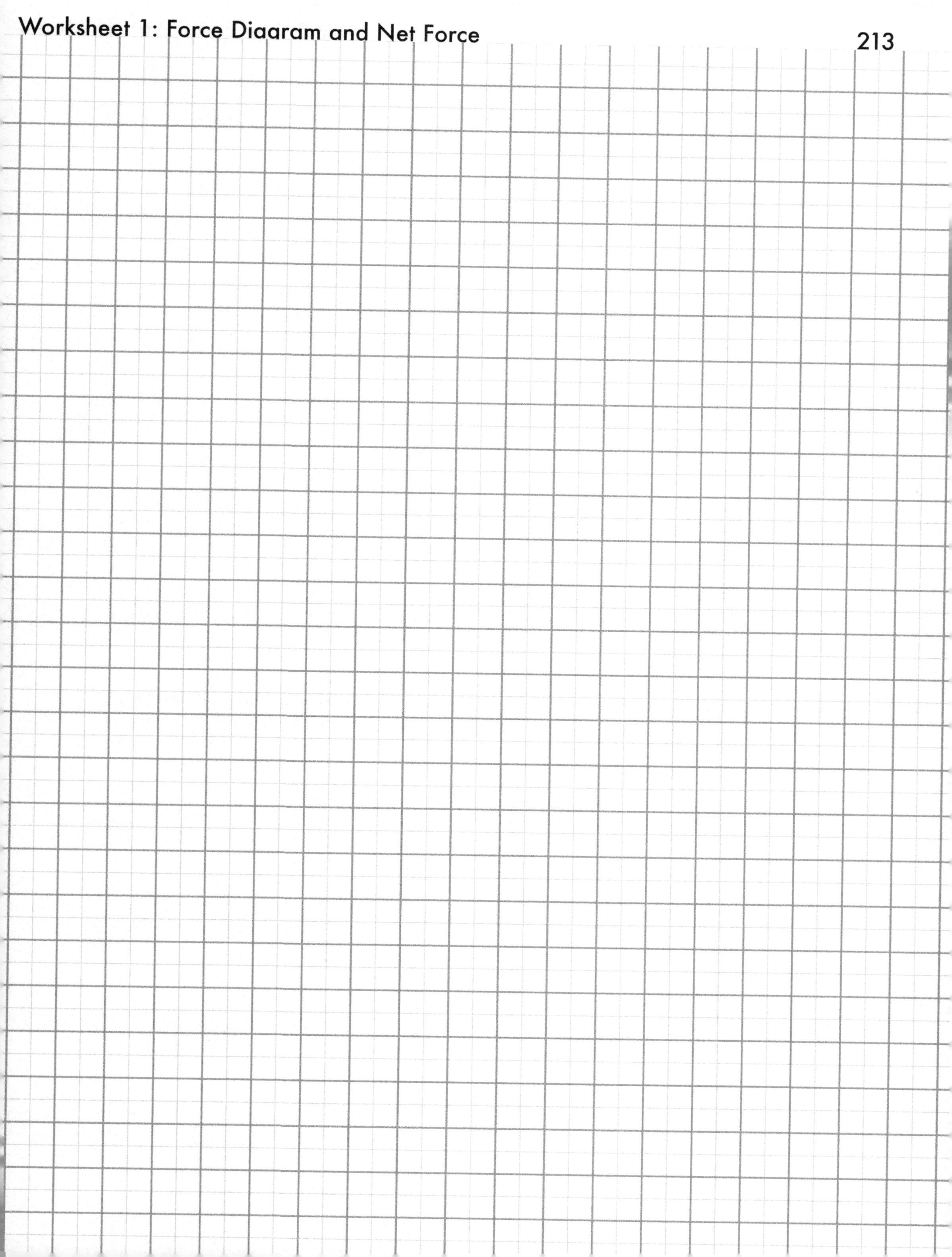

5.a. A 70 kg skydiver jumps out of an airplane. Immediately after jumping, how large is the skydiver's acceleration?

b. Upon reaching a downward velocity of 100 miles per hour, 300 newtons of drag resist the diver's motion. Draw a force diagram for the skydiver. How large is the skydiver's acceleration?

6. a. Draw a force diagram for a 900 kg car that exerts 5000 N of traction force on a level road while being opposed by 1000 Newtons of friction and drag forces combined.

b. Write a net force equation for the car.

c. Calculate the acceleration of the car.

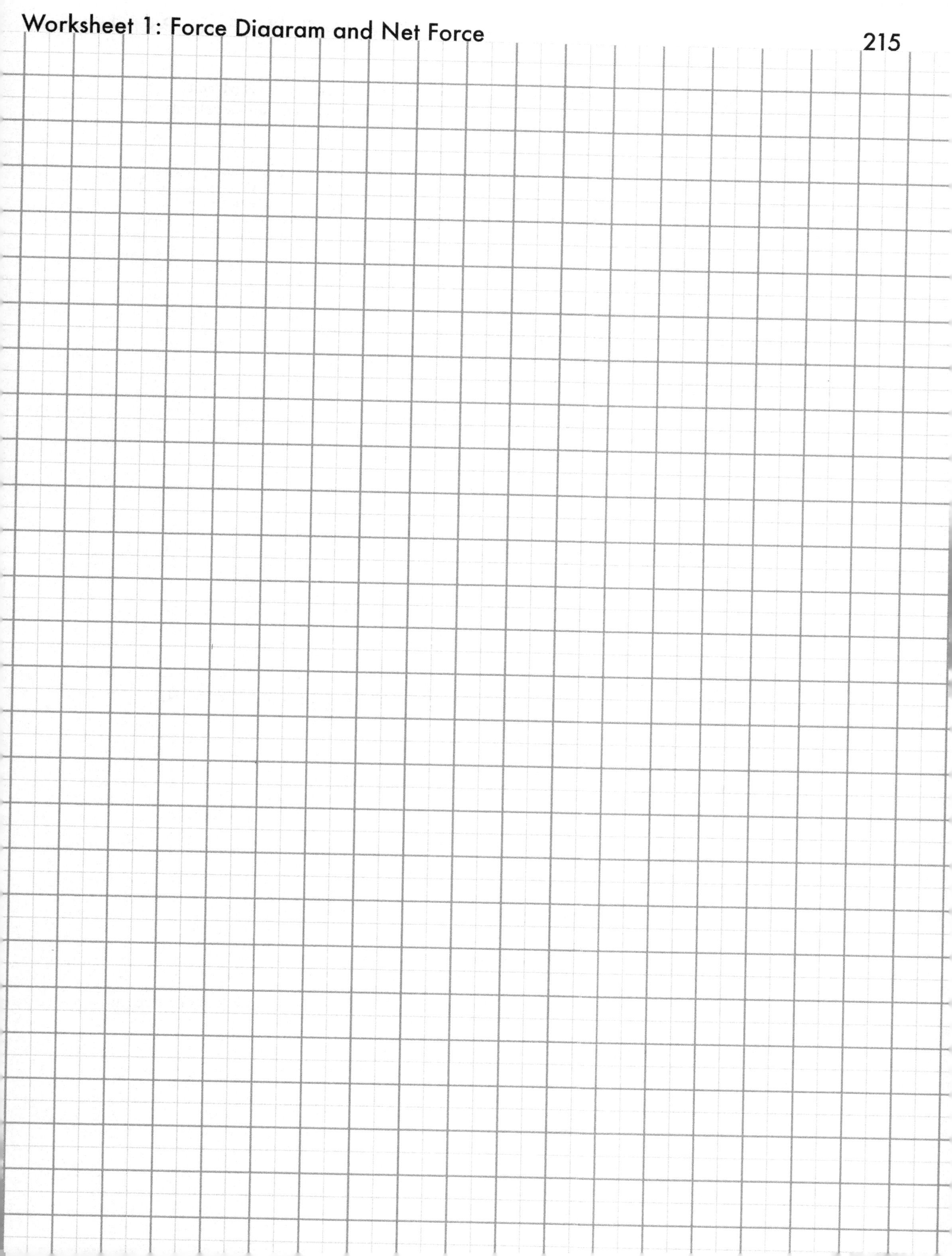

7. The three modified Atwood's machines shown below have blocks of mass M on a frictionless surface and hanging from a string. When the blocks are released, they accelerate as they did in our lab.

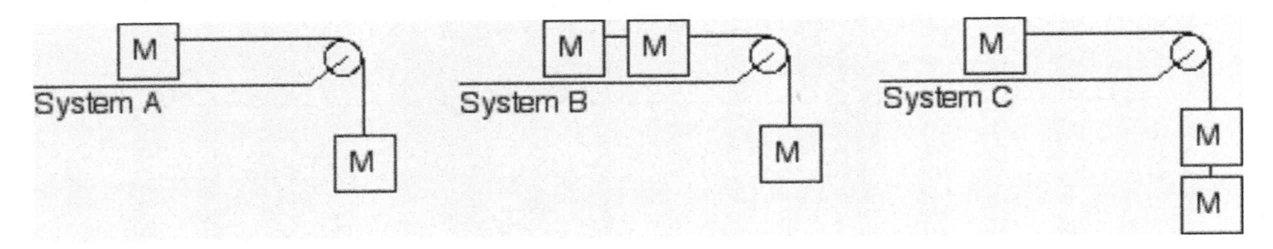

a. Which system has the greatest net force? Explain how you know.
b. Which system has the least inertia? Explain how you know.
c. Determine the acceleration for each system.

8. A child takes a trip down a slide.

a. Draw a quantitative force diagram for the 30kg child. The frictional force is 160 N.

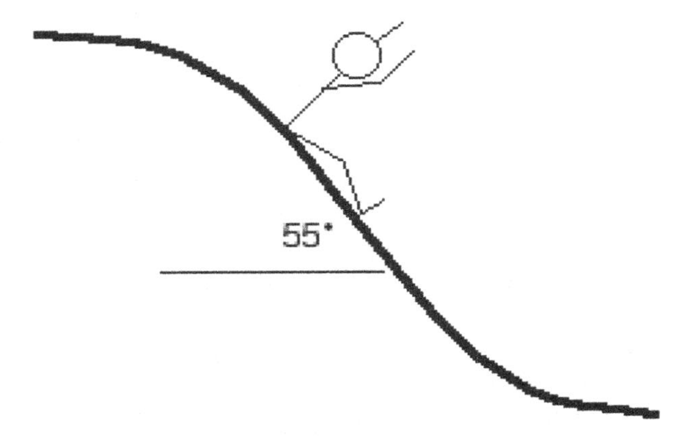

b. Write an equation for the forces on the child parallel to the slide and find the net force on the child.
c. Calculate child's acceleration.

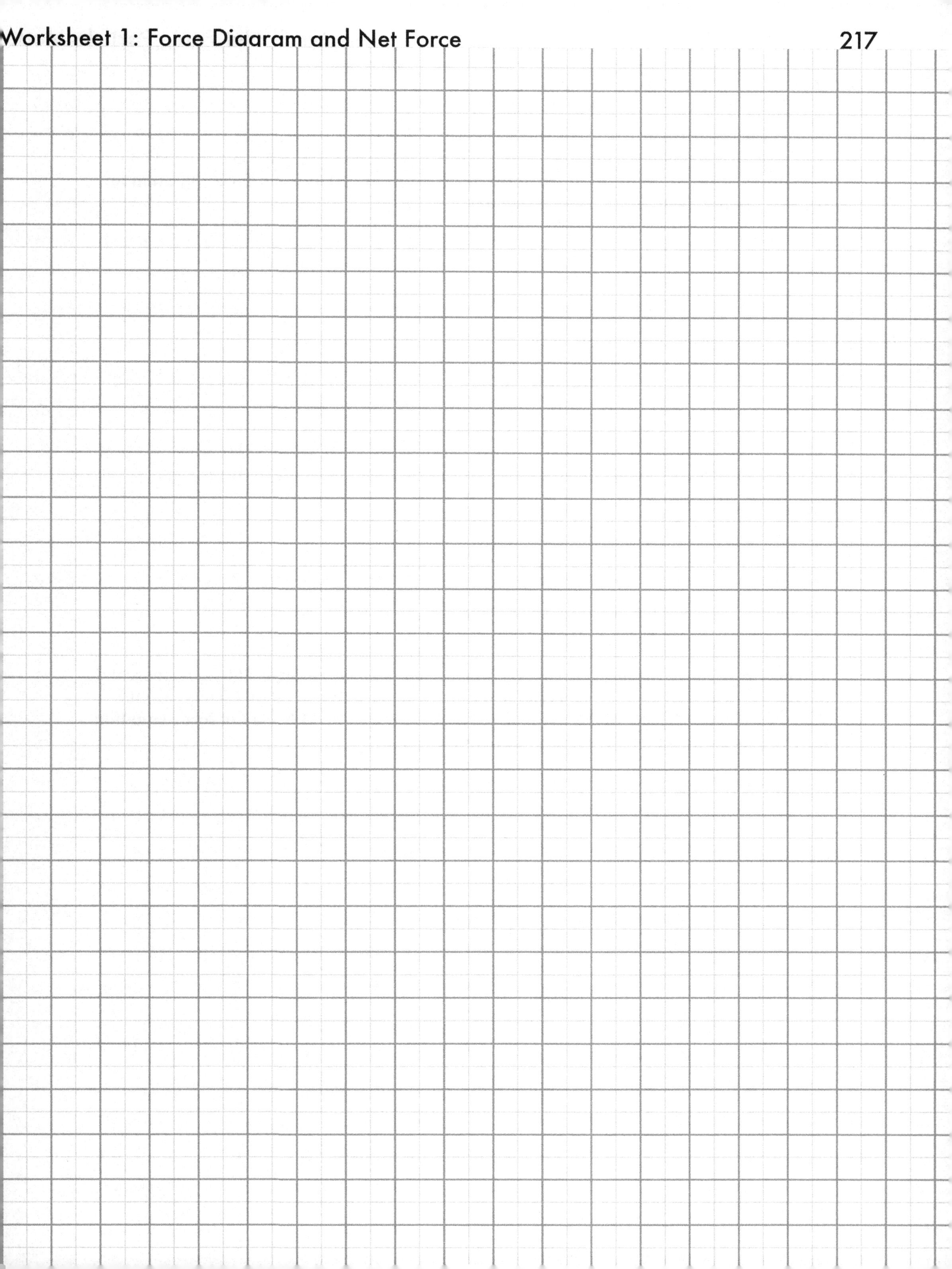

Worksheet 2: Newton's 2nd Law

1. A 4600 kg helicopter accelerates upward at 2.0 m/s^2. Determine the lift force exerted on the propellers by the air. **Make a quantitative force diagram. Write a net force equation for the axis along which forces are not balanced.**

2. The maximum force that a grocery bag can withstand without ripping is 250 N. Suppose that the bag is filled with 20 kg of groceries and lifted with an acceleration of 5.0 m/s^2. Do the groceries stay in the bag? **Make a quantitative force diagram. Write a net force equation for the axis along which forces are not balanced.**

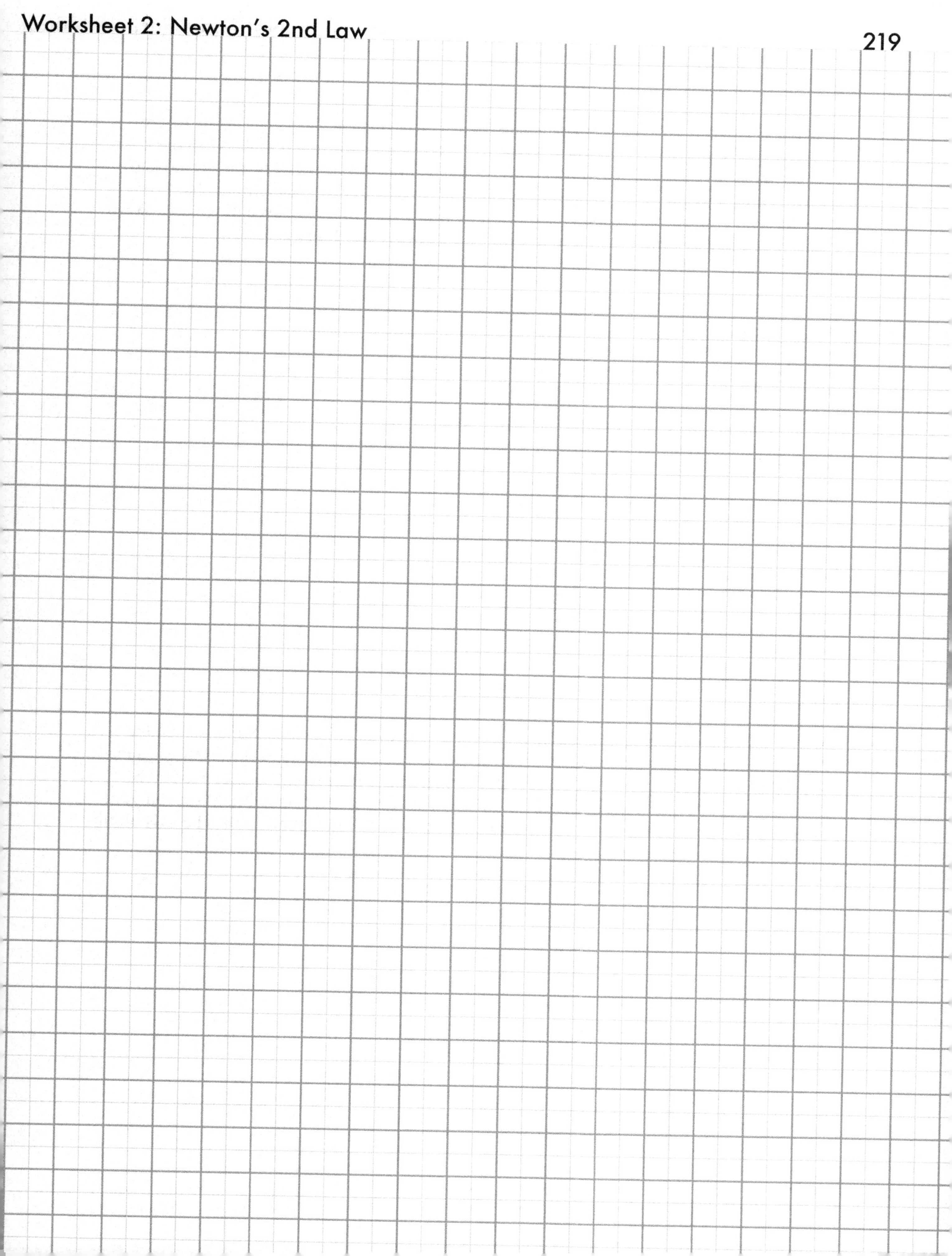

3. A student, standing on a scale in an elevator at rest, sees that his weight is 840 N. As the elevator rises, the scale reading increases to 1050 N, then returns to normal. When the elevator slows to a stop at the 10th floor, the scale reading drops to 588 N, then returns to normal. Draw a motion map for the student during his elevator ride. Determine the acceleration at the beginning and end of the trip. **Make quantitative force diagrams. Write a net force equation for the axis along which forces are not balanced.**

4. A sign in an elevator states that the maximum occupancy is 20 persons. Suppose that the safety engineers assume the mass of the average rider is 75 kg. The elevator itself has a mass of 500 kg. The cable supporting the elevator can tolerate a maximum force of 30, 000 N. What is the greatest acceleration that the elevator's motor can produce without snapping the cable? **Make a quantitative force diagram. Write a net force equation for the axis along which forces are not balanced.**

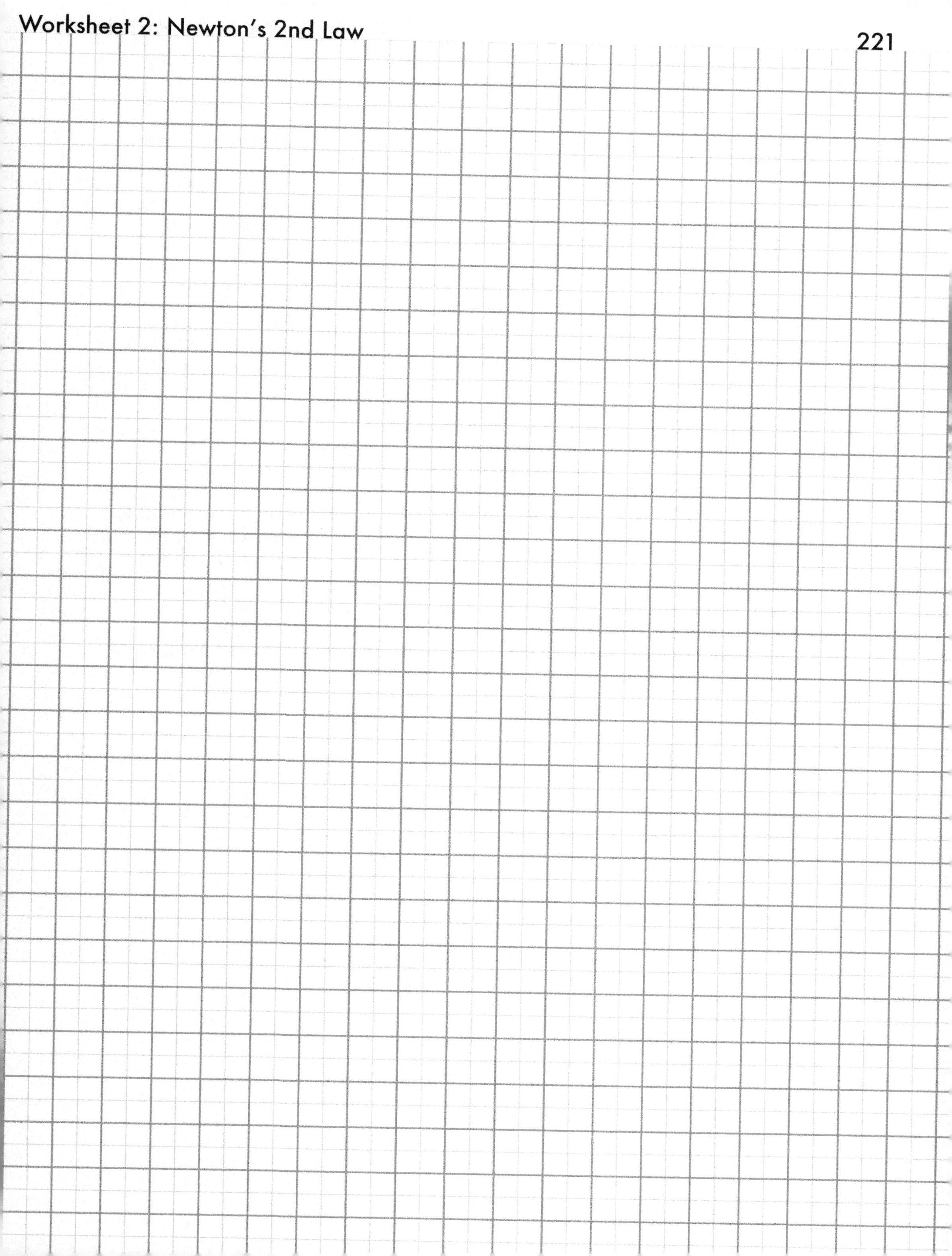

Worksheet 3: Kinematics & Newton's 2nd Law

The problems on the worksheet require you to use kinematics formulas in addition to Newton's second law. Use the following steps in your solutions:

a. use force diagram analysis to find the net (unbalanced) amount of force.
b. list knowns and unknowns for force and motion variables:

force variables	motion variables
acceleration	**acceleration**
mass	initial velocity
net force	final velocity
	change in time
	displacement
mathematical model	mathematical models
$F_{net} = m*a$	$v_f = a\Delta t + v_i$
	$\Delta x = \frac{1}{2}a\Delta t^2 + v_i\Delta t$
	$v_f^2 = v_i^2 + 2a\Delta x$

c. The variable that ties both lists of variables together is **acceleration**. Depending on the variables you know, use either the force or motion mathematical models to solve for acceleration, and then use the acceleration value to solve for the unknown quantity.

1. A race car has a mass of 710 kg. It starts from rest and travels 40.0m in 3.0s. The car is uniformly accelerated during the entire time. How big is the net force acting on the car? **Make a quantitative force diagram. Write a net force equation for the axis along which forces are not balanced.**

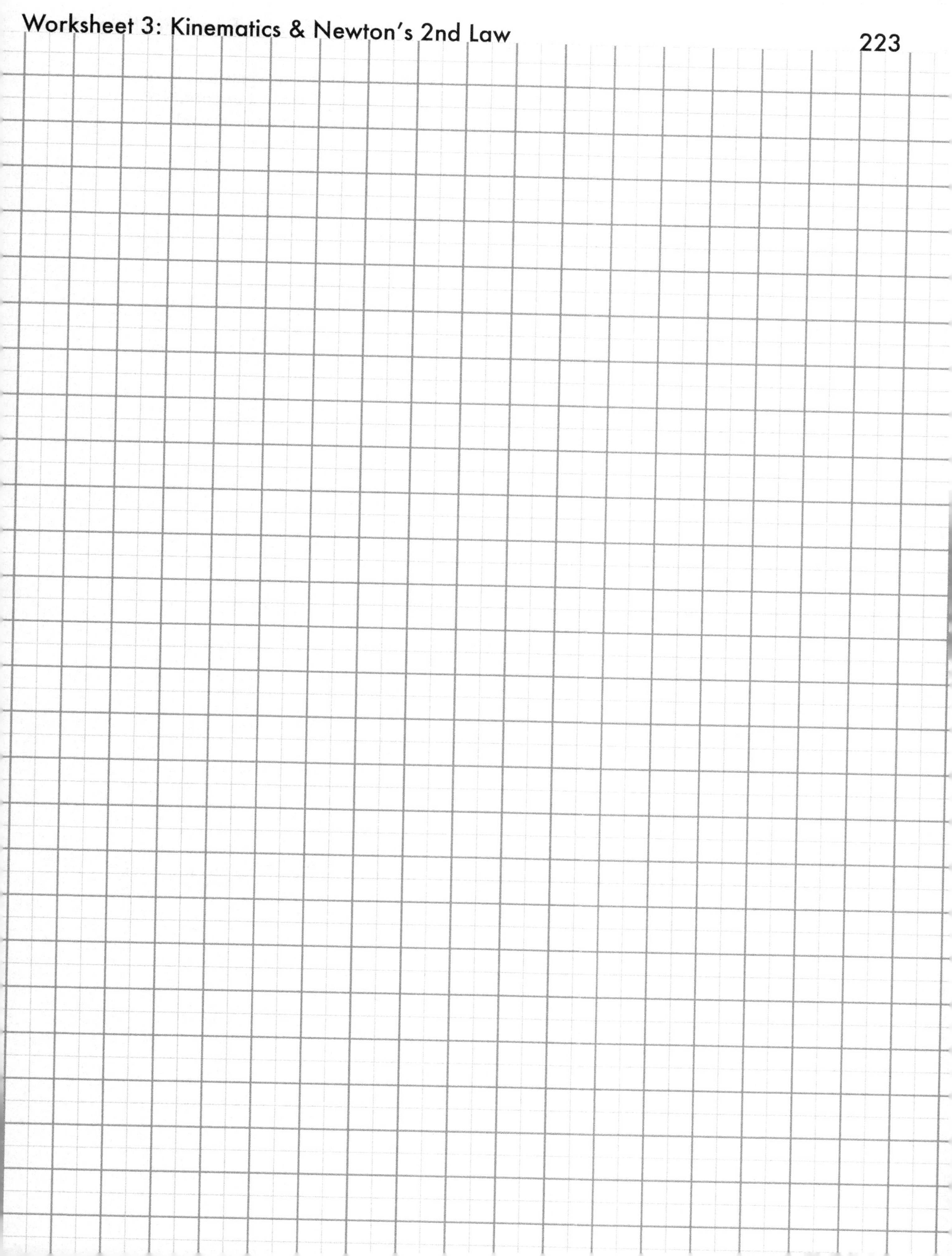

2. Suppose that a 1000 kg car is traveling at 25 m/s (55 mph). Its brakes can apply a force of 5000 N. What is the minimum distance required for the car to stop? **Make a quantitative force diagram. Write a net force equation for the axis along which forces are not balanced.**

3. A 65 kg person dives into the water from the 10 m platform.
   a. What is her speed as she enters the water?

   b. She comes to a stop 4.0 m below the surface of the water. Find the force on the swimmer by the water.

4. During a head-on collision, a passenger in the front seat of a car accelerates from 13.3 m/s (30 miles/hour) to rest in 0.10 s.
   a. Calculate the acceleration of the passenger.

   b. The driver of the car holds out his arm to keep his 25 kg child (who is not wearing a seat belt) from smashing into the dashboard. How much force must he exert on the child?

   c. What is the weight of the child?

   d. Convert the forces in parts b and c from Newtons to pounds. (1 lb = 4.45N). What are the chances the driver will be able to stop the child?

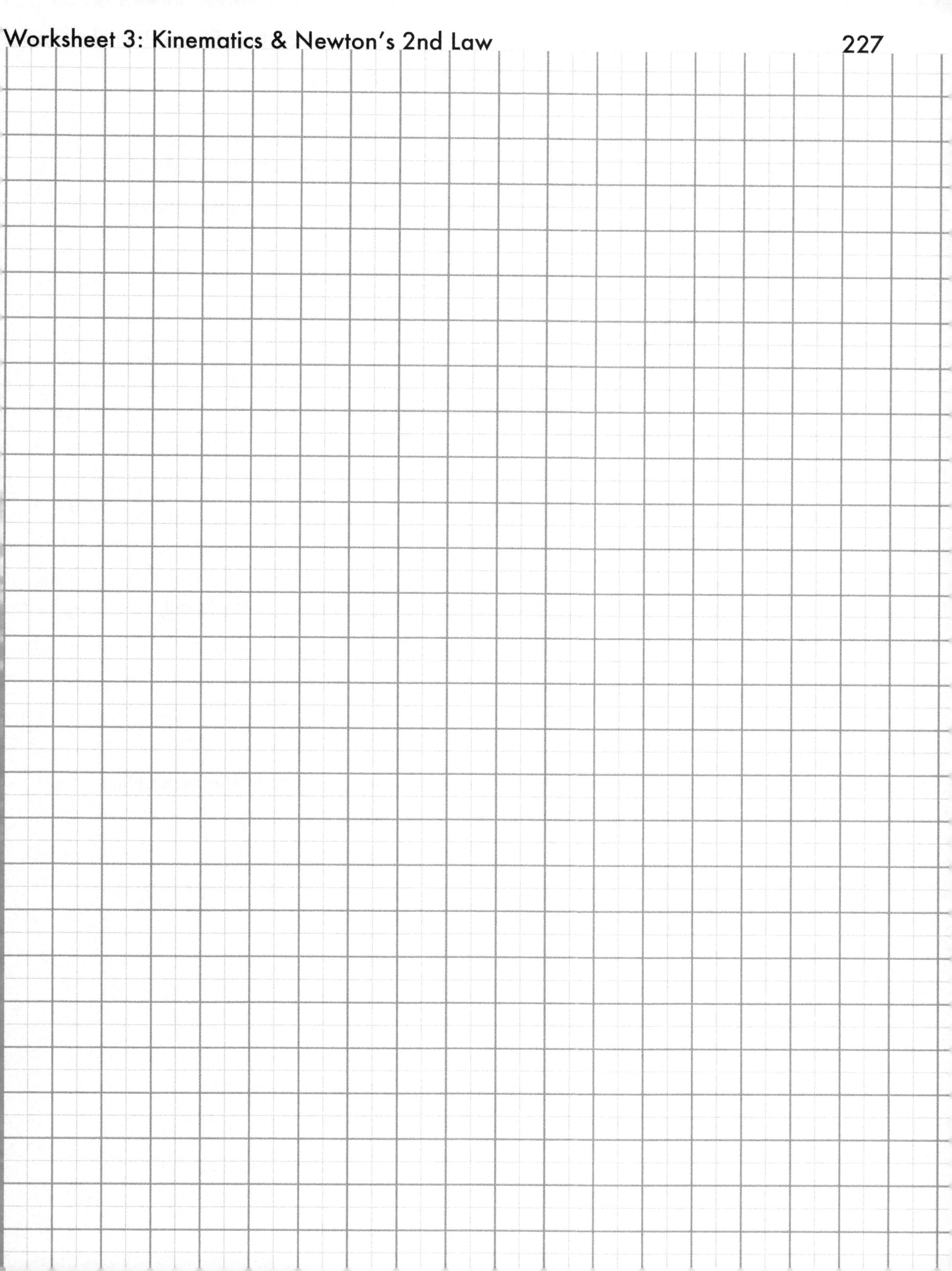

Worksheet 4: Newton's 2nd Law & Component Forces

1. A rollercoaster car, 300 kg with passengers, accelerates down a 65° hill. We will assume that friction is small enough that it can be ignored.

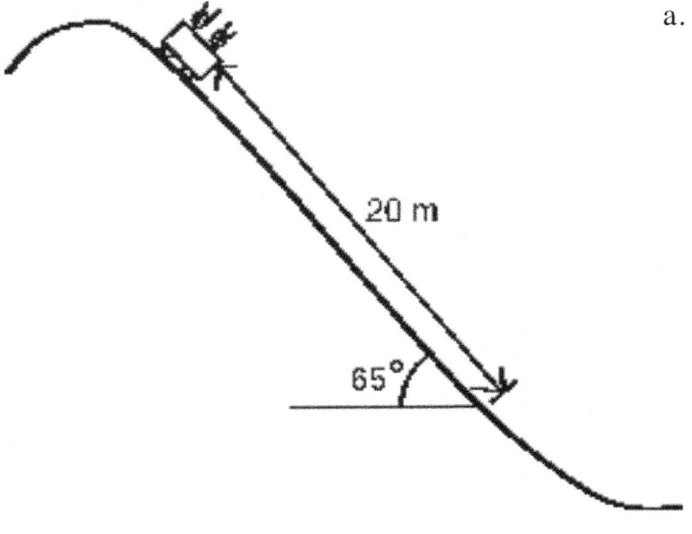

   a. Draw a force diagram for the system of car and riders.

   b. Determine the value of the component of the gravitational force parallel to the hill.

   c. What is the acceleration of the rollercoaster down the hill?

   d. If they are traveling 4 m/s at the time shown in the picture, how fast will they be traveling at the end of the straight stretch, 20 m later?

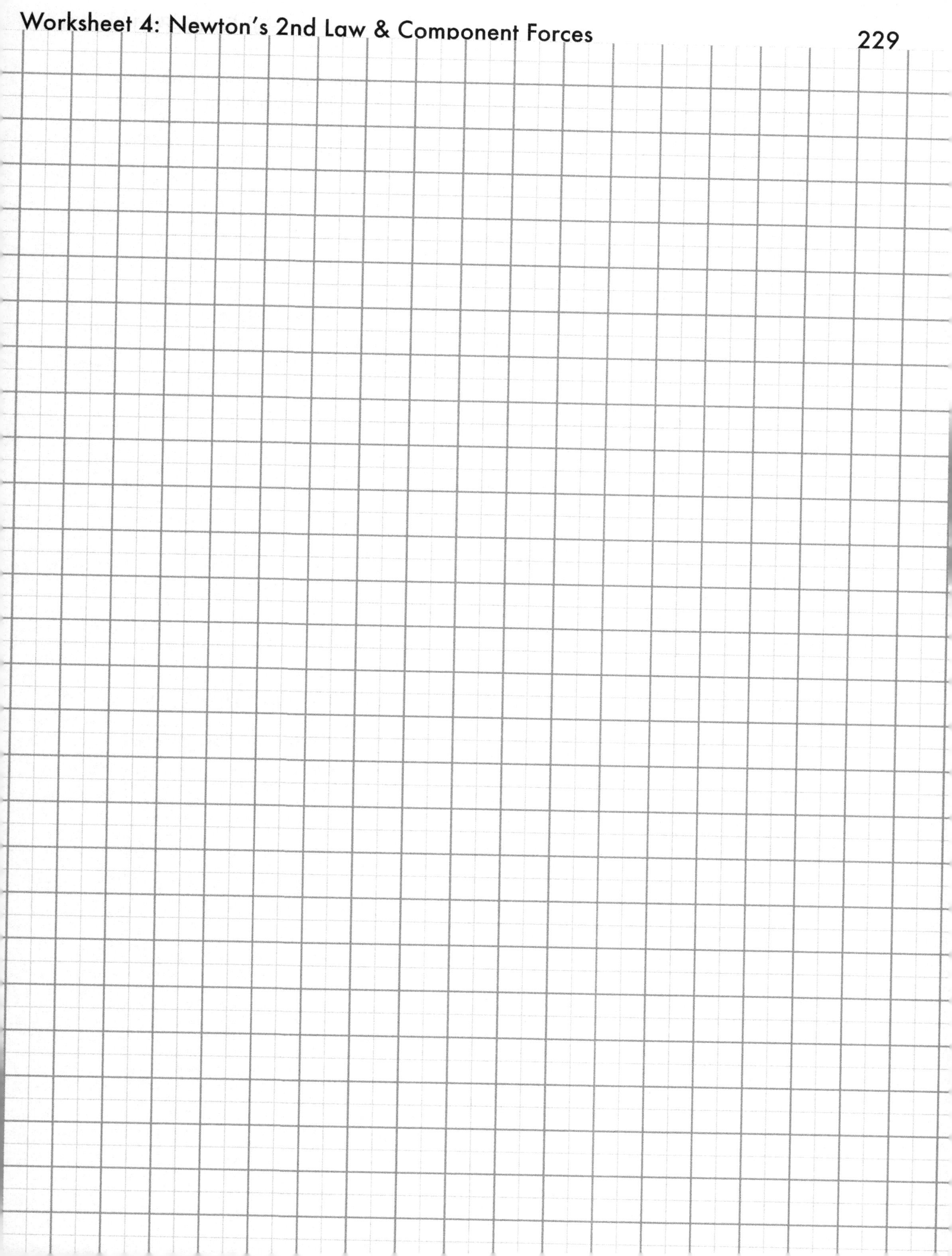

2. A worker pushes a 7 kg shipping box along a roller track. Assume friction is small enough to be ignored because of the rollers. The worker's push is 25 N directed down and to the right at an angle of 20°.

a. Draw a force diagram for the block.

b. Determine the horizontal-component of the worker's push.

c. Write a net force equation for the horizontal forces on the block.

d. Determine the acceleration of the block.

e. Determine the normal force on the block.

3. A 70 kg box is pulled by a 400 N force at an angle of 30° to the horizontal. The force of kinetic friction is 75 N.

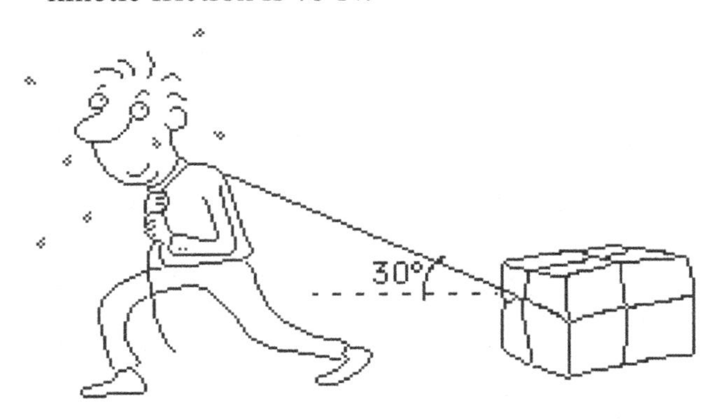

a. Draw a quantitative force diagram for the box.

b. Determine the acceleration of the box.

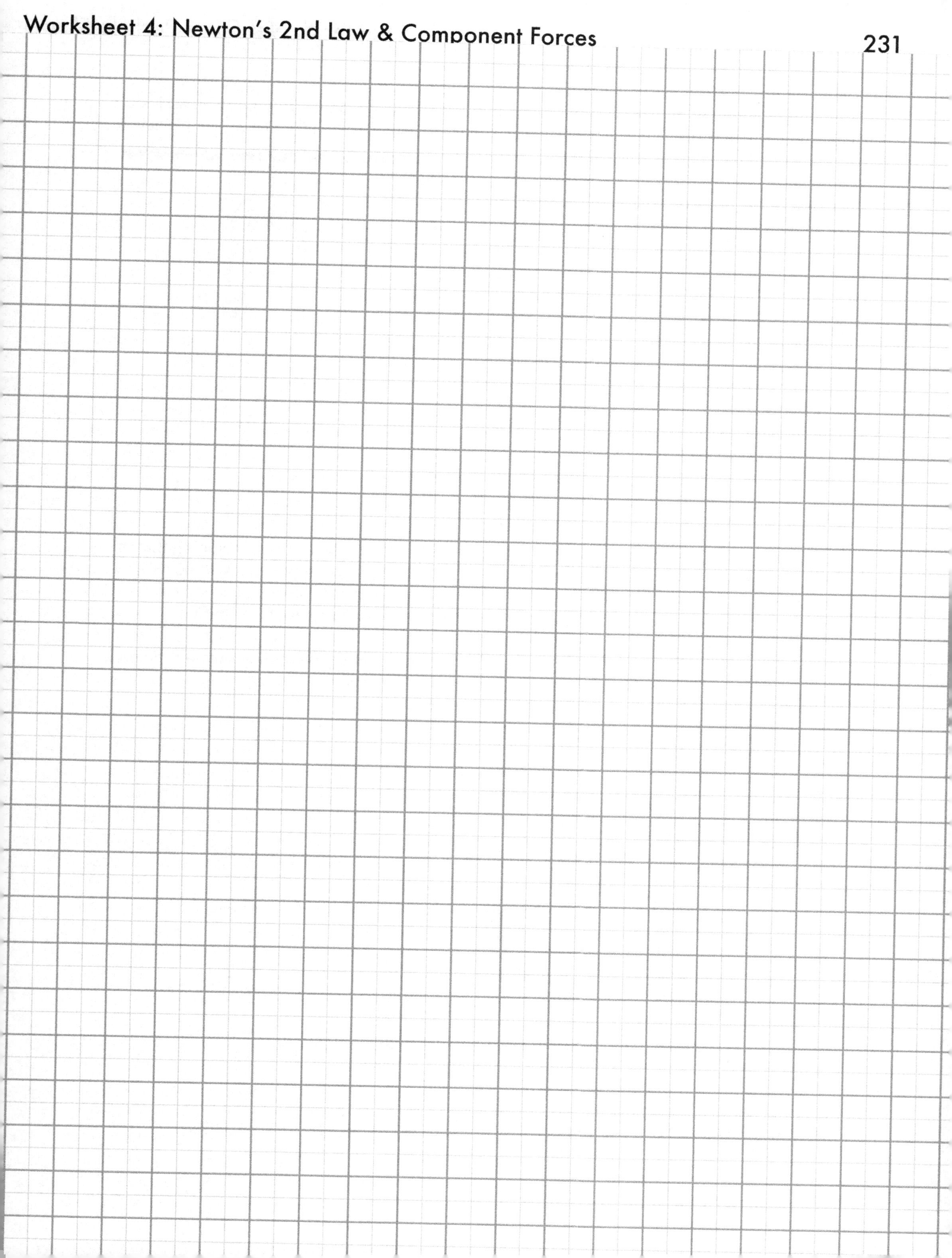

4. Below is a picture of an Atwood's Machine: two masses attached to a frictionless, massless pulley (pretty neat how physicists dream up equipment like this, huh?). The mass of block A is 5.0 kg, and the mass of B is 2.0 kg.

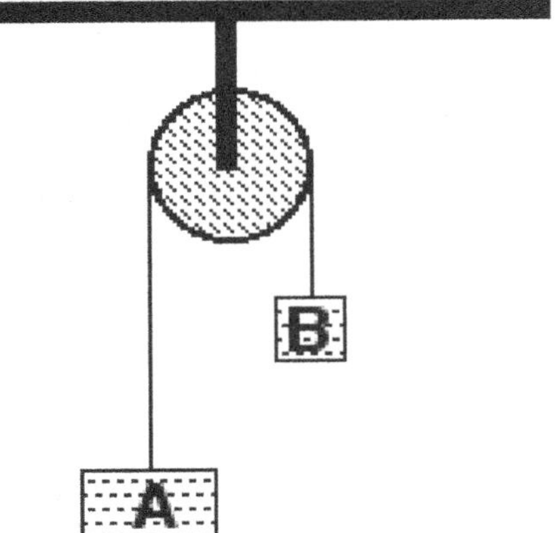

   a. Determine the acceleration of the system when the blocks are released.

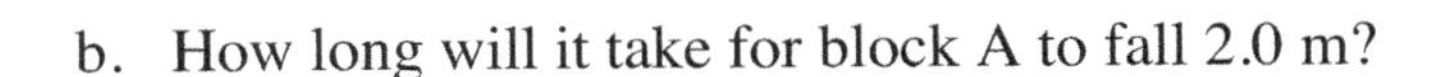

   b. How long will it take for block A to fall 2.0 m?

5. Two lovers are parked 10.0 m from the edge of a cliff in a car whose mass, including that of the occupants is 1000 kg. A jealous suitor ties a rope to the car's bumper and a 50 kg rock to the other end of the rope. He then lowers the rock over the edge of the cliff, and the car, which is in neutral, accelerates toward the edge. (Note the similarity to the modified Atwood's machine lab, and ignore frictional effects.)

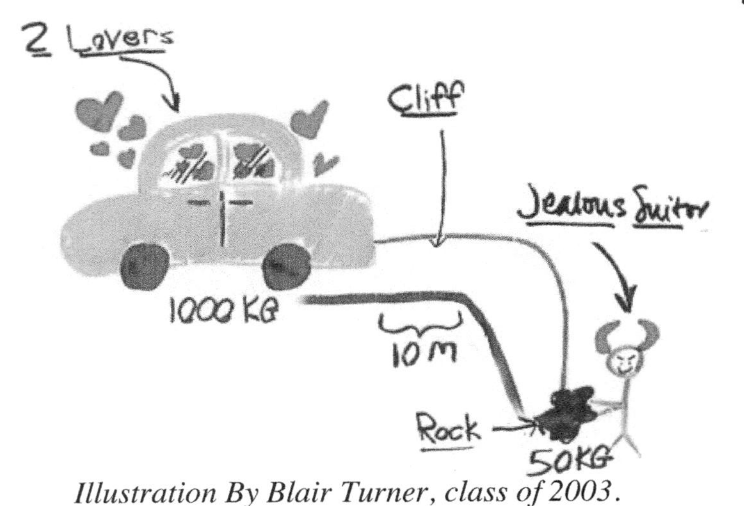

Illustration By Blair Turner, class of 2003.

   a. Draw force diagrams for the rock and the car:

   b. Determine the acceleration of the car towards the edge.

   c. How long do the lovers have to apply the brakes before they go over the edge?

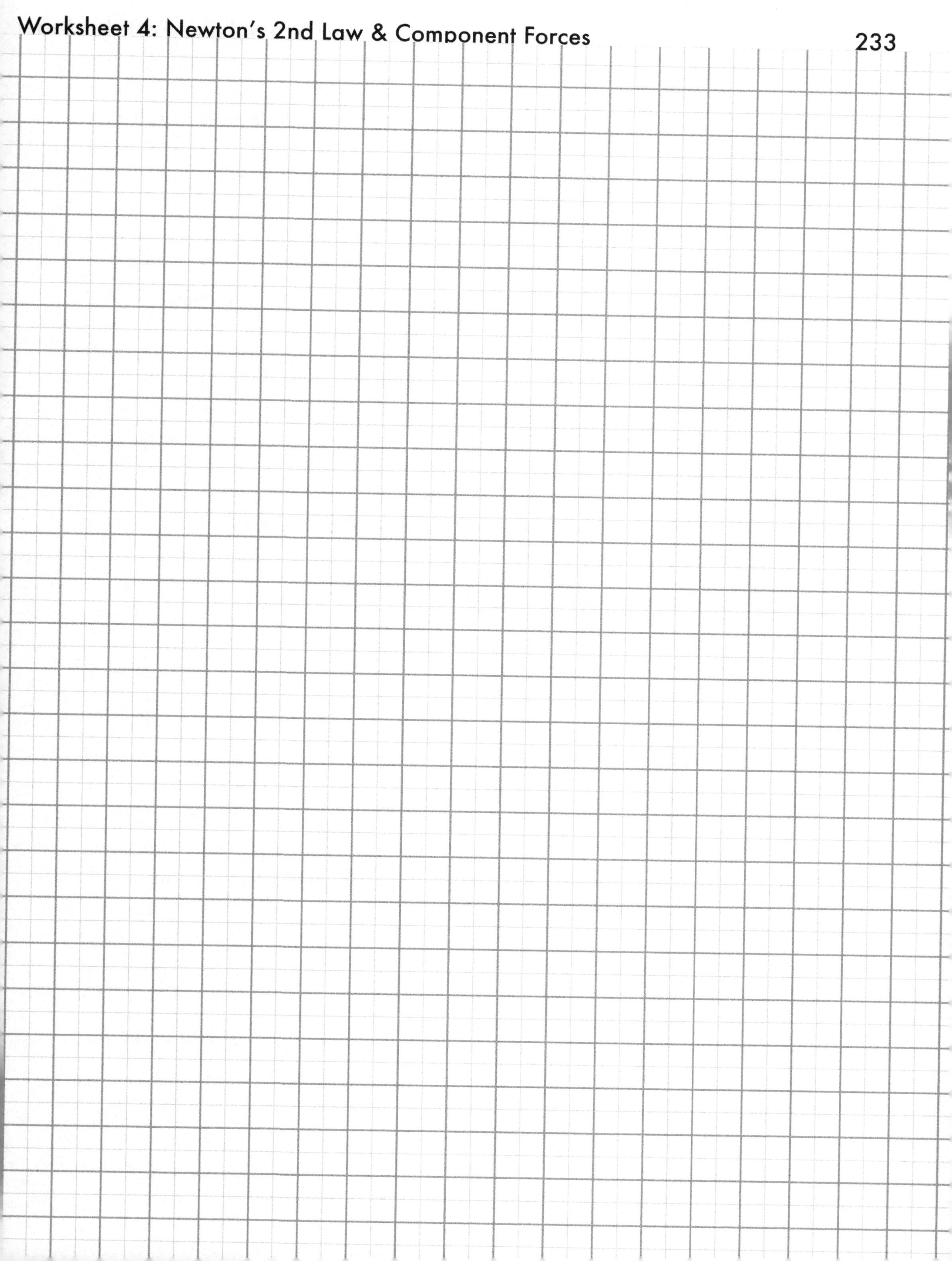

Worksheet 5: Newton's 2nd Law and Friction

1. A sled weighing 300 N is moved *at constant speed* over a horizontal floor by a force of 50 N applied parallel to the floor.

   a. Construct a force diagram for the sled.

   b. Determine the coefficient of kinetic friction, μ_k, between the sled and the floor.

   c. What would be the acceleration of the sled if $\mu_k = 0$?

2. Suppose a hanging 1.0 kg lab mass is attached to a 4.0 kg block on the table.

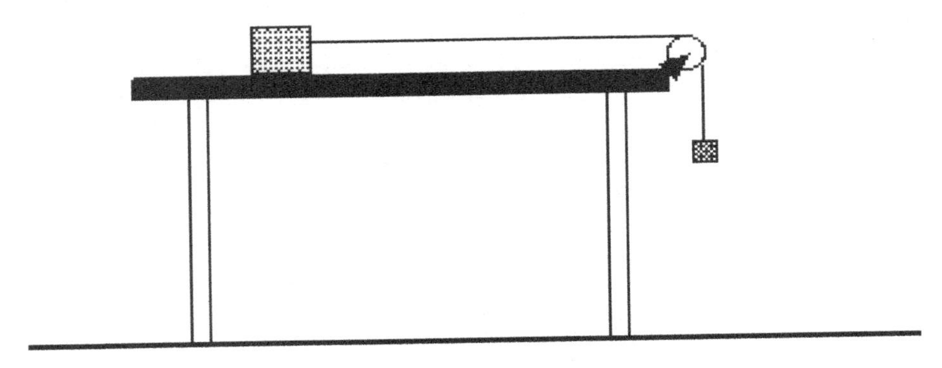

   a. Draw a force diagram for the block on the table.

   b. What would be the minimum value of the coefficient of static friction, μ_s, in order for the block to remain motionless?

   c. If the coefficient of kinetic friction, μ_k is 0.20, what is the acceleration of the block?

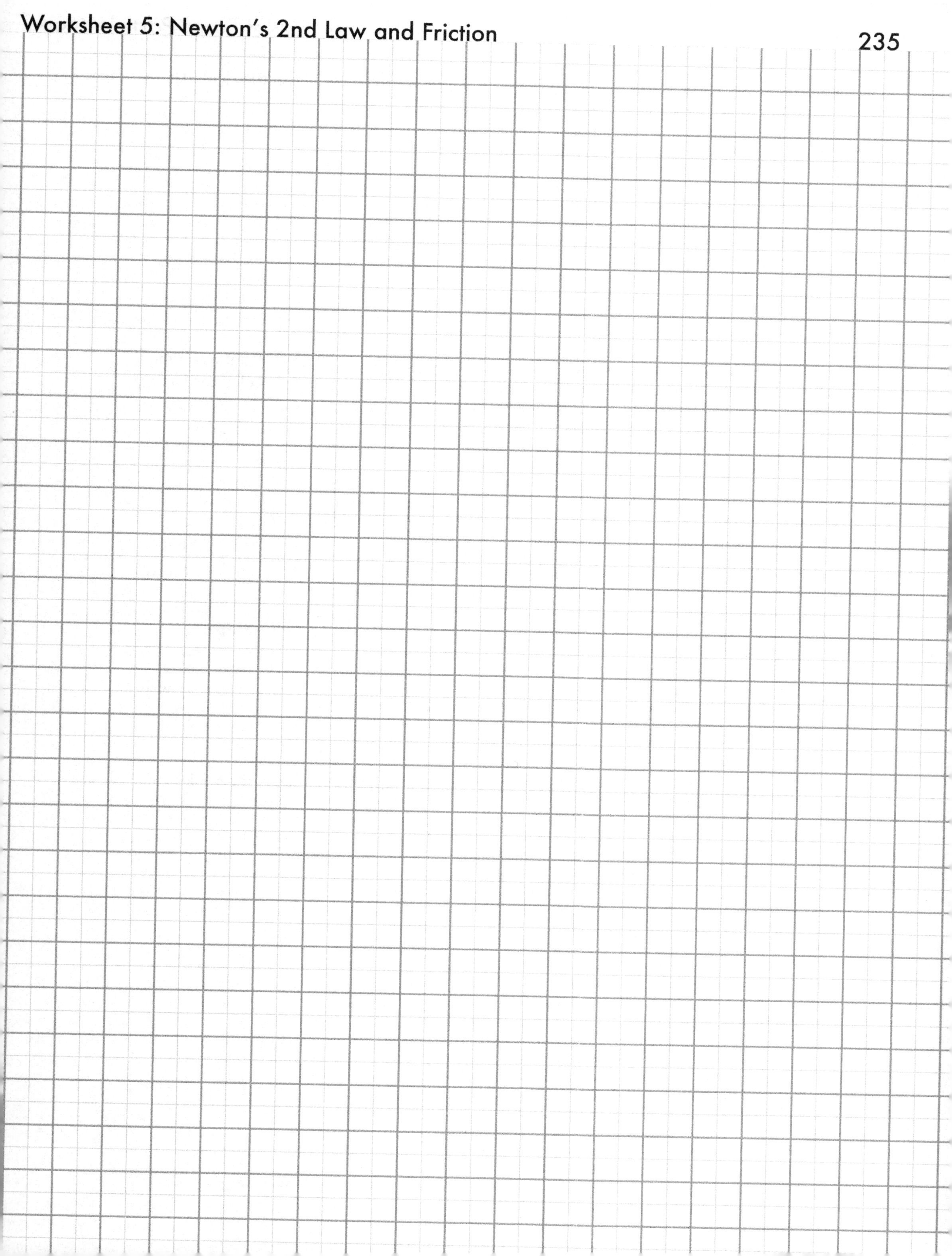

3. A horizontal 100 N force is applied to a 50 kg classmate resting on a level tile floor. The coefficient of kinetic friction is 0.15.

   a. Draw a force diagram to represent this situation.

   b. What is the acceleration of the classmate?

   c. Suppose the classmate in was resting on a carpet where the coefficient of static friction is 0.25. Is the horizontal 100 N force sufficient to cause the classmate to accelerate? Draw a force diagram, and then explain why or why not.

4. When 15 newtons of force is applied to the 0.50 kg book, the friction keeps the book from sliding down the wall.

   a) Make a force drawing for the book. Include the amount of each force.

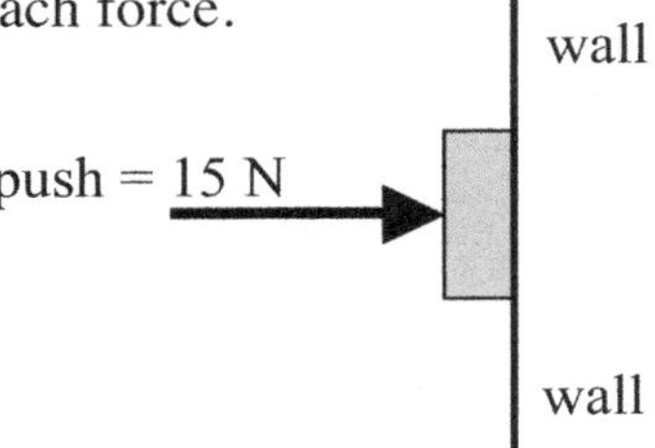

   b) What is the minimum force and minimum coefficient of friction to keep the book from sliding?

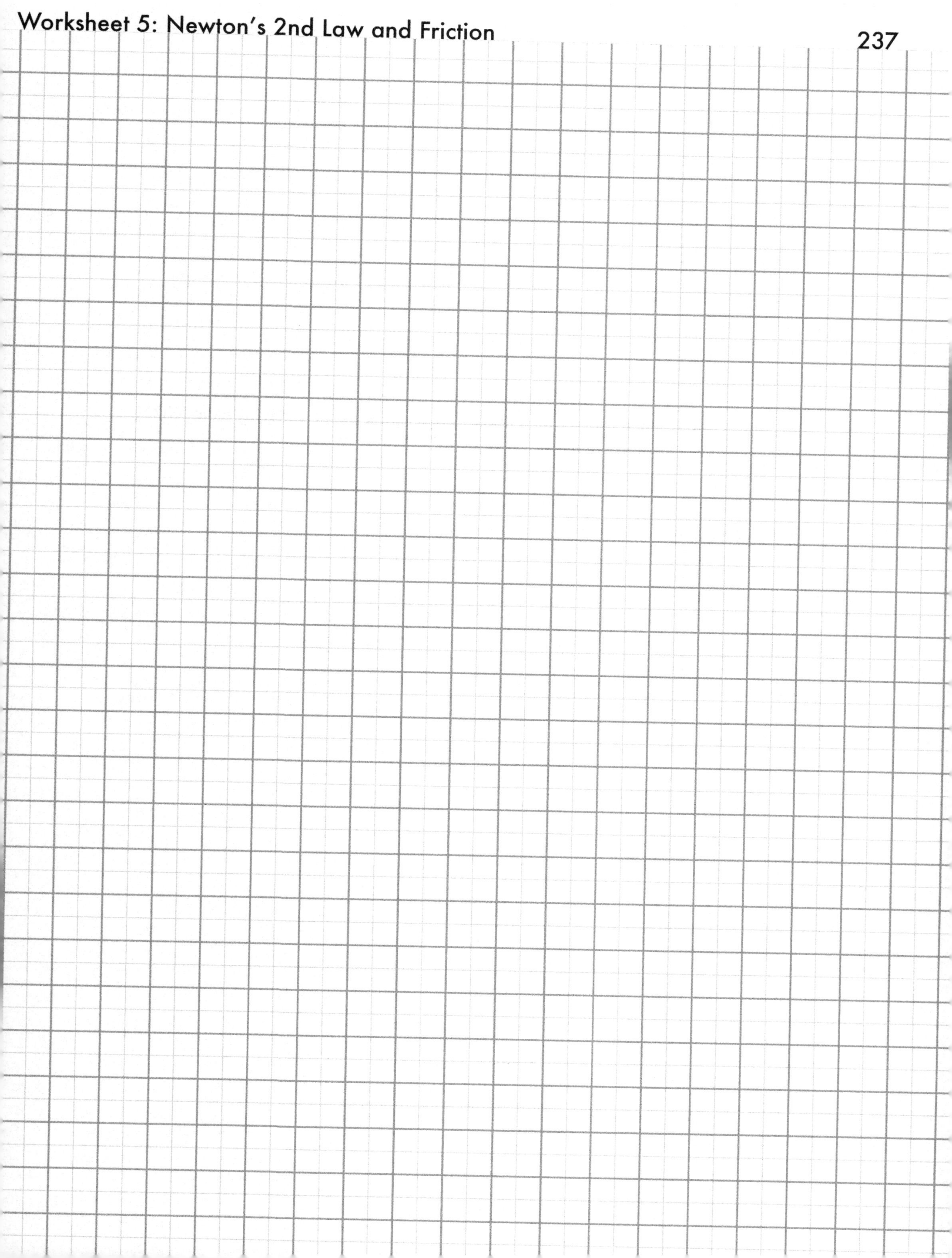

5. An 84 kg skier glides down a hill with $\mu_k = 0.15$.

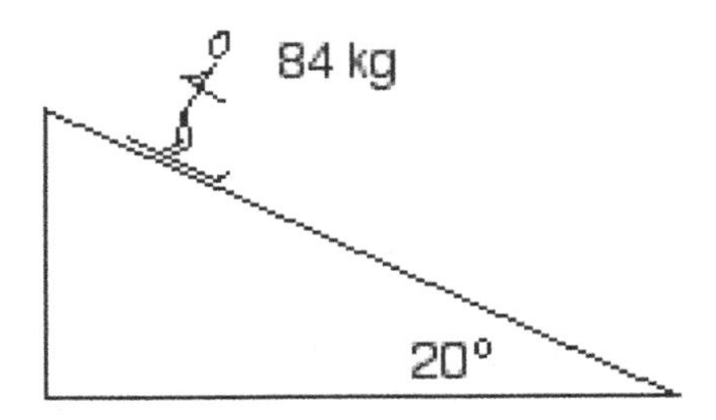

a. Draw a force diagram for the skier.

b. What is the value of the frictional force opposing the skier's slide down the hill?

c. Calculate the acceleration of the skier.

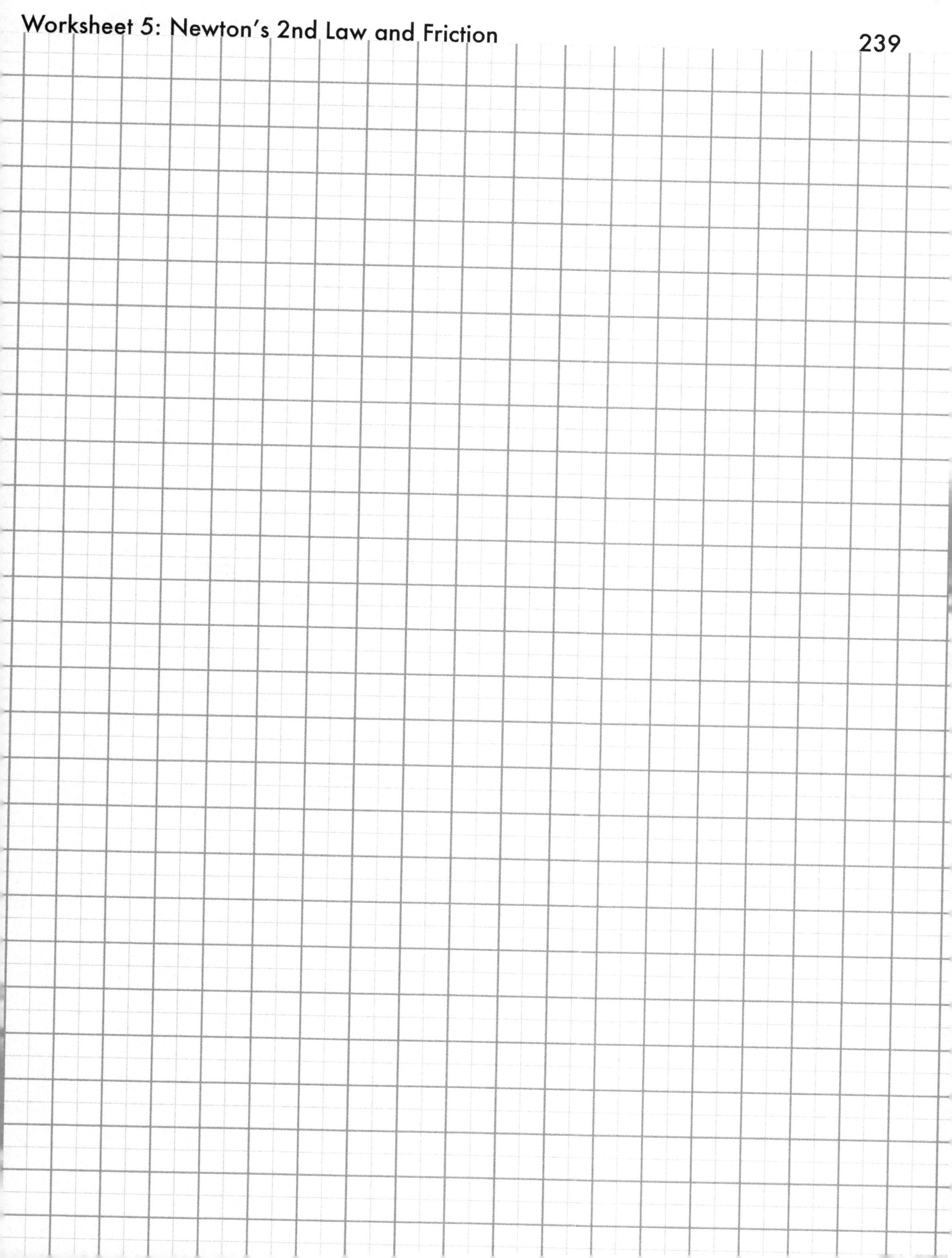

Review Problems

1. An 80 kg water skier is being pulled by a boat with a force of 220 N causing the skier to accelerate at 1.8 m/s^2. Find the drag force on the skier.

2. A 2000 kg car is slowed down uniformly from 20 m/s to 5 m/s in 4 seconds. Determine the average net force on the car during this time, and how far the car traveled while slowing down.

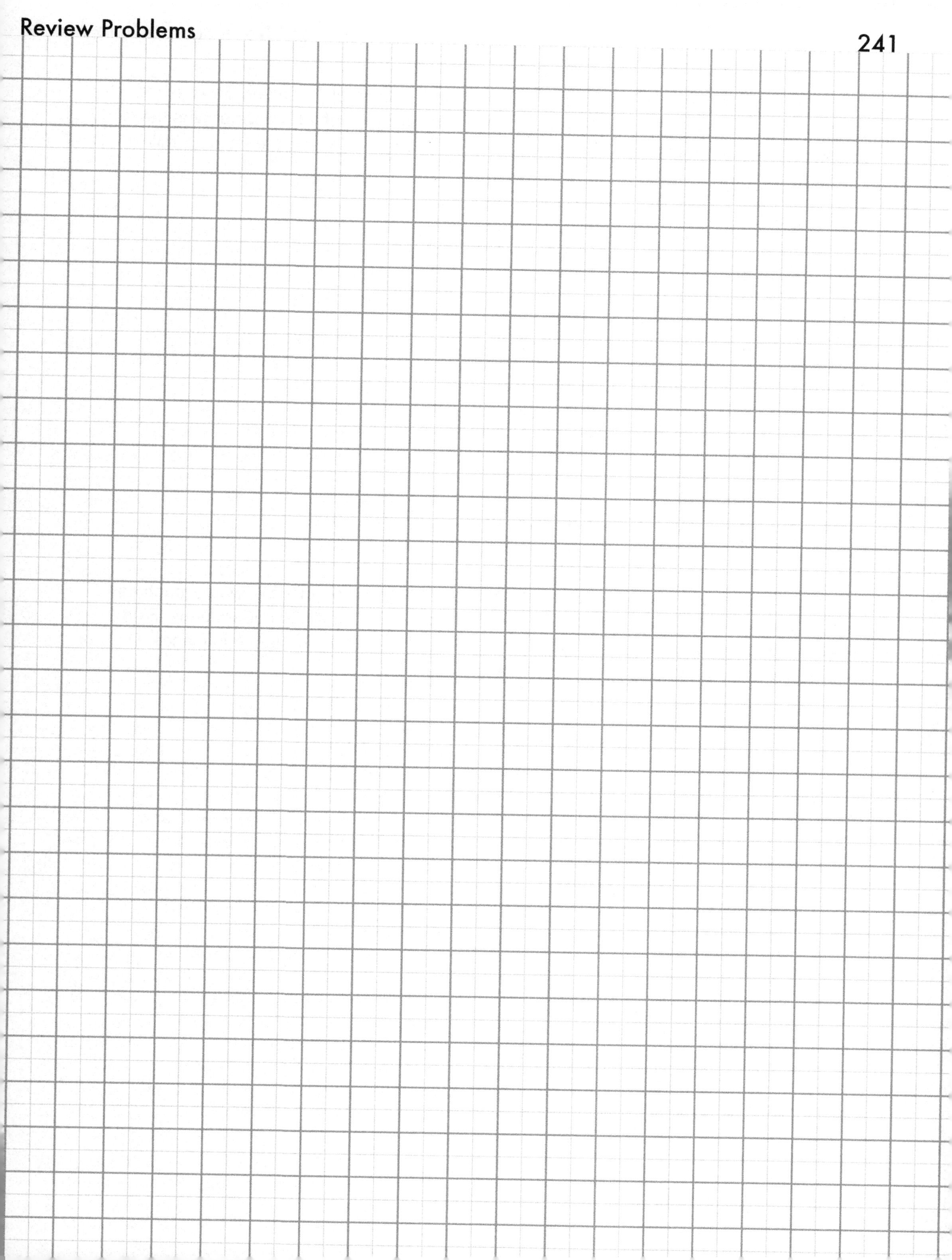

3. Some baseball pitchers are capable of throwing a fastball at 100 mi/hr. The pitcher achieves this speed by moving his arm through a distance of 1.5 m. Determine the average net force that must be exerted on the 0.15 kg ball during the pitch. (1 mile = 1600 meters)

4. After falling from rest at a height of 30 m, a 0.50 kg ball bounces upward, reaching a height of 20 m. The contact between the ball and ground lasted 20 milliseconds. Find the average force exerted on the ball by the ground. (Break the problem into pieces. Do a bunch of kinematics first, then apply Newton's 2nd law.)

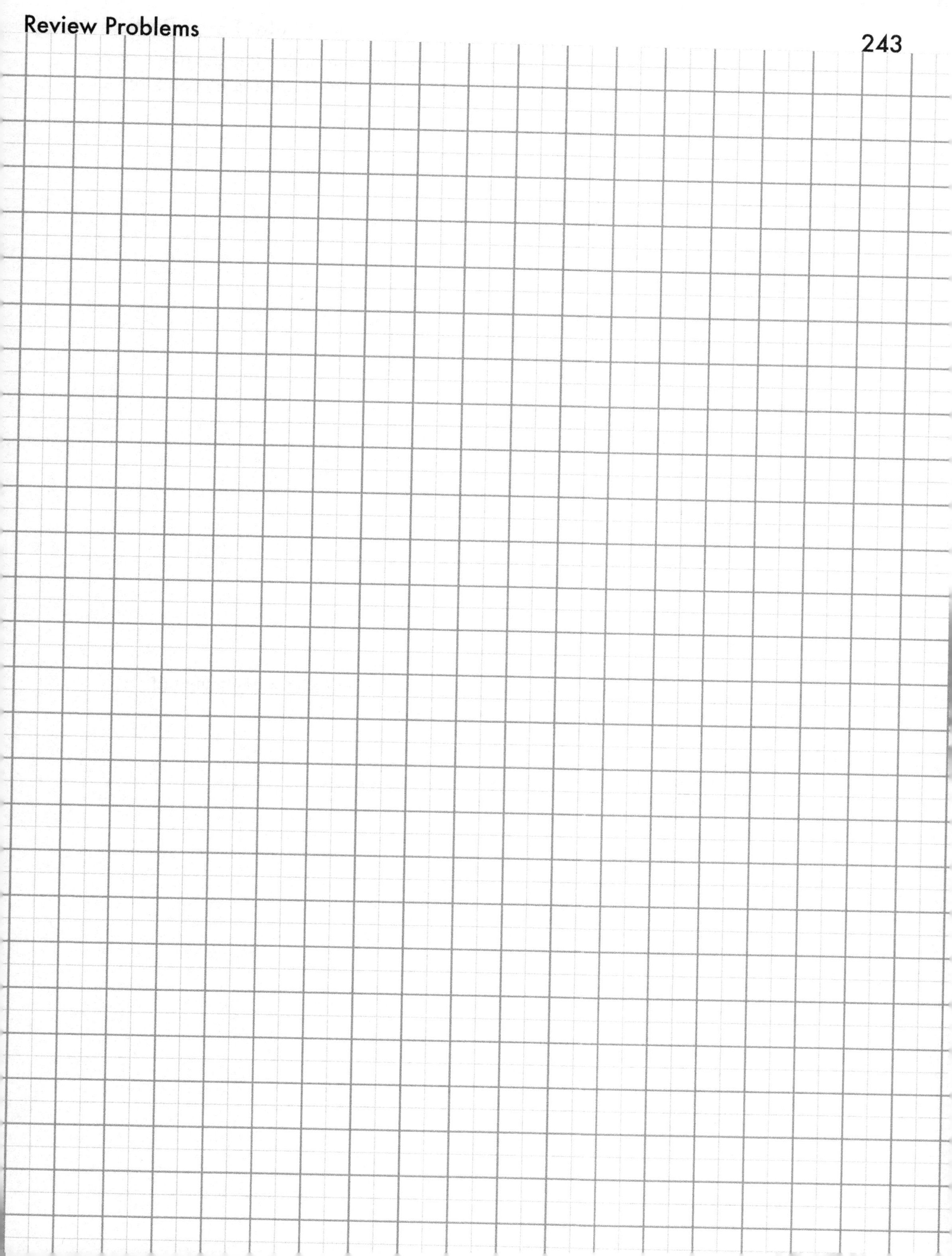

5. In the diagram below, the cord makes a 25° angle with the horizontal, the mass of the sled and occupants is 100 kg. The tension in the cord is 120 N and the friction force is 15 N. Find the acceleration of the sled.

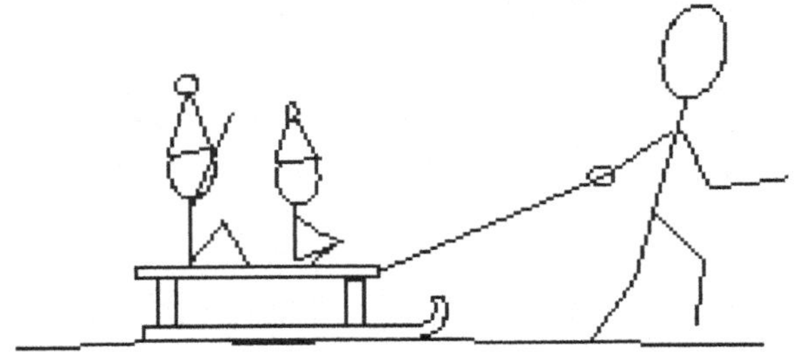

6. The 60 kg skier shown below is skiing down a 35° incline with a coefficient of friction is 0.08. Determine the acceleration of the skier.

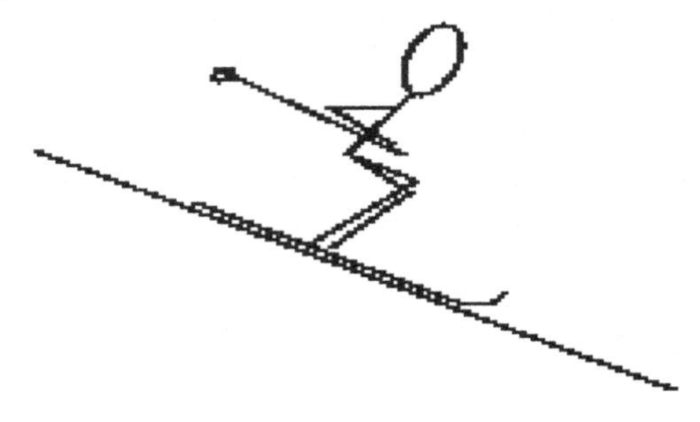

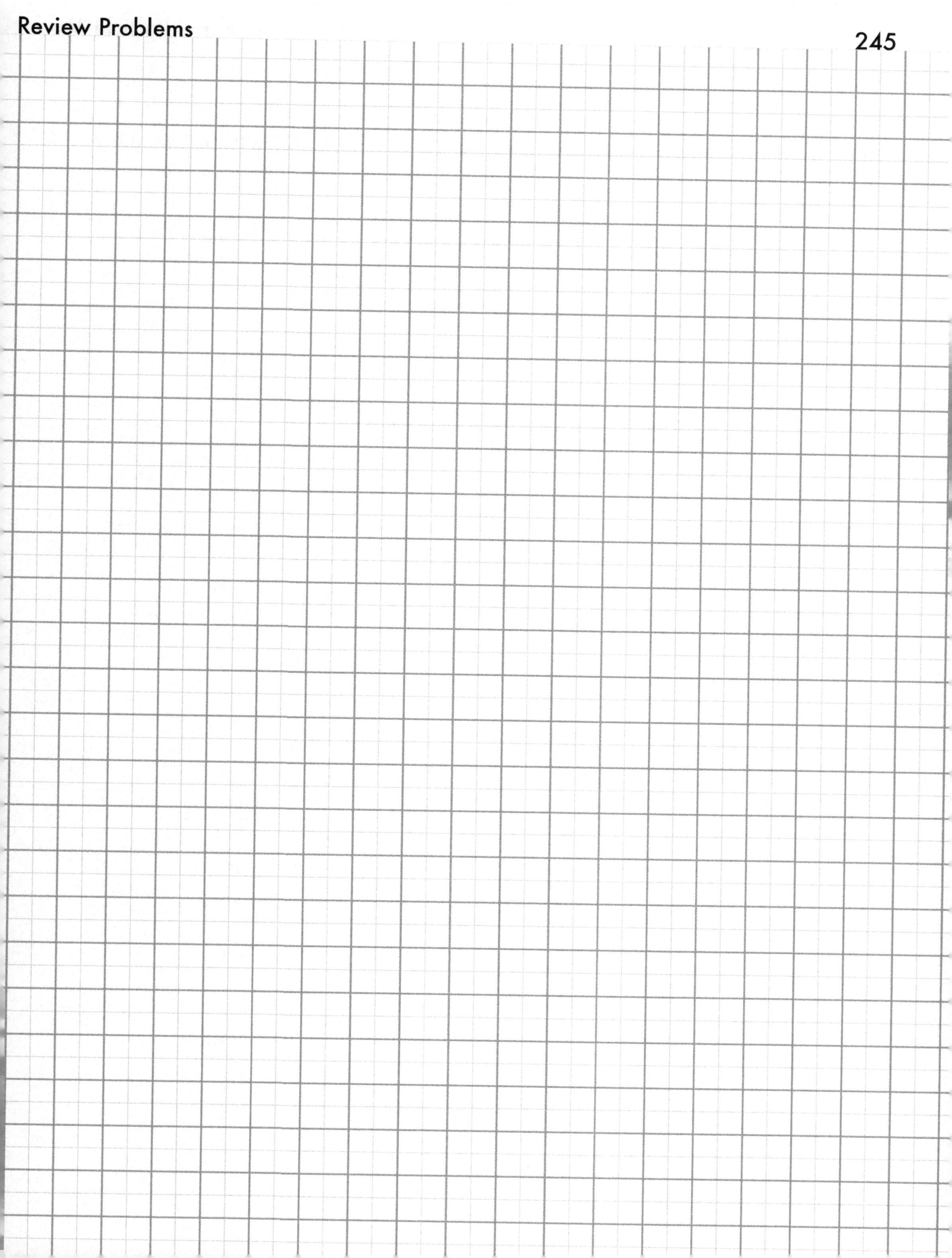

Model Summary

This is a place to summarize different representations of the Net Force Particle Model

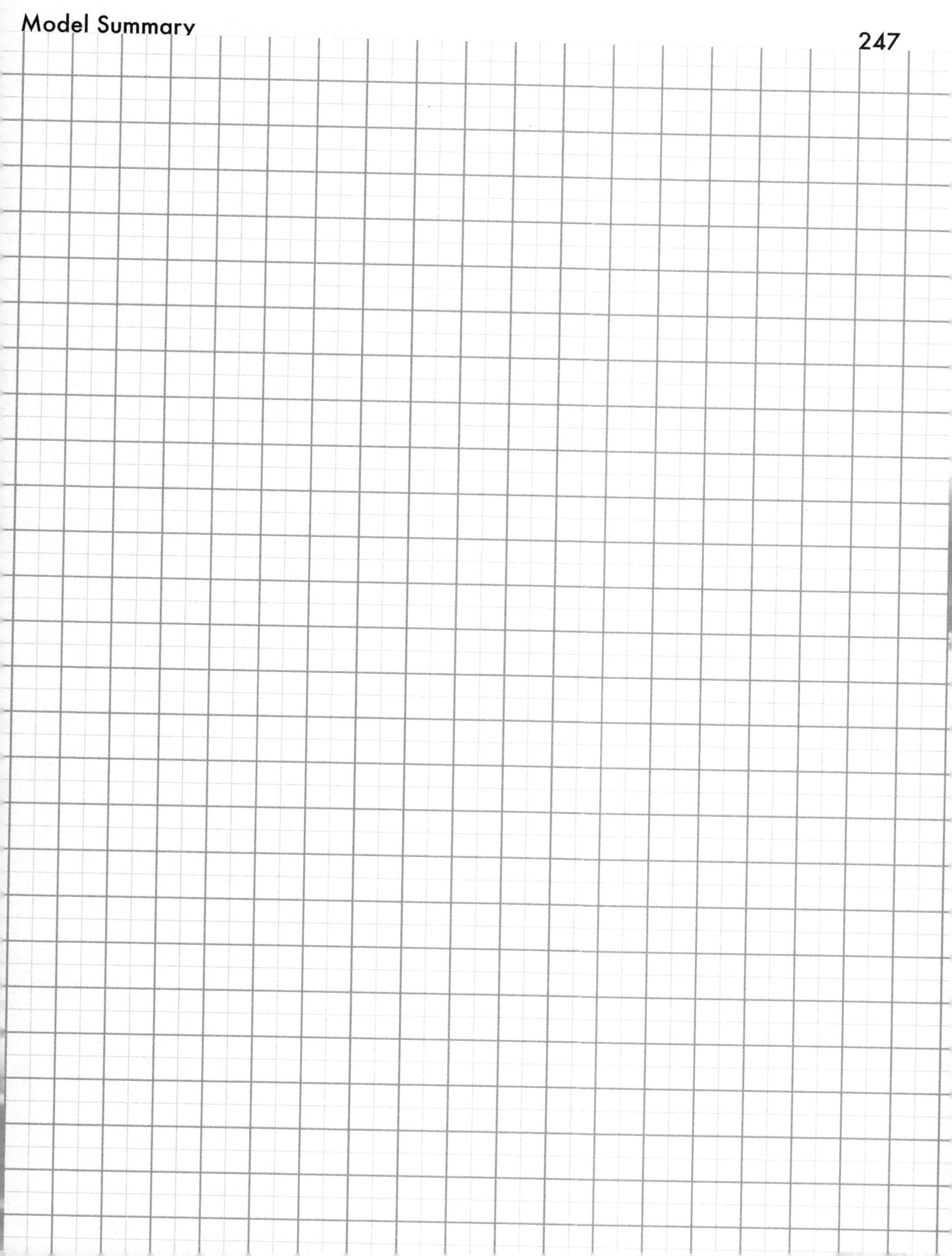

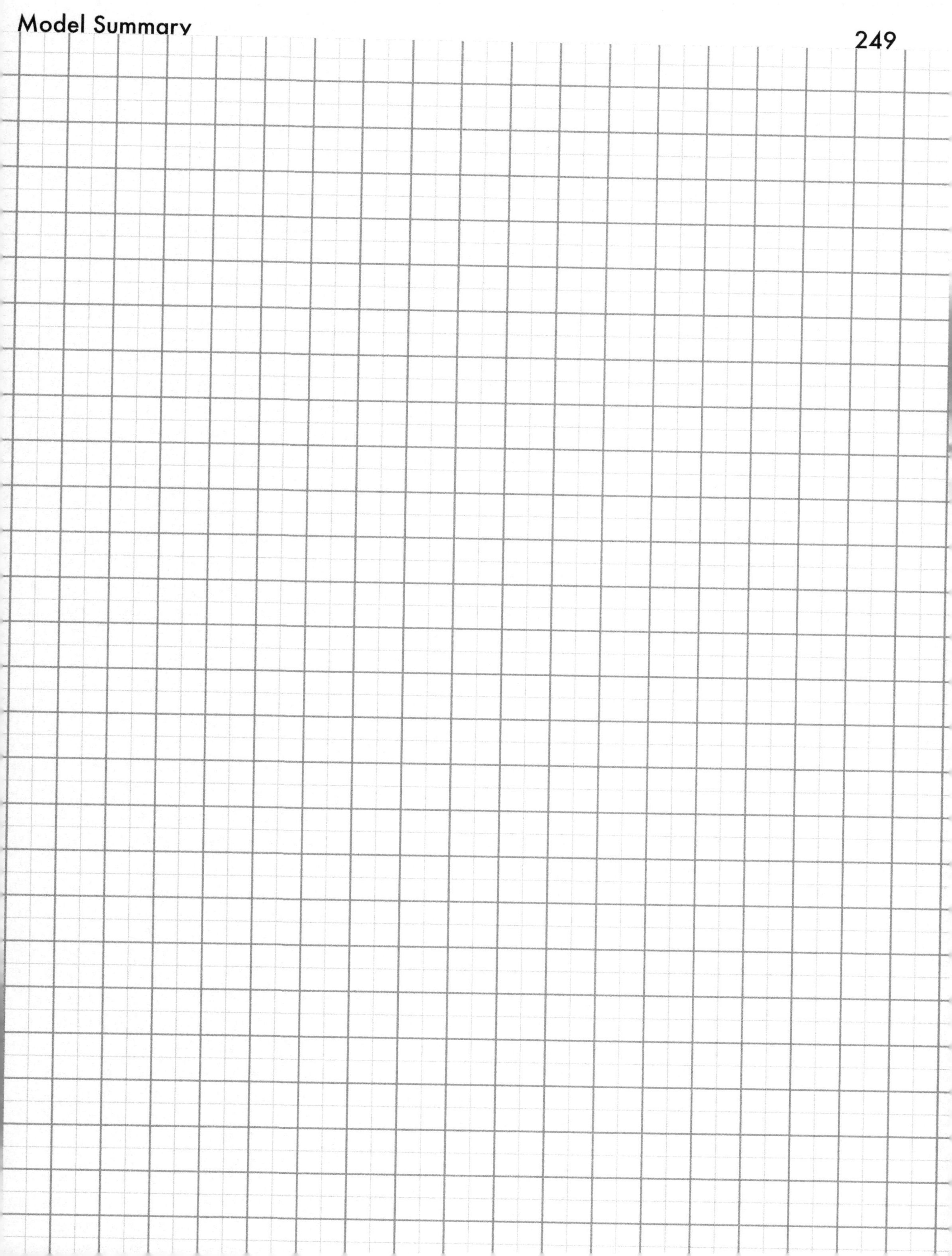

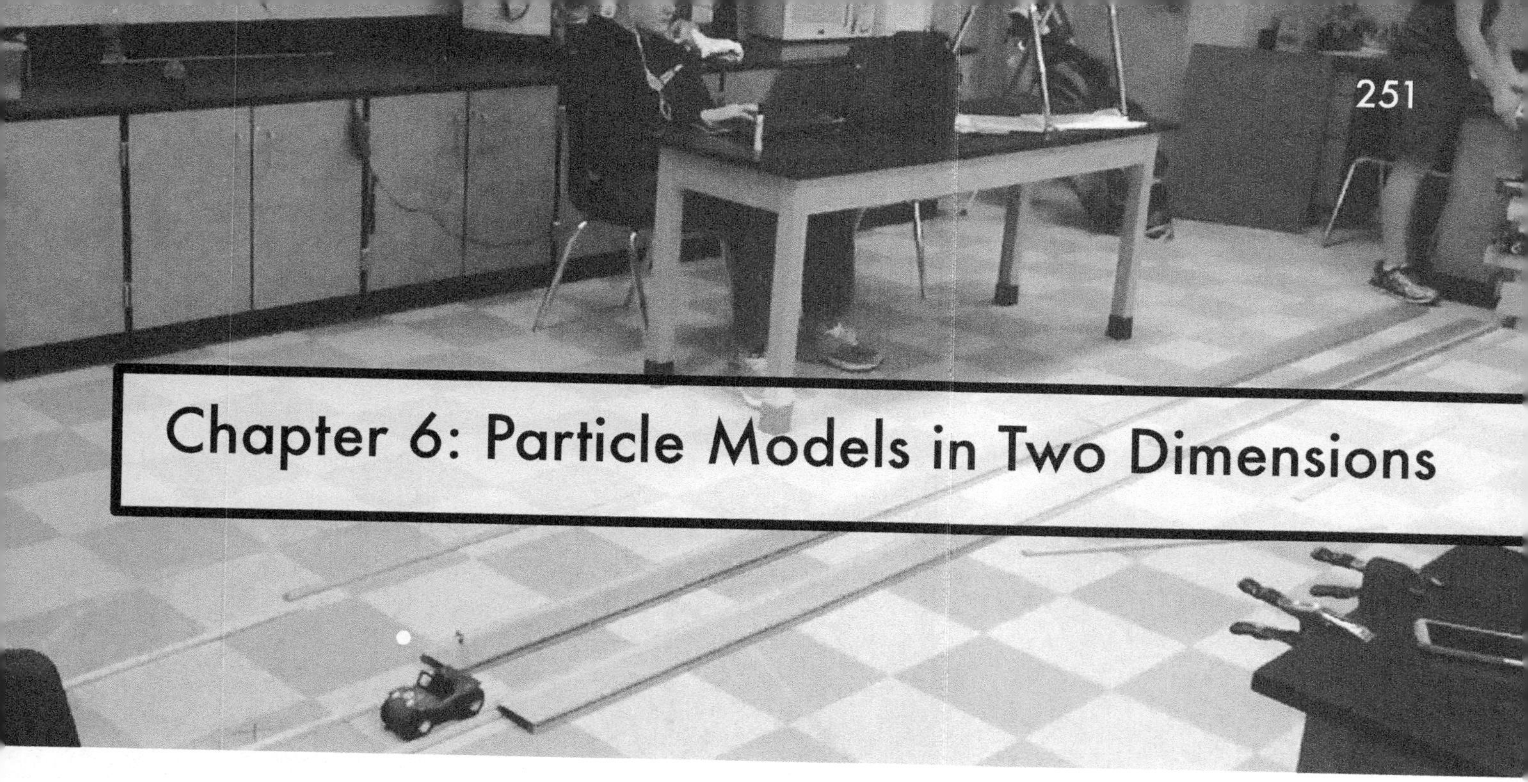

Chapter 6: Particle Models in Two Dimensions

Chapter Sections

chapter 6 online help

Lab Notes

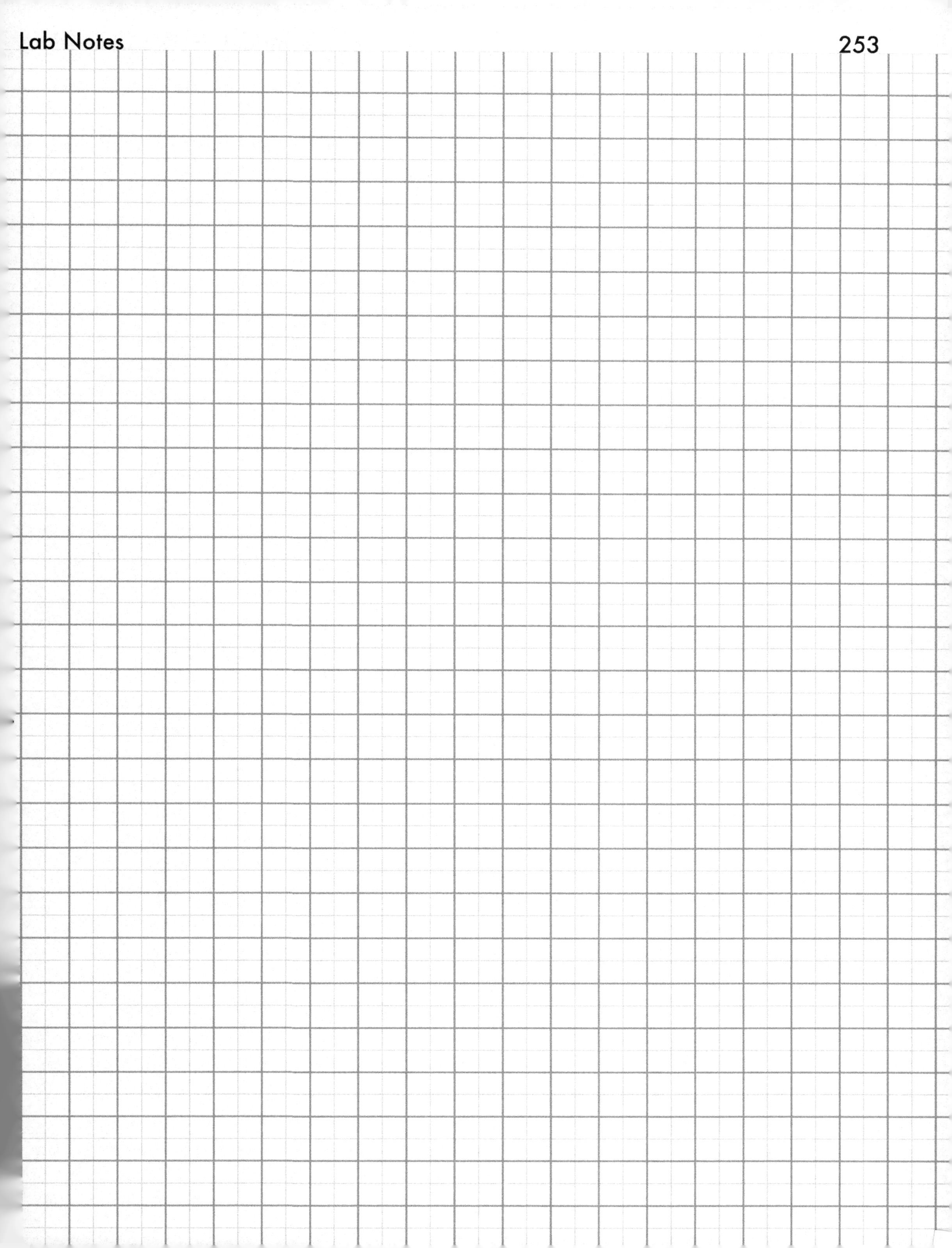

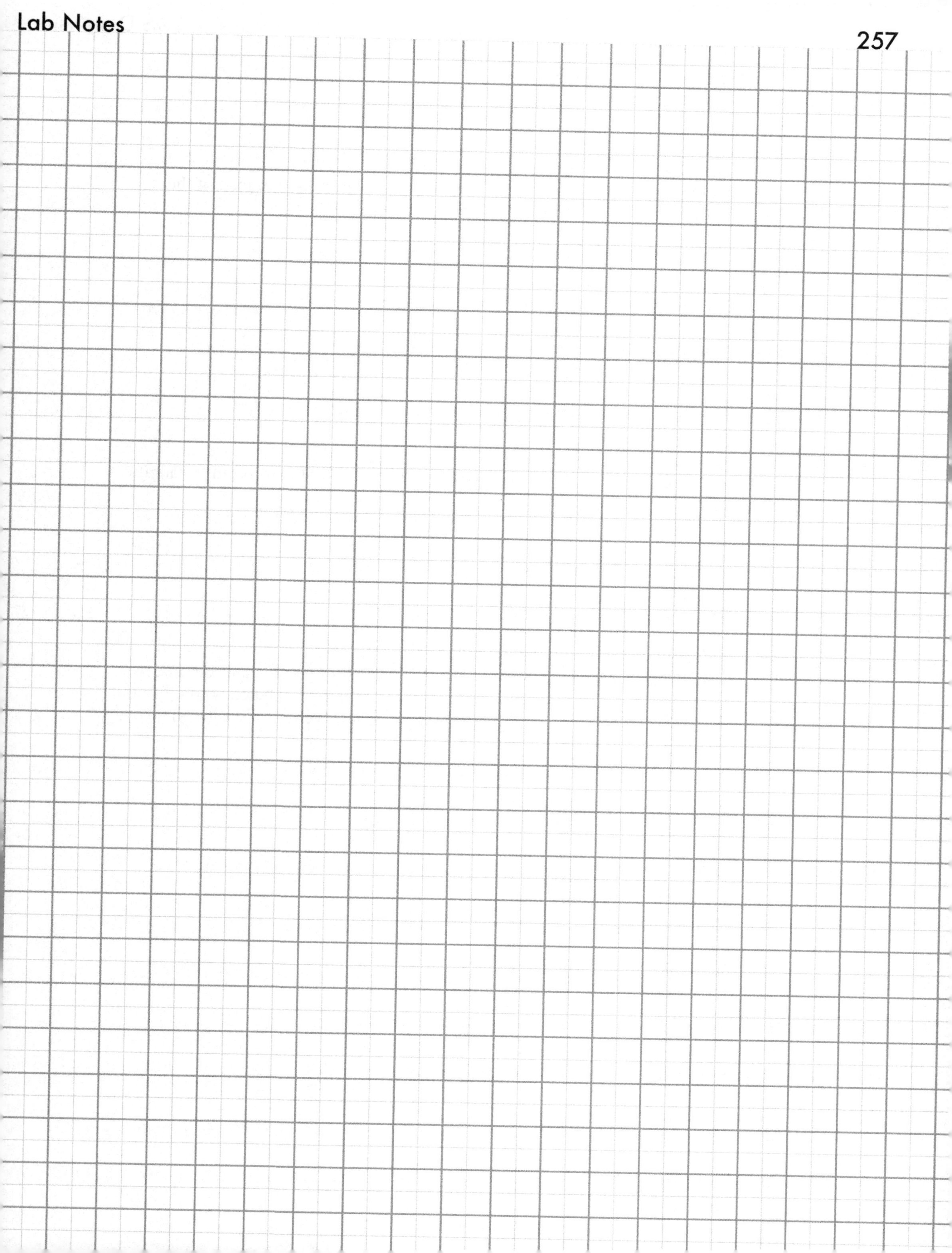

Worksheet 1: Free-Fall Kinematics

1. A ball is thrown downward with an initial speed of 20 m/s on Earth.
   a. Make a labeled diagram (specify the (+) direction), then make a motion map of the situation.

   b. What is the acceleration of the ball?

   c. Calculate the displacement during the first 4 s.

   d. Calculate the time required to reach a speed of 50 m/s.

   e. Calculate the time required to fall 300 m (Hint: factor the quadratic or use the quadratic formula).

   f. Calculate the speed after falling 100 m.

2. A rock is thrown upward with an initial speed of 15 m/s on Earth.
   a. Make a well-labeled diagram of the situation.

   b. Make a list of given quantities and quantities to find, labeled with units and appropriate algebraic signs (+, -).

   c. What is the acceleration of the rock?

   d. Calculate the rock's height after 1 sec.

   e. Calculate the time required to reach an upward speed of 3 m/s.

   f. Calculate the time required to reach a downward speed of 5 m/s.

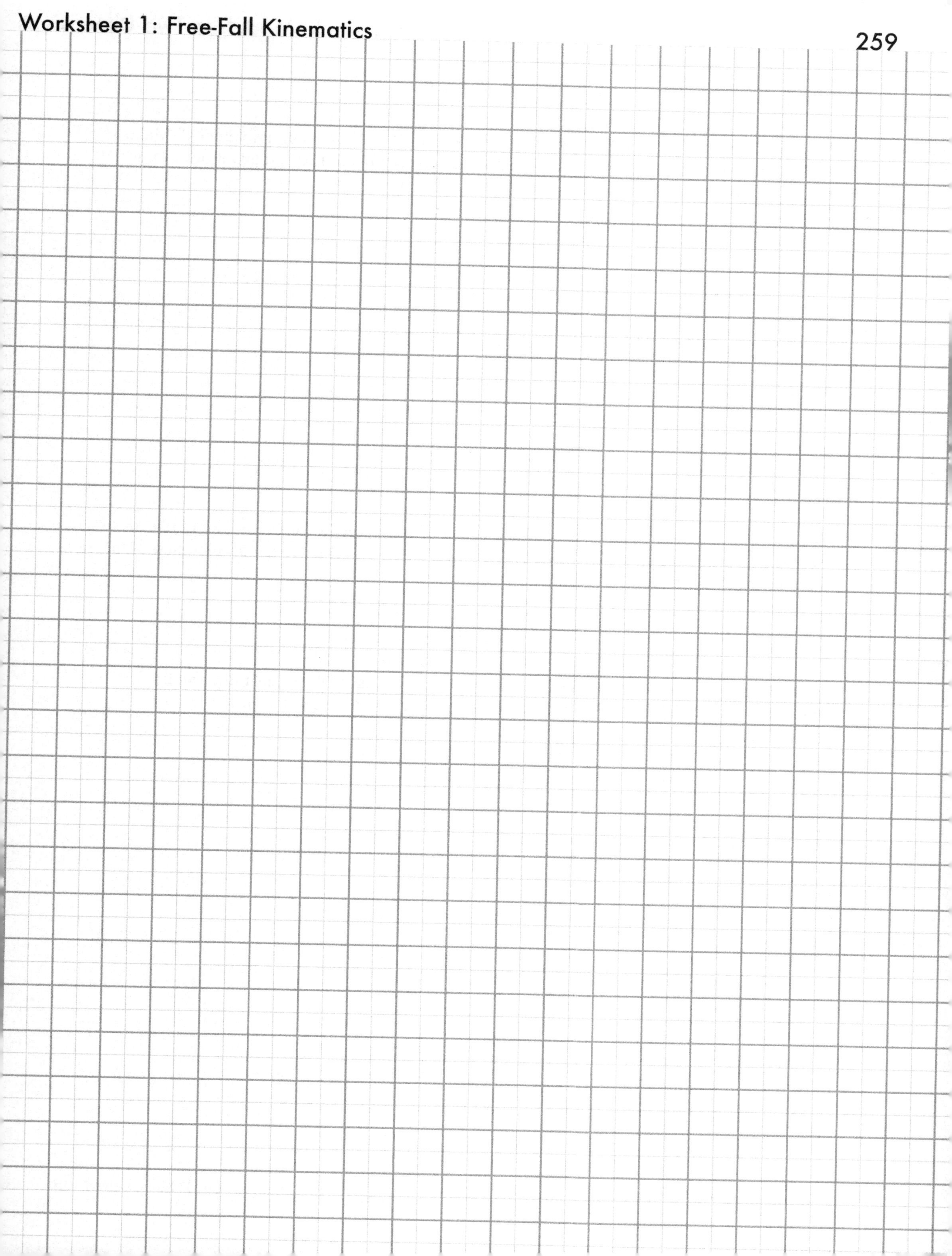

3. A ball punted vertically has a hang time of 3.8 seconds. What was its initial velocity? Make a well-labeled diagram of the situation. Make a list of given quantities and quantities to find, labeled with units and appropriate algebraic signs (+, -).

4. A rock is thrown straight up with an initial speed of 22 m/s. How long will it be in the air before it returns to the thrower? Graph the vertical position, velocity, and acceleration of the rock versus time on the graph page to the right.

a. Make a well-labeled diagram of the situation. Make a list of given quantities and quantities to find, labeled with units and appropriate algebraic signs (+, -).

b. Draw a velocity and an acceleration motion map for the trip.

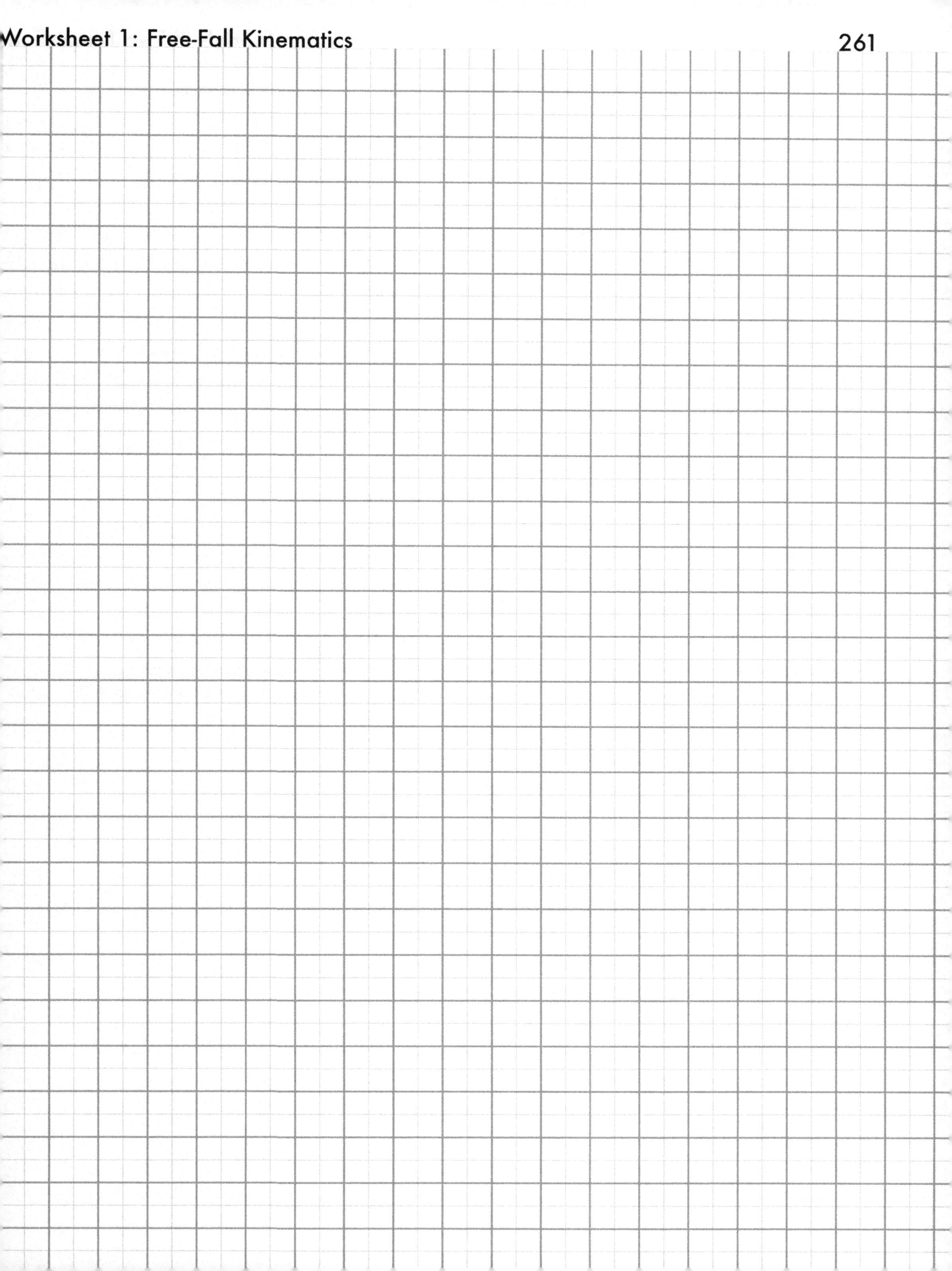

5. A student throws a baseball off a 120 m high bridge with an initial downward speed of 10 m/s
   a. How long does it take the ball to hit the ground below?

   b. How fast is the ball going at the moment of impact?

6. When a kid drops a rock off the edge of a cliff, it takes 4.0 s to reach the ground below. When she throws the rock down, it strikes the ground in 3.0 s. What initial speed did she give the rock?

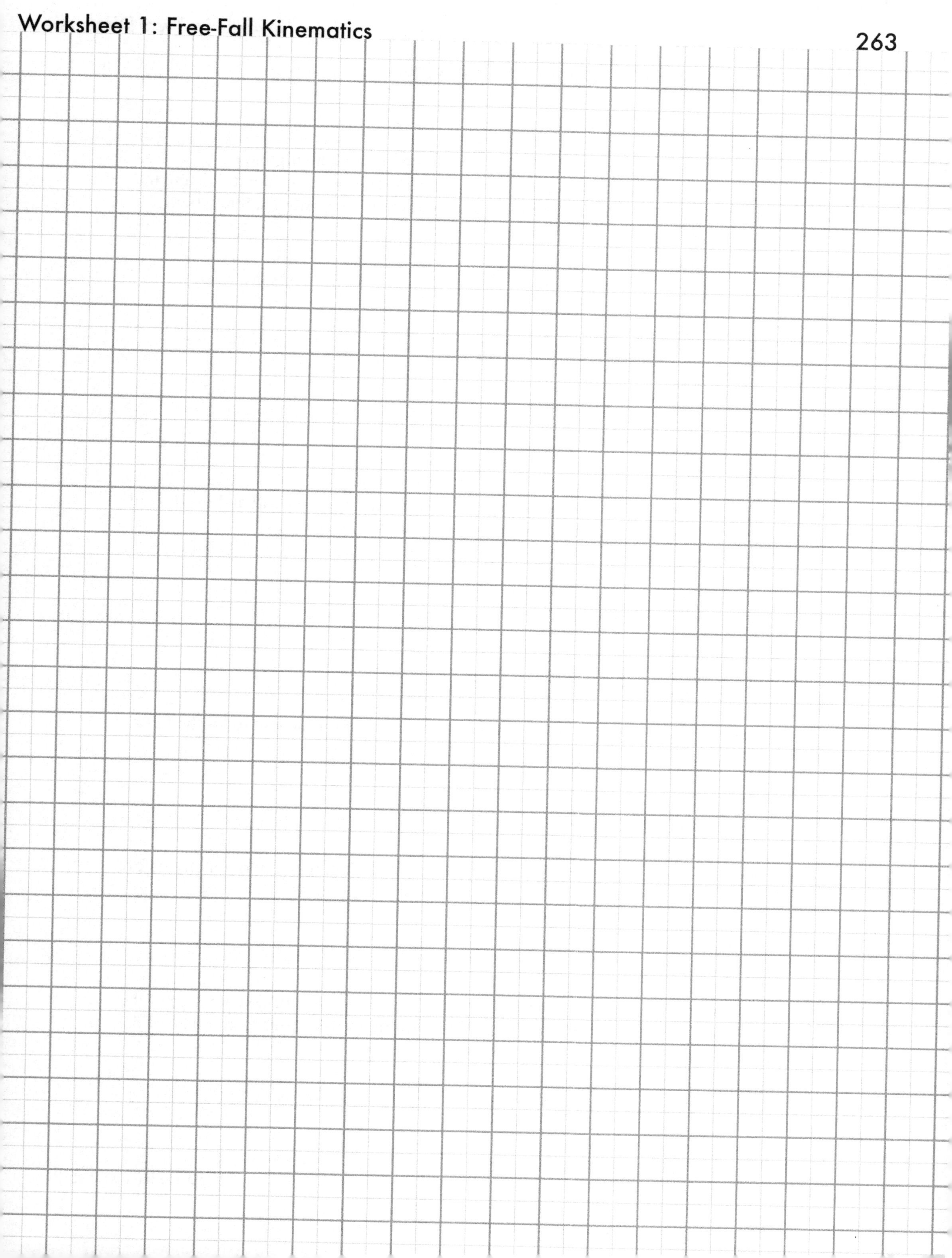

Worksheet 2: Horizontally Launched Projectiles

1. Given the following situation of a marble in motion on a rail with negligible $F_{friction}$:
   a. Sketch a motion map showing the motion of the marble after it leaves the rail, using the graph paper to the right to help you carefully locate the marble's positions. Show both horizontal and vertical velocity vectors on each dot.

   b. Sketch and label force diagrams for the marble both when it is on the rail and off the rail. Describe the horizontal and vertical motion of the ball in each case.

   c. Once the ball leaves the table, calculate how long it will take for the ball to hit the floor.

   d. In the time you have calculated in part c, how far will the ball travel horizontally before hitting the floor?

   e. Suppose the table was doubled in height to 3.0 m. Determine the horizontal range of the marble as it falls to the floor. What effect does doubling the height have on range of the marble? What other factors affect the range of the sphere?

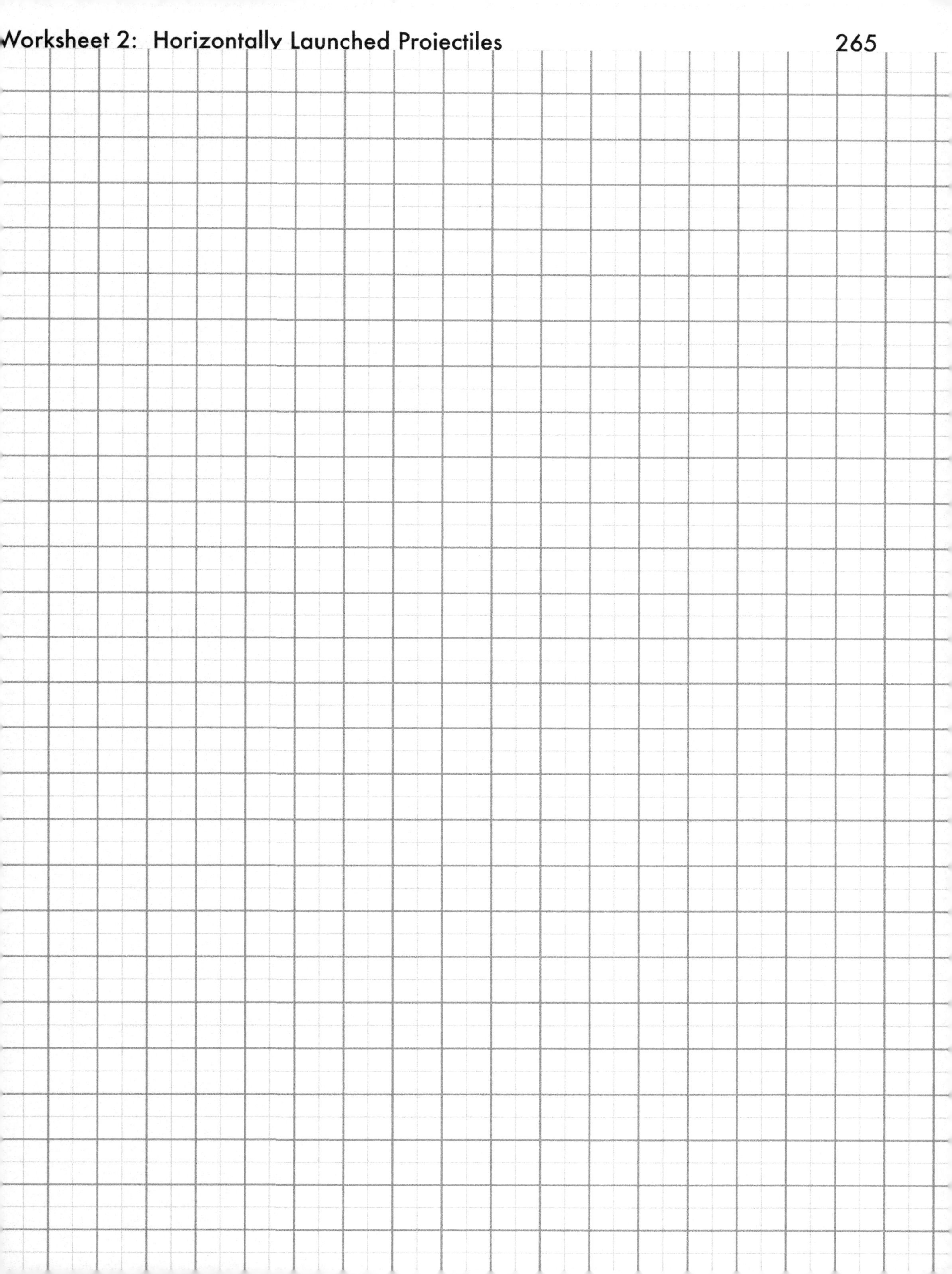

2. A student finds that it takes 0.20s for a ball to pass through photogates placed 30 cm apart on a level ramp. The end of the ramp is 92 cm above the floor. Where could a coin be placed so that the ball directly strikes the coin on impact with the ground?

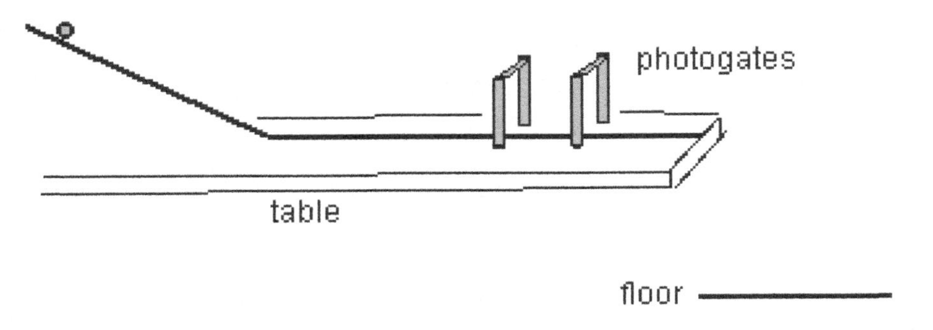

3. Suppose now that the same ball, released from the same ramp (92 cm high) struck a coin on the floor placed 25 cm from the end of the ramp.
   a. What was the ball's horizontal velocity?
   b. How long did it take for the ball to pass through the photogates?

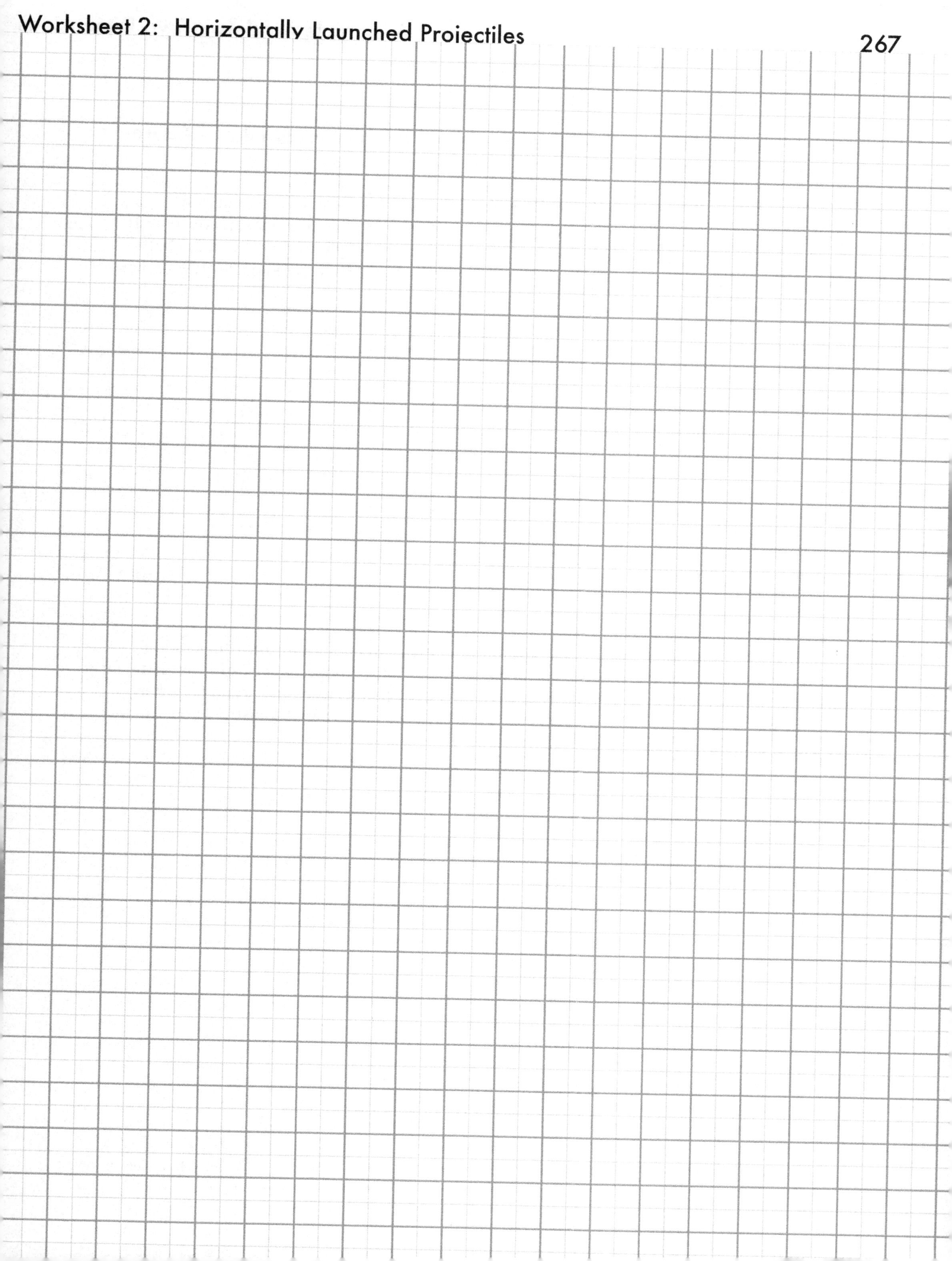

Worksheet 3: Projectile Motion Problems

In all the problems below, draw a diagram to represent the situation. Identify the knowns and unknowns and label clearly.

1. The movie "The Gods Must Be Crazy" begins with a pilot dropping a bottle out of an airplane. A surprised native below, who thinks it is a message from the gods, recovers it. If the plane from which the bottle was dropped was flying at a height of 500m, and the bottle lands 400m horizontally from the initial dropping point, how fast was the plane flying when the bottle was released?

   b. Draw a 2-dimensional motion map for the velocities and another for the acceleration.
2. Suppose that an airplane flying 60 m/s, at a height of 300m, dropped a sack of flour. How far from the point of release would the sack have traveled when it struck the ground? Where will the plane be in relation to the sack when the sack hits the ground? Illustrate your answer carefully using the graph paper to the right.

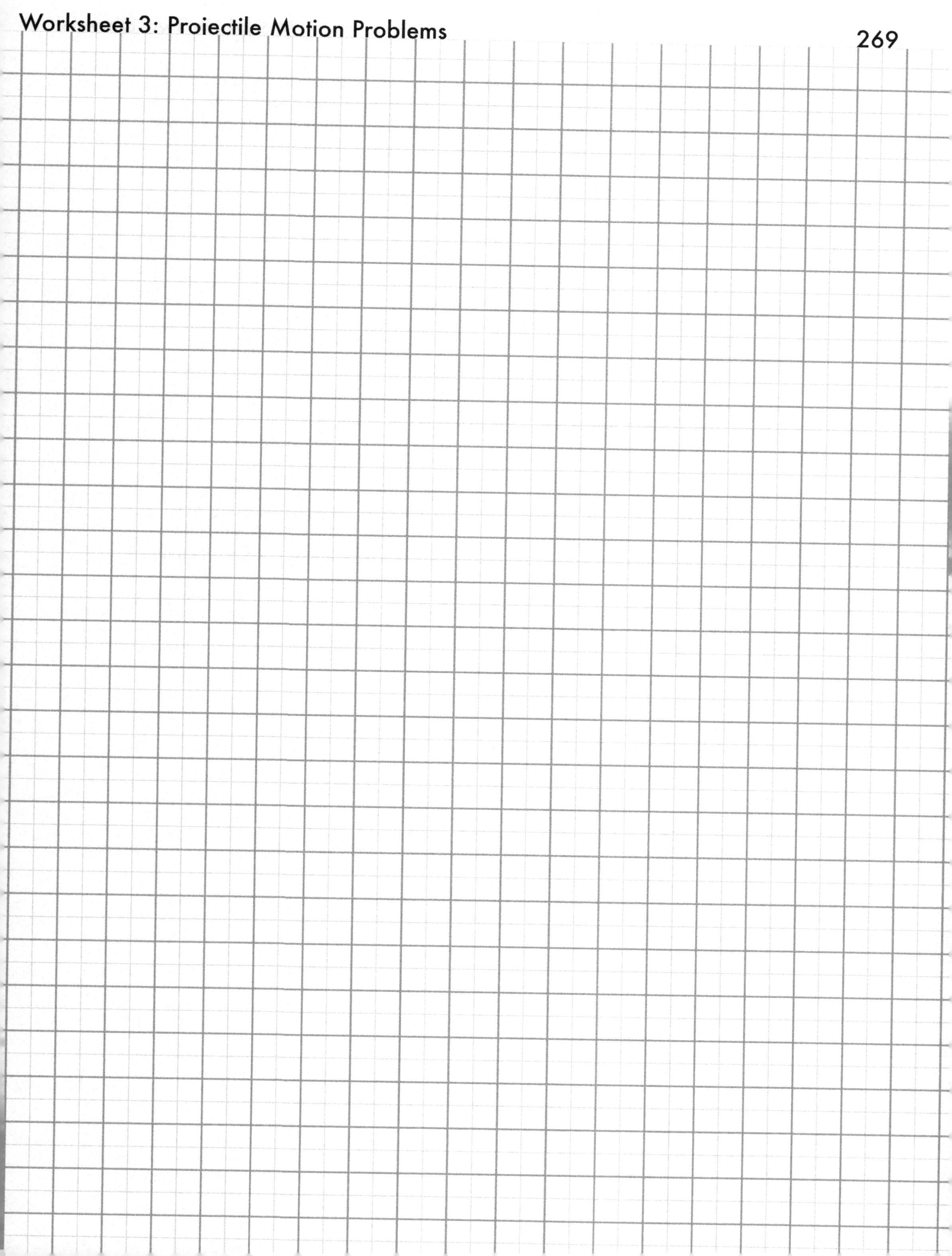

3. In many locations, old abandoned stone quarries have become filled with water once excavating has been completed. While standing on a quarry wall, a boy tosses a piece of granite into the water below. If he throws the rock horizontally with a velocity of 3.0 m/s, and it strikes the water 4.5 m away, how high above the water is the wall?

4. Tad drops a cherry pit out the car window 1.0 m above the ground while traveling down the road at 18 m/s. How far, horizontally, from the initial dropping point will the pit hit the ground? If the car continues to travel at the same speed, where will the car be in relation to the pit when it lands?

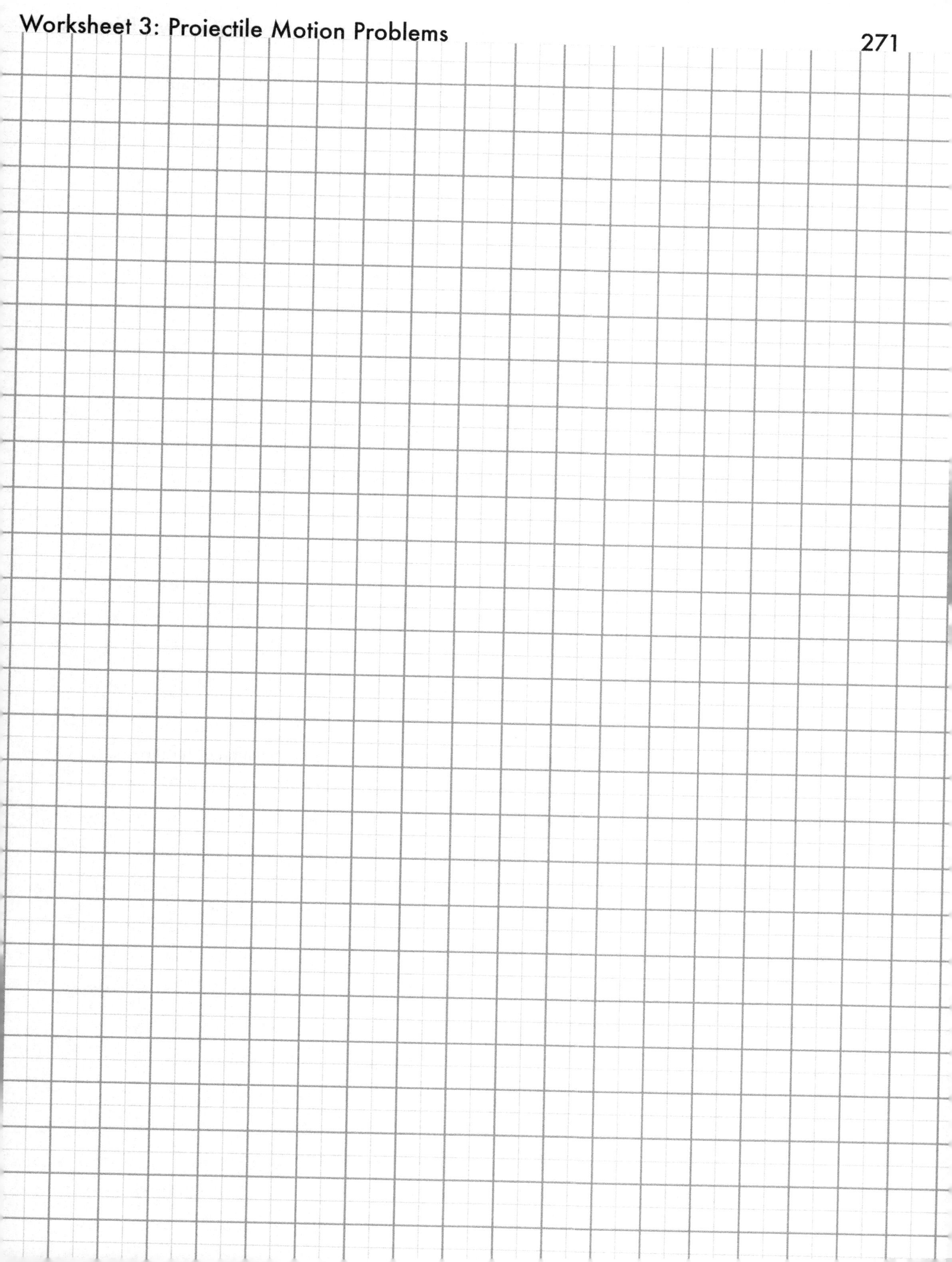

5. A kickoff sends a football with an initial velocity of 25 m/s at an angle of 50 degrees above horizontal.

a. Find the x and y-components of the velocity

b. Find the time the ball is in the air

c. Find the horizontal distance the ball travels before hitting the ground.

d. Find the maximum height of the ball.

e. Draw a 2-dimensional motion map for the velocities (v_x, v_y, and v) and another for the acceleration.

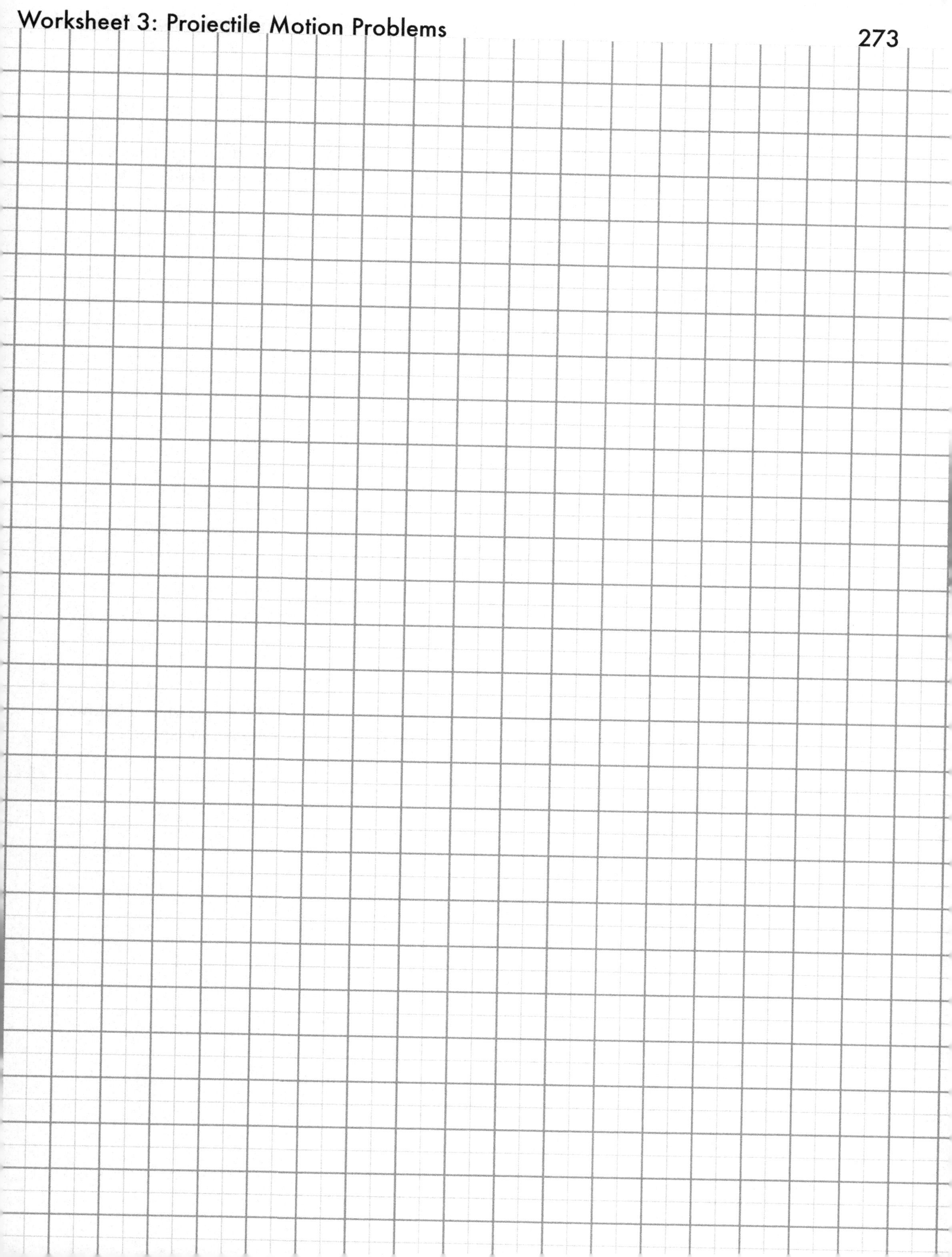

Worksheet 4: Projectile Motion Problems

1. A metal sphere is launched with an initial velocity of 1.5 m/s as it leaves the ramp. The end of the ramp is 1.20 m above the floor. Calculate the range of the sphere. (*Range* is the horizontal displacement of the projectile.)

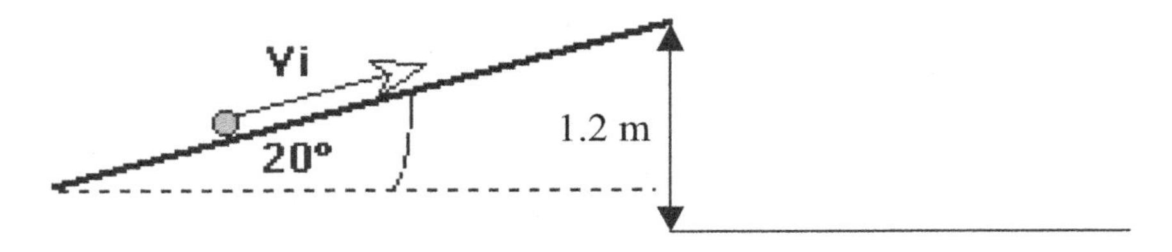

2. Now the ramp is tilted downwards and the sphere leaves the ramp at 1.5 m/s as shown below. The bottom of the ramp is 0.90 m above the floor. Calculate the range of the sphere.

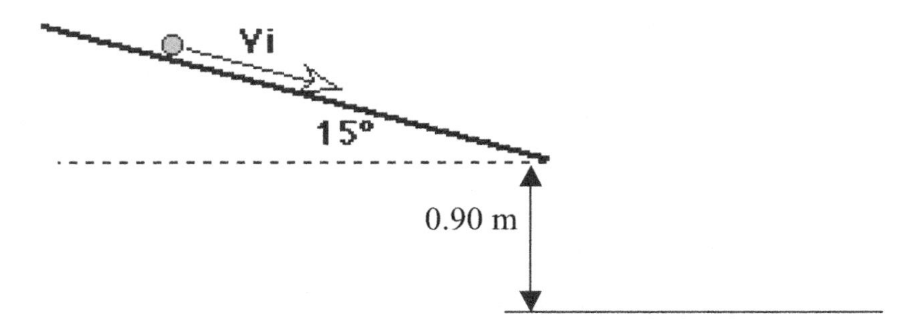

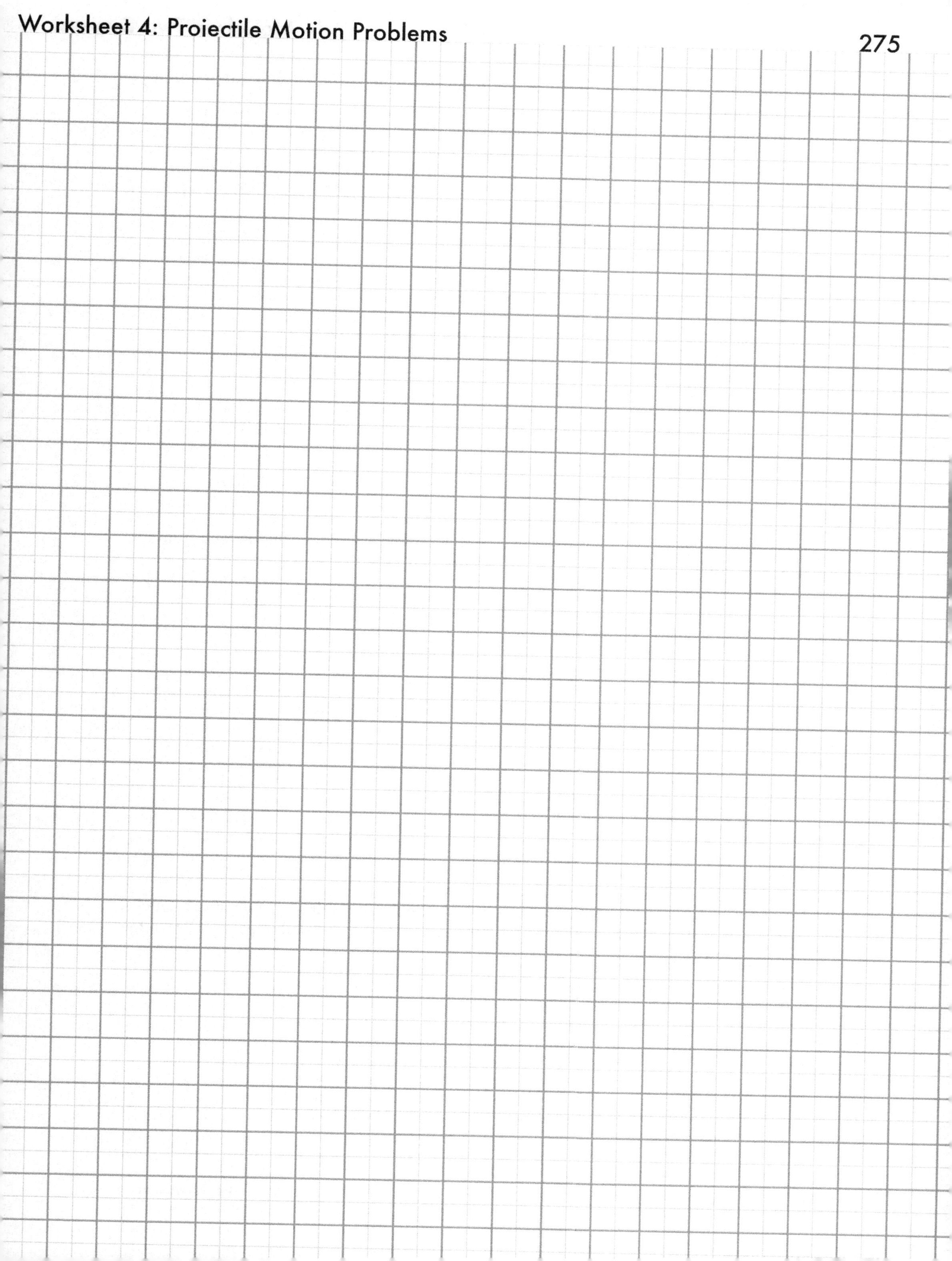

3. A water balloon is launched at a building 24 m away with an initial velocity of 18 m/s at an angle of 50° above the horizontal.
   a. At what height will the balloon strike the building?

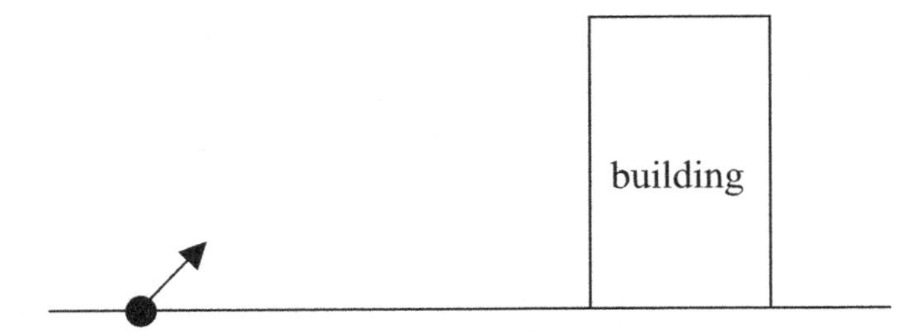

   b. If the balloon misses or shoots over the building, how far will the balloon land from its launch location?

   c. The balloon can be launched from less than 24 m away from the building at the same speed and angle and still hit exactly the same height you calculated in part a. Determine this second launch location.

Review Problems: Projectile Motion

1. A soccer goalie makes a save and then kicks the ball through the air to the middle of the field.

   a. Graph the **horizontal** component (position, velocity, and acceleration) of the ball's motion while in the air.

   b. Explain what each graph shows in words.

   c. Graph the **vertical** component of the ball's motion while in the air.

   d. d. Explain what each graph shows in words.

   e. Draw a force diagram for the soccer ball while it is in the air.

   f. Draw a motion map for the soccer ball's trajectory.

2. Tom the cat is chasing Jerry the mouse across a table surface 1.5 m high. Jerry steps out of the way at the last second, and Tom slides off the edge of the table at a speed of 5 m/s.
   a. Where will Tom strike the floor?
   b. What are his vertical and horizontal velocity components just before he hits the floor?

3. A lacrosse player slings the ball at an angle of 30 degrees above the horizontal with a speed of 20 m/s. How far away should a teammate position herself to catch the ball?

4. A ball is thrown straight upward and returns to the thrower's hand after 3 seconds in the air. A second ball is thrown at an angle of 30 degrees with the horizontal. At what speed must the second ball be thrown so that it reaches the same height as the one thrown vertically?

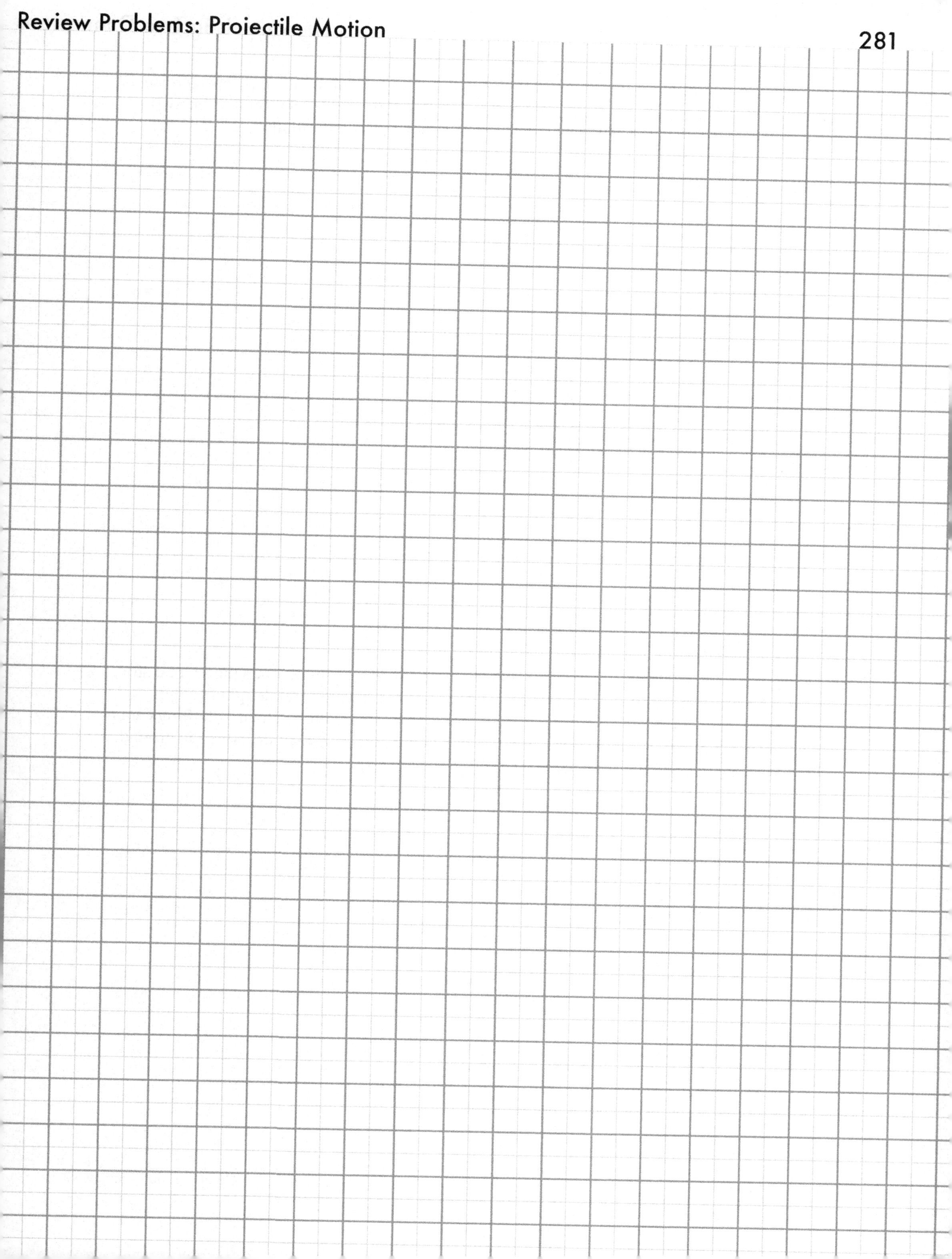

5. Two objects are initially the same height above the ground. Simultaneously, one is released from rest and the other is shot off horizontally with an initial speed of 2.5 m/s. The two objects collide after falling 20 m. How far apart were the objects initially?

6. Frustrated with HISTORY, (you never get frustrated in physics) you open the second story classroom window and (to the horror of your teacher but to the secret delight of your classmates) violently hurl your history book out the window with a velocity of 18 m/s at an angle of 35 degrees above the horizontal. If the launch point is 6 meters above the ground, how far from the building will the book hit the parking lot?

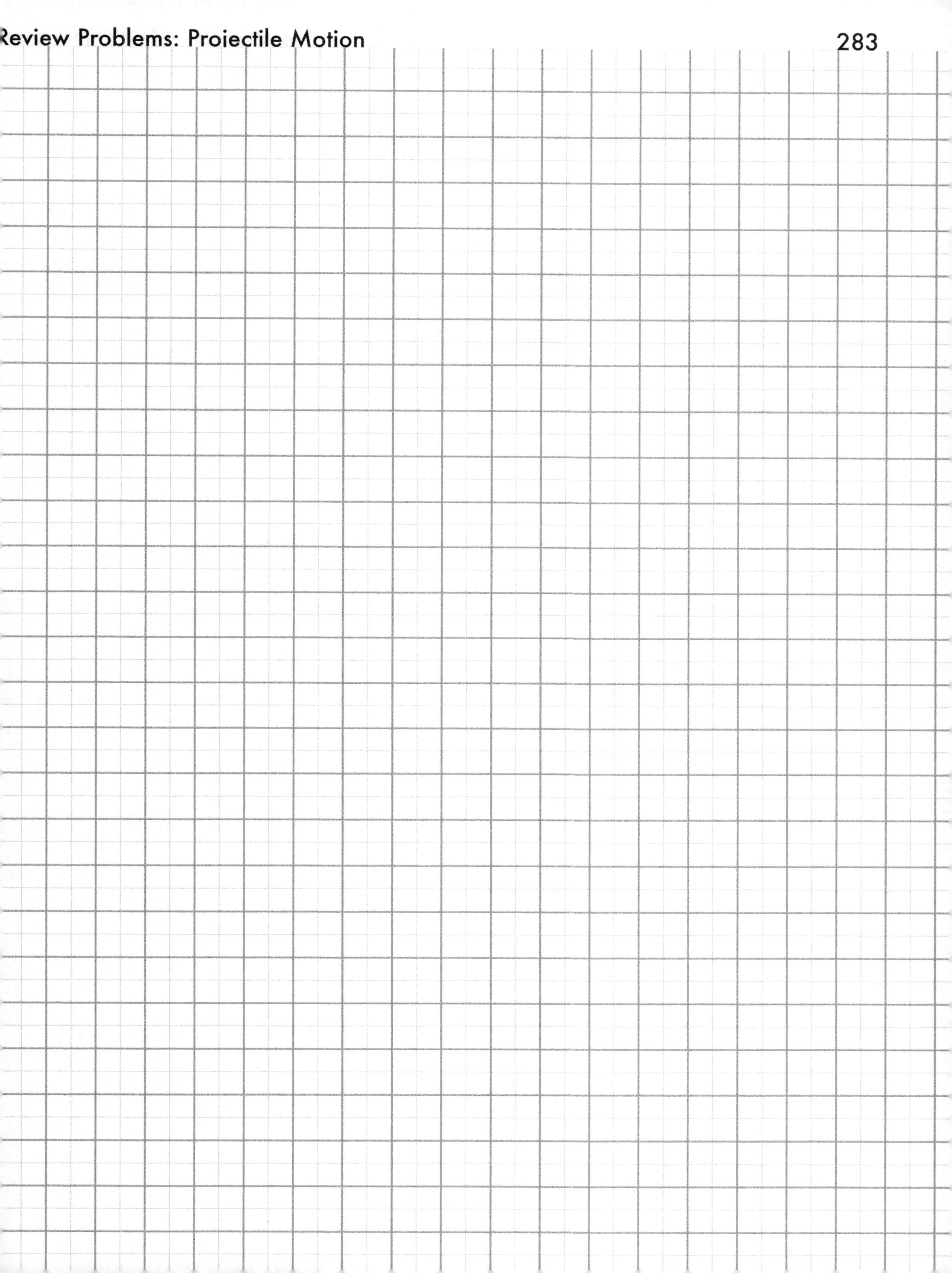

Model Summary

This is a place to summarize the Big Ideas for Particle Models in Two Dimensions.

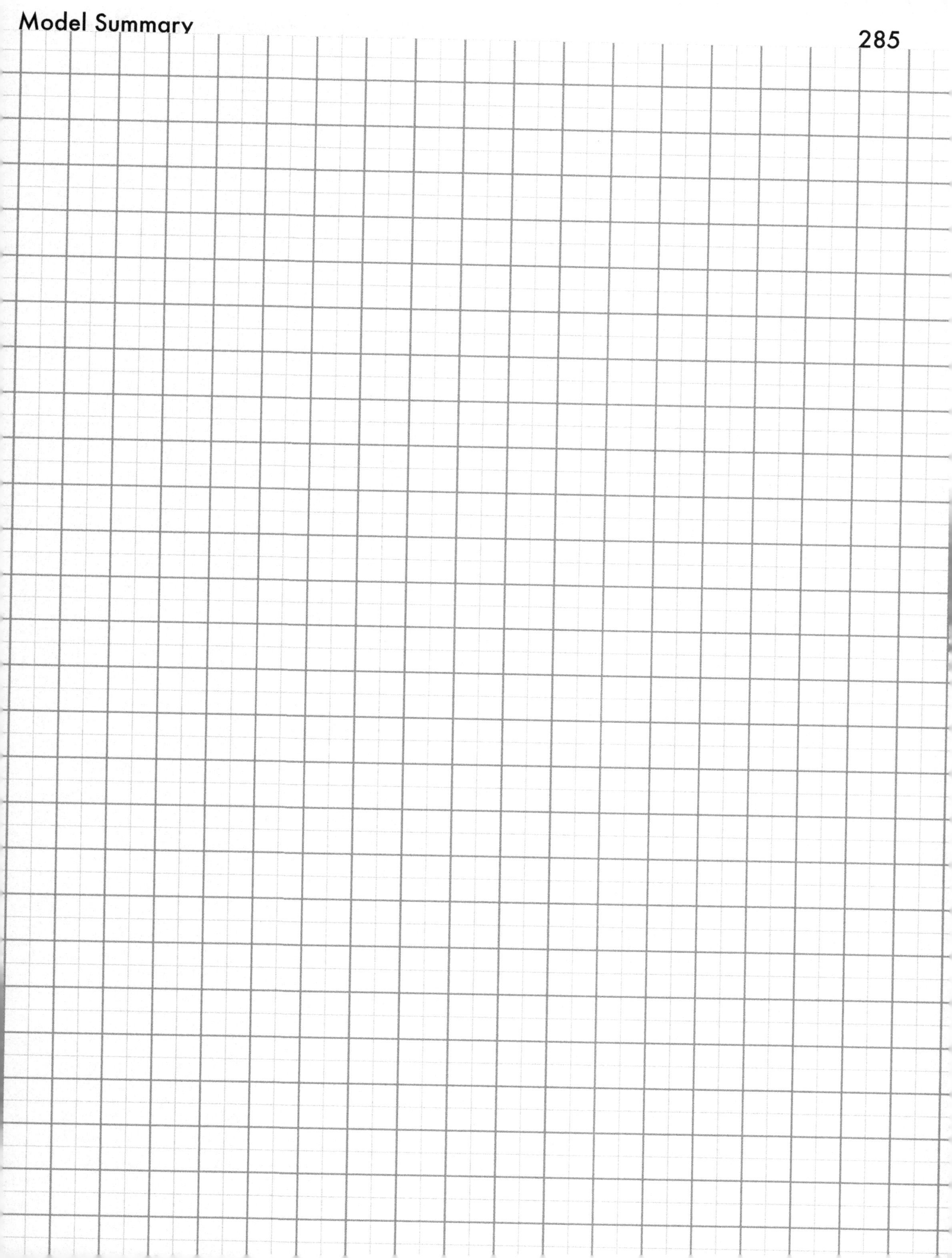

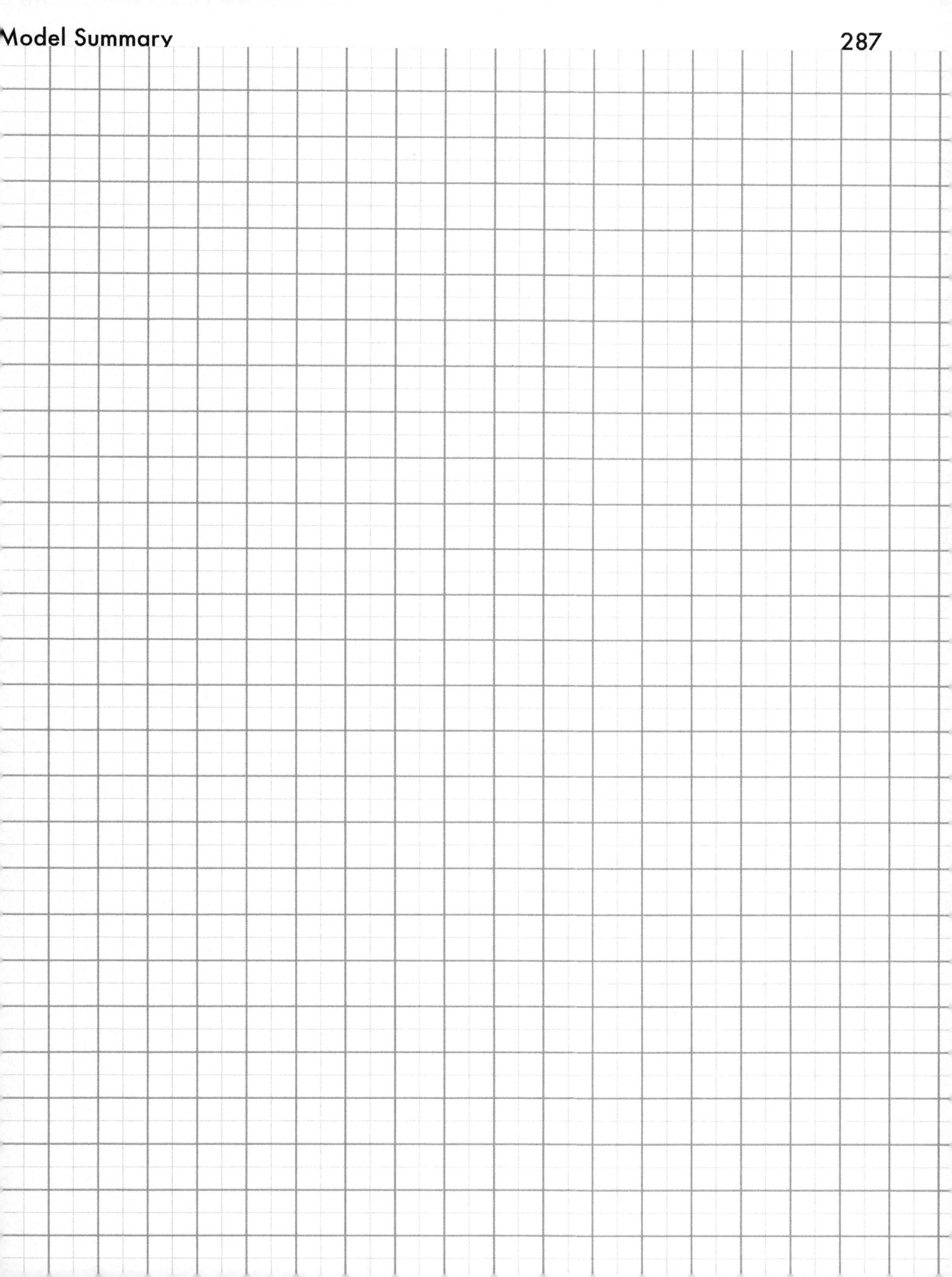

Chapter 7: Central Net Force Model

Chapter Sections

chapter 7 online help

Lab Notes

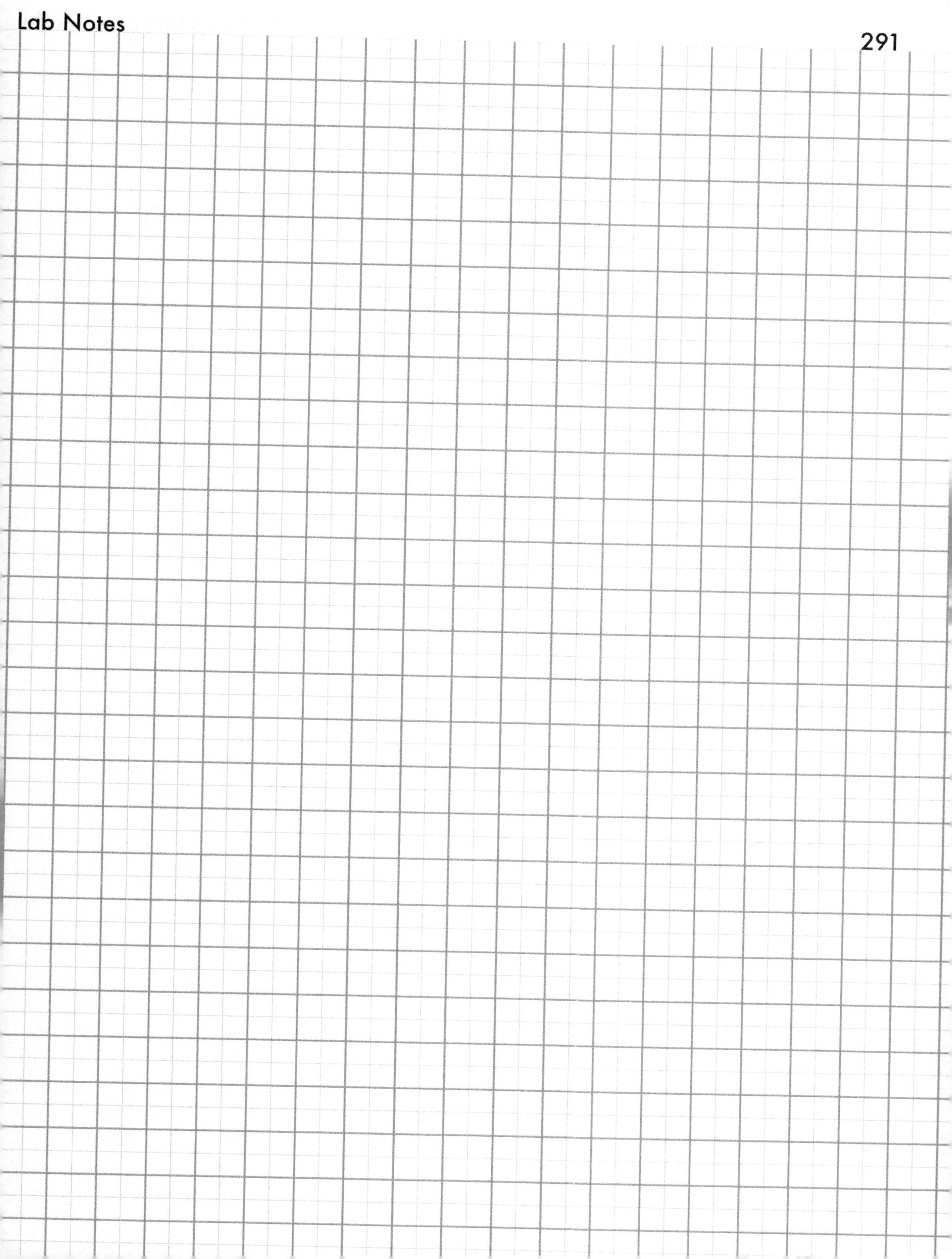

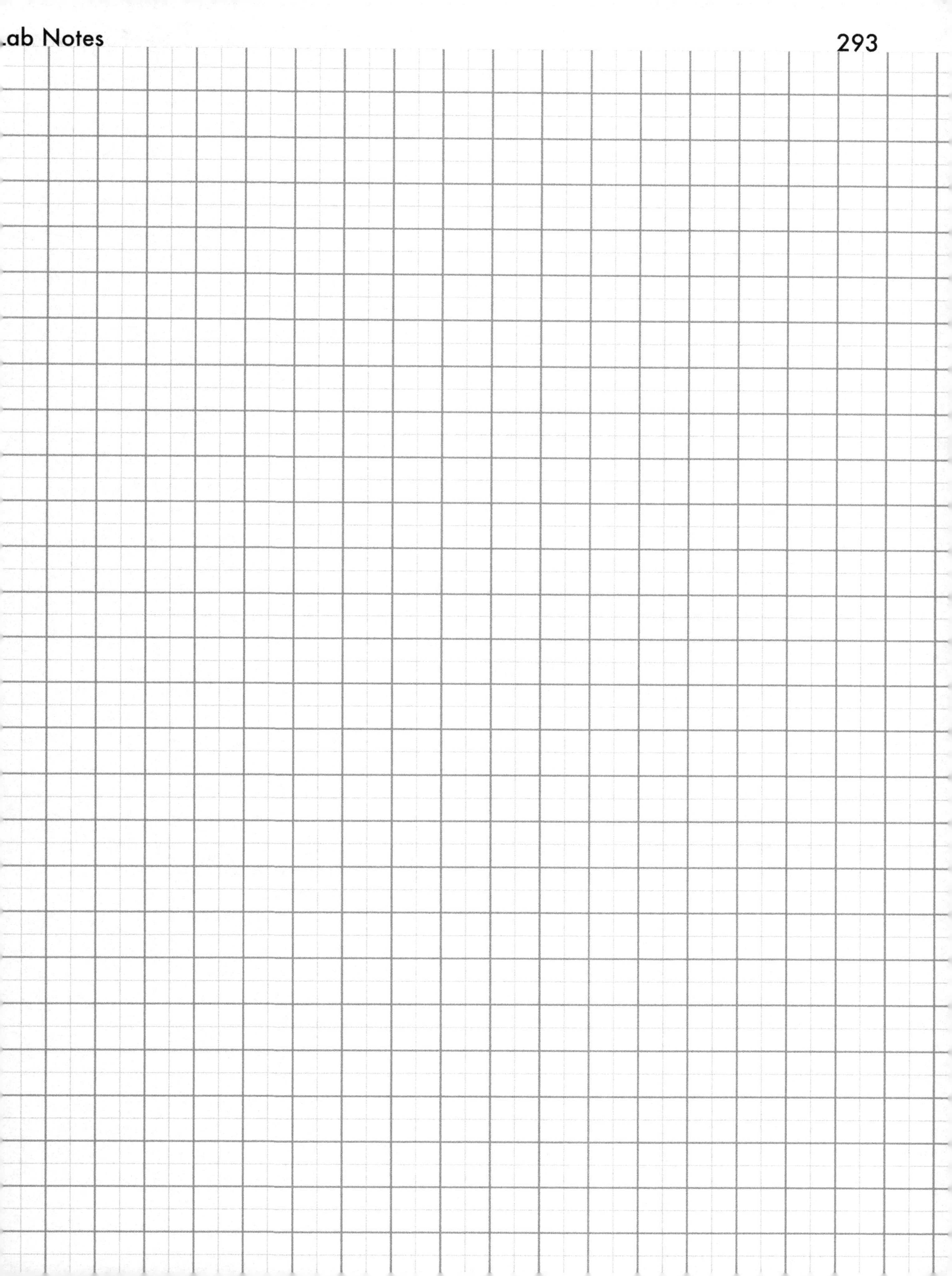

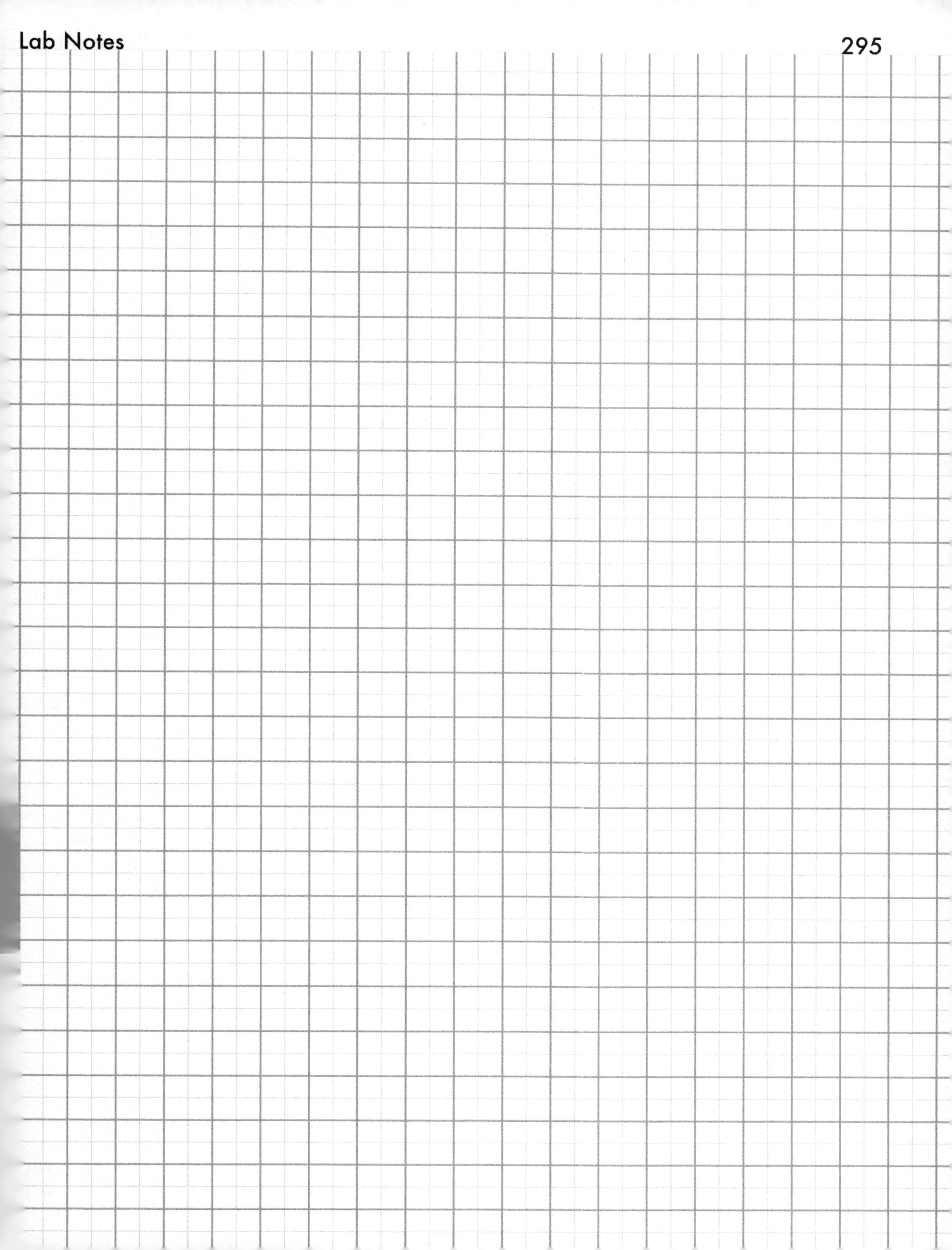

Worksheet 1: Radial Net Forces and Circular Motion

1. A bowling ball rolls down the hallway.

   a. To curve the ball turn in a smooth circular turn to the right, draw a picture to indicate how you would push on the ball to make it turn.

   b. While you are curving the ball's path, are the forces on the ball balanced? Draw a force diagram for the ball.

   c. Is the ball accelerating? If so, what is changing about the velocity?

2. An airplane banks and makes a wide circle.

   a. Draw a force diagram for a head-on view of the banking plane.

   b. Name the force that allows the plane to travel in a circle.

3. A car enters a circular turn.

   a. Name the force (the interaction between objects) that allows the car to travel in a circle. In what direction does this force push on the car? Draw a force diagram for the car as it approaches head-on.

   b. Describe the motion of the car if the force you described in part "a" suddenly vanished.

   c. If the 35 meter radius turn is level, the car has a mass of 1200 kg, and the coefficient of friction between the tires and the road is .85, what is the maximum speed that a car can travel through the turn?

4. The international space station orbits earth once every 90 minutes.

   a. Name the force that allows the ISS to orbit earth.

   b. Explain why the space station doesn't crash to earth due to the force on it.

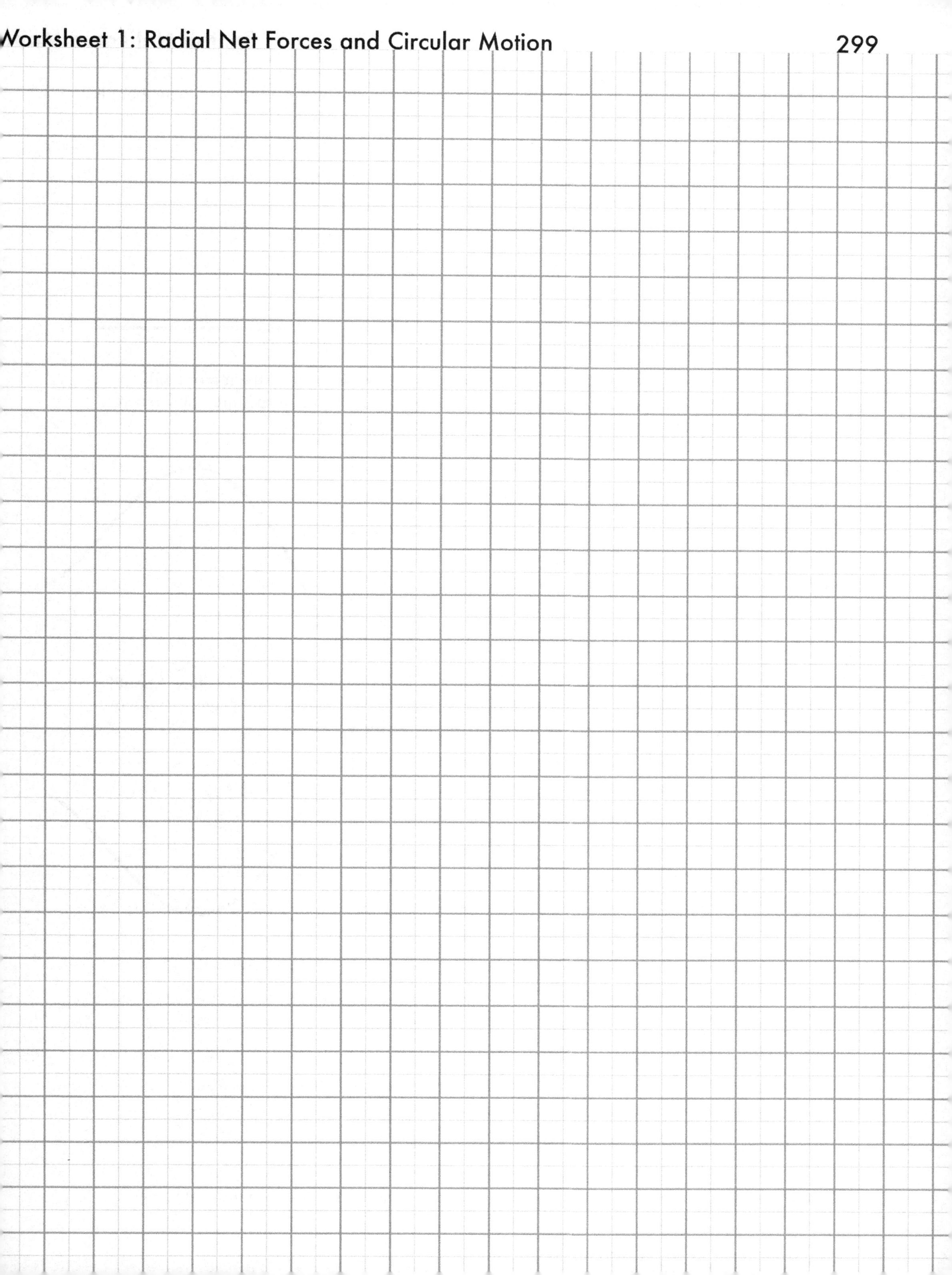

5. a. Draw a force diagram (side view) for a rollercoaster on level track. Should the forces perpendicular to the track be balanced? If the forces are unbalanced, explain why there is a net force and the direction of the net force.

b. Draw a force diagram (side view) for a rollercoaster traveling over the top of a hill. Should the forces perpendicular to the track be balanced? If the forces are unbalanced, explain why there is a net force and the direction of the net force.

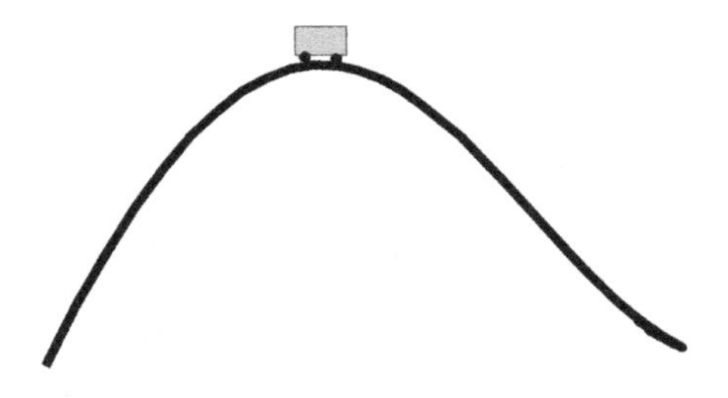

c. Draw a force diagram (side view) for a rollercoaster traveling through a valley. Should the forces perpendicular to the track be balanced? If the forces are unbalanced, explain why there is a net force and the direction of the net force.

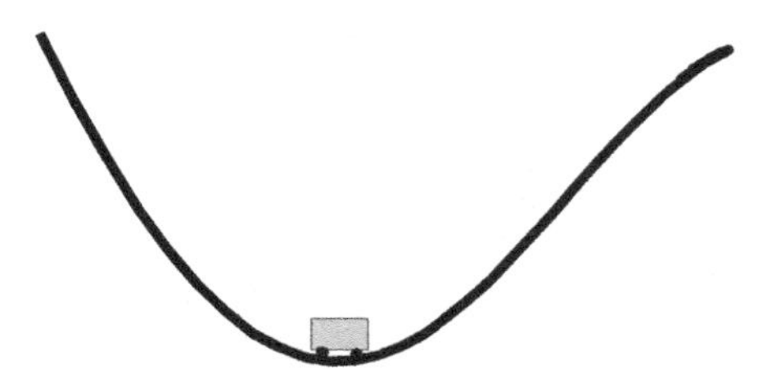

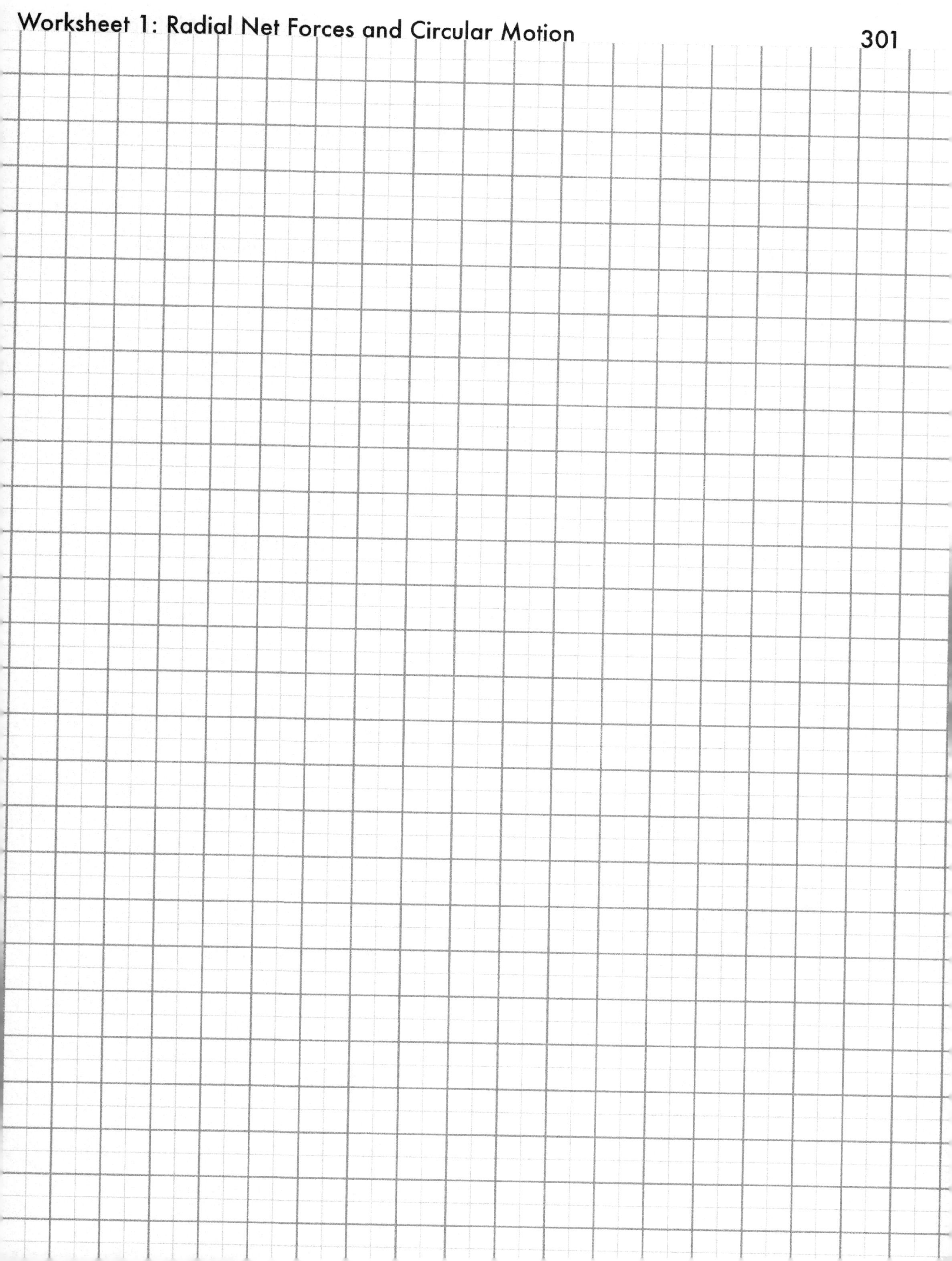

Reading: Circular Motion Problem Solving

When we did Newton's 2nd law, we established: sum of forces = net force = ma

Now, for circular motion: sum of radial forces = centripetal force = $\frac{mv^2}{r}$

Note that "Centripetal force" is just a fancy name for the net force. It is not a kind of interaction (like gravity or normal forces) and is NOT drawn on force diagrams.

EXAMPLES:

1. What frictional force is needed to keep a penny from sliding off a record rotating at 33 $^1/_3$ revolutions per minute when it is placed 10 cm from the center of the record. (mass of penny = 2.5 grams)

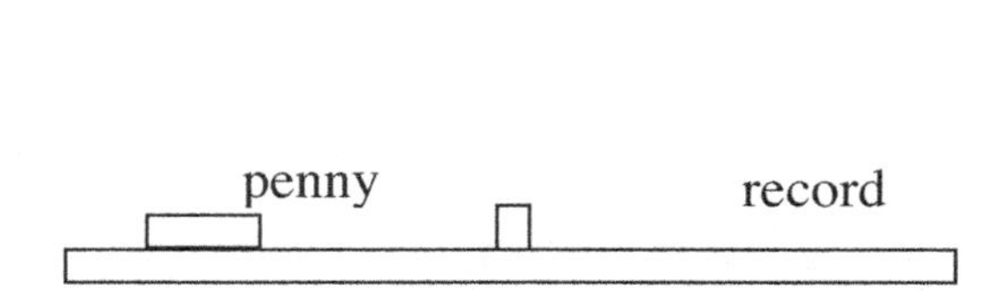

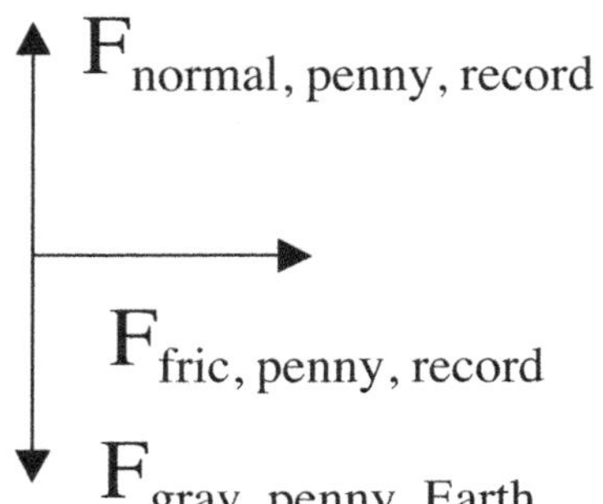

Net radial force = $F_{fric} = (mv^2)/r = [(0.0025kg)(2\pi\ 0.1\ m/1.8\ sec)^2] / 0.1\ m$

2. A ferris wheel with a 20 m radius and tangential speed of 4 m/s has all 70 kg of you riding it. How big is the normal force exerted on you at **a**) the top **b**) the bottom?

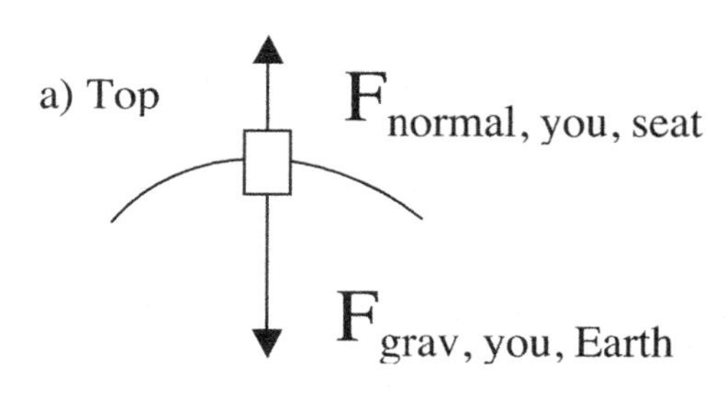

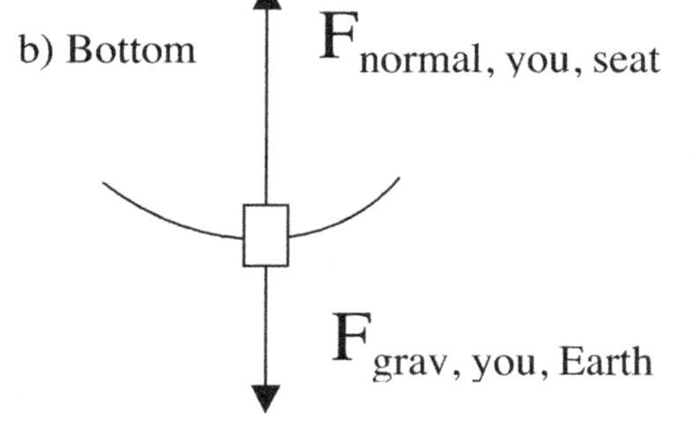

$F_g - F_N = (mv^2)/r$

$F_N = F_g - (mv^2)/r$

$F_N - F_g = (mv^2)/r$

$F_N = F_g + (mv^2)/r$

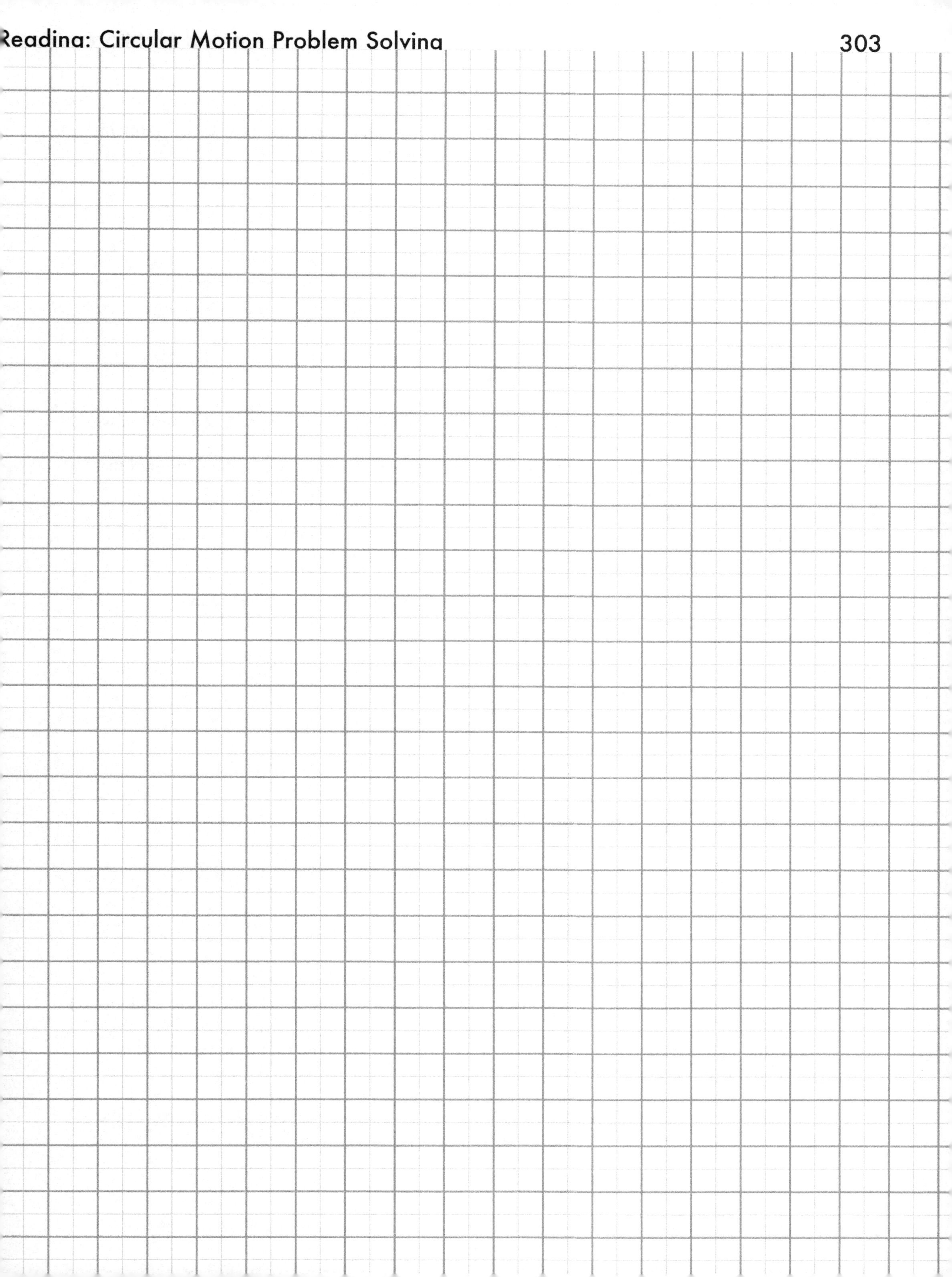

Worksheet 2: Radial Net Force

1. a. A car travels through a valley at constant speed, though not at constant velocity. Explain how this is possible.

   b. Construct a qualitative motion map for the car.

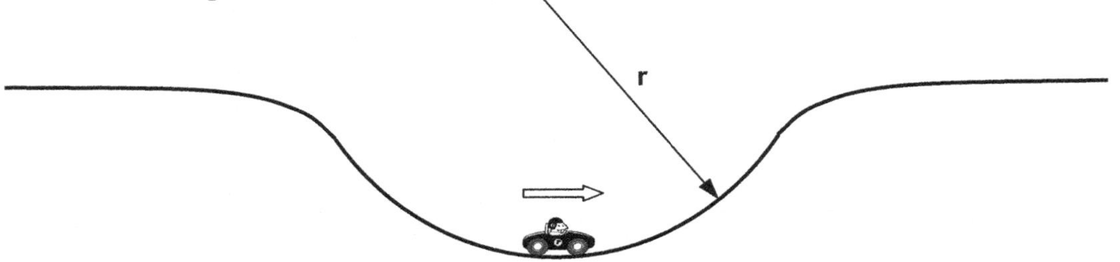

   c. Is the car accelerating? What direction is the car's acceleration? (Explain how you know.)

   d. Construct a **qualitative** force diagram for the car at the moment it is at the bottom of the valley. Are the forces balanced? Justify the relative sizes of the forces.

   e. If the car's speed is 25 m/s, its mass is 1200 kg and the radius of valley (r) is 25 meters, determine the magnitude of the centripetal force acting on the car.

   f. Construct a **quantitative** force diagram for the car at the bottom of the valley.

2. A car travels over a hill at constant speed.
   a. Construct a qualitative motion map for the car.

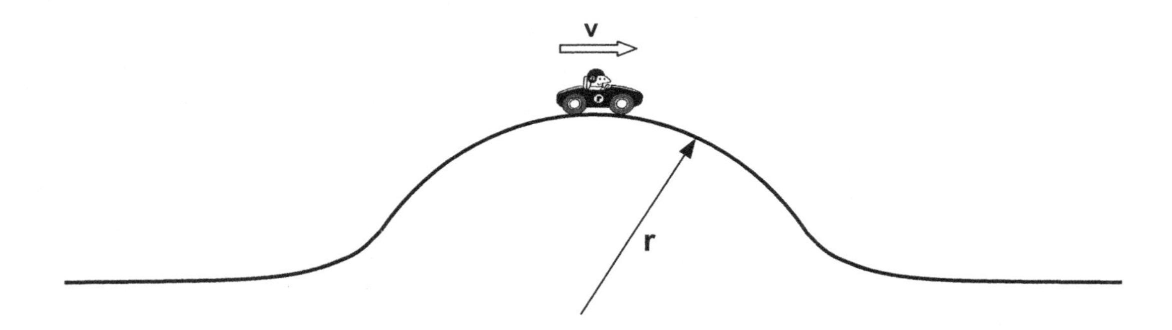

   b. Is the car accelerating? What direction is the car's acceleration? (Explain how you know.)

   c. If the speed of the car is 43 km/h, its mass is 1200 kg and the radius of the hill (r) is 25m, determine the magnitude of the centripetal force acting on the car.

   d. Construct a **quantitative** force diagram for the car at the moment it is at the top of the hill. Are the forces balanced? Justify the relative sizes of the forces.

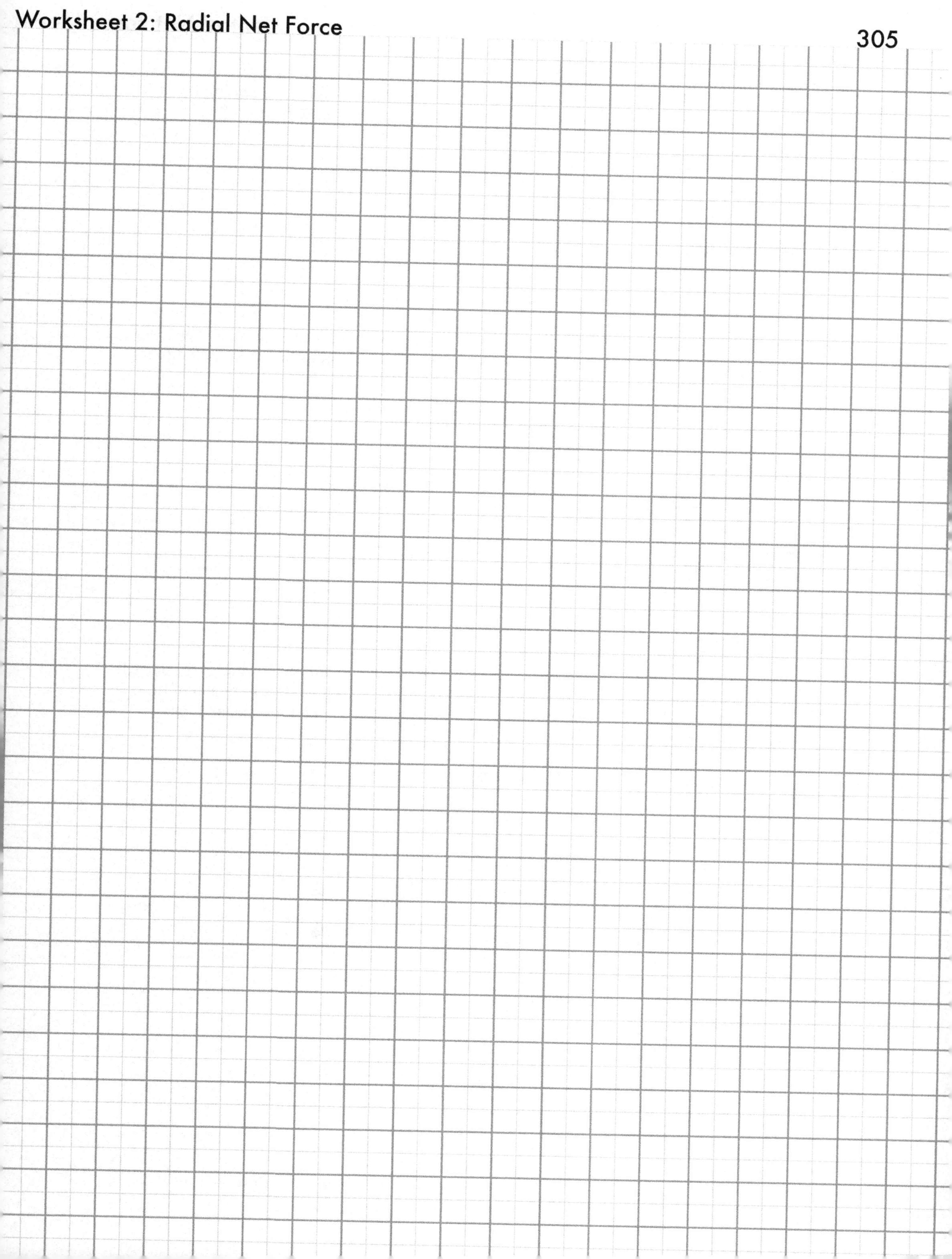

3. Roads are banked (tilted) in curves in order to make turning a car at high speeds safer.
   a. For the situation of an unbanked road, draw a force diagram for a car coming toward you as it is turning. Which force provides the force needed to make the turn?

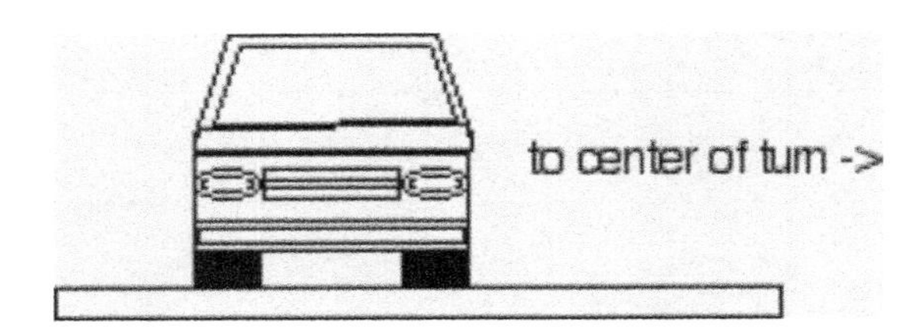

   b. For the situation of a banked road, draw a force diagram for a car coming toward you as it is turning. Identify all of the forces and components of forces that contribute to the force needed to make the turn.

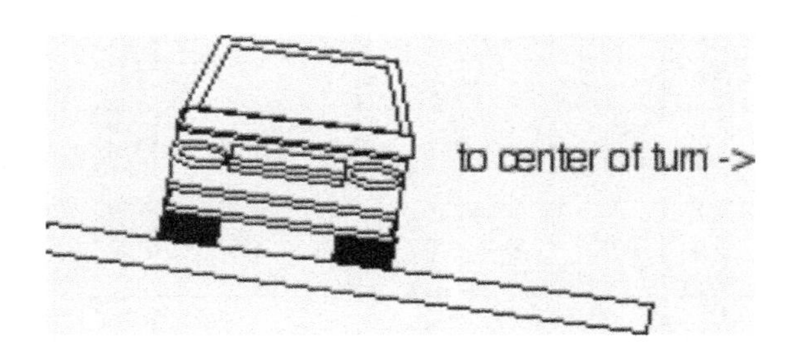

4. A yo-yo pro swings the yo-yo "around the world." Draw force diagrams for the yo-yo at each of the four positions shown: top, descending side, bottom, ascending side. For each of the positions, indicate which force or combination of forces provides the force needed for circular motion.

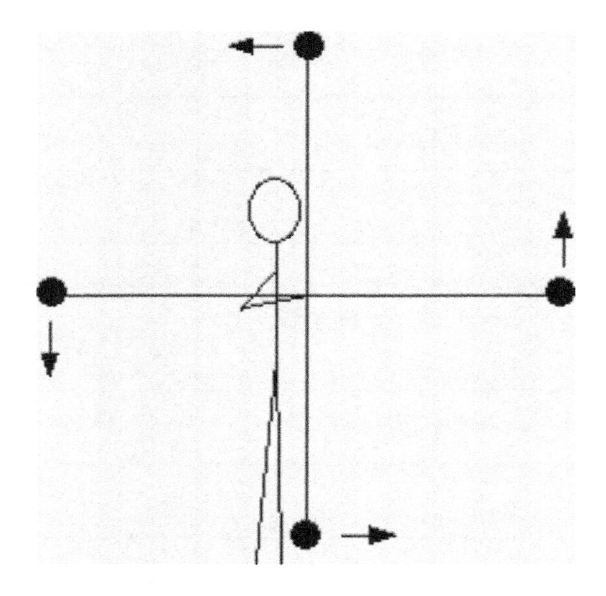

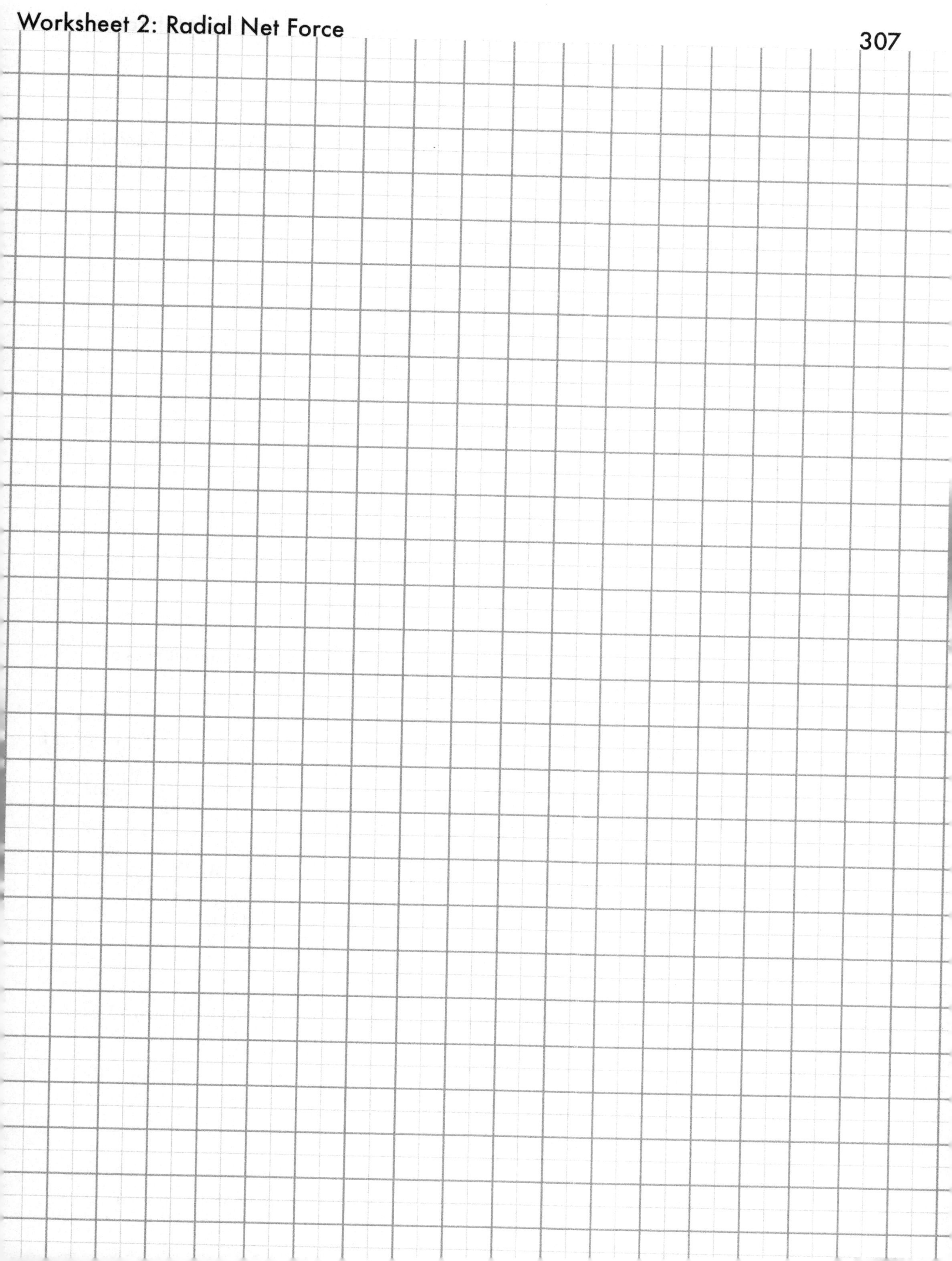

Worksheet 3: Circular Motion Examples

1. A woman flying aerobatics executes a maneuver as illustrated below. Construct a **quantitative** force diagram of all relevant forces acting on the woman flying the airplane when upside-down at the top of the loop.

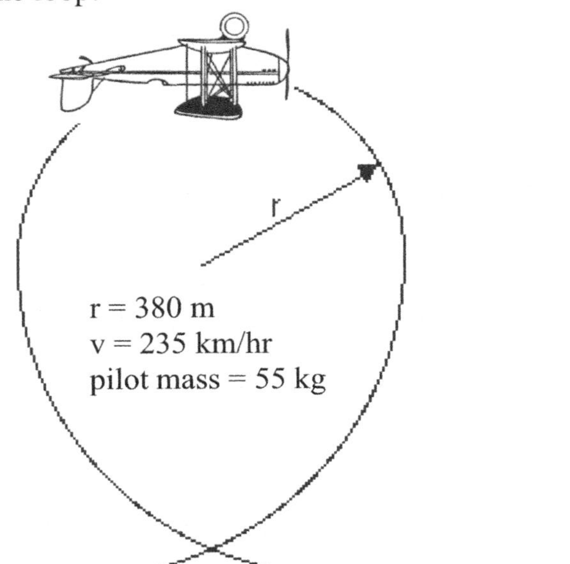

2. Six children run on a track with equal speeds. Their masses are expressed in multiples of mass "M" and their path radii are expressed in multiples of radius "R."

   a. Rank the centripetal acceleration of the lettered children from largest to smallest. (Ties are possible.)

   largest -> ____ ____ ____ ____ ____ ____ <-smallest
   Explain how you determined your ranking:

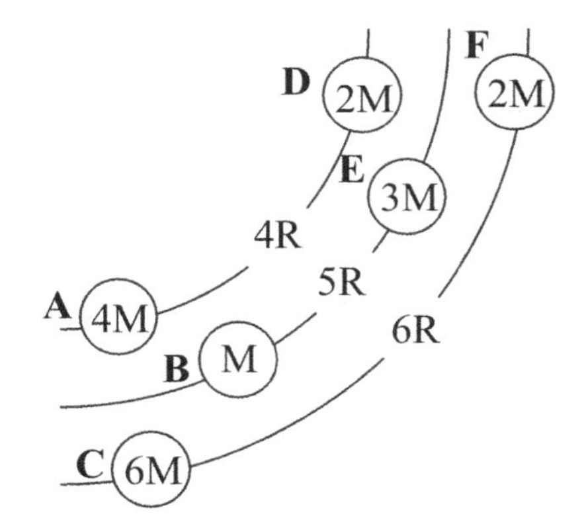

   b. Rank the centripetal force needed for each child to remain in circular motion. (Ties are possible.)

   largest -> ____ ____ ____ ____ ____ ____ <-smallest
   Explain how you determined your ranking:

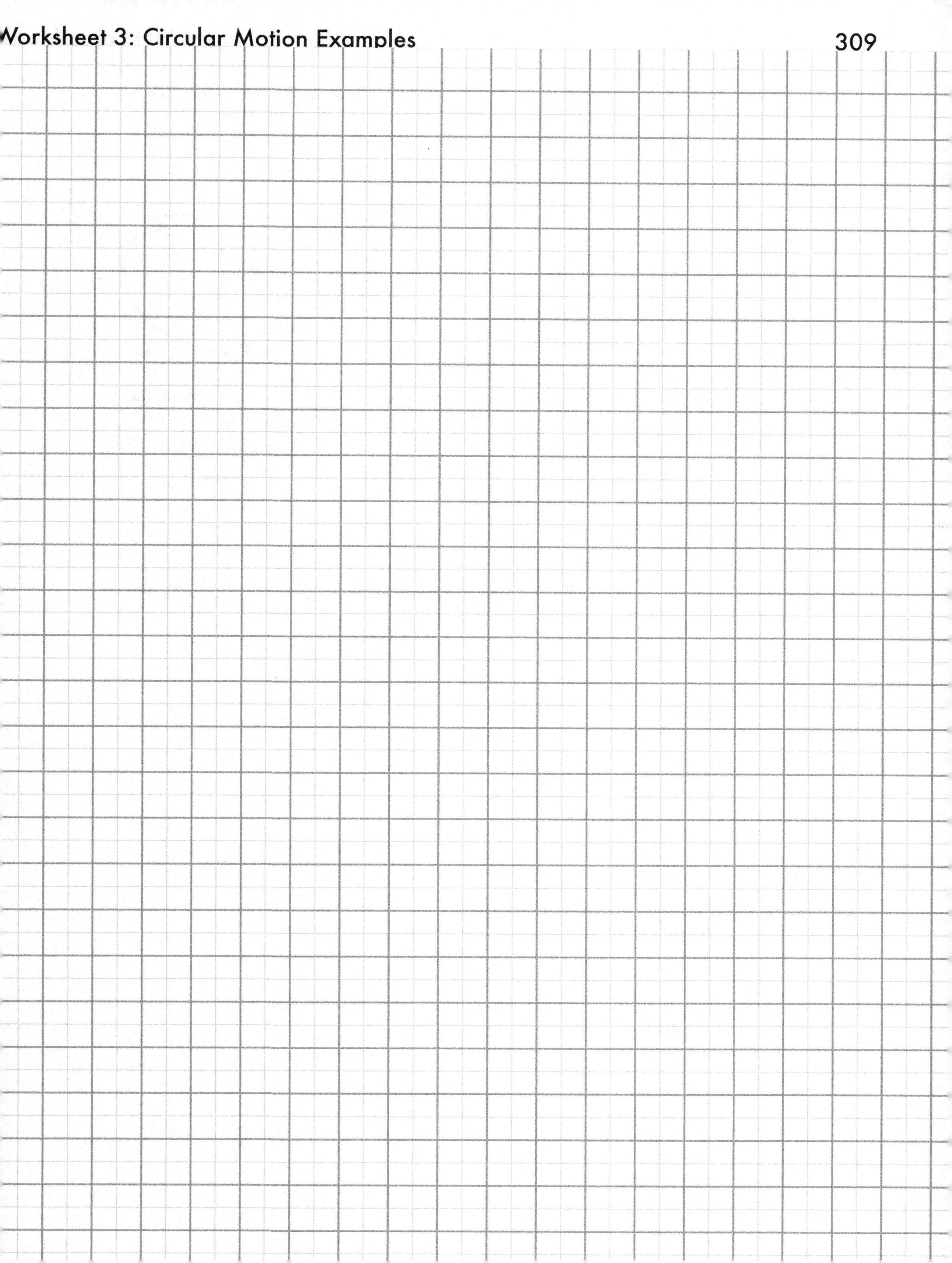

3. Rollercoasters use a hill for riders to gain speed followed by an upside down loop. The loops are designed with large radius bottoms and small radius tops, and such a shape is called a clothoid. Answer the following questions in order to find out why the clothoid is used.

The speed of the rollercoaster is 22 m/s at the bottom of the loop and 8 m/s at the top of the loop.

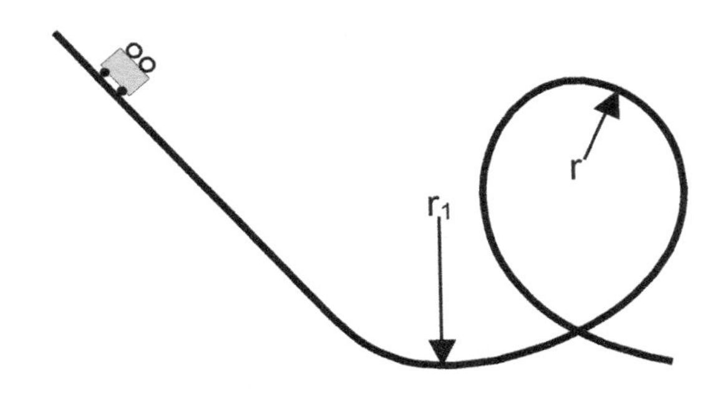

a. Use quantitative force diagrams to determine the size of the force on the rider by the seat at the top and bottom of the loop.

b. Now suppose the rollercoaster had been designed with the small 5 meter radius at the bottom and the large 10 meter radius at the top. Use quantitative force diagrams to determine the size of the force on the rider by the seat at the top and bottom of the loop.

c. Why is the clothoid shape used in rollercoasters?

4. 80 kg Tarzan grabs a vine to swing to another tree.

a. As Tarzan swings from point A to point B, describe qualitatively how the tension in the vine changes and why.

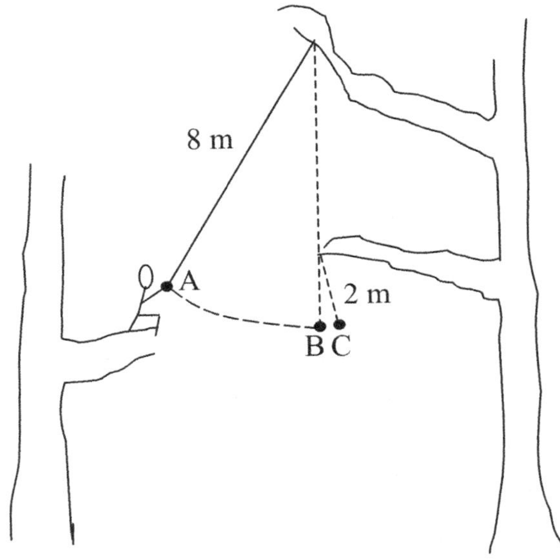

b. At point B he is swinging at 7 m/s and the vine is 8 meters long. How hard does he have to hang on to the vine to keep from slipping off?

c. A moment later, at point C, the vine catches on a branch, reducing the radius of the swing to 2 m. If Tarzan is still traveling at 7 m/s, how hard does he now have to hold on to the vine?

d. If Tarzan slips off at point C what will be the path he takes? (Sketch the path on the diagram.) How does this path differ from circular motion?

5. Six children of equal masses run on a track. Their speeds are expressed in multiples of velocity "V" and their path radii are expressed in multiples of radius "R."

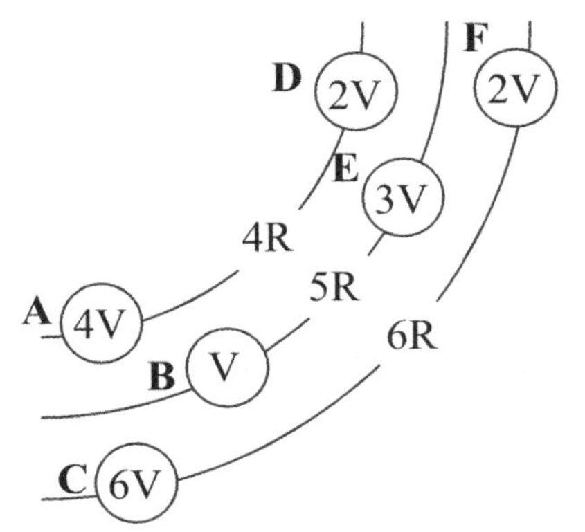

a. Rank the centripetal acceleration of the lettered children from largest to smallest. (Ties are possible.)

largest -> ____ ____ ____ ____ ____ ____ <-smallest
Explain how you determined your ranking:

b. Rank the centripetal force needed for each child to remain in circular motion. (Ties are possible.)

largest -> ____ ____ ____ ____ ____ ____ <-smallest
Explain how you determined your ranking:

6. An amusement park ride operates as follows: riders enter the cylindrical structure when it is stationary with the floor at the point marked "a". They then stand against the wall as the cylinder then begins to rotate. When it is up to speed, the floor is lowered to the position marked "b", leaving the riders "suspended" against the wall high above the floor.

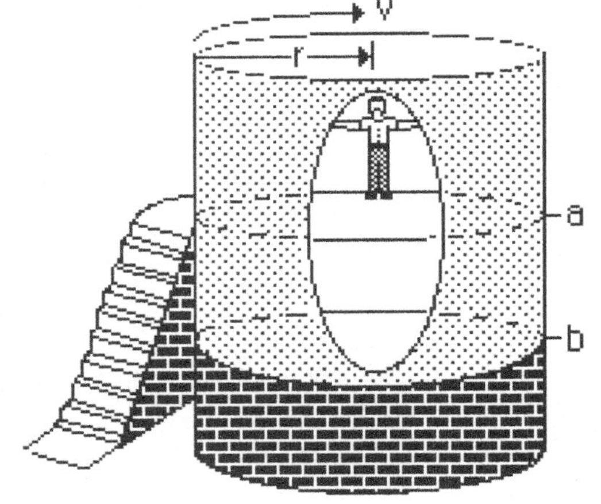

$r = 1.5\,m$
$u_s = 0.50$
$m_b = 73\,kg$

Determine the period of rotation necessary to keep the riders from sliding down the wall when the floor is lowered from point "a" to point "b". (Show all of your work and explain your reasoning.)

Worksheet 4: Orbital Motion

gravitational constant: $G = 6.67 \times 10^{-11} \frac{Nm^2}{kg^2}$

1. Suppose you are at mission control on the moon, in charge of launching a moon-orbiting communications satellite.

   Moon mass = 7.36×10^{22} kg Moon radius = 1.74×10^{6} m

   a. First, how much would a 1500 kg satellite weigh near the surface of the moon? (The gravitational field strength on Earth's moon is 1.6 N/kg.)

   b. The satellite is to have an altitude of 100 km above the moon's surface. What is the radius of the orbit of the satellite?

   c. When the satellite is in orbit, how big will the centripetal force be? Explain.

   d. Find the required orbital velocity for the satellite.

   e. How long will it take the satellite to orbit the moon? (This time is called the orbital period.)

   f. Is this satellite accelerating while in orbit? If so, what is the direction and magnitude of the acceleration?

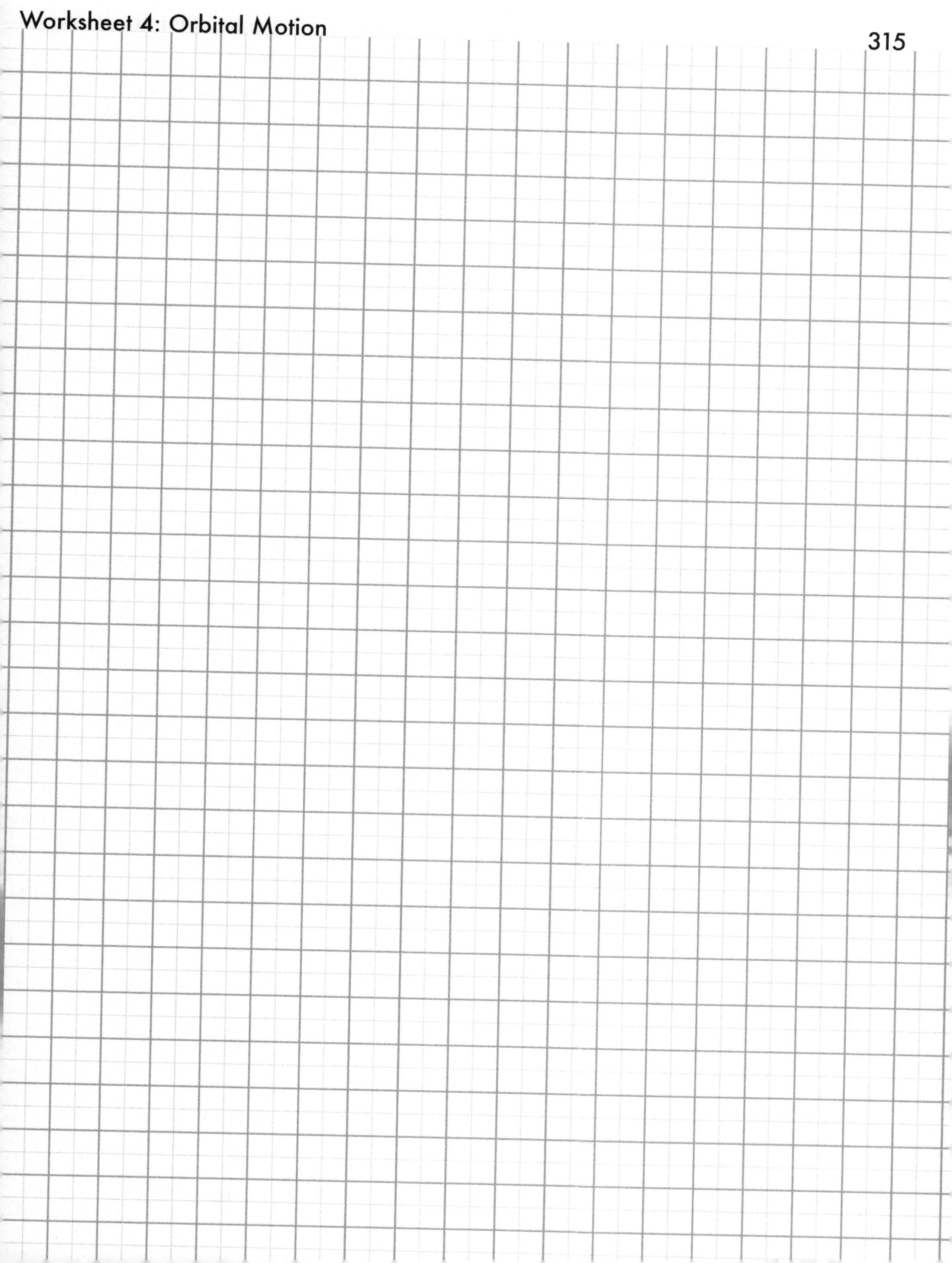

2. a. Why do astronauts float aboard the international space station? What sensation does an astronaut feel while in orbit?

   b. Are astronauts in orbit really "weightless"? What might be a better description?

3. The space shuttle aims for an orbit about 250 km above the surface of the earth. In orbit, the mass of the space shuttle is about 95,000 kg.

   Earth mass = 5.98×10^{24} kg   Earth radius = 6.38×10^{3} km .

   a. Calculate the orbital speed of the space shuttle.

   b. Calculate the orbital period of the space shuttle.

Earth mass = 5.98×10^{24} kg Earth radius = 6.38×10^{3} km

4. Back in Galileo's day, one of the objections to the heliocentric model of the solar system is that if the earth is spinning, we should all be "thrown off the earth." Actually, you do weigh a bit less on the equator than you would at the poles. Calculate how much. (Hint: Construct force diagrams for a 100 kg person standing on a bathroom scale at the equator and at the pole, and do the F_{net} calculations.

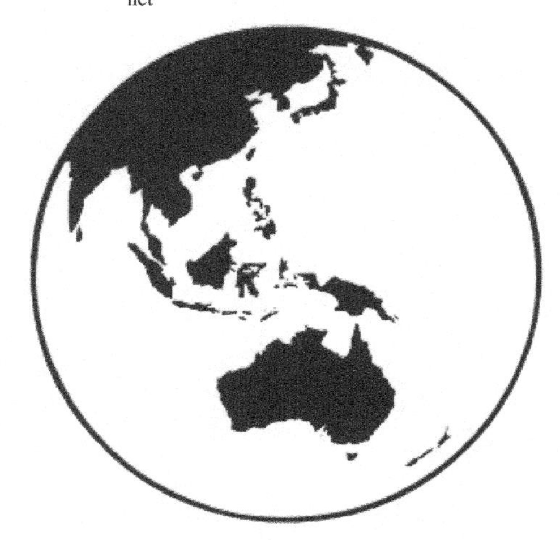

5. The earth's orbit around the sun is very nearly circular, with an average radius of 1.5×10^{8} km.

   a. Determine the average speed of the earth in its orbit around the sun.

   b. What is the magnitude of the earth's average acceleration in its orbit around the sun?

   c. Determine the gravitational force on the earth by the sun. How does the force on the earth by the sun compare to the force on the sun by the earth? Explain.

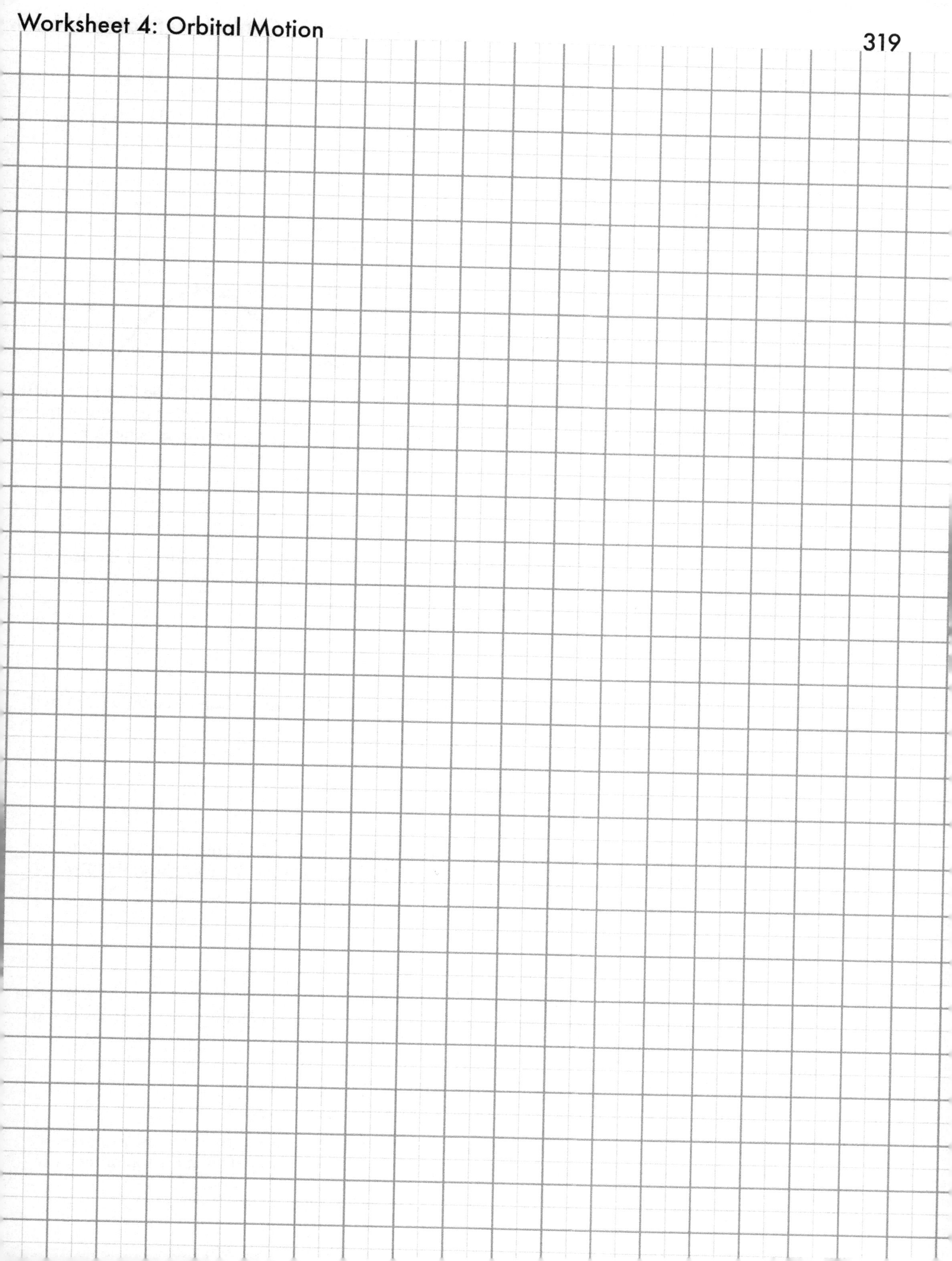

Review Problems

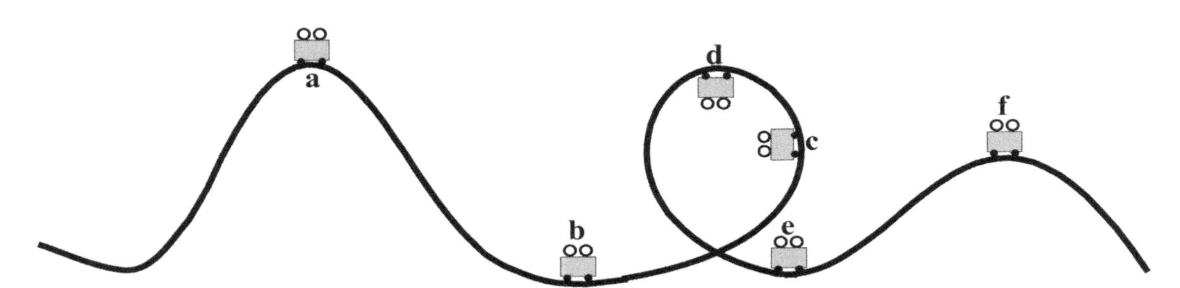

1. At the top of the first hill of the rollercoaster, point "a," a 60 kg passenger feels as if she "weighs" 500 N. Explain which force provides the sensation of weight. How fast is the rollercoaster going over the 3.0 m radius hilltop to create this sensation? Draw a quantitative force diagram for the situation.

2. At point "b" the rollercoaster has reached a speed of 28 m/s. How large must the radius of the valley be so that a 100 kg rider will experience a normal force of five times their weight (5 G's)? Draw a quantitative force diagram for the situation.

3. At point "c" a 70 kg rider is traveling at 20 m/s in a 7.0-meter radius curve. Draw a quantitative force diagram for the rider.

4. At point "d" a 40 kg child is upside-down at the top of the loop. How fast would the train have to pass through the 4.0-meter radius curve to produce a 200 N downward normal force on the child? Draw a quantitative force diagram for the child.

5. Exiting the loop at valley "e" the 2000 kg rollercoaster exerts a downward normal force on the track of 90,000 N. The track radius is 130 meters. Draw a quantitative force diagram for the rollercoaster train.

6. At the top of hill "f" the rollercoaster crests the 5.0-meter radius curve at 6.0 m/s. Draw a quantitative force diagram for a 60 kg passenger. How many G's would any passenger feel at the top of the hill?

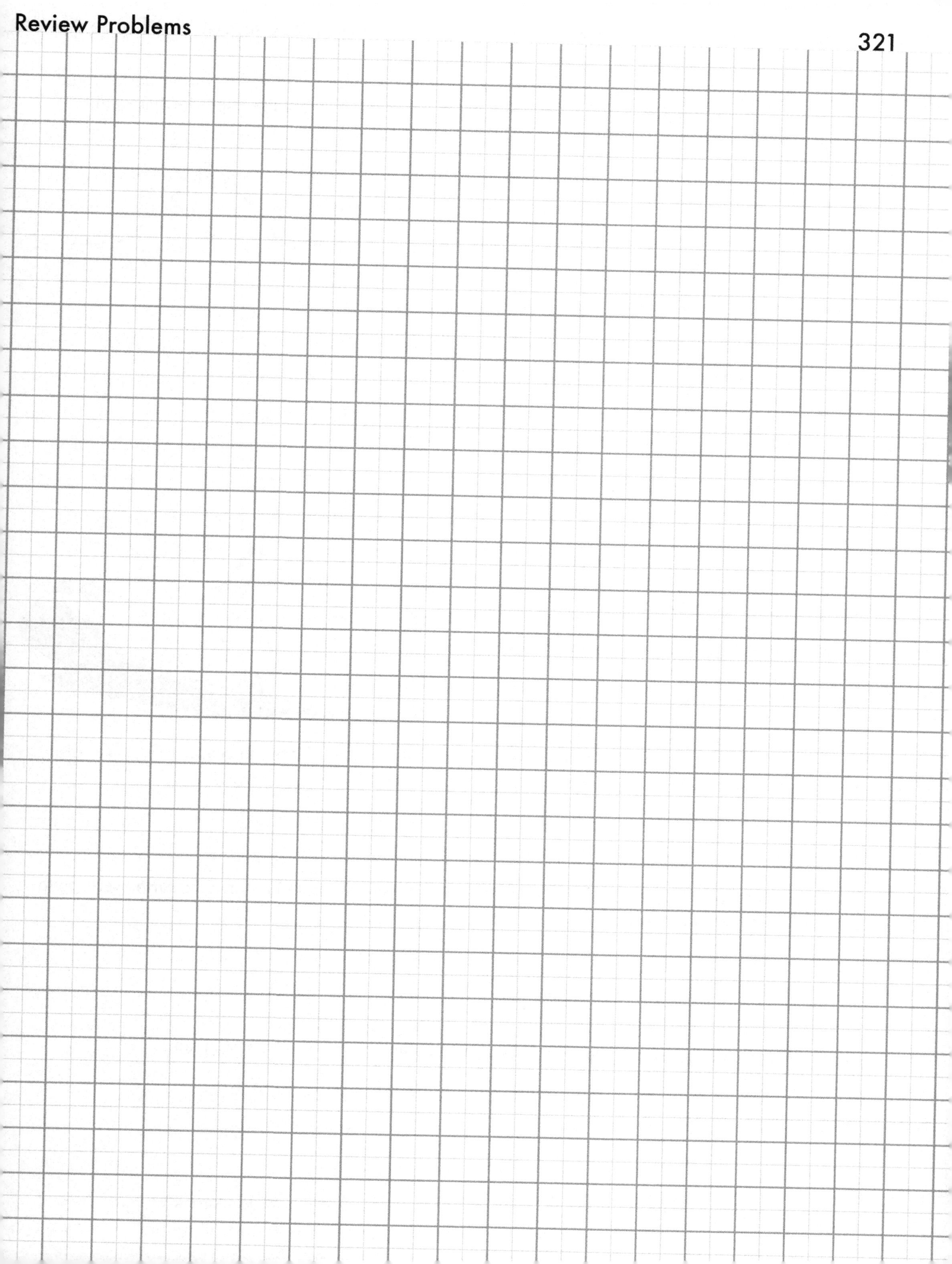

7. A car travels over a hill at constant speed. If the radius of the hill is 30 meters, at what speed would the centripetal force equal the force of gravity? If the car were to exceed this speed, what would happen to the car?

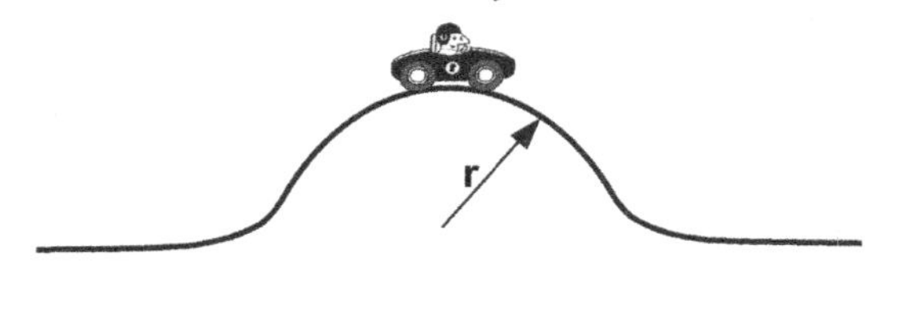

8. Here is the data for the space shuttle in its orbit around earth:
Shuttle mass in orbit = 94,802 kg
mass of the earth = 6×10^{24} kg
shuttle orbital height above the earth = 2.76×10^{5}m
radius of the earth = 6.38×10^{6} m
shuttle tangential velocity when in orbit = 7823 m/sec

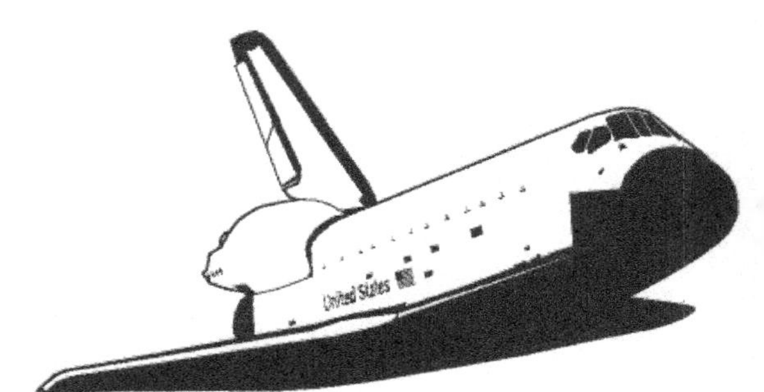

a. Use the principles of circular motion to find the centripetal force necessary to keep the shuttle in its circular orbit around earth.

b. Use Newton's Law of Universal Gravitation to find the gravitational force the earth exerts on the shuttle when the shuttle is in orbit.

c. How do the values calculated in parts *a* and *b* compare to one another? Explain.

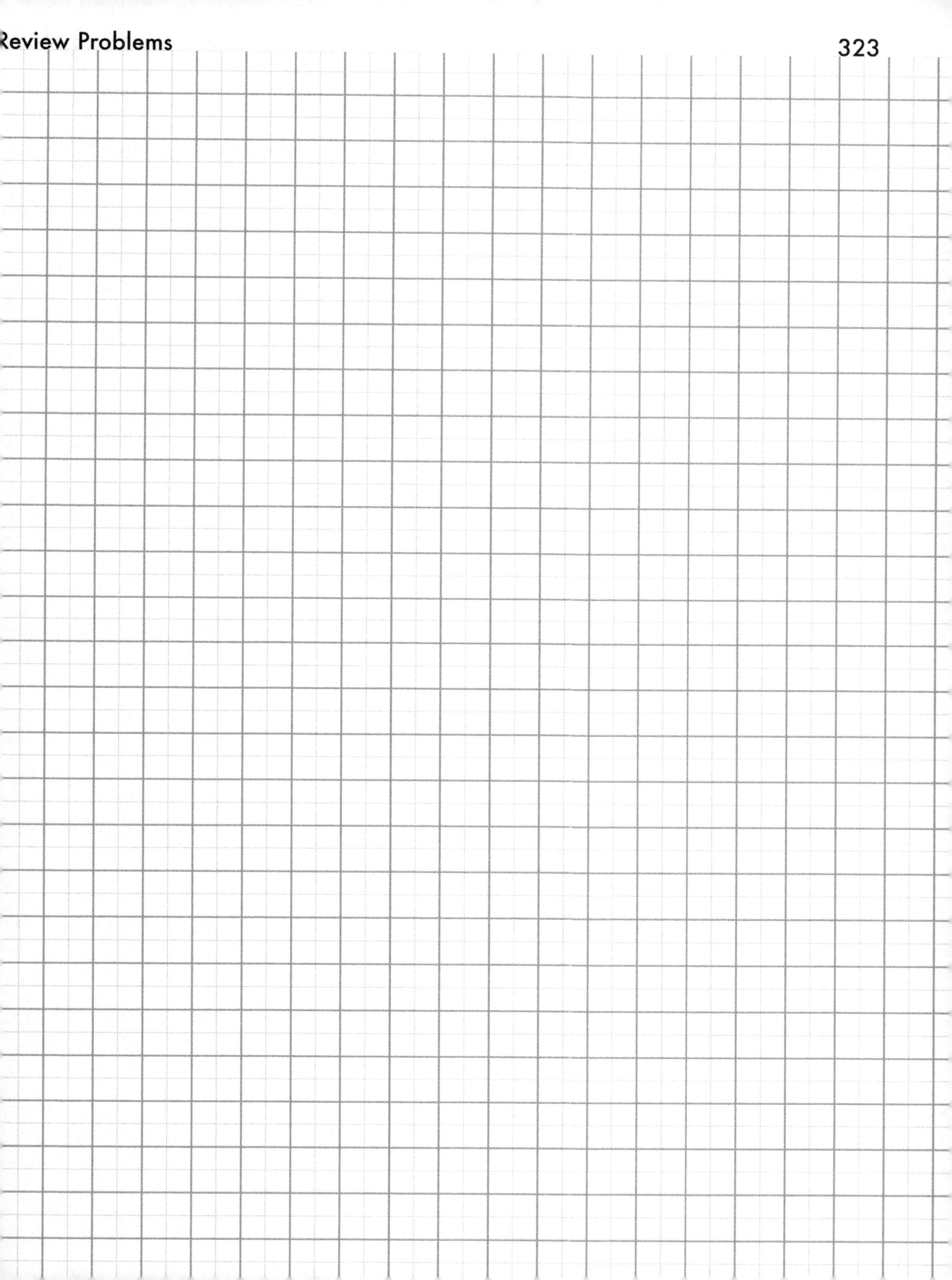

Model Summary

This is a place to summarize different representations of the Central Net Force Model

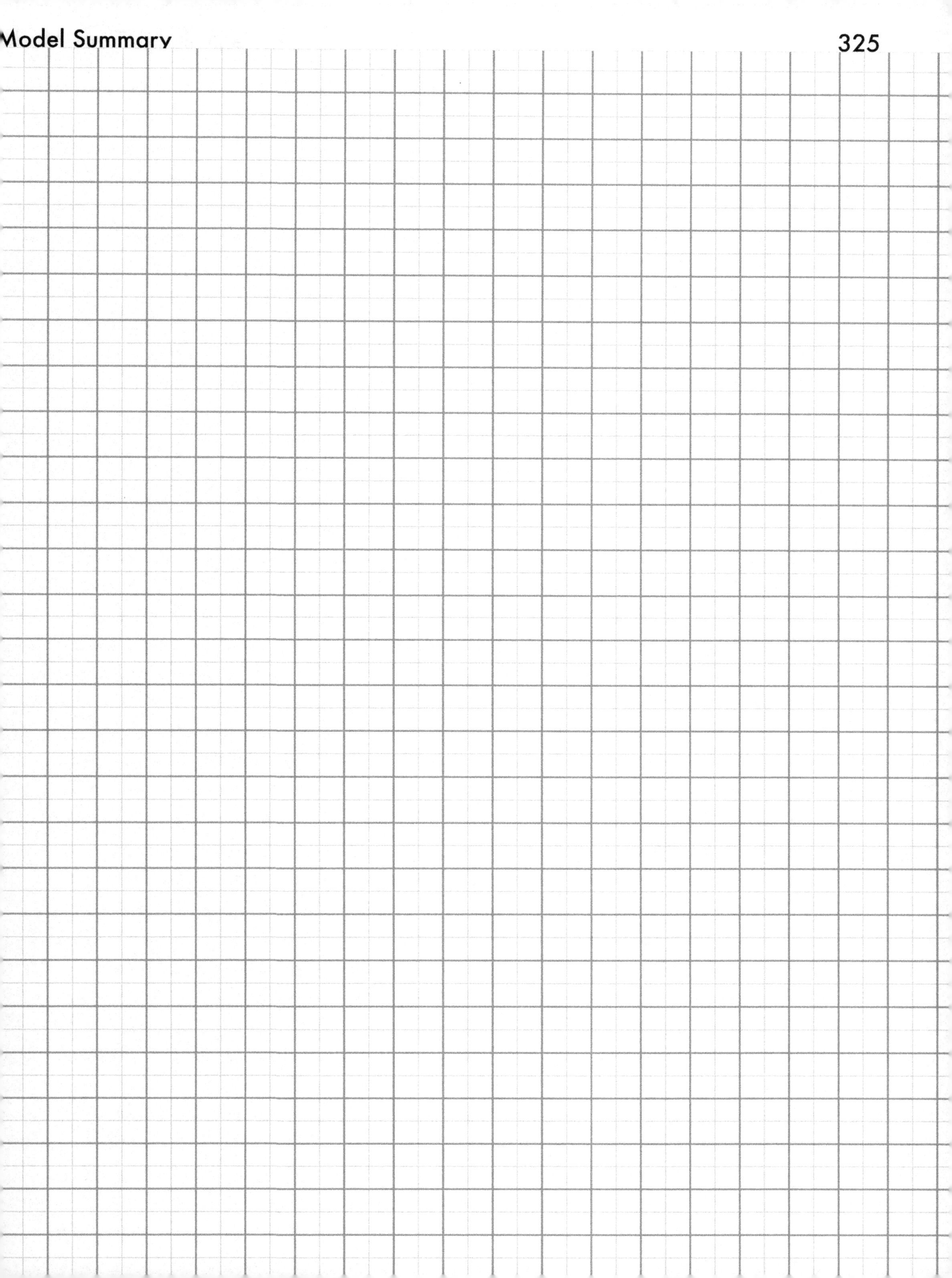

Chapter 8: Energy Storage and Transfer Model

:hapter Sections

chapter 8 online help

Lab Notes

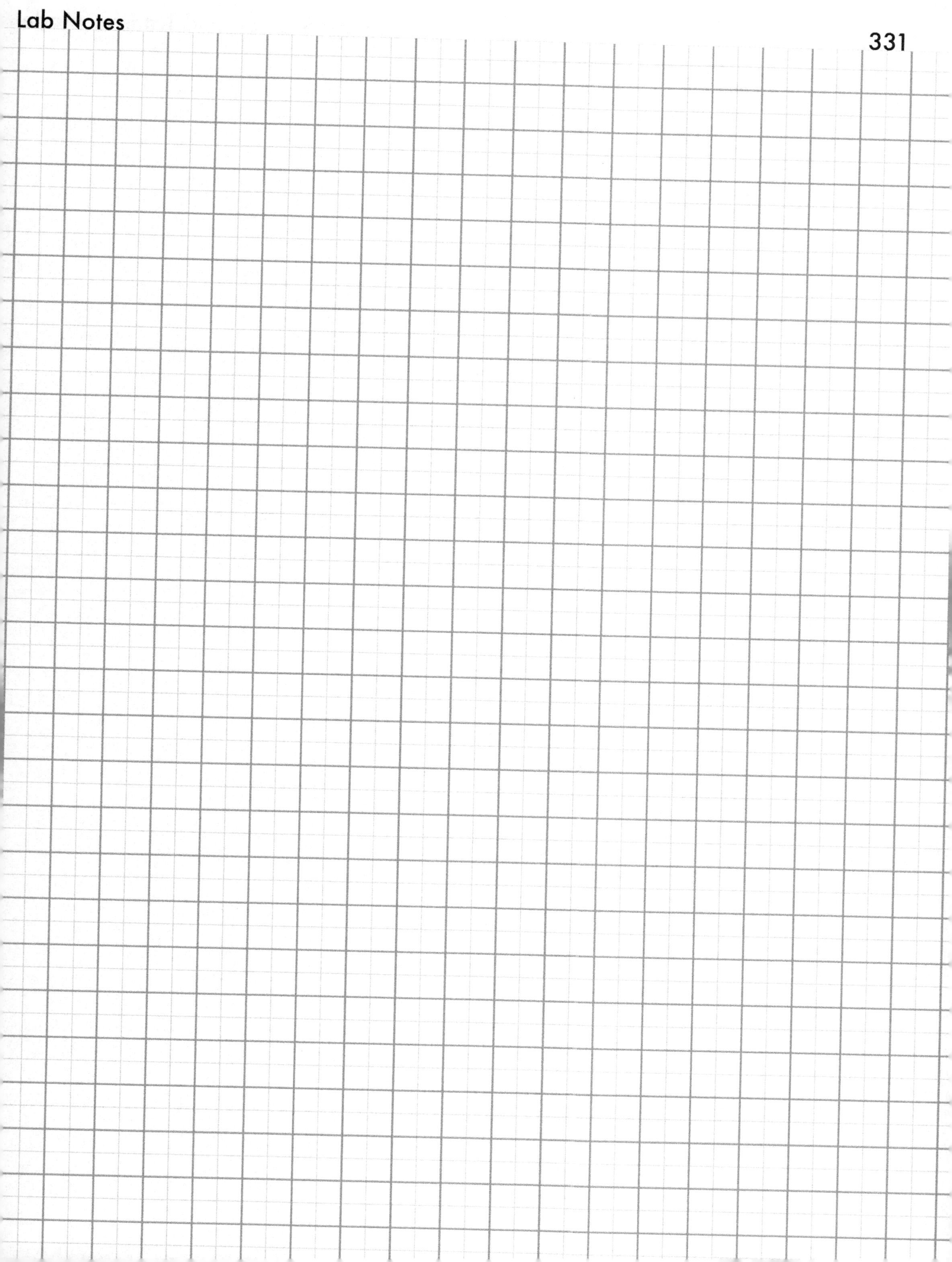

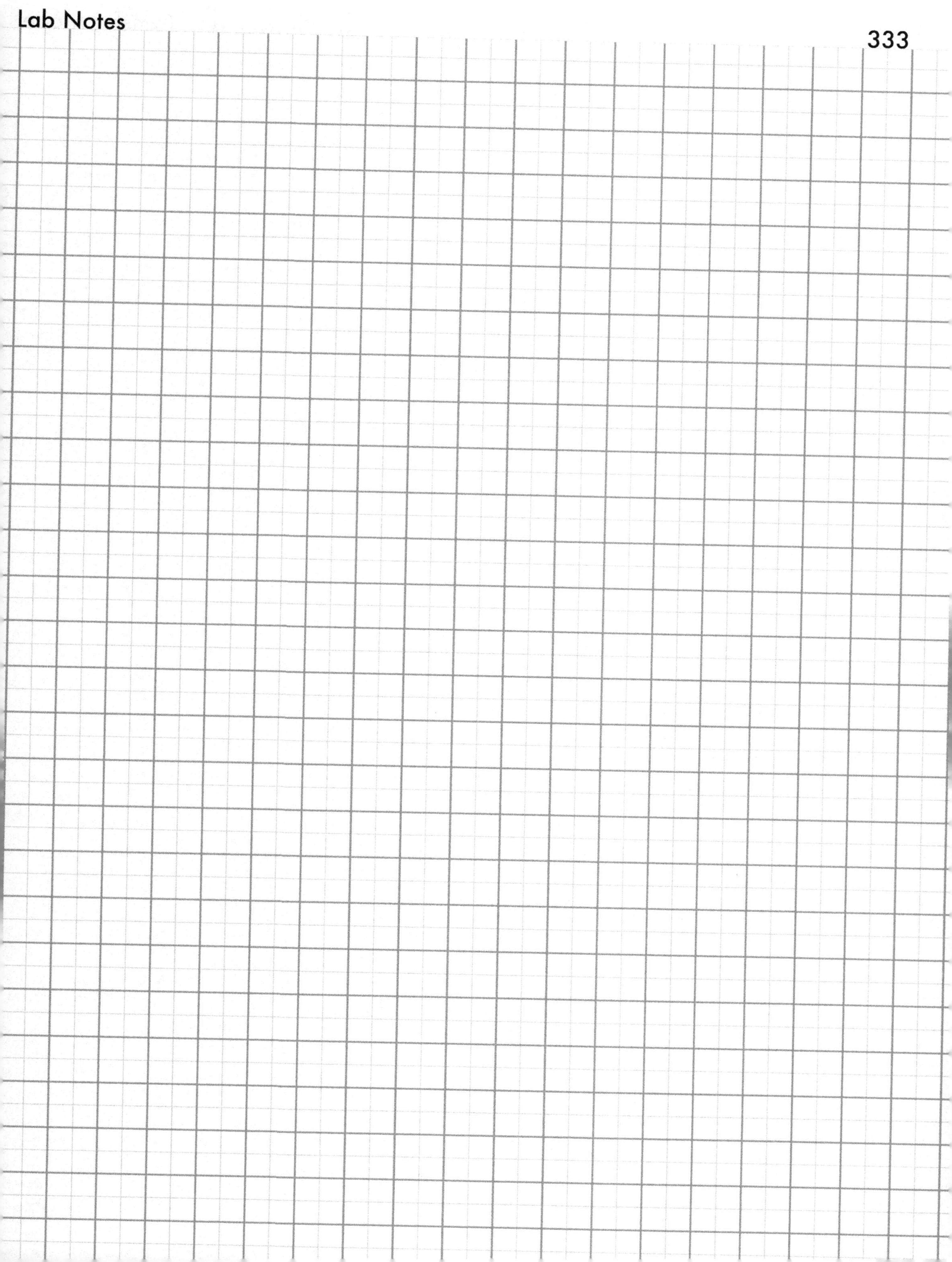

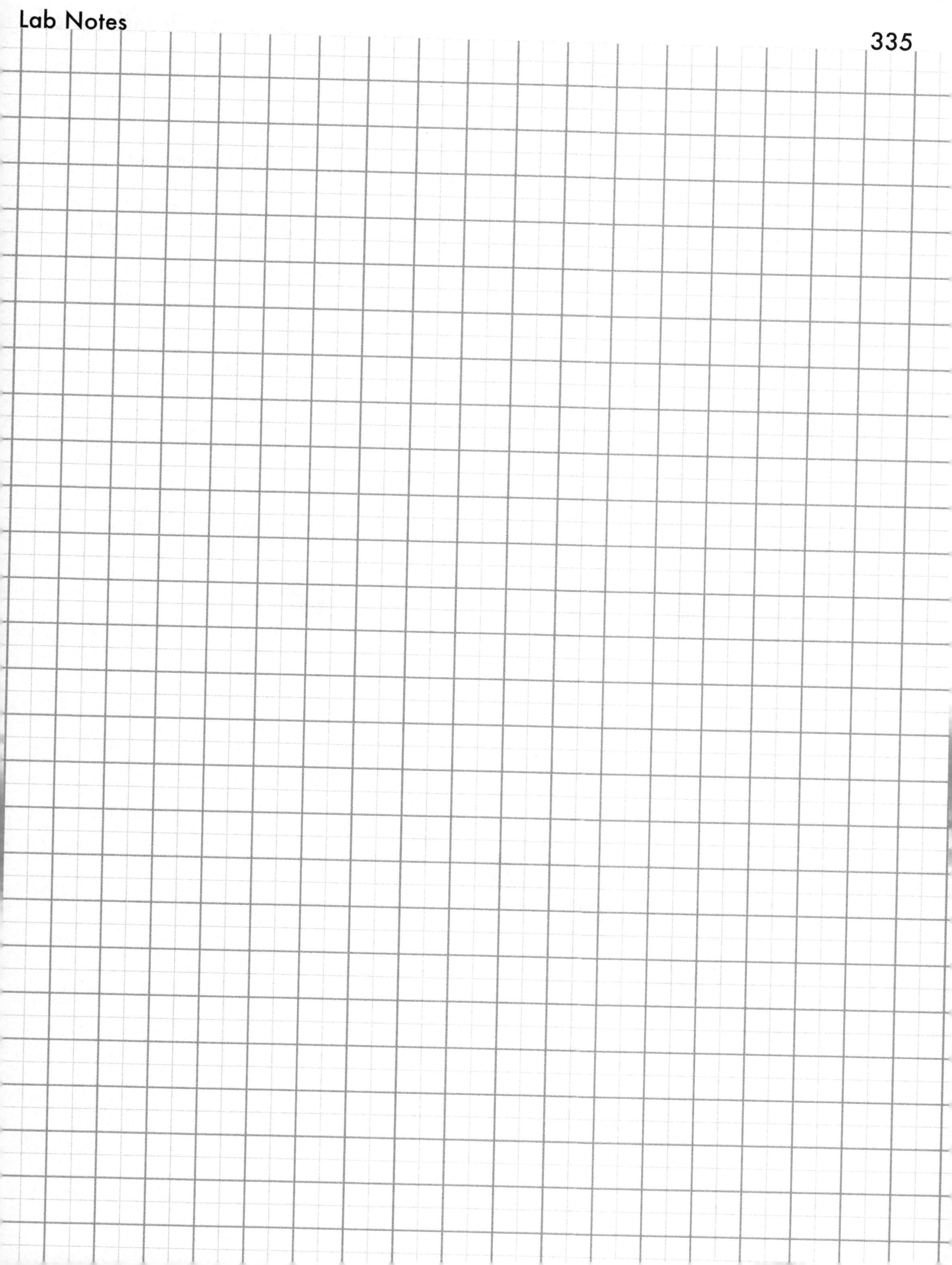

Worksheet 1a: Qualitative Analysis - Pie Charts

Use pie charts to analyze the energy changes in each situation given.

- Designate your choice of system with a dotted line. Choose your system so that the energies involved are internal (within the system).
- Carefully label the pies to correspond with the positions of the objects given. (A, B,C, etc.)
- The pies should be accurately divided and labeled with the energy storage mechanisms involved.
- Remember the 3 energy questions in deciding about the energy changes:
  1. Where does the energy come from? (What's the source of the energy?)
  2. What does the energy do?
  3. Where does the energy go?

1. A wind-up toy is fully wound and at rest.

2. A wind-up toy is wound up and moving across level ground. The toy is speeding up.

3. The toy is wound up and is moving at a constant speed up an incline.

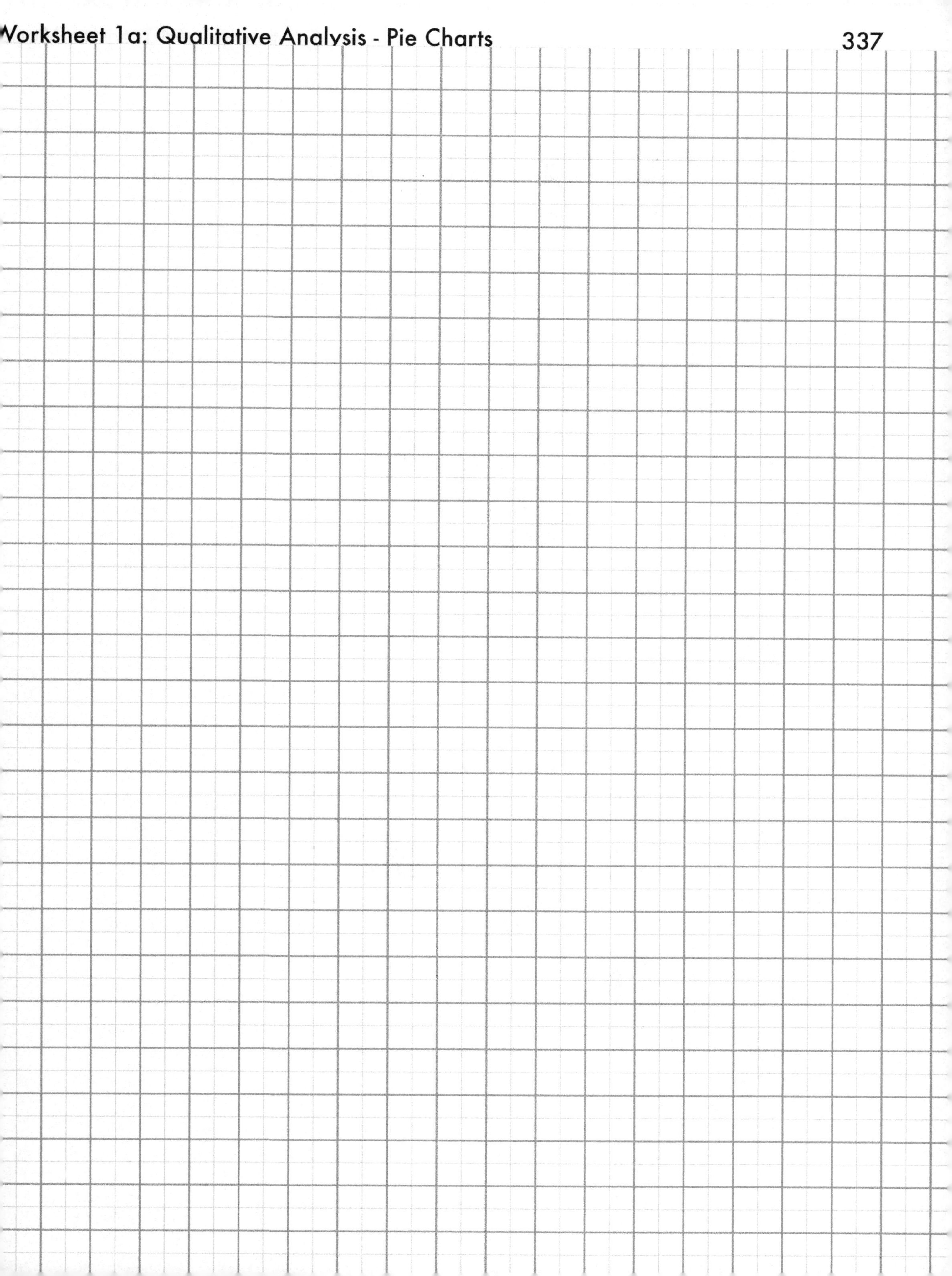

4. The toy is wound up and moving along at a constant speed.

5. The toy is wound up and slowing down as it moves up an incline.

6. The toy is wound up and speeding up as it moves up an incline.

Worksheet 1b: Qualitative Analysis - Pie Charts

Use pie charts to analyze the energy changes in each situation given.
Designate your choice of system with a dotted line. Choose your system so that the energies involved are internal (within the system).
Carefully label the pies to correspond with the positions of the objects given. (A, B,C, etc.)
The pies should be accurately divided and labeled with the energy storage mechanisms involved.
Remember the 3 energy questions in deciding about the energy changes:
1. Where does the energy come from? (What's the source of the energy?)
2. What does the energy do?
3. Where does the energy go?

1. A ball is held above the ground, and then is dropped so it falls straight down. (Restrict your analysis to the ball being in the air, BEFORE it hits the ground.)

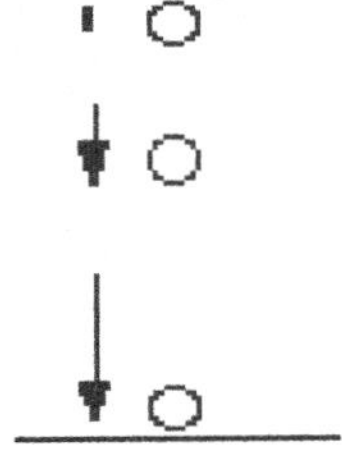

2. A wind-up toy is wound up, then "walks" across a table and comes to a stop.

3. A baseball is thrown up in the air and then falls back down. Place velocity vectors beside each corresponding baseball in the drawing, and draw an energy storage pie for each lettered position.

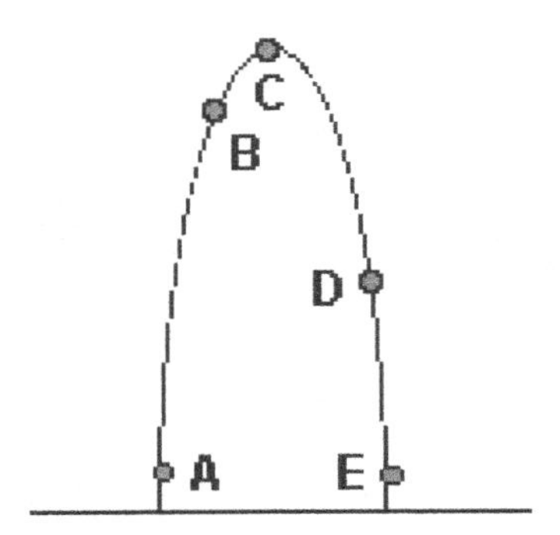

4. An object rests on a coiled spring, and is then launched upwards.

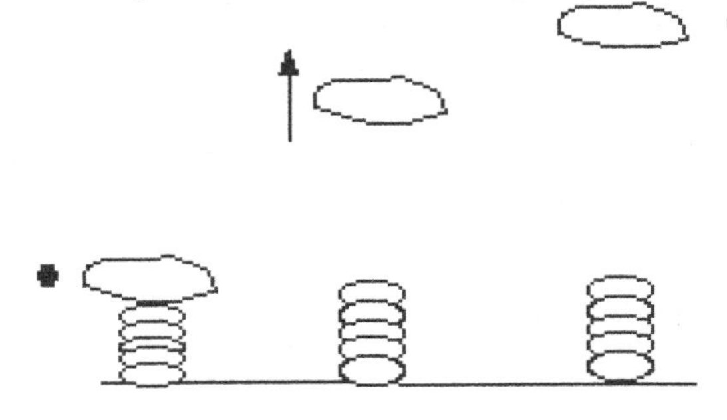

5. A piece of clay is dropped to the floor.

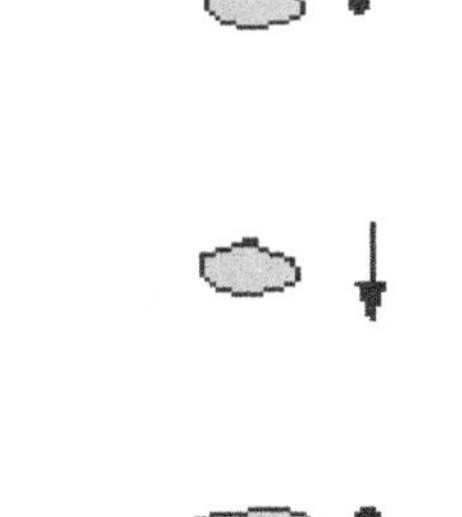

6. A ball rolls to a stop on the floor.

7. A truck being driven down the street.

8. A superball is dropped and bounces up and down. Draw a pie chart for each position of the ball shown. Why does the ball not bounce as high each time? Where does the energy "go"?

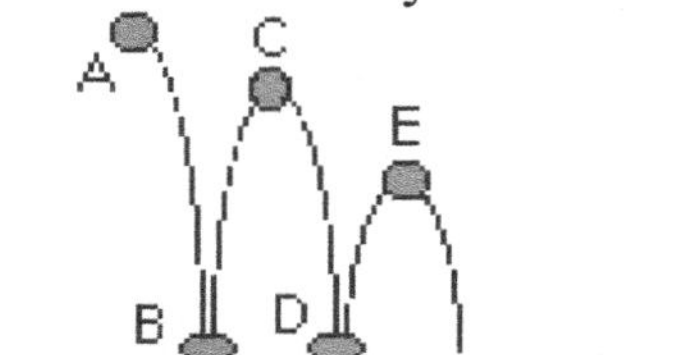

Worksheet 2: Hooke's Law and Elastic Energy

Suppose one lab group found that F = 1000 N/m (Δx). Construct a graphical representation of force vs. displacement. (Hint: make the maximum displacement 0.25 m.)

1. Graphically determine the amount of energy stored while stretching the spring described above from x = 0 to x = 10. cm.

2. Graphically determine the amount of energy stored while stretching the spring described above from x = 15 to x = 25 cm.

The graph to the right was made from data collected during an investigation of the relationship between the amounts two different springs stretched when different forces were applied.

3. Determine the spring constant for each spring.

4. For each spring, compare:
   a. the amount of force required to stretch the spring 3.0 m.

   b. the E_{el} stored in each spring when stretched 3.0m.

5. Determine the amount that spring 2 needs to be stretched in order to store 24 joules of energy.

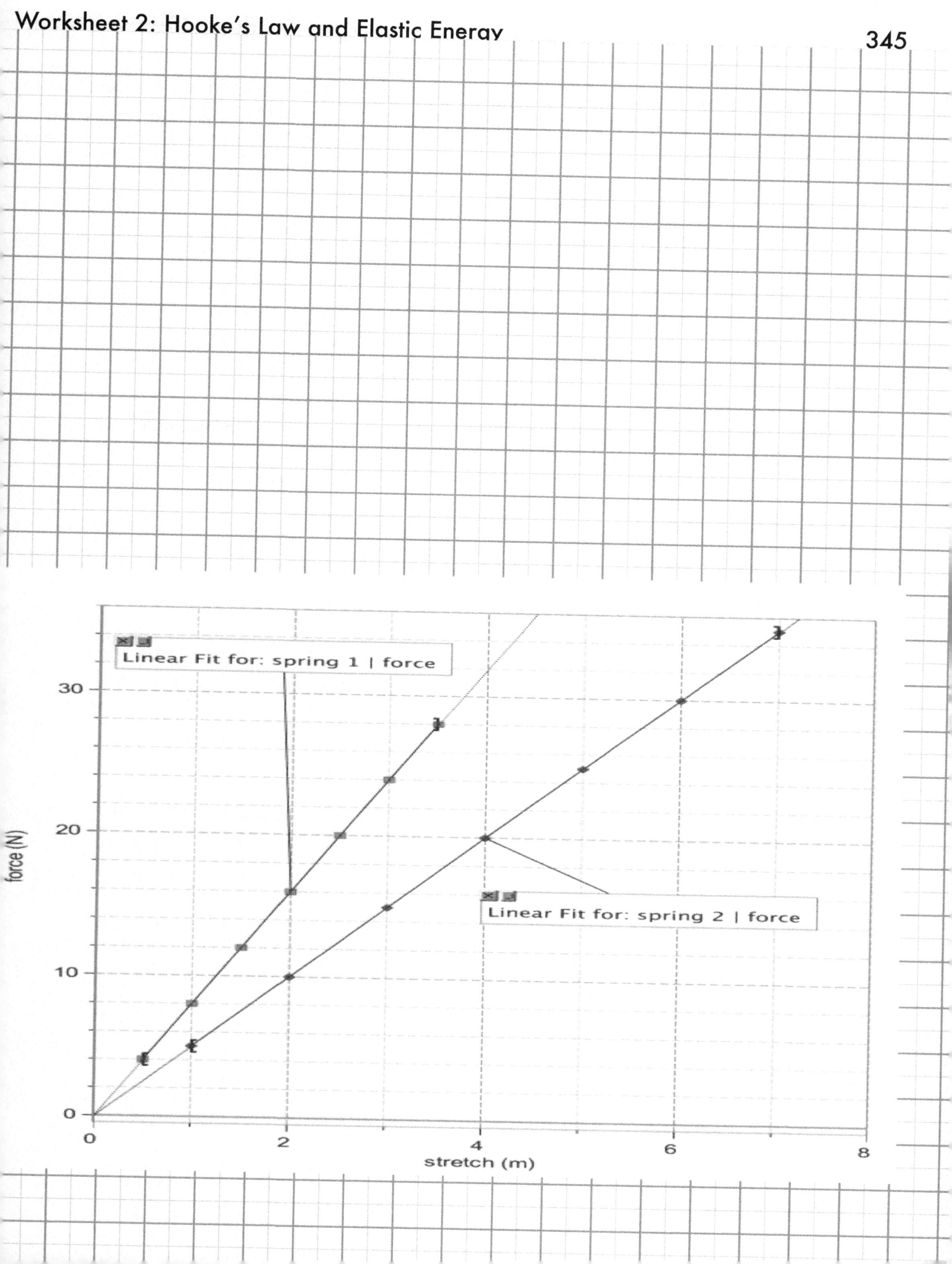
Linear Fit for: spring 1 | force
Linear Fit for: spring 2 | force
force (N)
30
20
10
0
0
2
4
6
8
stretch (m)

6. The spring below has a spring constant of 10. N/m. If the block is pulled 0.30 m horizontally to the right, and held motionless, what force does the spring exert on the block? Sketch a force diagram for the mass as you hold it still. (Assume a frictionless surface.)

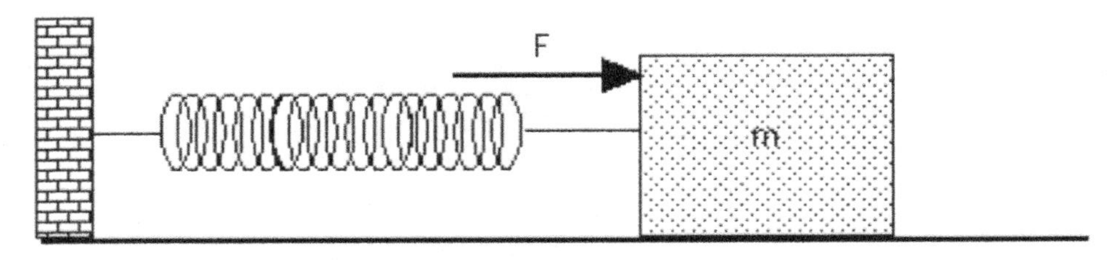

7. The spring below has a spring constant of 20. N/m. The μ_s between the box and the surface is 0.40.

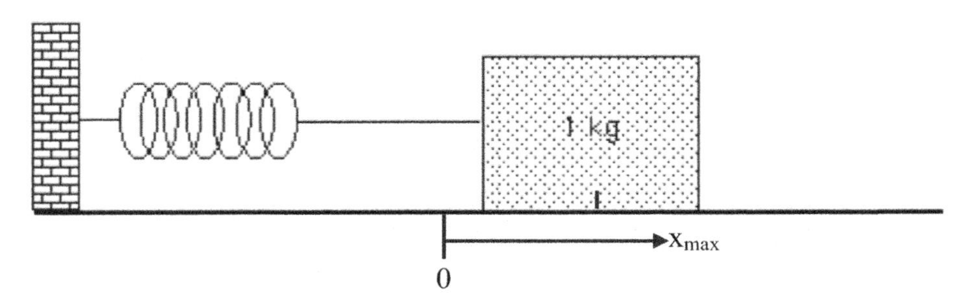

a. The box is pushed to the right, then released. Draw a force diagram for the box above when the spring is stretched, yet the box is stationary.

b. What is the maximum distance that the spring can be stretched from equilibrium before the box begins to slide back?

c. Do pie chart analysis for this situation, when the spring is stretched beyond its maximum (from part b above) so it slides back, and then the box oscillates back and forth until it comes to a stop. Assume your system includes the spring, box, and table top.

Reading:

Energy- a conserved, substance-like quantity with the capability to produce change.

The idea of energy is an invention that proves very useful. Energy is universal - it does not come in different "kinds" or exist in different "forms." To help us describe the interaction of energy and matter, we create various "accounts" in which energy can be stored in a given system, but the energy itself is unchanged. It can be transferred from one account to another as some aspect of the system undergoes a change. It can be transferred between system and surroundings via several mechanisms, although "working" (W) is the primary transfer mechanism used in this unit.

Energy always has a home; it is either stored in an object - which we label kinetic energy when the object is moving or elastic energy when it undergoes a restorable deformation - or it is stored by a field (gravitational, electric or magnetic), which we label potential energy. In this unit you will develop expressions that will enable you to determine the amount of energy stored in these various accounts. As energy is transferred from one account (or storage mode) to another, or between the system and the surroundings, the total amount of energy stays constant; we say that energy is conserved. The choice of which objects are in the system affects the way you calculate energy transfers. Generally, the smallest system that contains all the needed ways of storing energy is the easiest.

Money analogy: A useful analogy to help understand energy storage and transfer is to compare energy to money. We will define "the system" as the personal and institutional places where you keep your money. You can store your money in a number of ways: in a checking account, savings account, cash in a piggy bank, or a stock mutual fund. As you transfer money between your various accounts the amount of money stays the same (is conserved) even though some features of your resources may be different (e.g., using cash may be easier than a check in some transactions). Some transfers cost you money, such as using a debit card or getting a cash advance. In such cases, while the money is still there, you may no longer be able to transfer it to some other account. This is our analog to thermal energy.

Diagrammatical representations for Energy:
Energy is a scalar (amount only, no direction) so it can't be represented with the arrows we use for vectors. Instead, we use pie charts and bar graphs and energy flow diagrams.

Thus far you have used pie charts to show how energy is stored within a system and how energy moves from one storage mode to another as change occurs within the system. The size of the pie reflects the total energy of the system, and the size of each piece of the pie indicates how the energy is distributed among the various storage modes. Making ıe size of each slice represent the exact value of the energy in each mode is not an asy task in a pie chart model, so we tend to use pie charts for qualitative epresentations.

he next representational tools you will use are energy bar graphs and flow diagrams. hey will help as you perform quantitative analysis of the energy flow during a change. he initial energy state of a system is represented with a bar graph showing the amount f energy stored in each account (or storage mode). To the right of the bar graph, an nergy flow diagram indicates which items are inside and outside of the system and vhether energy is transferred into or out of the system by working or heating. Finally, to ıe right of the energy flow diagram, another bar graph indicates the final distribution of nergy stored within the system. To use the representation for quantitative analysis, a ıathematical expression or energy value can be written below each bar and the energy ow diagram. The sum of the initial stored energy in the system plus or minus any energy owing in or out of the system equals the sum of the final stored energy in the system. Consider the example below in which a water balloon tossed by Buffy lands and bursts n Biff's head.

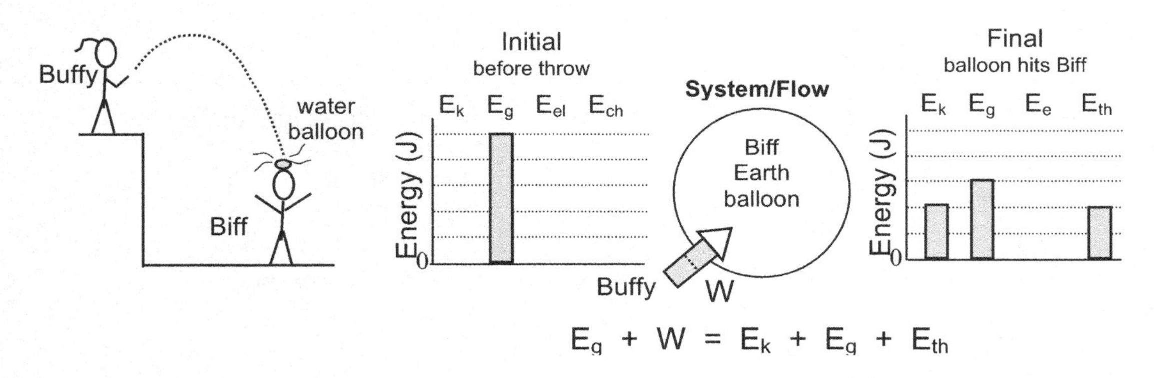

$$E_g + W = E_k + E_g + E_{th}$$

he system contains Biff, the Earth and the water balloon. The zero reference position for ıe gravitational potential energy, E_g , is the floor on which Biff stands. In the Initial state, ıe Earth-balloon system has some E_g as the balloon rests in Buffy's hand. Buffy, an xternal agent, applies a force through some distance to the balloon, transferring ıdditional energy to the system via the mechanism we call working (W). This is shown in ıe system/flow portion of the diagram. In the Final state, the moving balloon and water ave some kinetic energy, E_k, and the Earth balloon system has some lower amount of ıravitational energy (due to the decreased height of the balloon). In addition, some nergy ends up in the thermal energy account due to the increase in the kinetic energy of ıe molecules of water, balloon scraps and Biff's head.

Had Buffy been included in the system, then a separate account for chemical energy, E_{ch} vould need to be shown on the energy bar charts with two more bars in the initial state ıan in the final state.

Worksheet 3: Qualitative Energy Storage & Conservation with Bar Graphs

For each situation shown below:

1. List objects in the system within the circle. ***Always include the earth's gravitational field in your system.*
2. On the physical diagram, indicate your choice of zero height for measuring gravitational energy.
3. Sketch the energy bar graph for position A, indicate any energy flow into or out of the system from position A to position B on the System/Flow diagram, and sketch the energy bar graph for position B.
4. Write a qualitative energy equation that indicates the initial, transferred, and final energy of your system.

1a. In the situation shown below, a spring launches a roller coaster cart from rest on a frictionless track into a vertical loop. Assume the system consists of the cart, the earth, the track, and the spring,

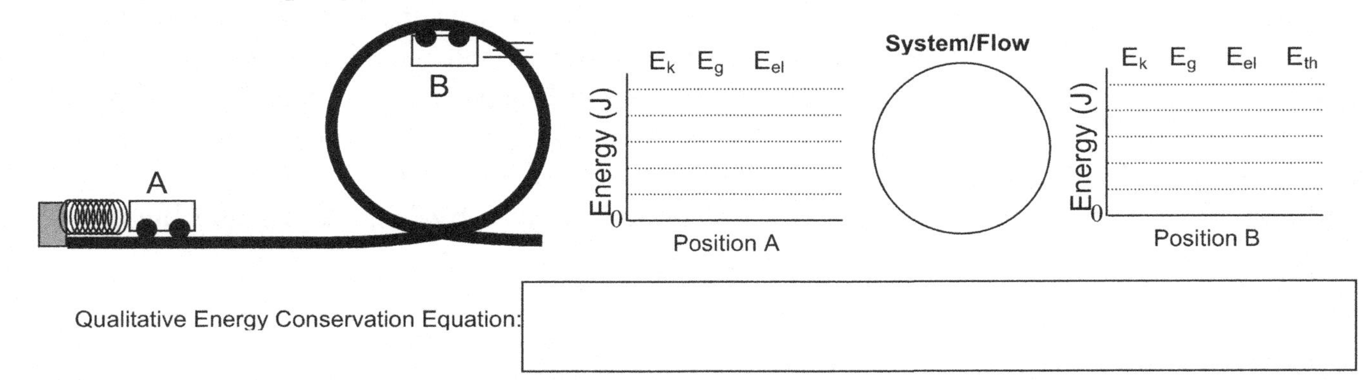

Qualitative Energy Conservation Equation:

1b. Repeat problem 1a for a frictionless system that includes the cart, the earth, and the track, but not the spring.

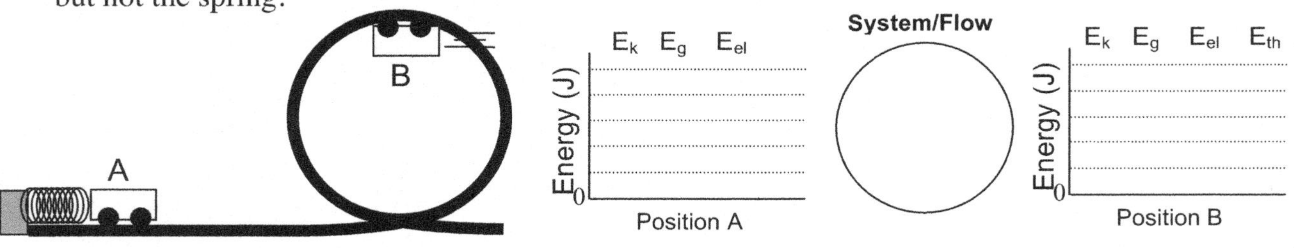

Qualitative Energy Conservation Equation:

1c. Use the same system as problem 1a, but assume that there is friction between the cart and the track.

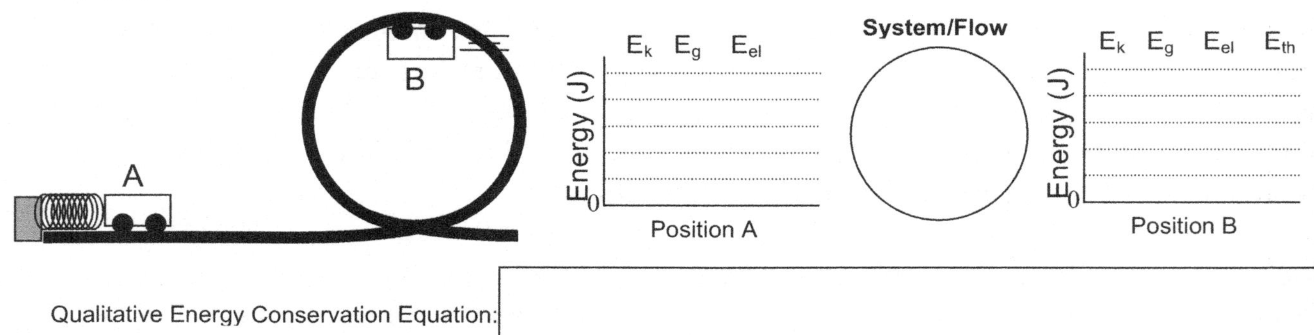

Qualitative Energy Conservation Equation:

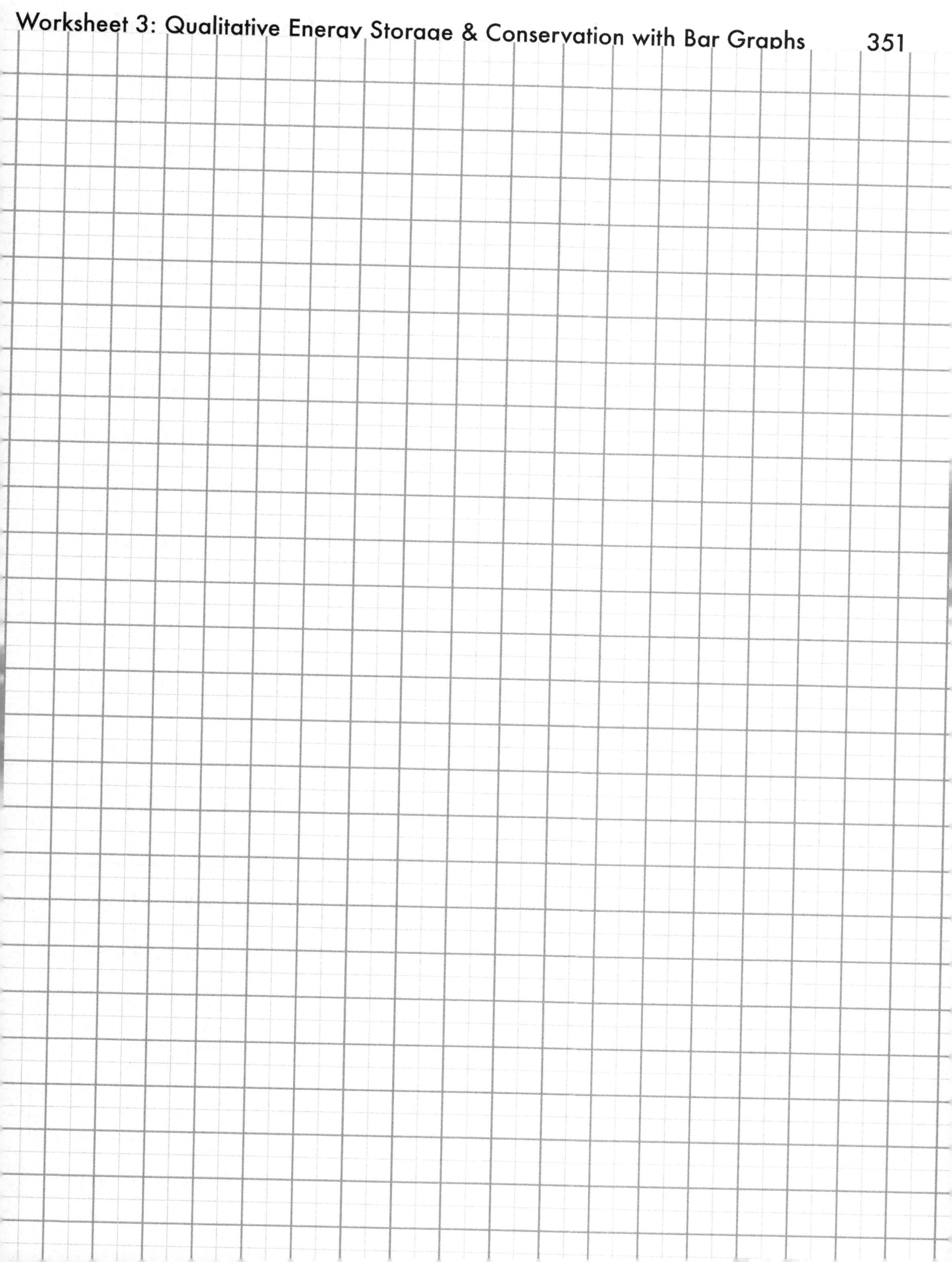

1d. This situation is the same as problem 1a except that the final position of the cart is lower on the track. Make sure your bars are scaled consistently between problem 1a and 1d. Assume the system consists of the cart, the earth, the track, and the spring.

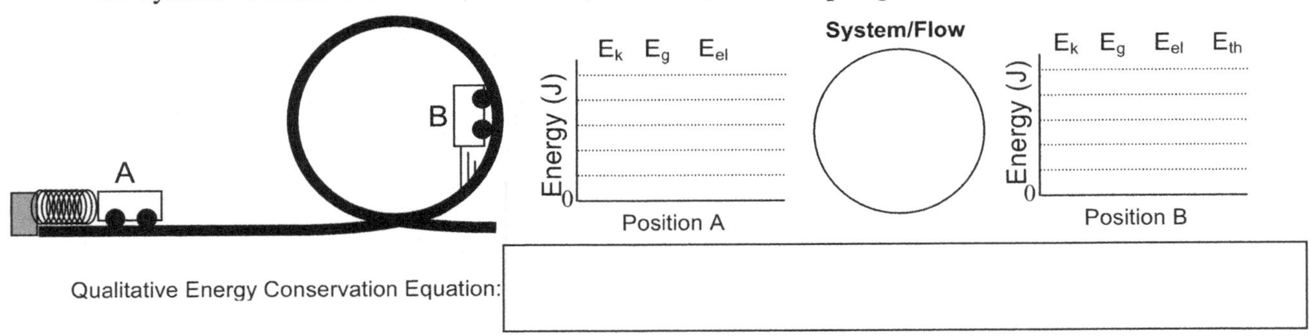

Qualitative Energy Conservation Equation:

2a. A moving car rolls up a hill until it stops. Do this problem for a system that consists of the car, the road, and the earth. Assume that the engine is turned off, the car is in neutral, and there is no friction.

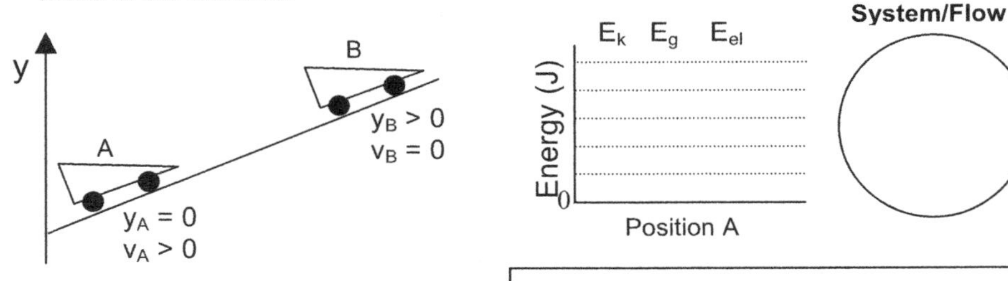

E_k E_g E_{el} E_{th}

Energy (J)

Position B

Qualitative Energy Conservation Equation:

2b. Repeat problem 2a for the same system with friction.

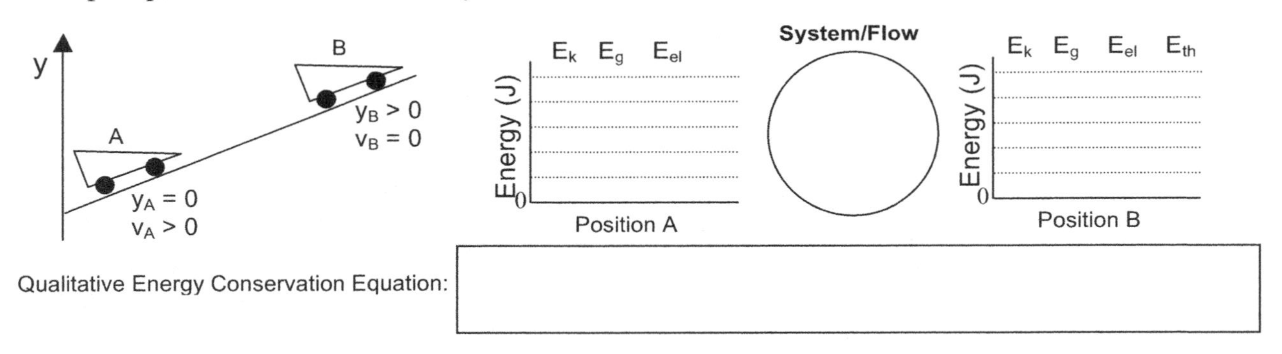

Qualitative Energy Conservation Equation:

3a. A person pushes a car, with the parking brake on, up a hill. Assume a system that includes the car, the road, and the earth, but does not include the person.

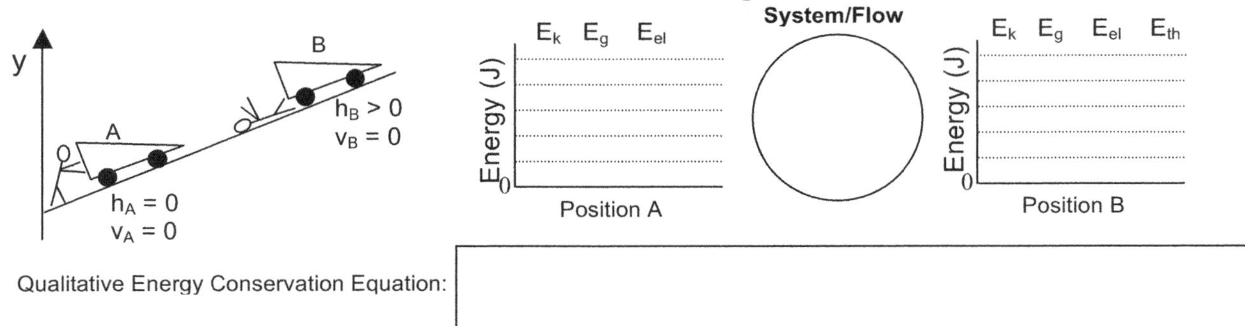

Qualitative Energy Conservation Equation:

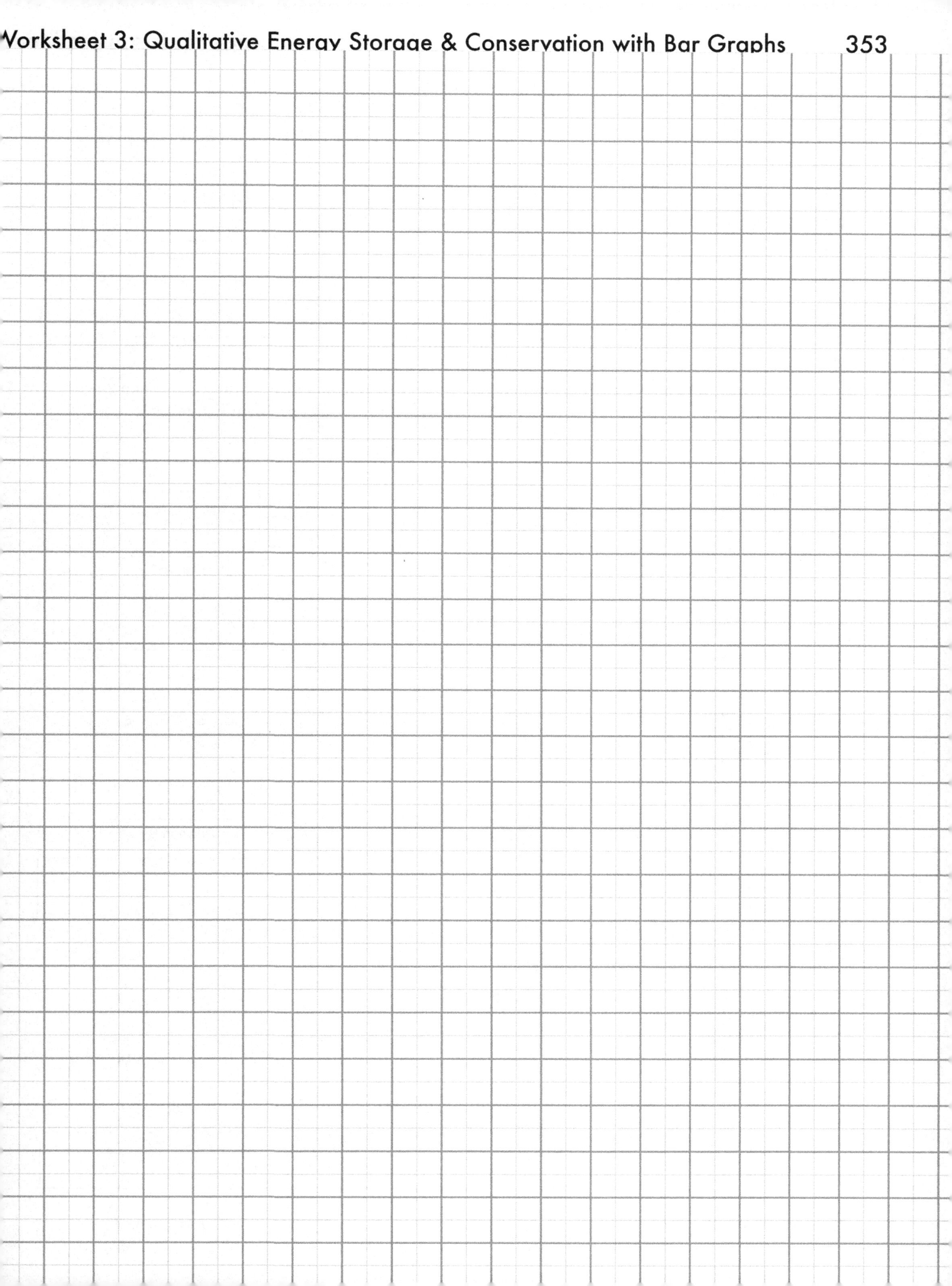

3b. Repeat problem 3a for a system that includes the person.

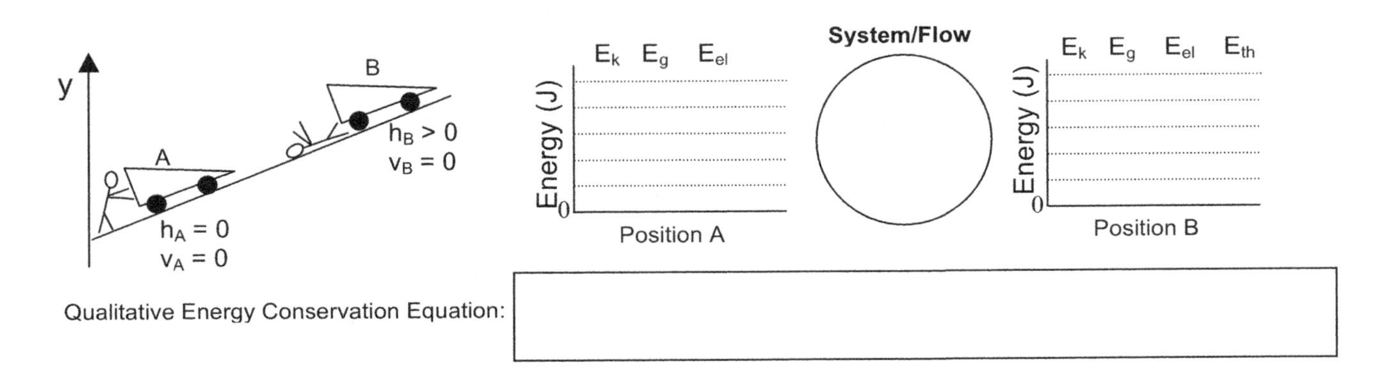

4a. A load of bricks rests on a tightly coiled spring and is then launched into the air. Assume a system that includes the spring, the bricks and the earth. Do this problem without friction.

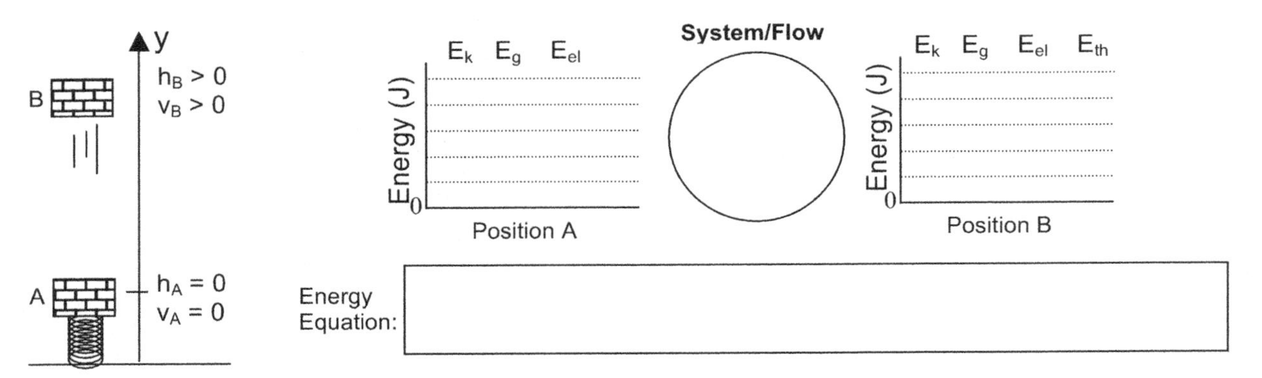

4b. Repeat problem 4a with friction.

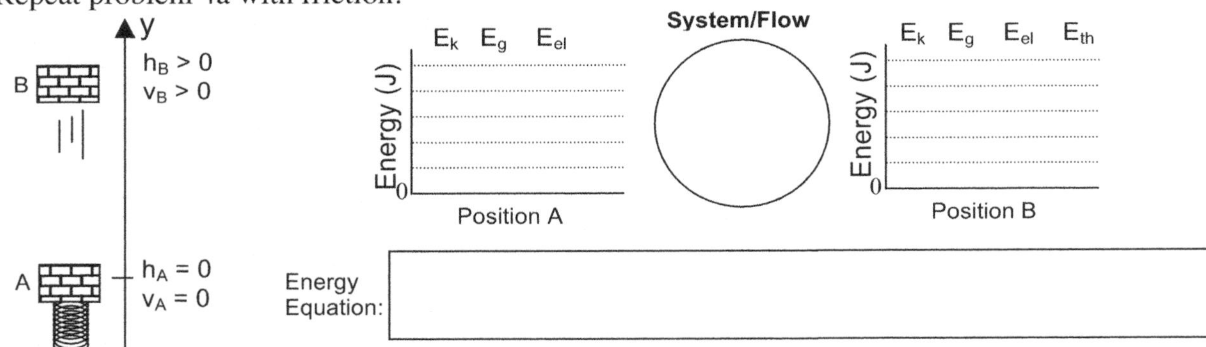

4c. Repeat problem 4a for a system that does not include the spring.

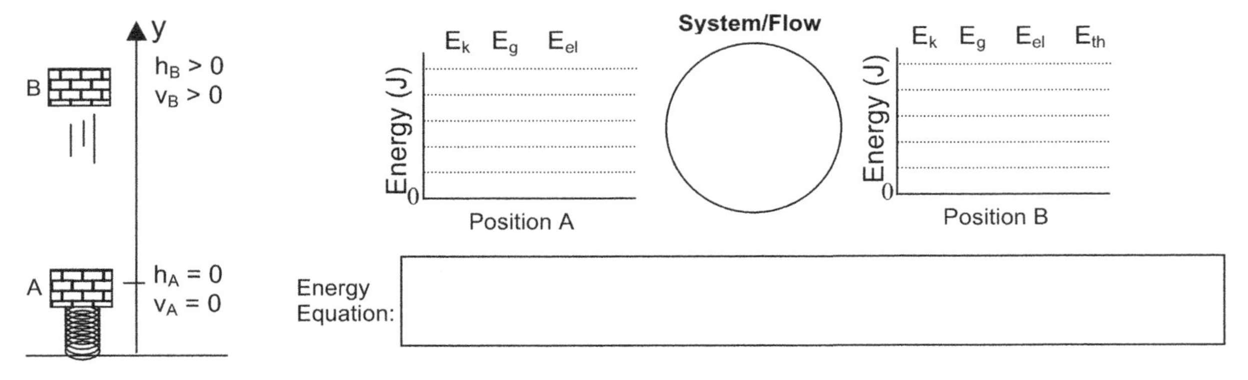

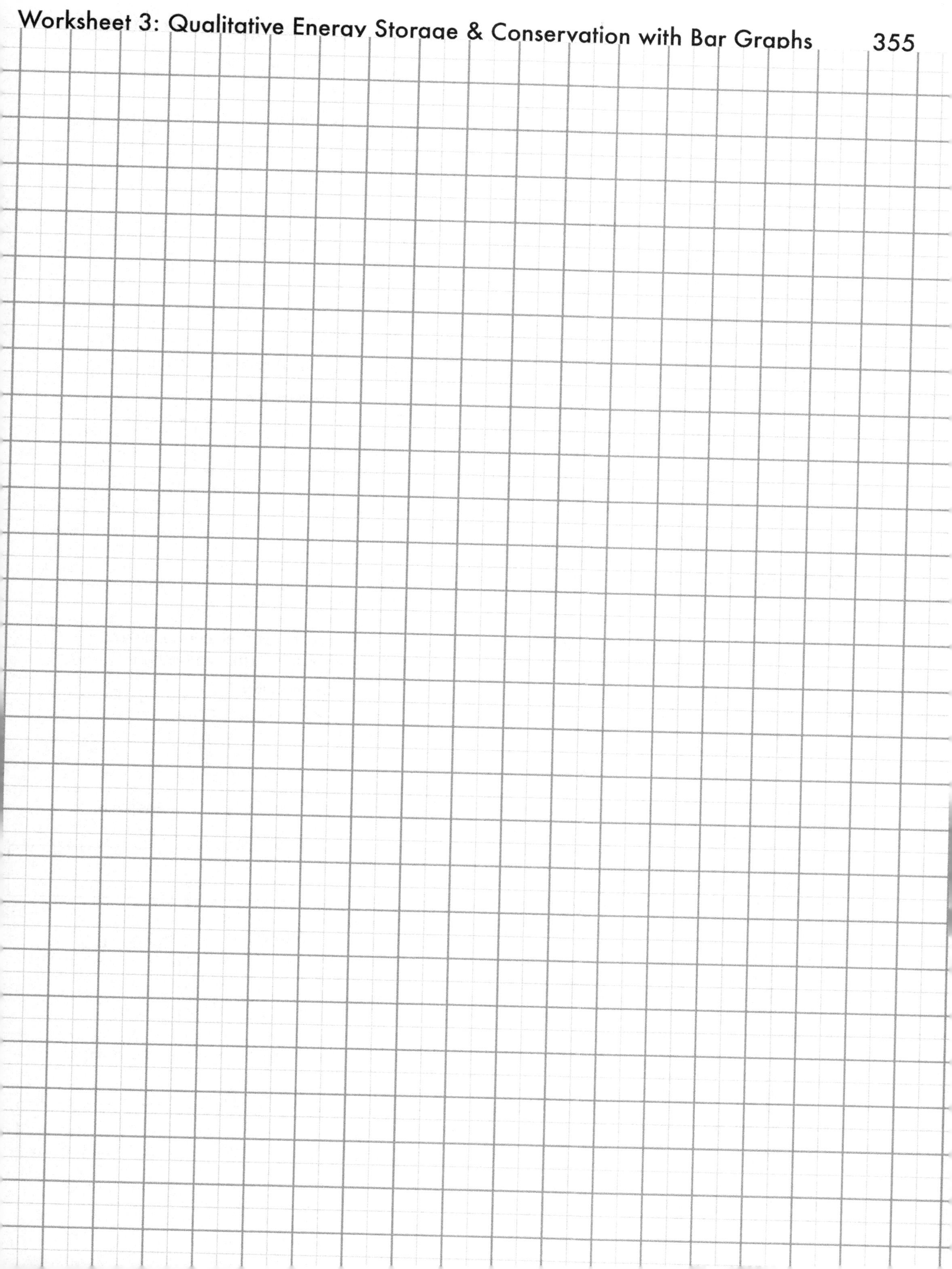

5a. A crate is propelled up a hill by a tightly coiled spring. Analyze this situation for a frictionless system that includes the spring, the hill, the crate, and the earth.

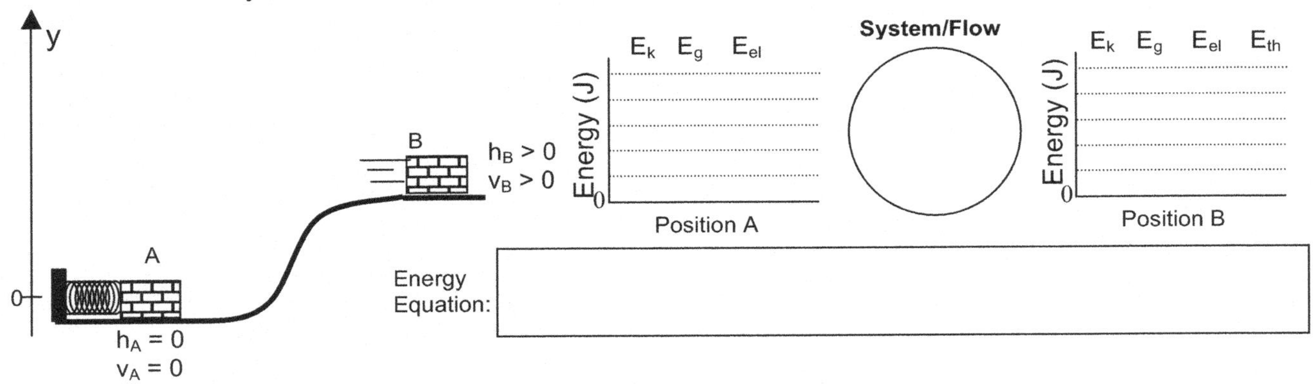

5b. Repeat problem 5a for a system that does not include the spring and does have friction.

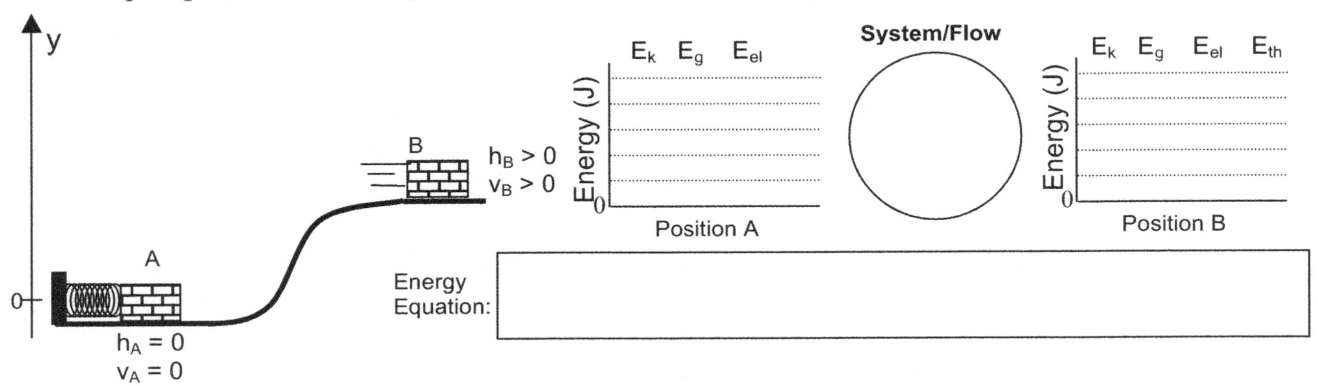

6a. A bungee jumper falls off the platform and reaches the limit of stretch of the cord. Analyze this situation for a frictionless system that consists of the jumper, the earth, and the cord.

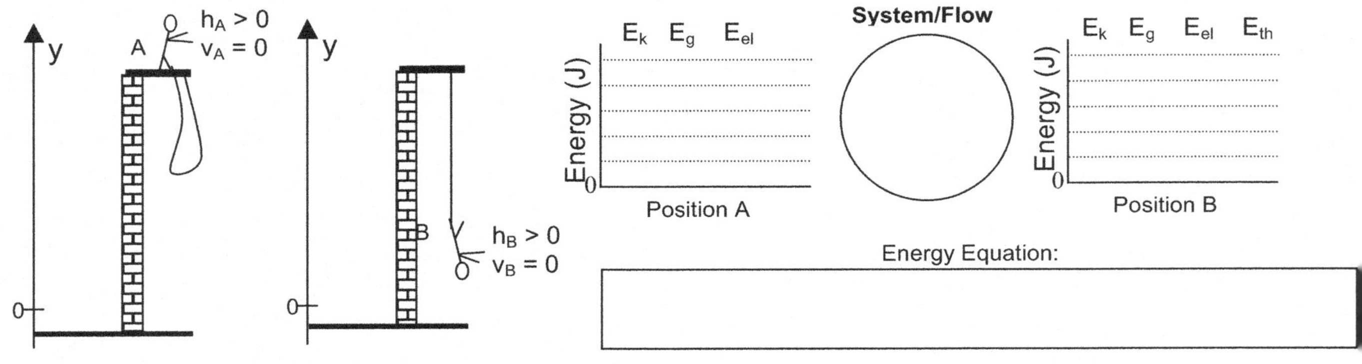

6b. Repeat problem 6a if the cord is not part of the system.

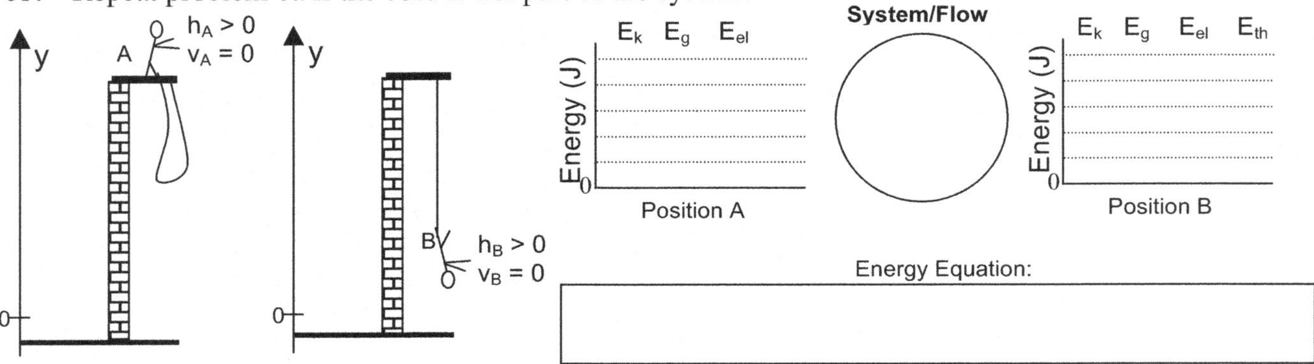

Worksheet 4: Quantitative Energy Calculations & Energy Conservation

Be careful with units and unit conversions!

1. How much kinetic energy does a 2000 kg SUV traveling 70 mph have? (1 mile = 1600 meters)

2. How much energy does a 180 Calorie, half-pint carton of chocolate milk store? (One food Calorie = 4186 Joules)

3. Consider your 3 kg physics binder resting on the table in the classroom. Determine the gravitational energy of the earth-book system if the zero reference level is chosen to be:

   a) the table

   b) the floor, 0.68 meters below the book

   c) the ceiling, 2.5 meters above the book

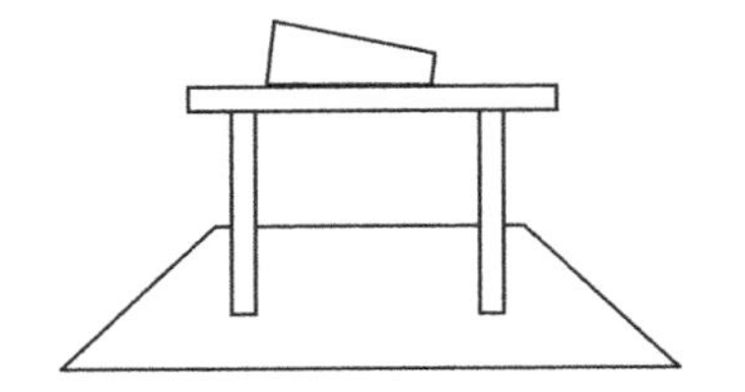

4. A bungee cord stretches 25 meters and has a spring constant of 140 N/m. How much energy is stored in the bungee?

5. How fast does a 50 gram arrow need to travel to have 40 joules of kinetic energy?

6. How much energy is stored when a railroad car spring is compressed 10.0 cm? (The spring requires about 10,000 N to be compressed 3.0 cm.)

7. A cart moving at 5.0 m/s collides with a spring. At the instant the cart is motionless, what is the largest amount that the spring could be compressed? Assume no friction.
   a. Define the system with the energy flow diagram, then complete the energy bar graphs qualitatively.

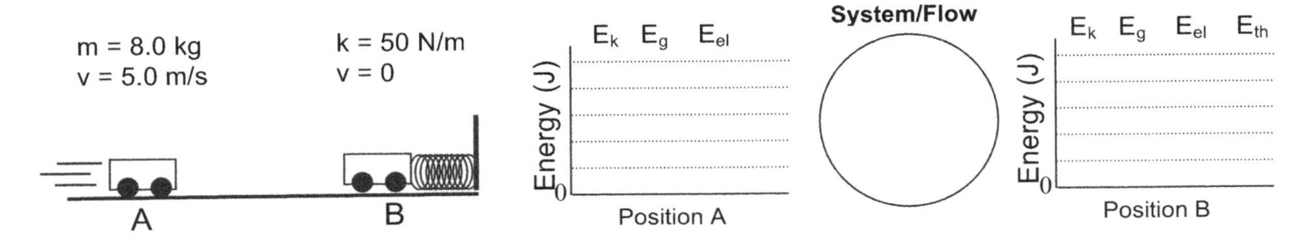

   b. Quantitative Energy Conservation Equation:

   c. Determine the maximum compression of the spring.

8. A rock is shot straight up into the air with a slingshot that had been stretched 0.30 m. Assume no air resistance.
   a. Qualitatively complete the energy flow diagram and the energy bar graphs.

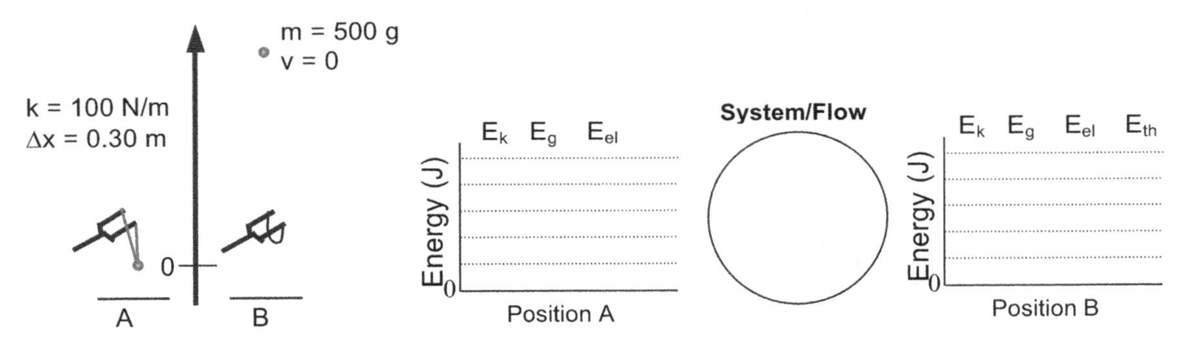

   b. Quantitative Energy Conservation Equation:

   c. Determine the greatest height the rock could reach.

9. Determine final velocity of the rollercoaster, assuming a 10% loss to friction.

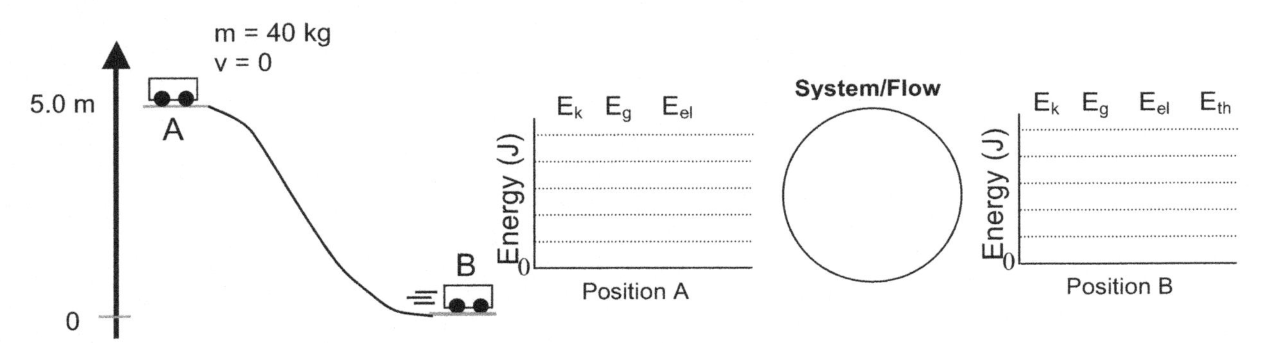

10. The moon could be an ideal spaceport for exploring the solar system. A moon launching system could consist of a magnetic rail gun that shoots items into moon orbit. How much energy would be needed from the rail gun to get a 10,000 kg capsule into an orbit 100 km above the moon surface? The moon's gravitational field strength is 1.6 N/kg and the orbital velocity for this altitude is 1700 m/s. Hint: Put the rail gun outside of the system.

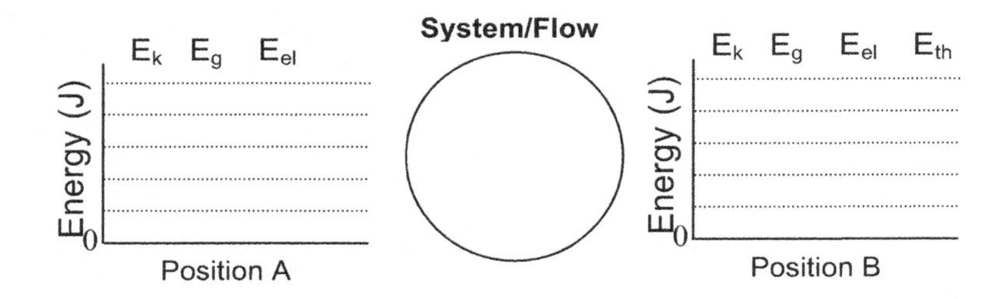

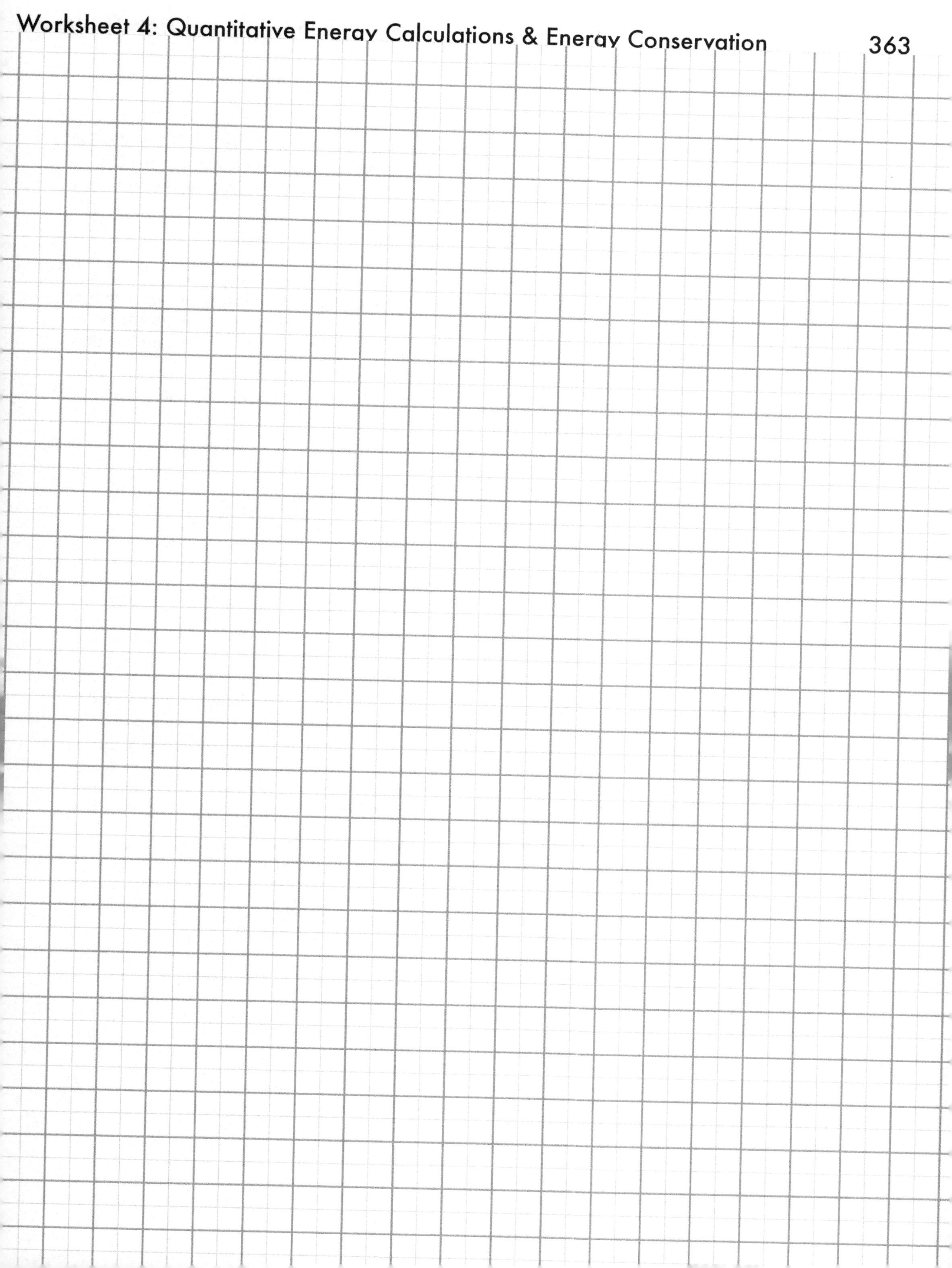

Worksheet 5: Energy Transfer and Power

1. A student eats a tasty school lunch containing 700. Calories. (One food Calorie = 4186 joules.) Due to basal metabolism, the student radiates about 100. joules per second into the environment.
   a. How long would the student have to sit on a couch to radiate away all of the energy from lunch?

   b. If all of the energy from the student's lunch did something useful, like lifting pianos weighing 5000. newtons to the top of a 10-meter tall apartment building, how many pianos could be lifted with the energy from lunch? (Ignore the energy radiated by the student.) Complete the energy bar graph below to aid your solution.

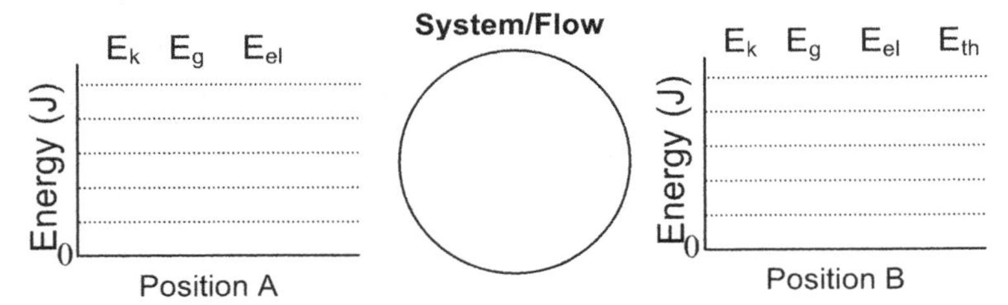

Energy Conservation Equation:

2. Jill pulls on a rope to lift a 12 kg pail out of a well, while the clumsy Jack watches. For a 10.0 meter segment of the lift, she lifts the bucket straight up at constant speed. How much power is required to complete this task in 5.0 seconds? Complete the energy bar graph as part of your solution.

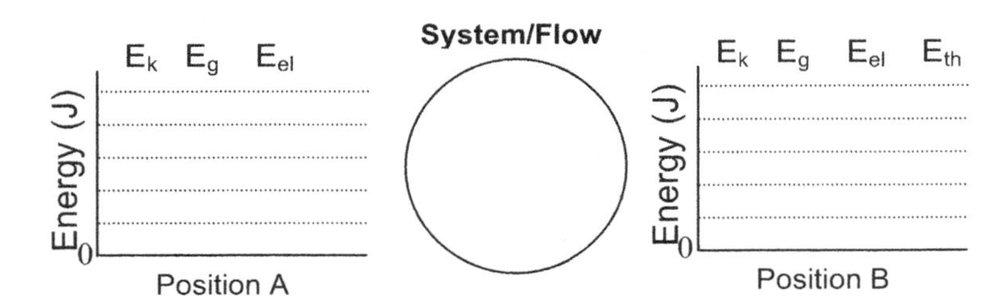

Energy Conservation Equation:

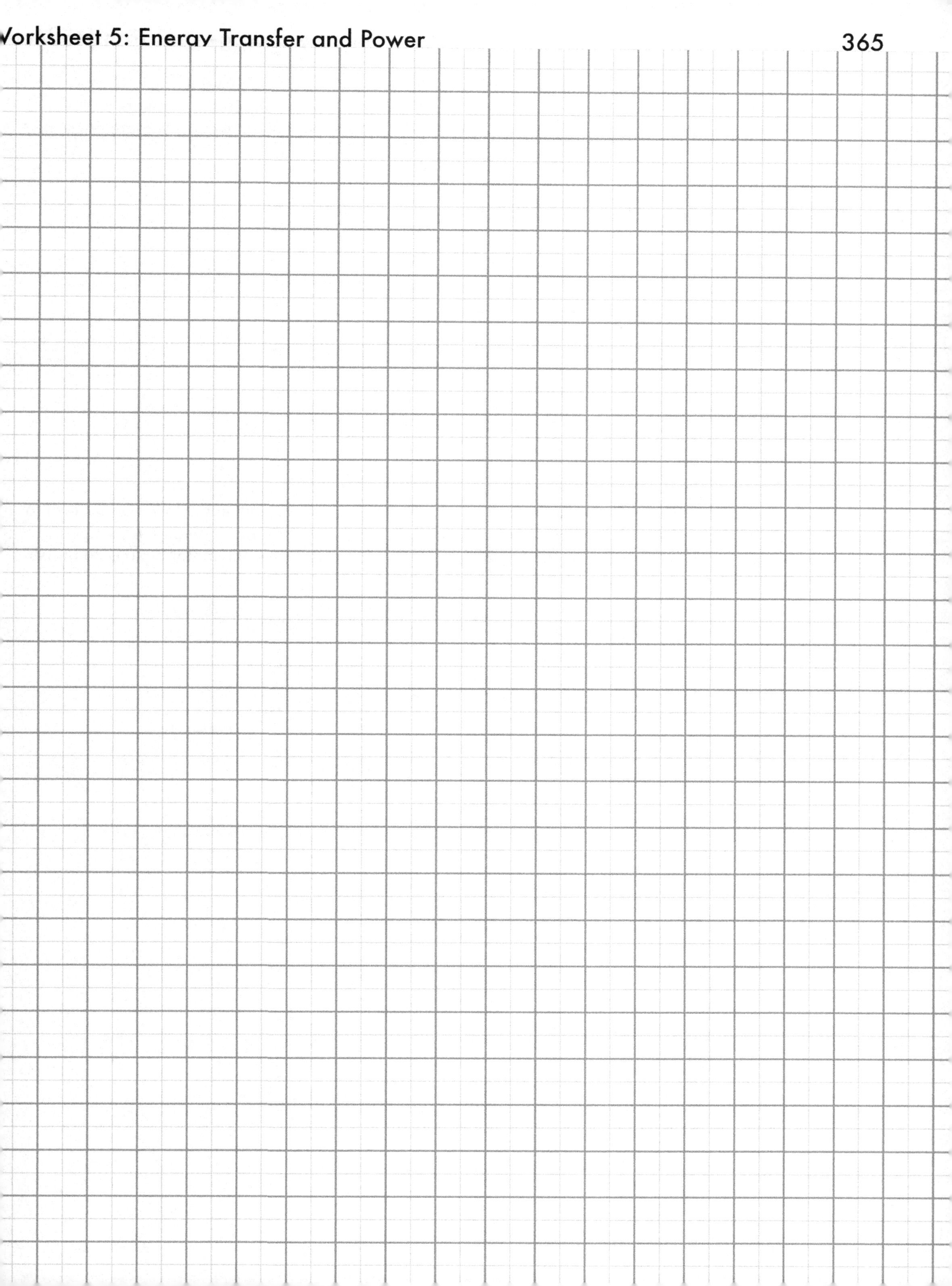

3. Hulky and Bulky are two workers being considered for a job at the UPS loading dock. Hulky boasts that he can lift a 100 kg box 2.0 meters vertically, in 3.0 seconds. Bulky counters with his claim of lifting a 200 kg box 5.0 meters vertically, in 20 seconds. Which worker is more powerful?

4. The trains on the Boss rollercoaster are raised from 10.0 m above ground at the loading platform to a height of 60.0 m at the top of the first hill in 45 s. Assume that the train (including passengers) has a mass of 2500 kg. Ignoring frictional losses, how powerful should the motor be to accomplish this task? Complete the energy bar graphs below.

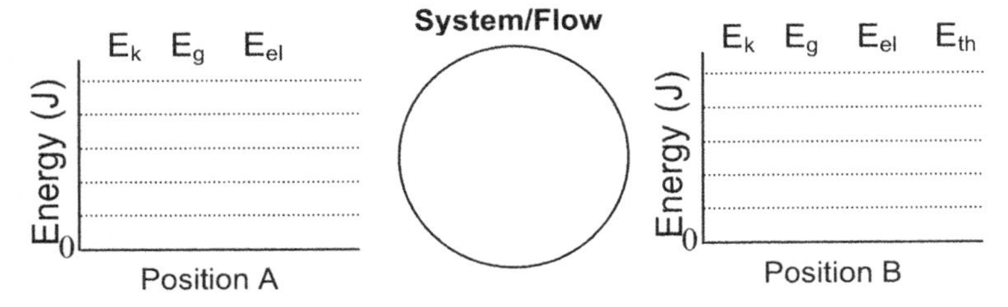

Energy Conservation Equation:

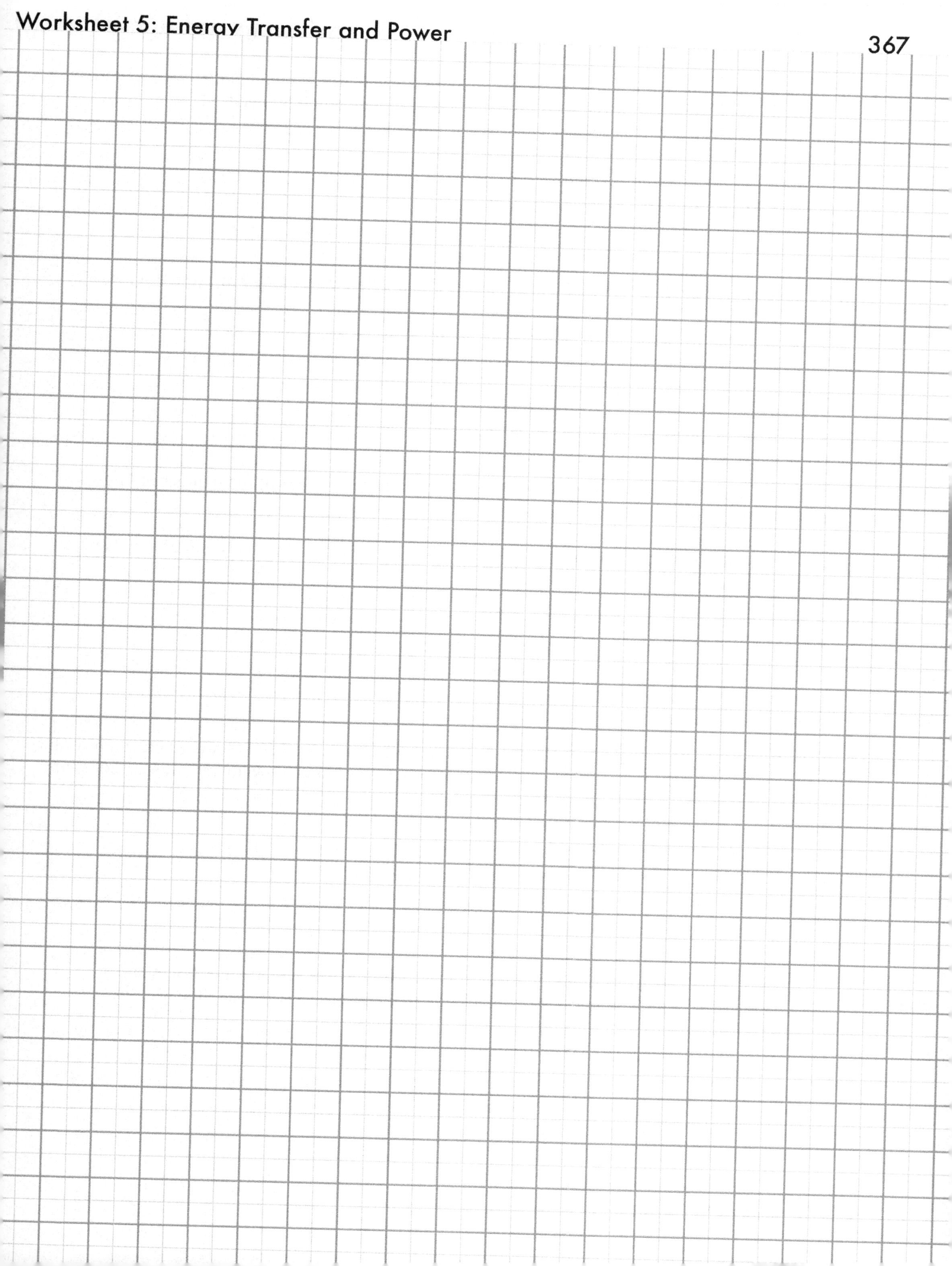

5. a. An aerodynamic 1,000 kg car takes about 270 newtons of force to maintain a speed of 25 m/s. How much horsepower is required from the engine to maintain this speed? (1 hp = 746 W)

b. How much horsepower is required for the same car to accelerate from 0-25 m/s in 6.0 seconds?

6. Your electric utility company sends you a monthly bill informing you of the number of kilowatt-hours of energy you have used that month.

   a. What is a kilowatt-hour (kilowatt x hour, or kWh)? Determine how many Joules equal one kilowatt-hour.

   b. A frost free, 17 cu. ft. refrigerator-freezer uses energy at a rate of 500. watts when you hear the compressor running. If the fridge runs for 200. hours per month, how many kilowatt-hours of energy does the refrigerator use each month?

   c. In the Phoenix area, electricity rates range from 8.0 cents per kilowatt-hour (winter) to 11.5 cents per kWh (summer). How much does the energy cost each month to run the refrigerator?

Review Problems

1. Three balls are rolled down three tracks starting from rest at the point marked "start."

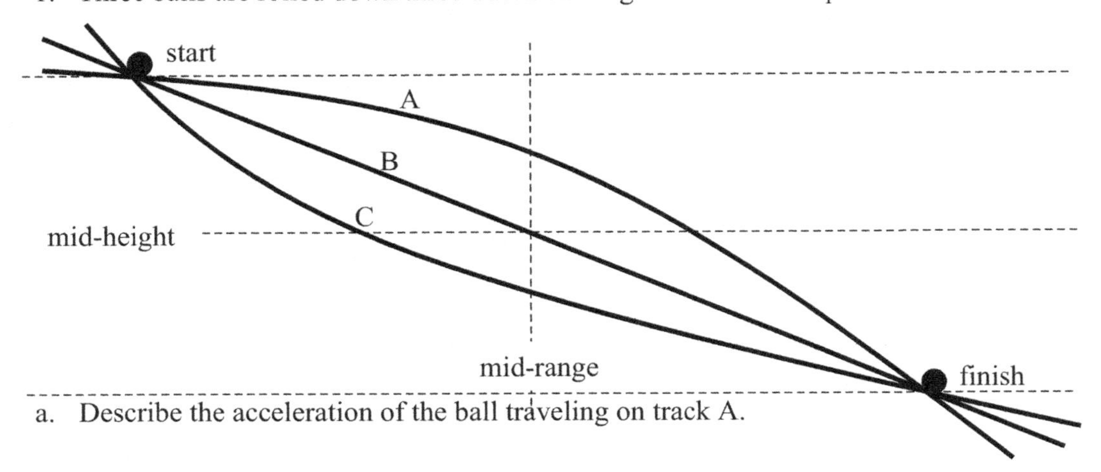

a. Describe the acceleration of the ball traveling on track A.

b. Describe the acceleration of the ball traveling on track B.

c. Describe the acceleration of the ball traveling on track C.

d. Describe the velocity of the ball traveling on track A.

e. Describe the velocity of the ball traveling on track B.

f. Describe the velocity of the ball traveling on track C.

g. Rank the time needed for the balls to travel from start to finish. Explain your ranking.

shortest:____ ____ _____:longest

h. Rank the instantaneous velocities of the balls at the mid-height line. Explain your ranking.

shortest:____ ____ _____:longest

i. Rank the instantaneous velocities of the balls at the mid-range line. Explain your ranking.

shortest:____ ____ _____:longest

j. Rank the instantaneous velocities of the balls at the finish point. Explain your ranking.

shortest:____ ____ _____:longest

k. If the start is 1.0 m higher than the finish, determine the heights at which A, B, and C will have half of their final kinetic energy.

l. If the start is 1.0 m higher than the finish, determine the heights at which A, B, and C will have half of their final velocity.

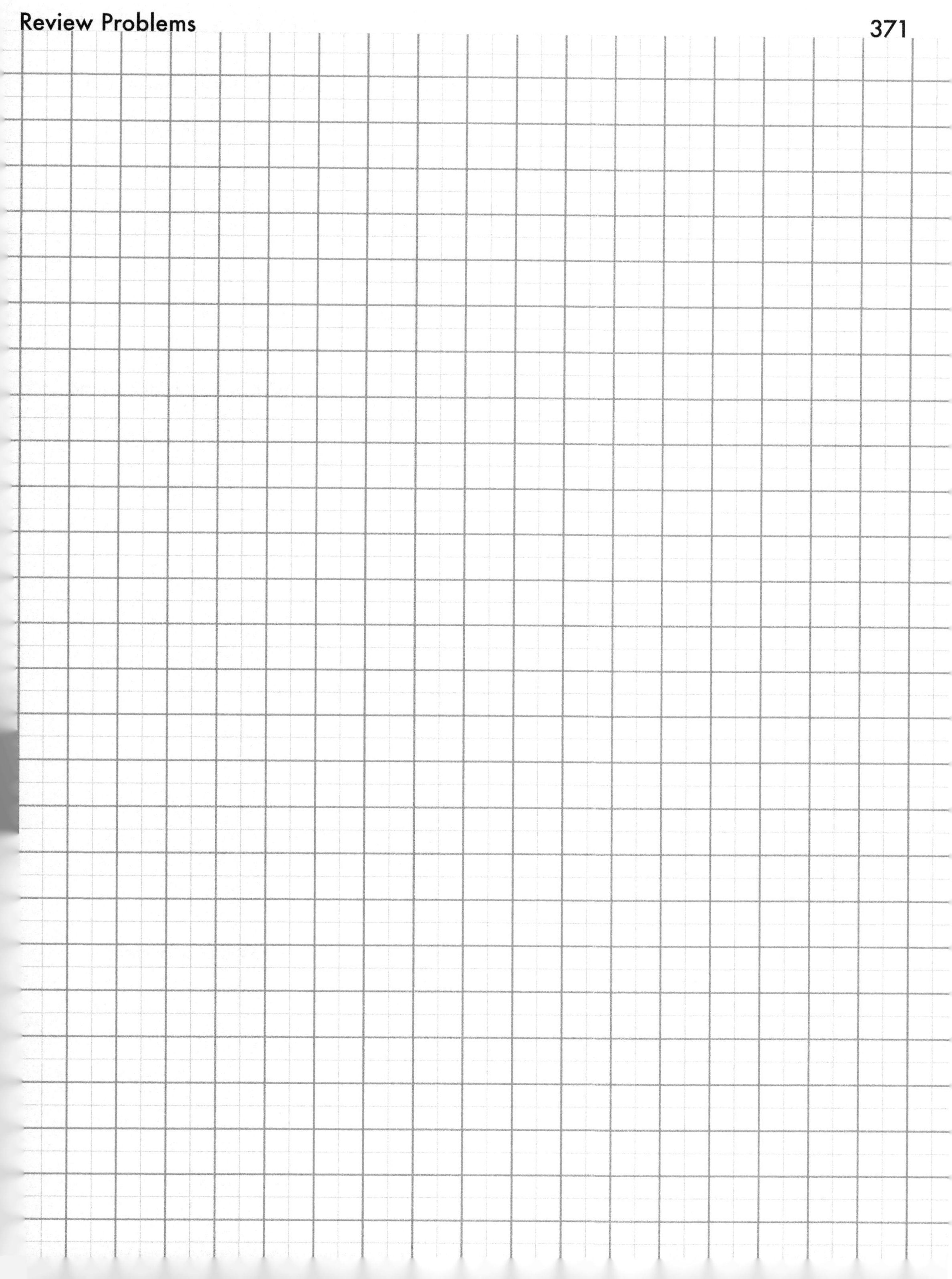

2. A baseball (m = 140 g) traveling at 30 m/s moves a fielder's glove backward 35 cm when the ball is caught.
   a. Construct an energy bar graph of the situation, with only the ball and Earth in the system.

   b. How large is the average force exerted by the ball on the glove?

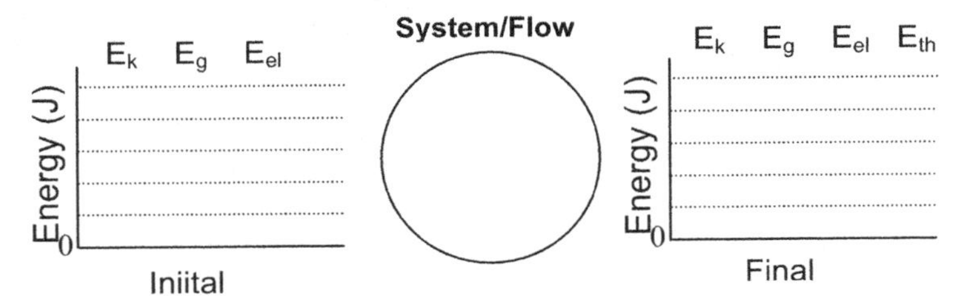

3. A spring whose spring constant is 850 N/m is compressed 0.40 m. What is the maximum speed it can give to a 500 g ball?

4. A bullet with a mass of ten grams is fired from a rifle with a barrel that is 85 cm long.
   a. Do an energy bar graph analysis of the situation.

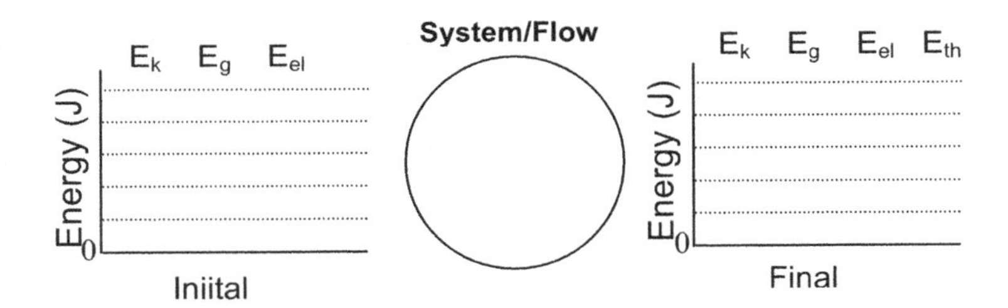

   b. Assuming that the force exerted by the expanding gas to be a constant 5500 N, what speed would the bullet reach?

5. A 24 kg child descends a 5.0 m high slide and reaches the ground with a speed of 2.8 m/s.
   a. Do a bar graph analysis for this situation.

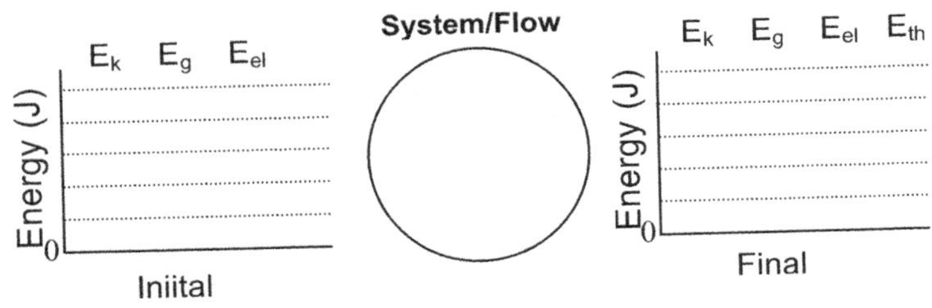

   b. How much energy was transferred to the thermal account due to friction in the process?

6. A 1500 kg car is traveling at 20 m/s.
   a. Calculate the E_k of the car relative to the road.

   b. If the average braking force applied to the car is 6000 N, how far would it travel before it came to a stop? (Draw an energy bar graph of the situation.)

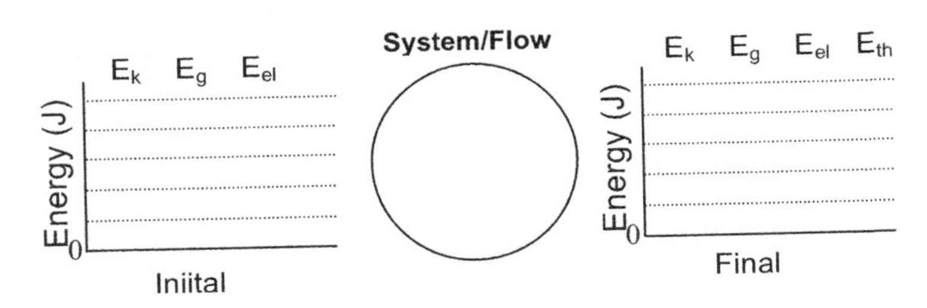

   c. If this same average braking force were applied to the car moving at twice the speed, what would be the stopping distance?

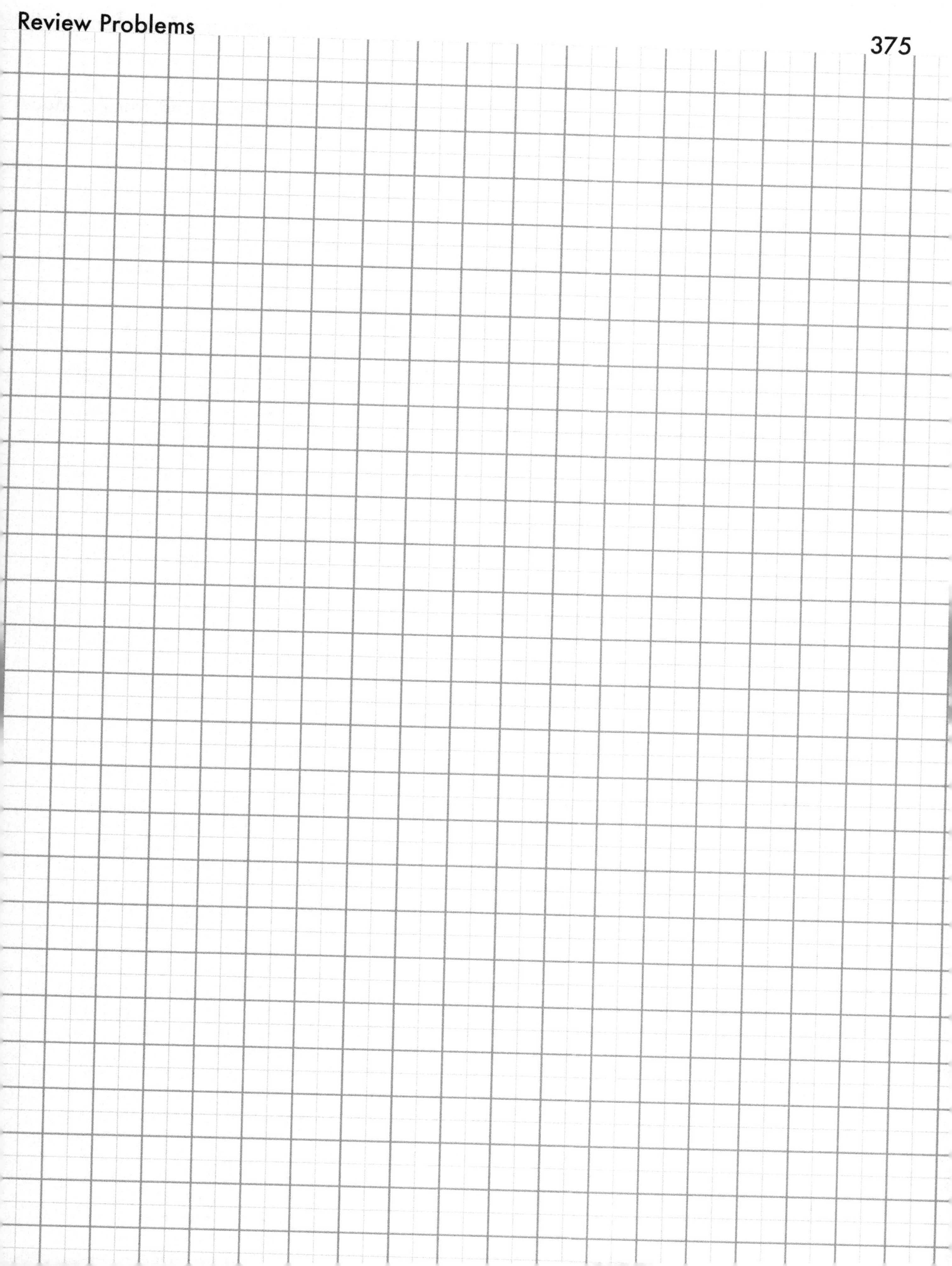

Model Summary

This is a place to summarize different representations of the Energy Storage and Transfer Mode

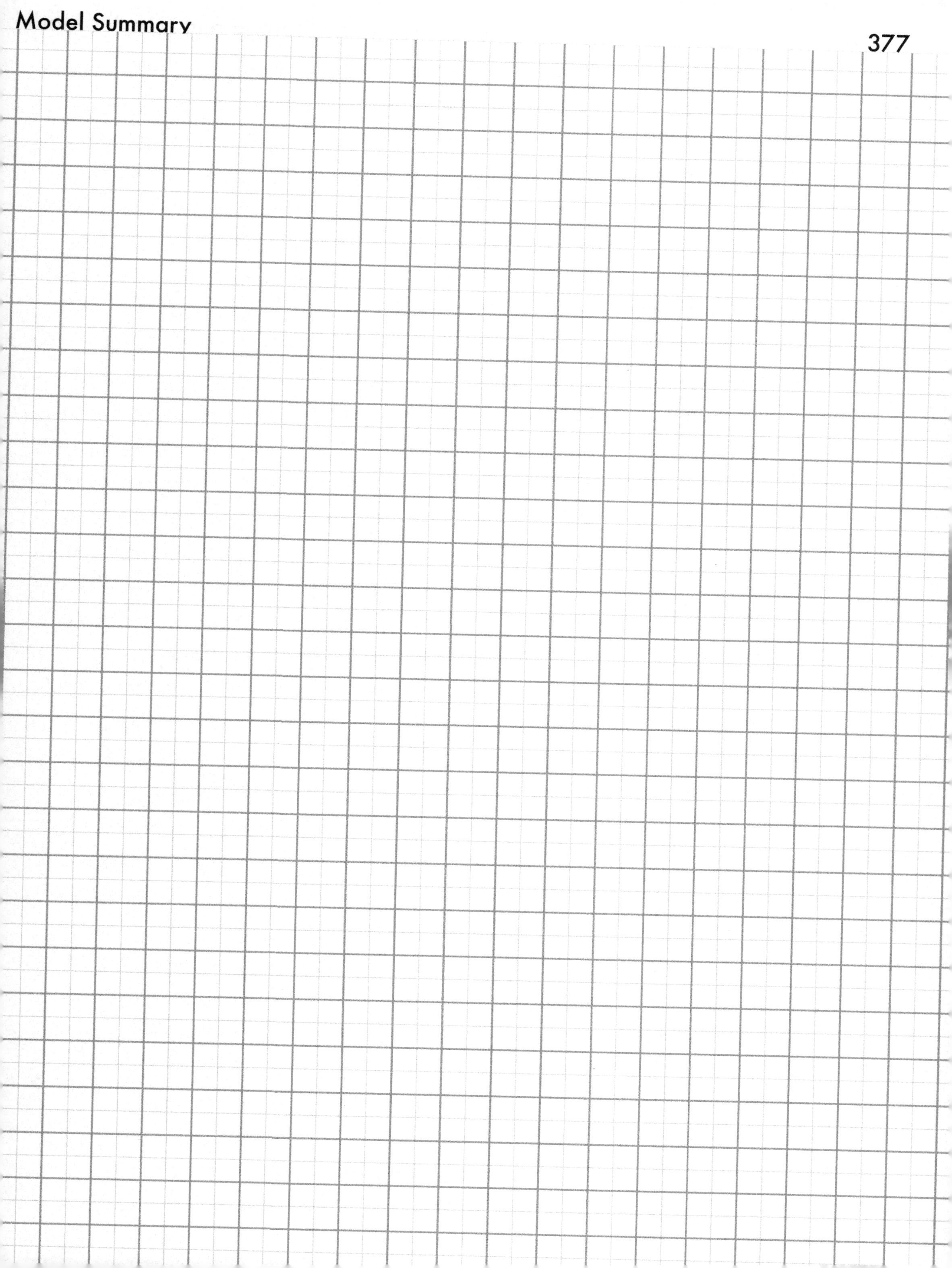

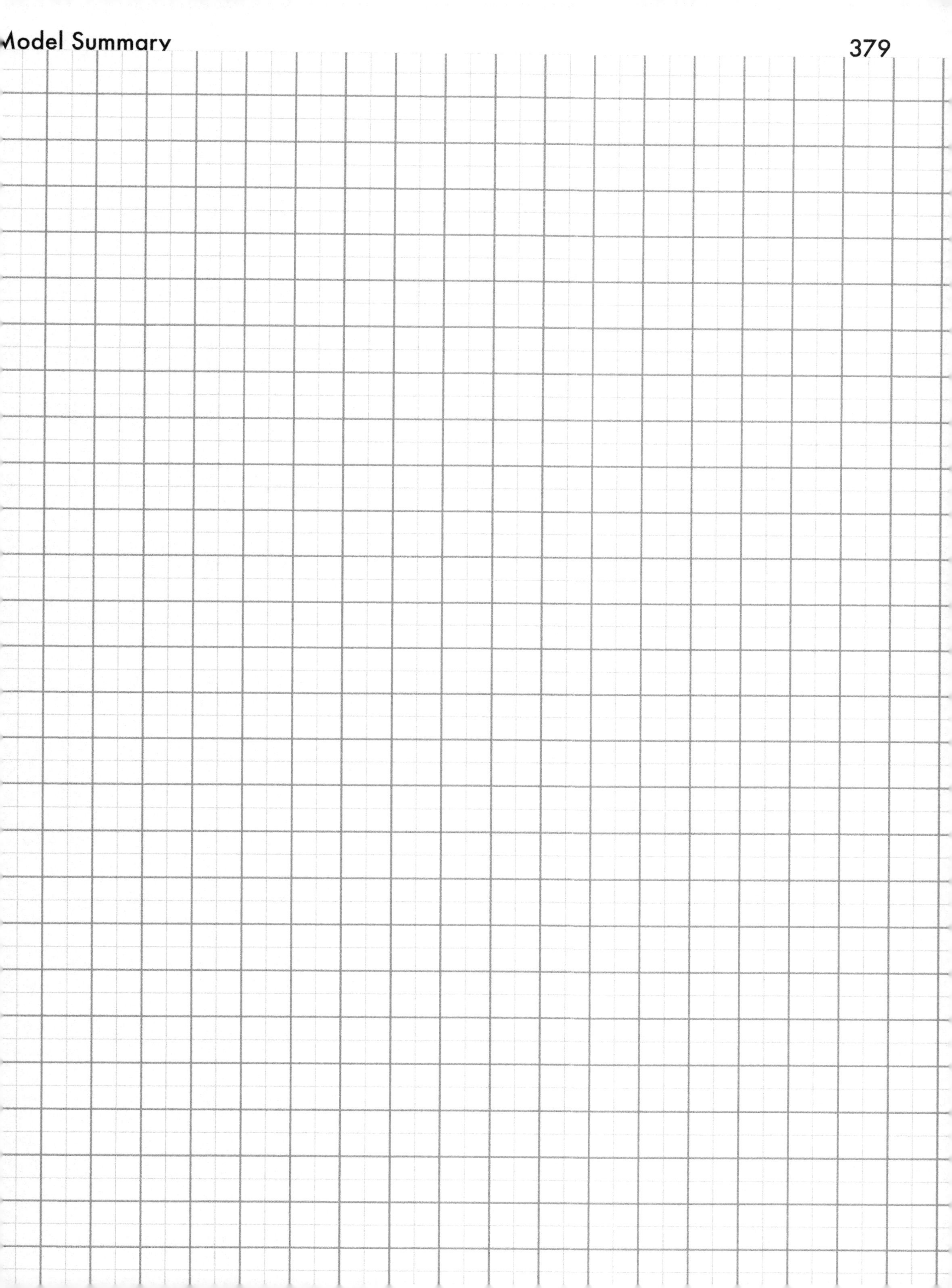

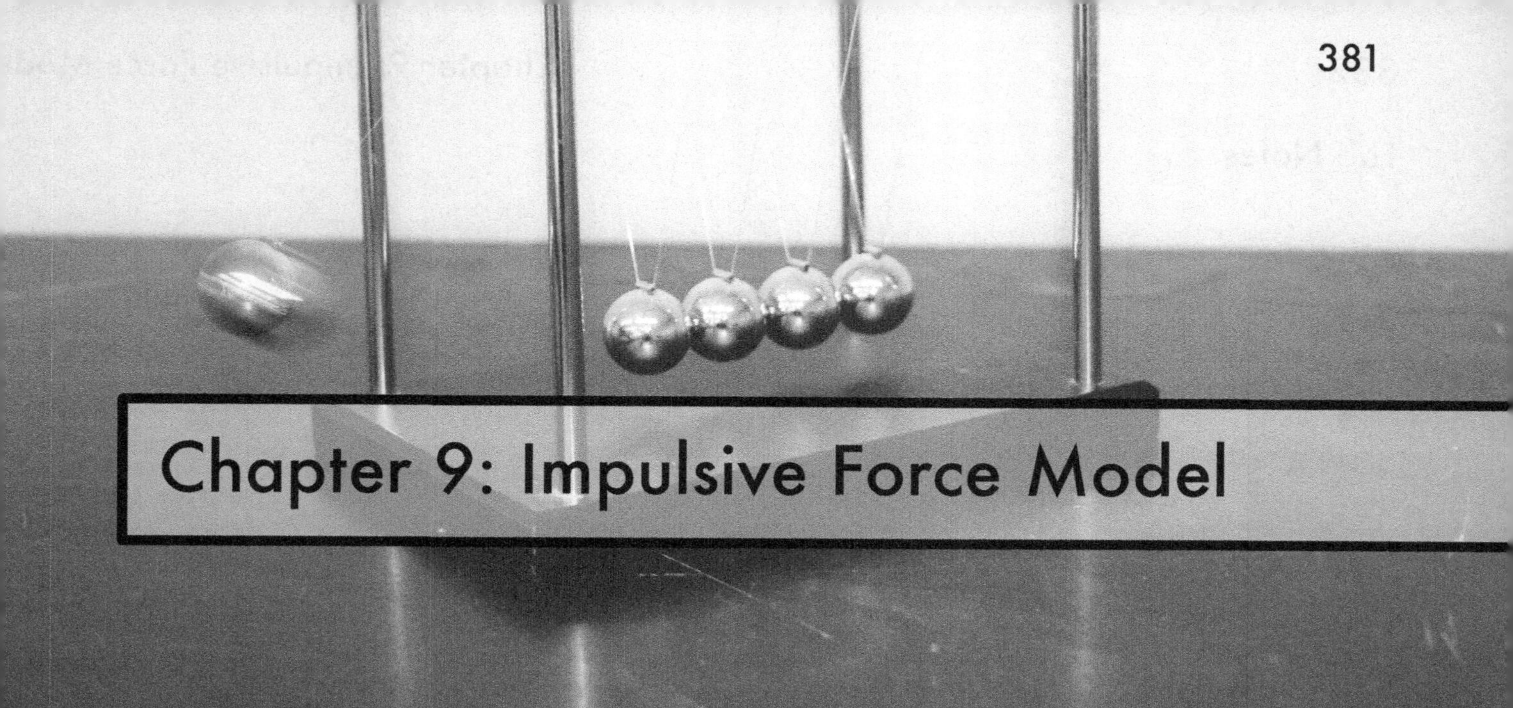

Chapter 9: Impulsive Force Model

:hapter Sections

chapter 9 online help

Lab Notes

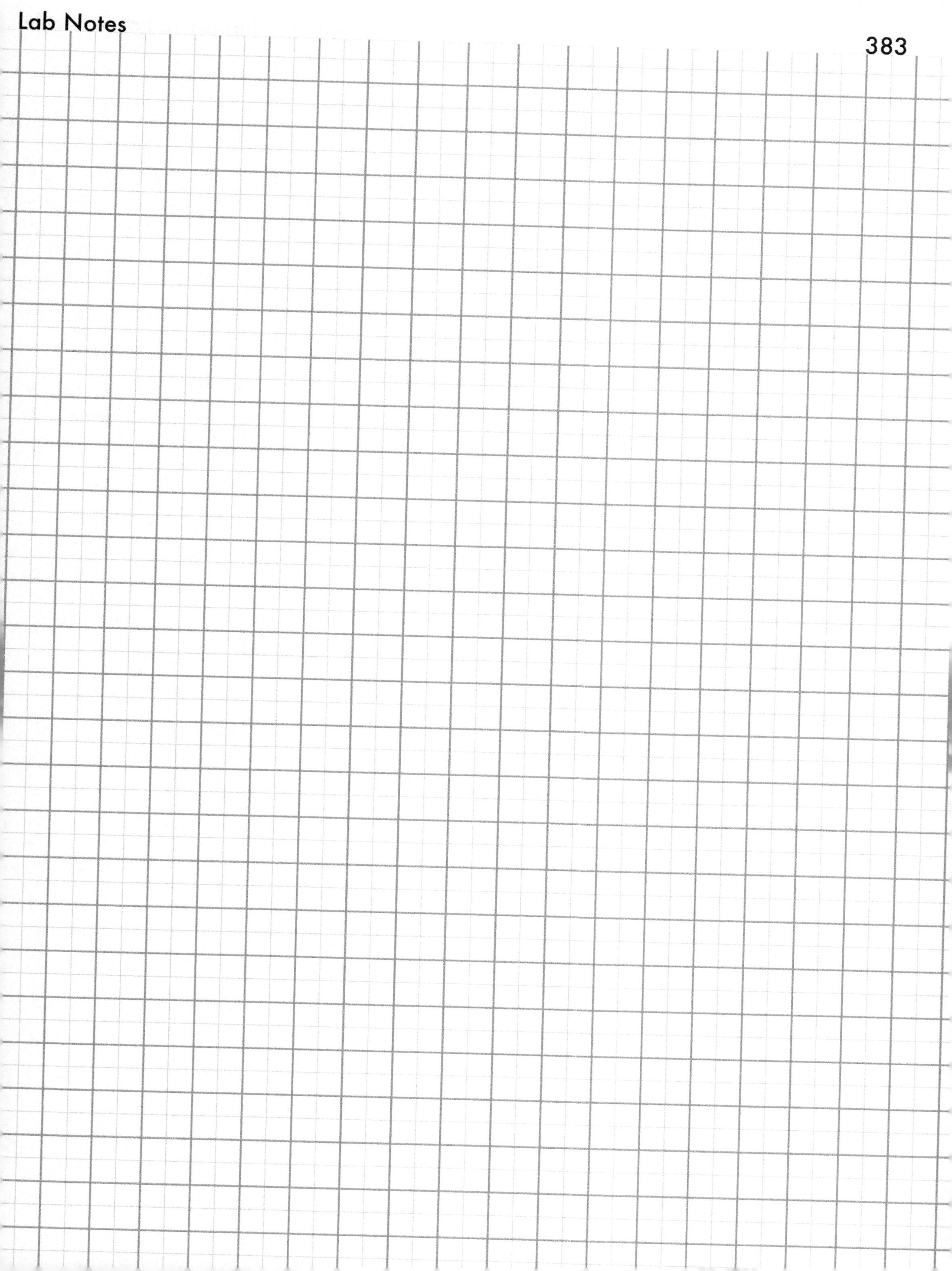

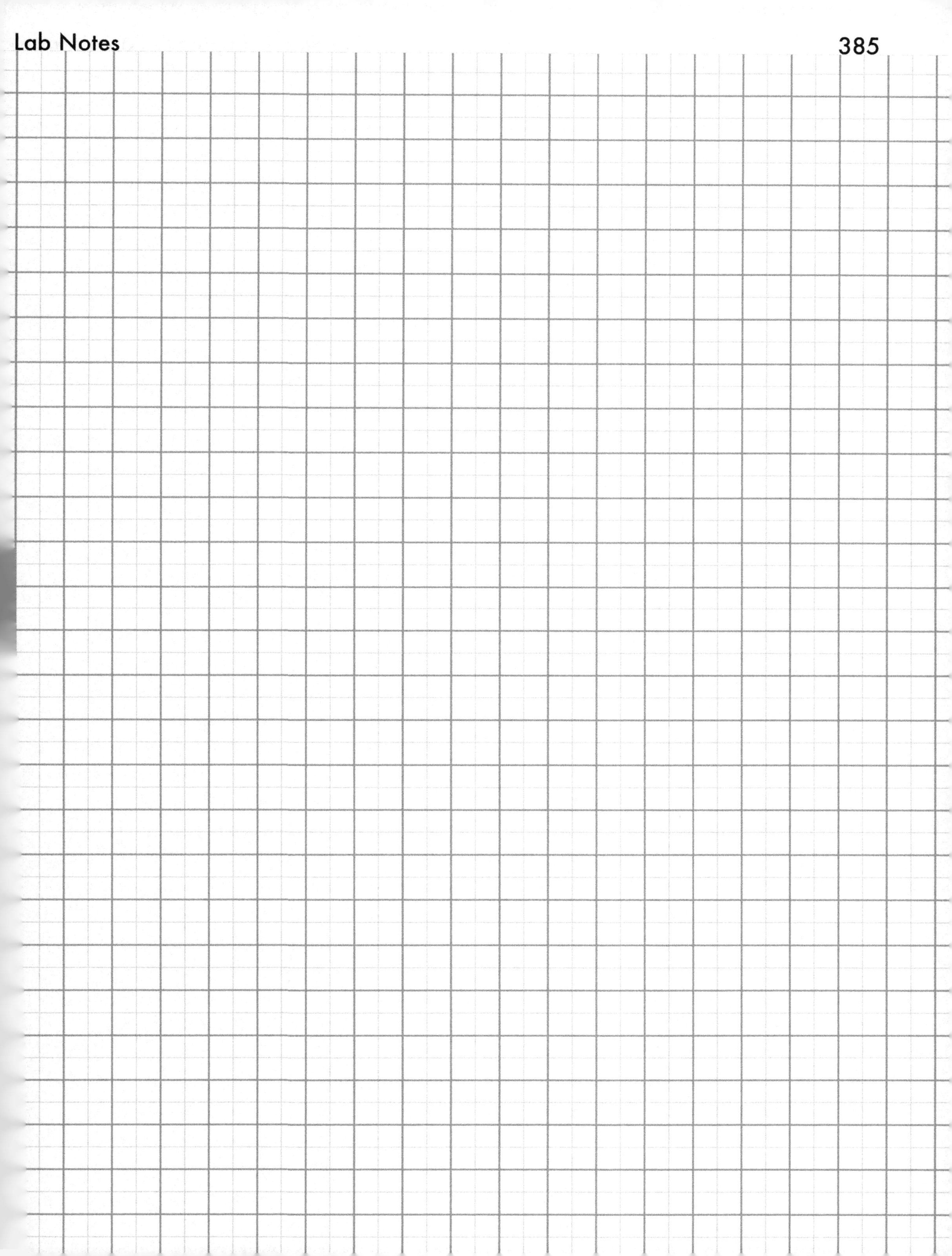

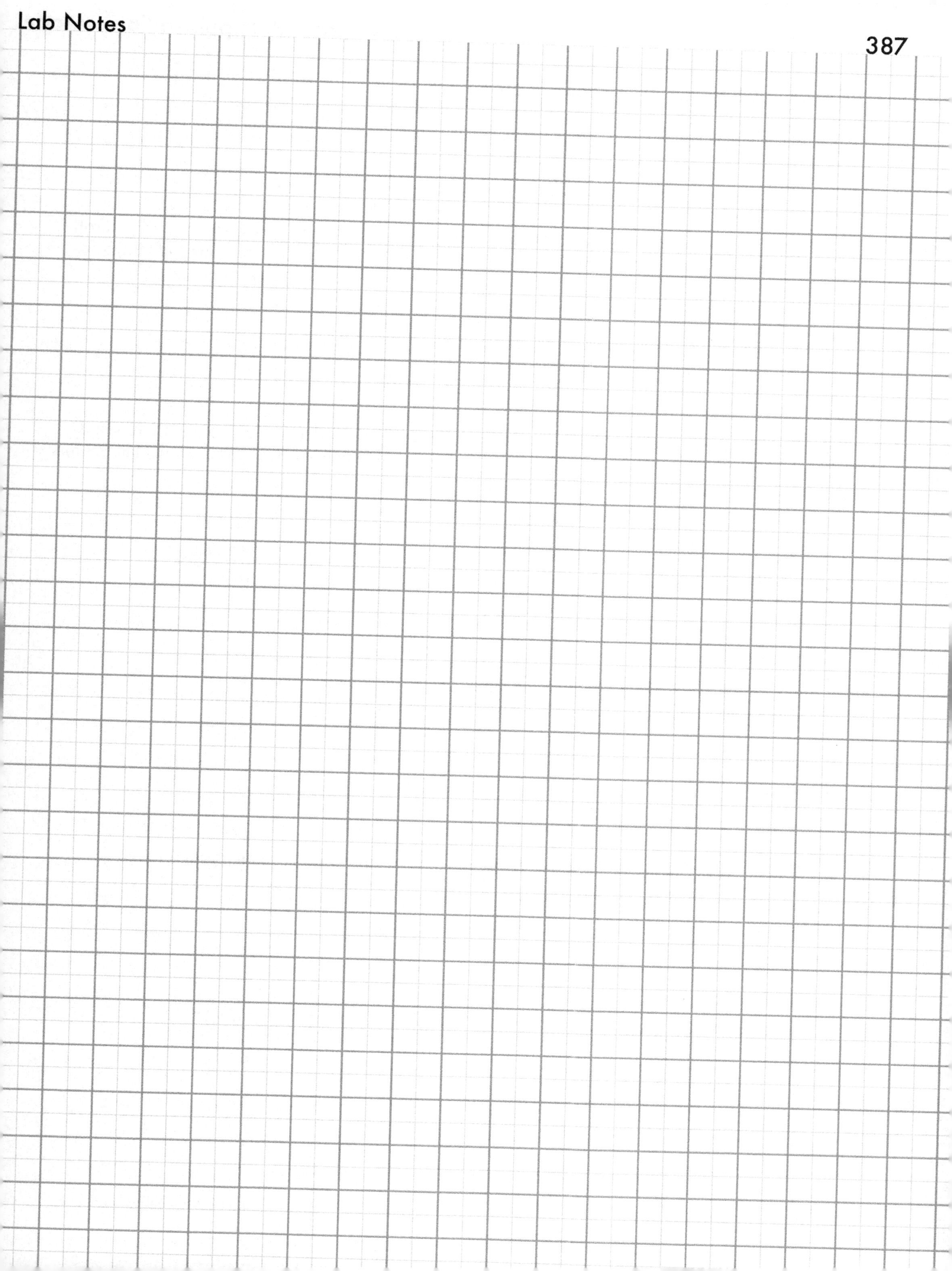

Worksheet 1: Qualitative Impulse-Momentum

The Impulse-Momentum theorem: $F_{net}\Delta t = \Delta(mv)$

1. If you throw a ball horizontally while standing on roller skates, you roll backwards. Will you roll backwards if you go through the motions of throwing the ball, but hold on to it instead? Explain your reasoning.

2. Which has the greater change in momentum, a 50 gram clay ball that strikes a wall at 1 m/s and sticks or a 50 gram superball that strikes a wall at 1 m/s and bounces away from the wall at 0.8 m/s? **Explain your reasoning.**

3. A Hummer and a VW Beetle traveling at equal speeds have a head-on collision.
   a. Which vehicle will experience the greater force of impact? Justify your answer.

   b. Which vehicle will experience the greater change in momentum? Justify your answer.

   c. Which vehicle will experience the greater acceleration? Justify your answer.

4. Discuss the following in terms of impulse and momentum:

   a. Why are padded dashboards safer than hard dashboards in automobiles?

   b. Why are nylon ropes, which stretch considerably under stress, favored by mountain climbers?

   c. When starting a heavy train, why will train engineers sometimes back up, stop, and then proceed forward? (This technique is called "bunching slack.")

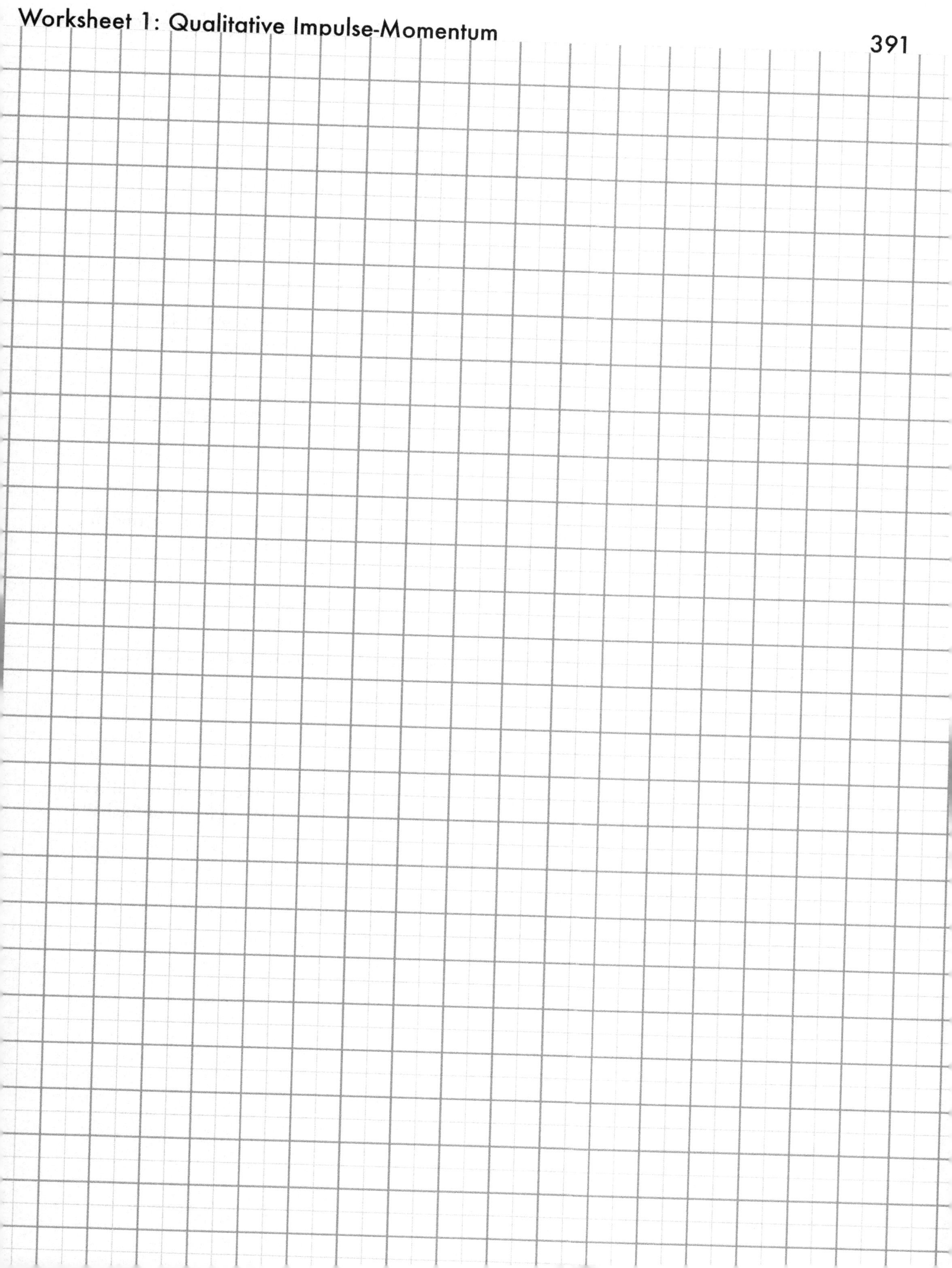

Worksheet 2: Impulsive Forces and Momentum

1. Two objects, A & B, have identical velocities. Object A has 3 times the mass of object B.
   a. Find the value of the ratio of momentum A to momentum B. Justify your answer.

   b. Find the value of the ratio of kinetic energy A to kinetic energy B. Justify your answer.

2. Two objects, C & D, have the same momentum. Object C has ½ the mass of object D.
   a. Find the value of the ratio of velocity C to velocity D. Justify your answer.

   b. Find the value of the ratio of kinetic energy C to kinetic energy D. Justify your answer.

3. The following questions refer to the motion of a baseball.

   a. While being thrown, a net force of 132 N acts on a baseball (mass = 140 g) for a period of 4.5×10^{-2} sec. What is the magnitude of the change in momentum of the ball?

   b. If the initial speed of the baseball is v = 0.0 m/s, what will its speed be when it leaves the pitcher's hand?

   c. When the batter hits the ball, a net force of 1150 N, opposite to the direction of the ball's initial motion, acts on the ball for 9.0×10^{-3} s during the hit. What is the final velocity of the ball?

   d. How large is the force the ball exerts on the bat? Explain.

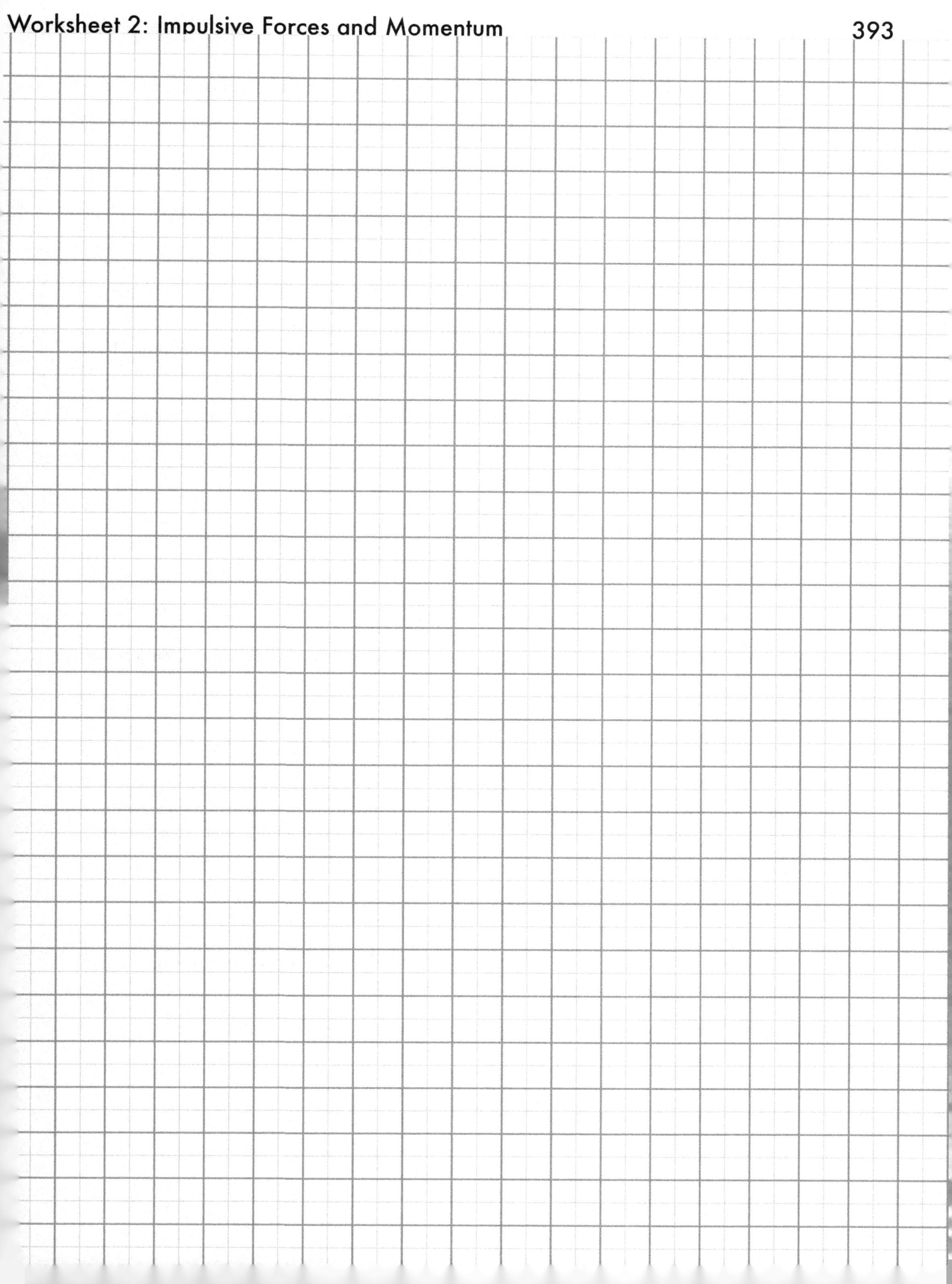

4. A rocket, weighing 4.36×10^4N, has an engine that provides an upward force of 1.2×10^5N. It reaches a maximum speed of 860 m/s.

   a. Draw a force diagram for the rocket.

   b. For how much time must the engine burn during the launch in order to reach this speed?

5. A golf ball that weighs 0.45 N is dropped from a height of 1.0 m. Assume that the golf ball has a perfectly elastic collision with the floor.

   a. Construct a motion map for the golf ball from the time it is dropped until it reaches its highest point of rebound.

   b. Determine the time required for the ball to reach the floor.

   c. What will the instantaneous momentum of the golf ball be immediately *before* it strikes the floor?

   d. What will be the change in momentum, (Δp) from the instant before the ball collides with the floor until the instant after it rebounds from the floor? (Illustrate with a vector diagram.)

   e. Suppose that the golf ball was in contact with the floor for 4.0×10^{-4}s. What was the average force on the ball while it was in contact with the floor?

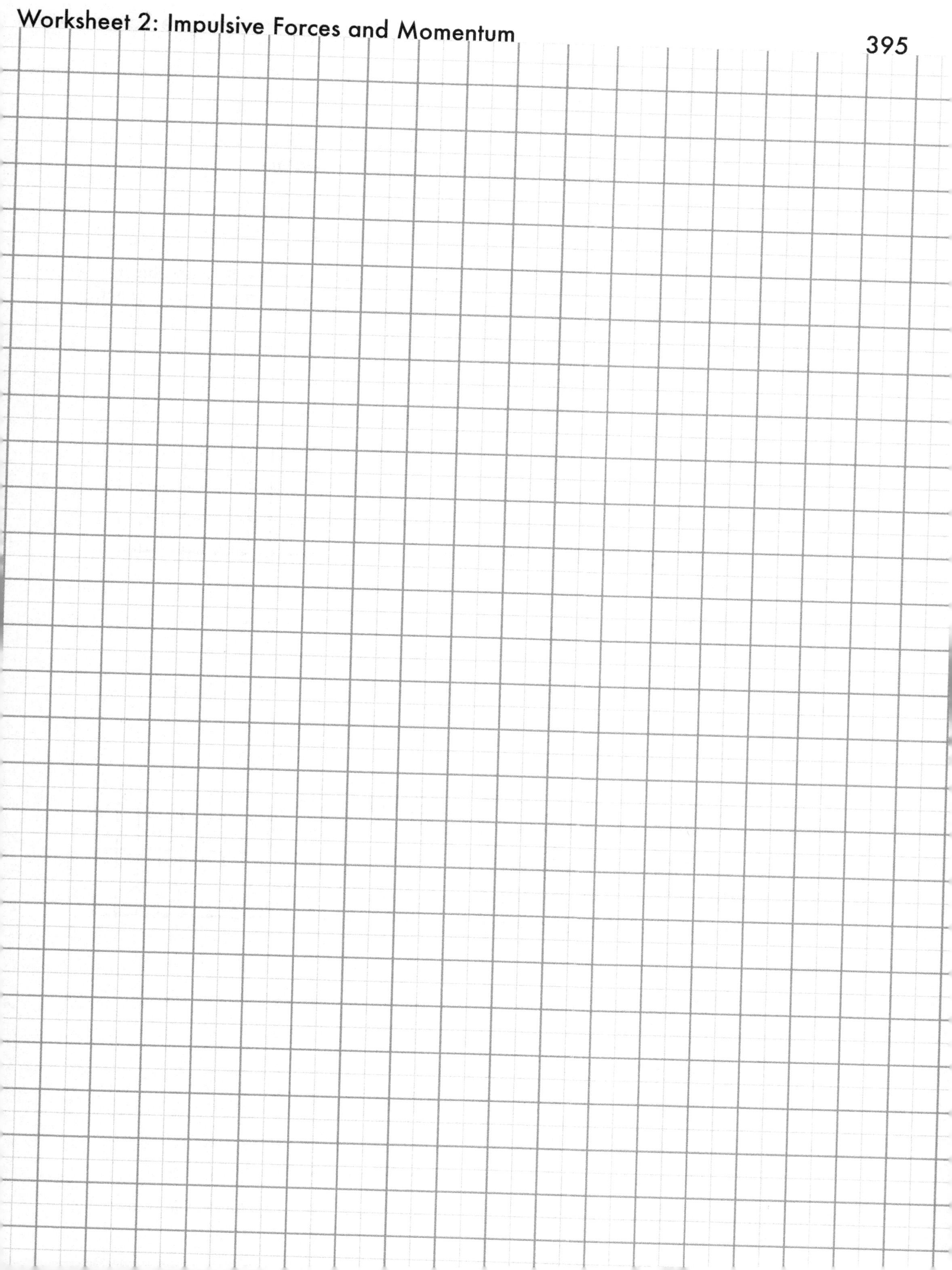

Worksheet 3a: Conservation of Momentum Examples

As long as no objects external to the system contribute to net forces on the system,

Total initial momentum = Total final momentum

1. Specify the impulsive force event that separates initial and final situations.
2. Designate objects in the system by listing the object, its mass, and its velocity in the chart -- use variables for unknown quantities.
3. Draw a horizontal bar to represent the size and direction of the momentum for each object.
4. Write the conservation of momentum equation for the bars and solve for the unknown quantity.

Example 1:

event:

initial
object/mass/velocity

– 0 +

final
object/mass/velocity

– 0 +

Example 2:

event:

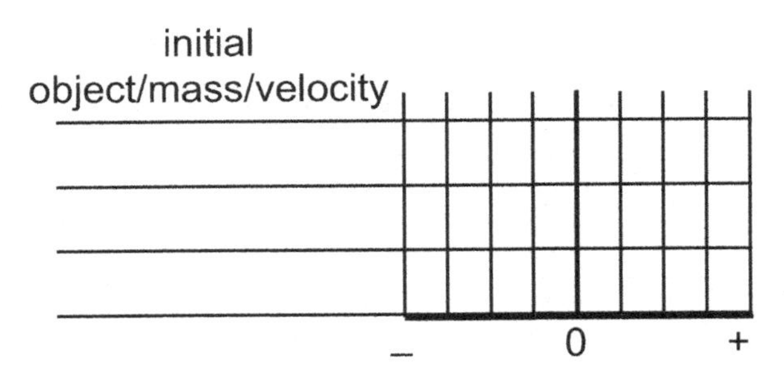

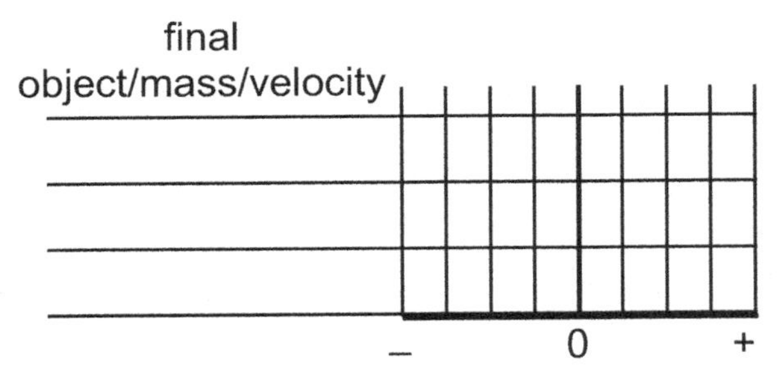

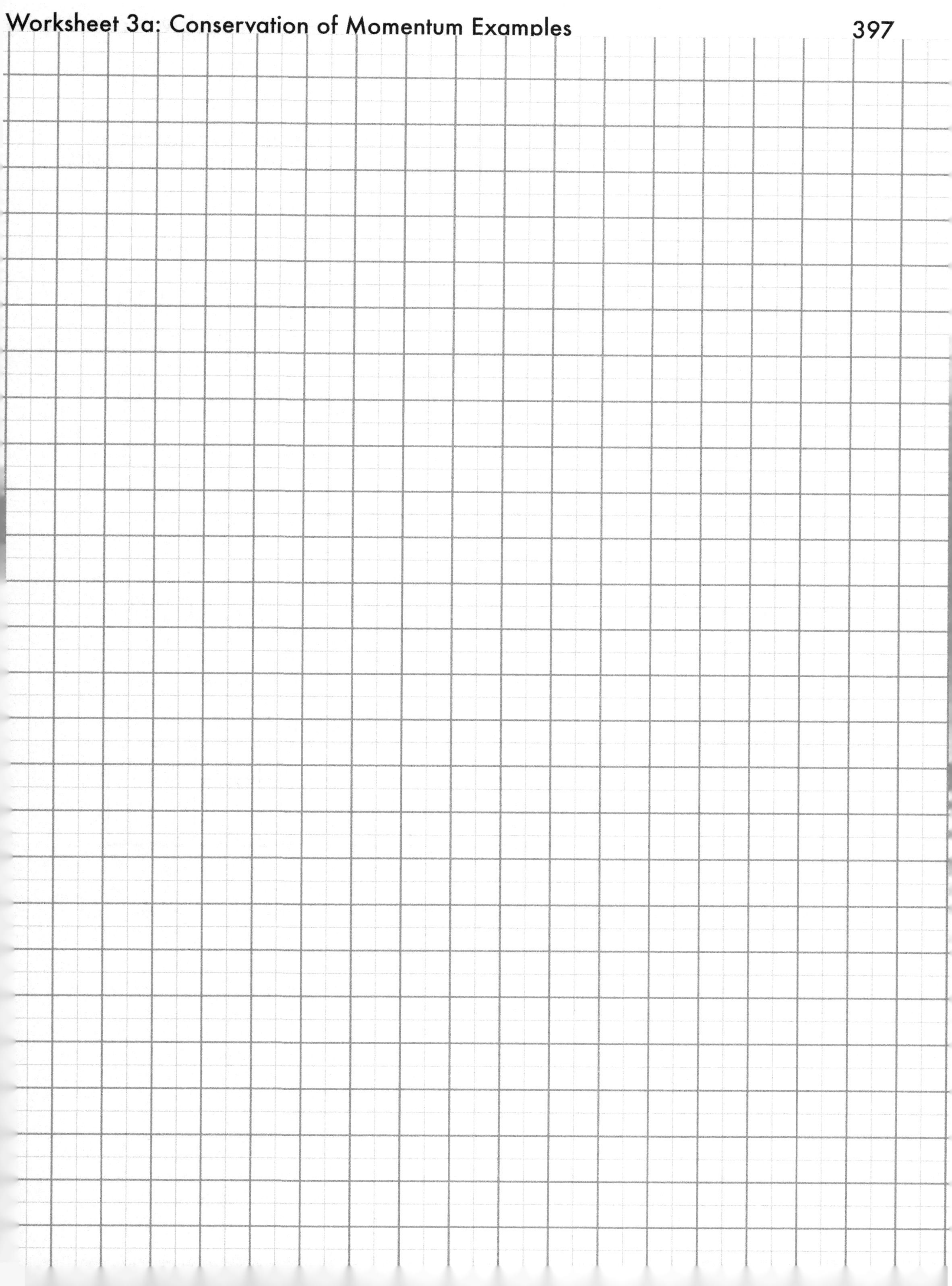

Worksheet 3b: Conservation of Momentum I

1. In a railroad yard, a train is being assembled. An empty boxcar, coasting at 3.0 m/s, strikes a loaded car that is stationary, and the cars couple together. Each of the boxcars has a mass of 9000 kg when empty, and the loaded car contains 55,000 kg of lumber.
   a. Complete the momentum conservation diagram.

event:

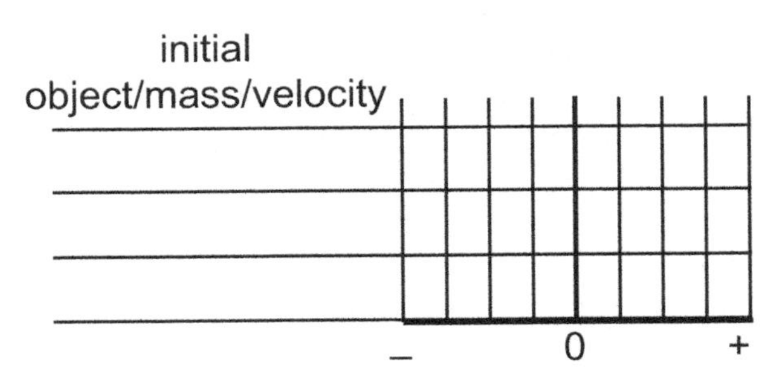

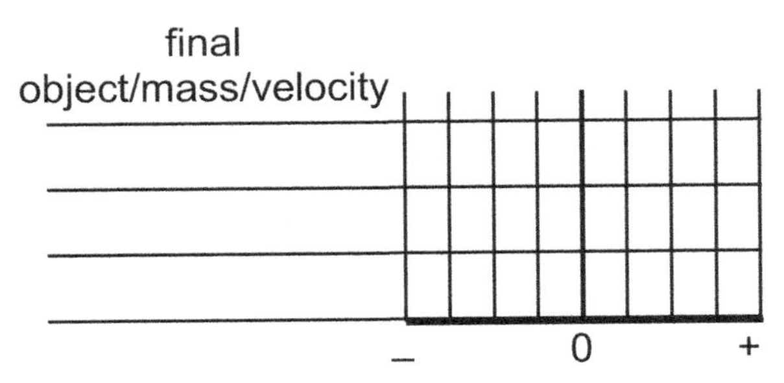

   b. Momentum conservation equation:

   c. Find the speed of the coupled boxcars.

2. An astronaut of mass 80.0 kg carries an empty oxygen tank of mass 10.0 kg. By pushing the tank away with a speed of 2.0 m/s, the astronaut recoils in the opposite direction.
   a. Complete the momentum conservation diagram.

event:

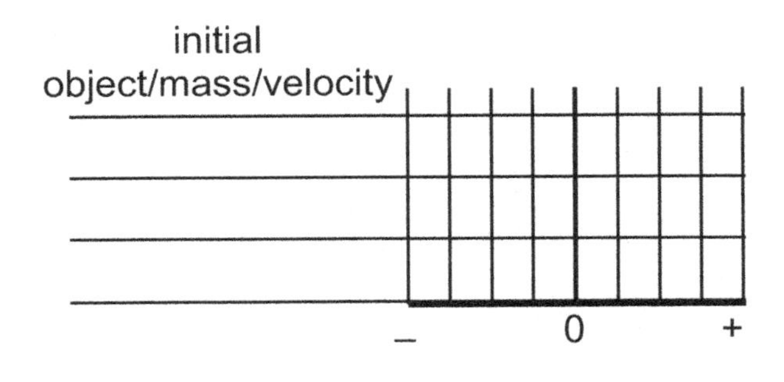

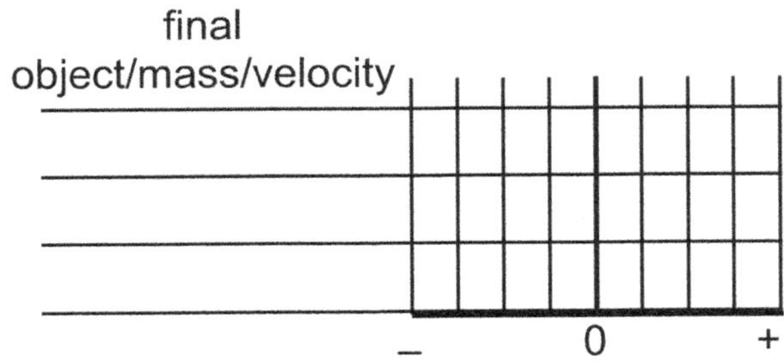

   b. Momentum conservation equation:

   c. Find the speed with which the astronaut moves off into space.

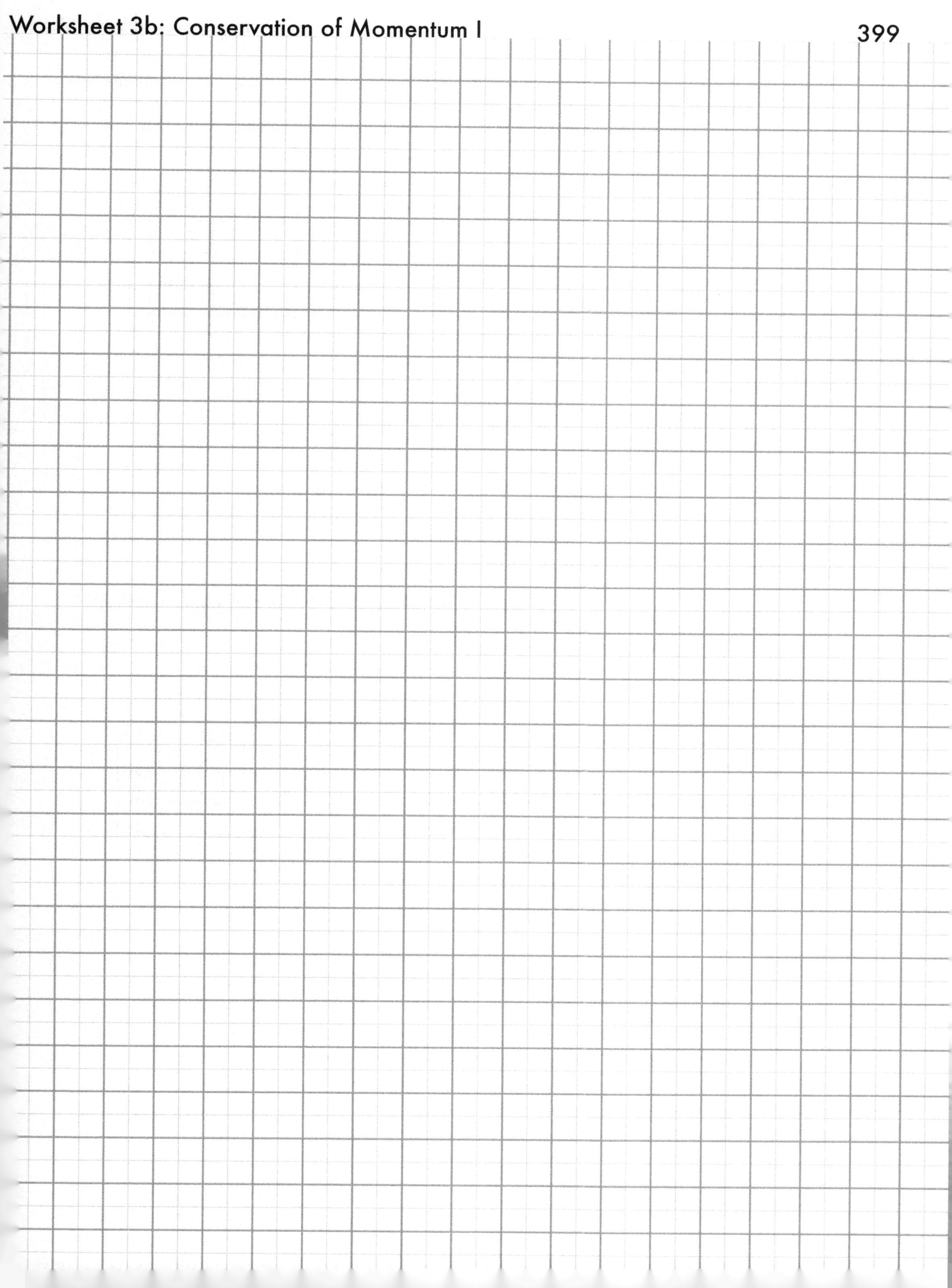

3. A tennis player returns a 30.0 m/s serve straight back at 25 m/s, after making contact with the ball for 0.50 s. The ball has a mass of 0.20 kg.
   a. Use a momentum conservation diagram to show the change in momentum of the ball.

event:

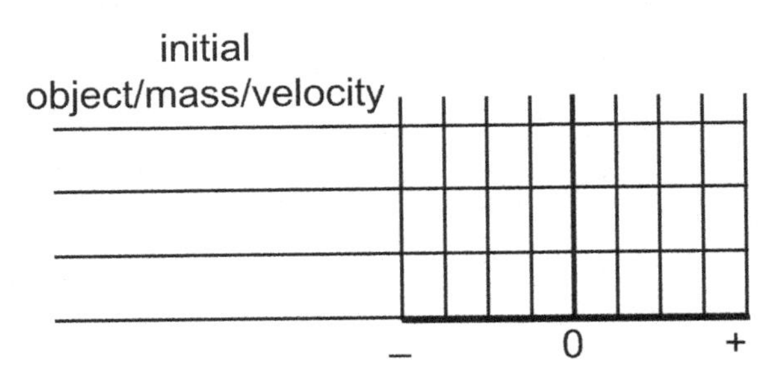

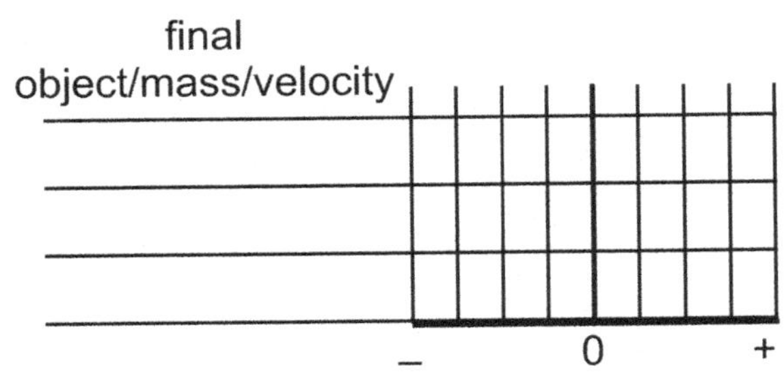

   b. Impulse-Momentum equation:

   c. How much force did the racket exert on the ball?

4. A 50.0 kg cart is moving across a frictionless floor at 2.0 m/s. A 70.0 kg boy, riding in the cart, jumps off so that he hits the floor with zero velocity.
   a. Complete the momentum conservation diagram.

event:

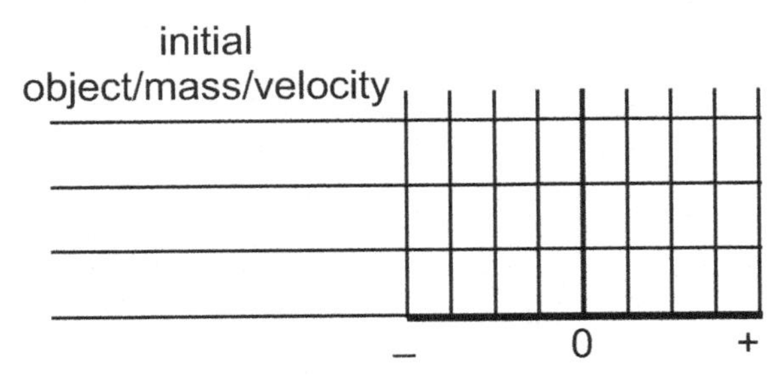

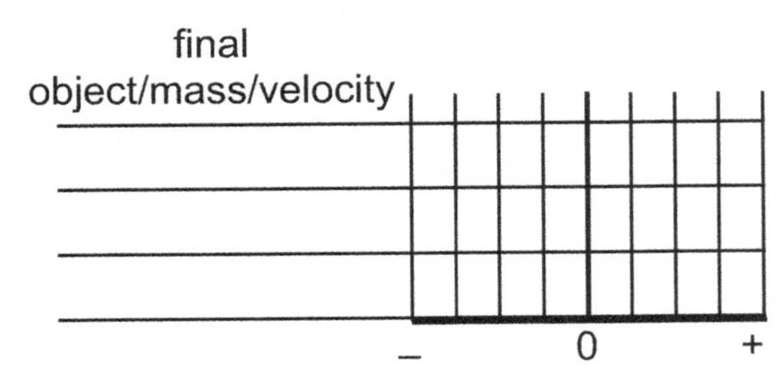

   b. Momentum conservation equation:

   c. How large an impulse did the boy give to the cart?

   d. What was the velocity of the cart after the boy jumped?

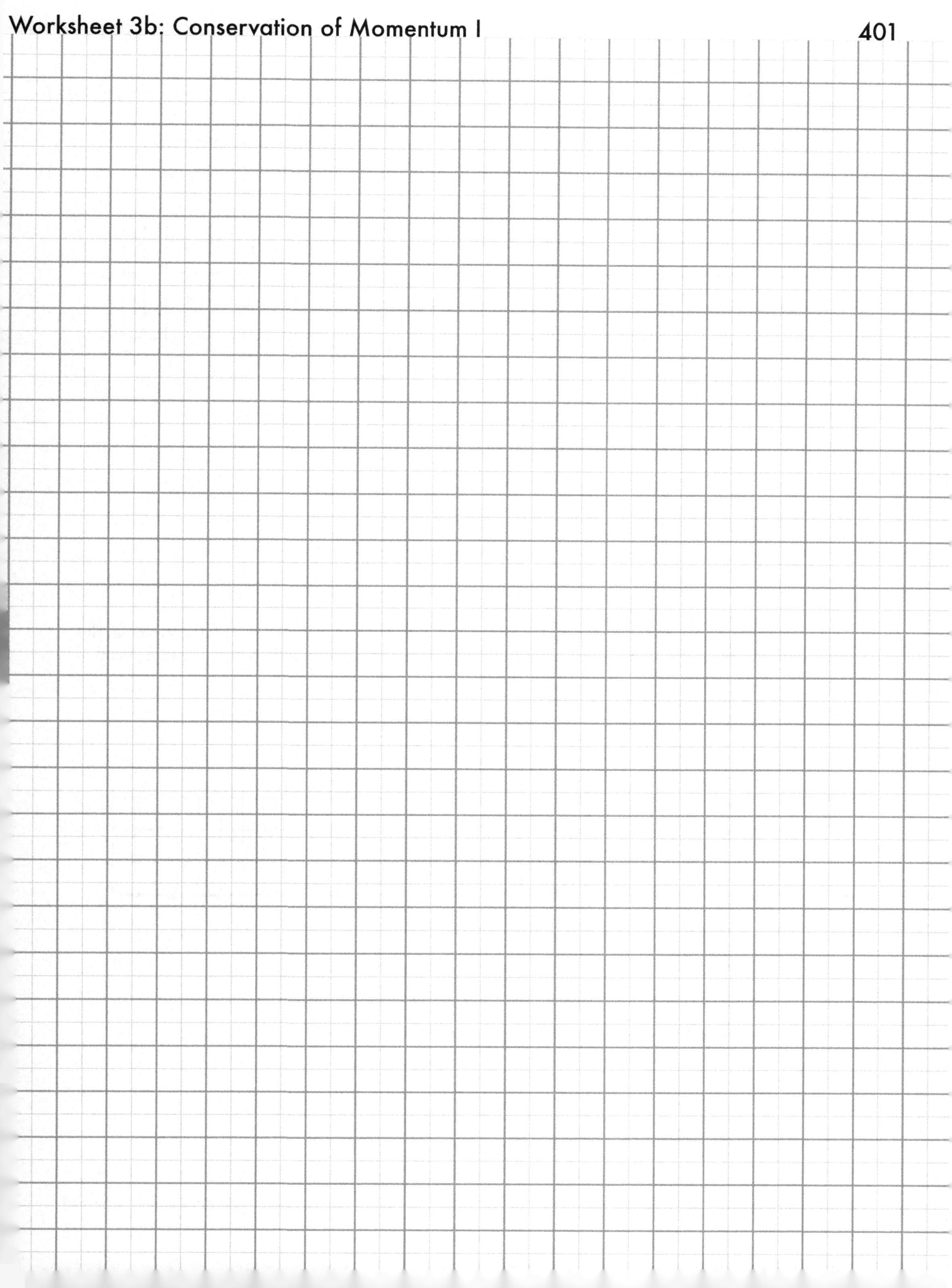

5. Two girls with masses of 50.0 kg and 70.0 kg are at rest on frictionless in-line skates. The taller girl pushes the shorter girl so that the shorter girl rolls away at a speed of 10.0 m/s.
   a. Show the effect of the push on both girls with a momentum conservation diagram.

event:

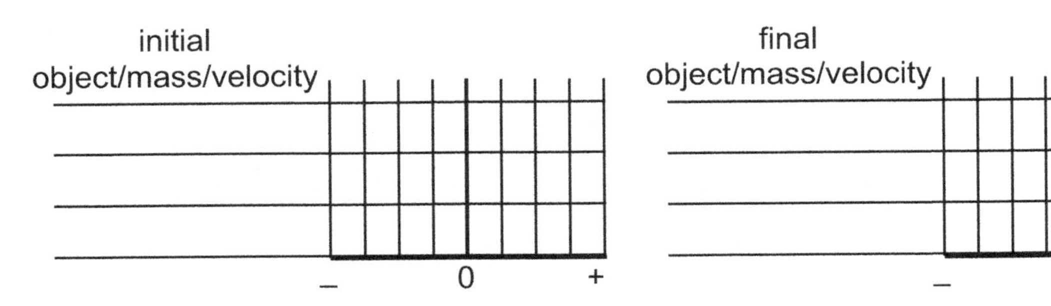

   b. Momentum conservation equation:

   c. Calculate the impulse that each girl imparts to the other.

6. A 2.0 kg melon is balanced on a circus performer's head. An archer shoots a 50.0 g arrow at the melon with a speed of 30 m/s. The arrow passes through the melon and emerges with a speed of 18 m/s.
   a. Draw a momentum conservation diagram for the stunt.

event:

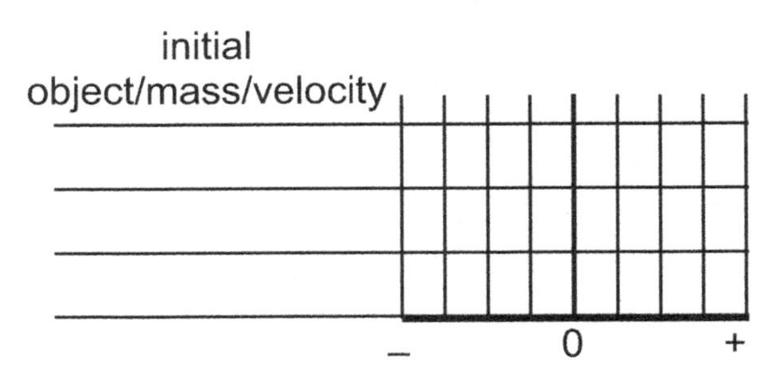

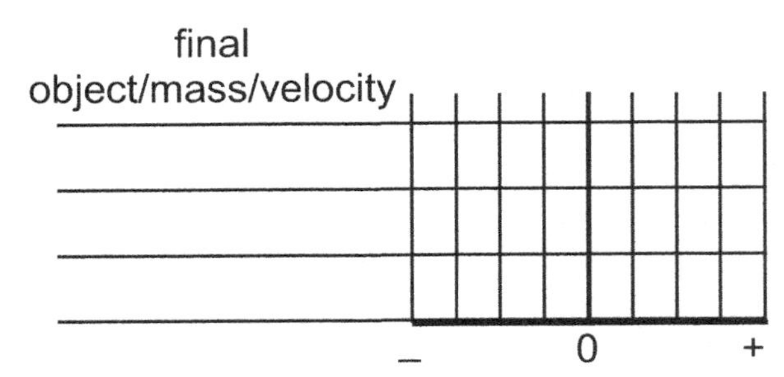

   b. Momentum conservation equation:

   c. Find the speed of the melon as it flies off the performer's head.

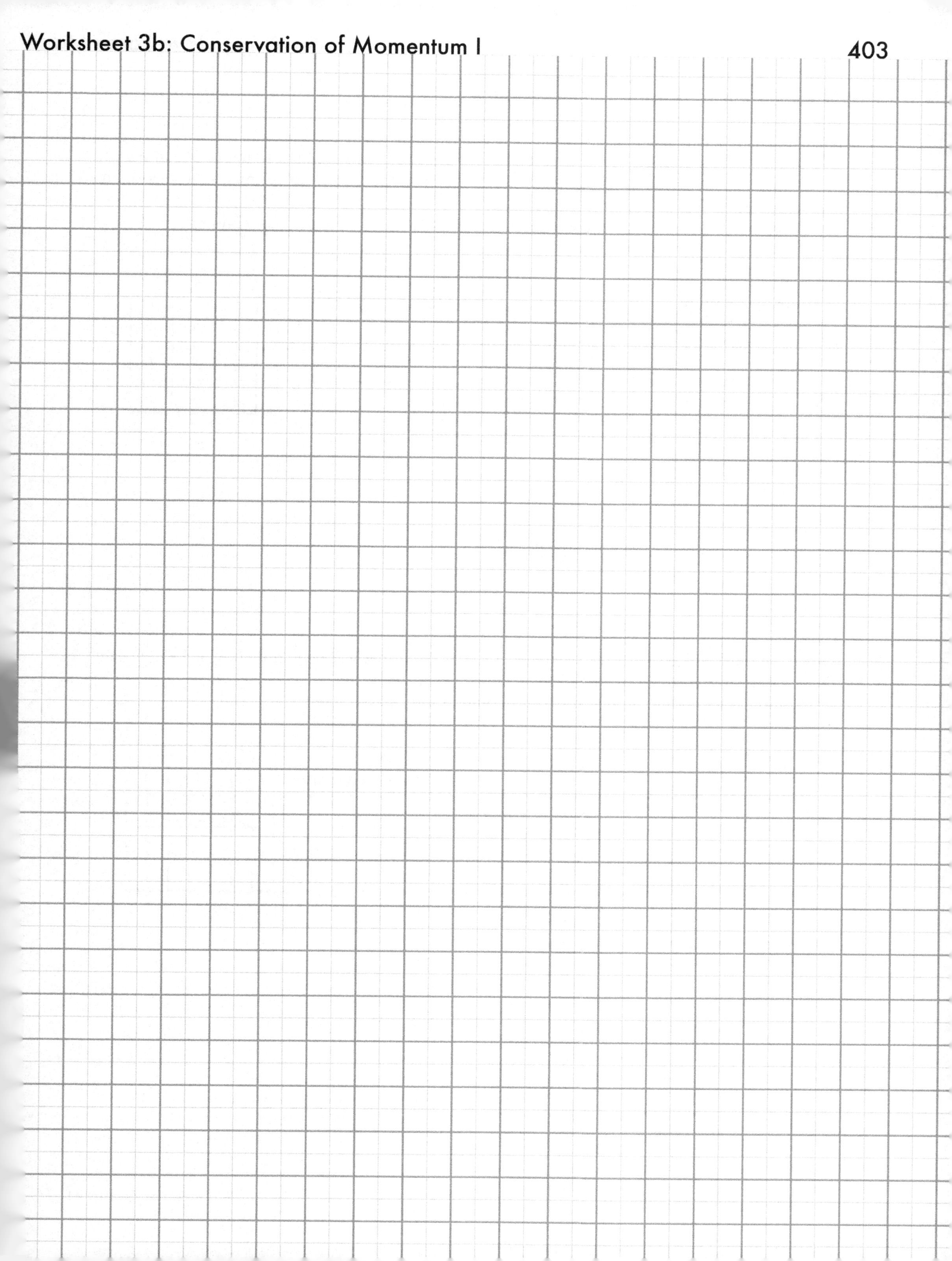

Worksheet 4: Conservation of Momentum II

1. Old cannons were built on wheeled carts, both to facilitate moving the cannon and to allow the cannon to recoil when fired. When a 150 kg cannon and cart recoils at 1.5 m/s, at what velocity would a 10.0 kg cannonball leave the cannon?
   a. Complete a conservation of momentum diagram for firing one of these cannons.

event:

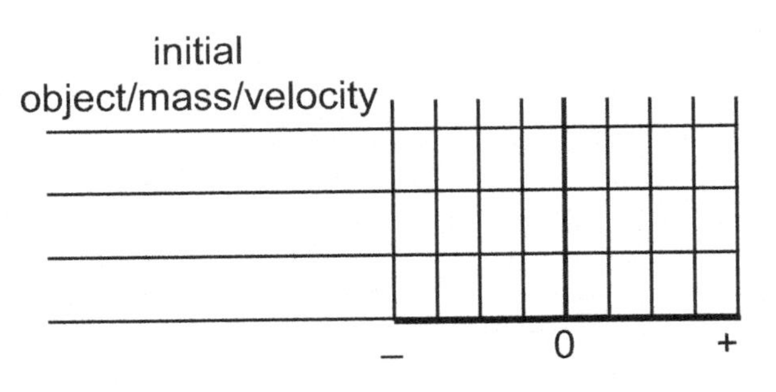

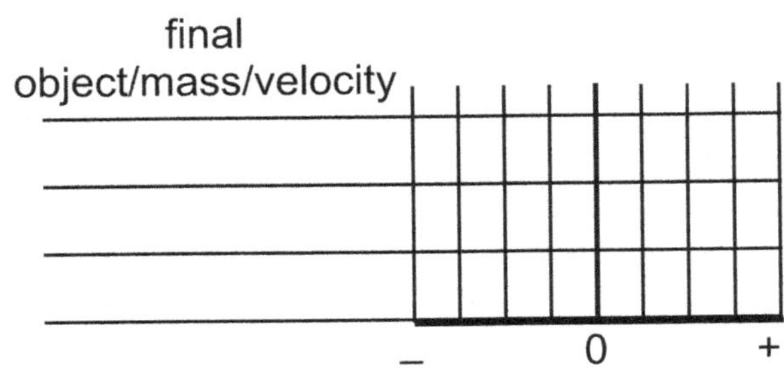

   b. Momentum conservation equation:

   c. Find the velocity of the cannonball.

2. On an icy road, a 5000 kg truck rear-ends a 1200 kg car that had been traveling at 13 m/s, causing the truck to slow from 14 m/s to 12 m/s and the car to speed up.
   a. Complete the momentum conservation diagram for the accident.

event:

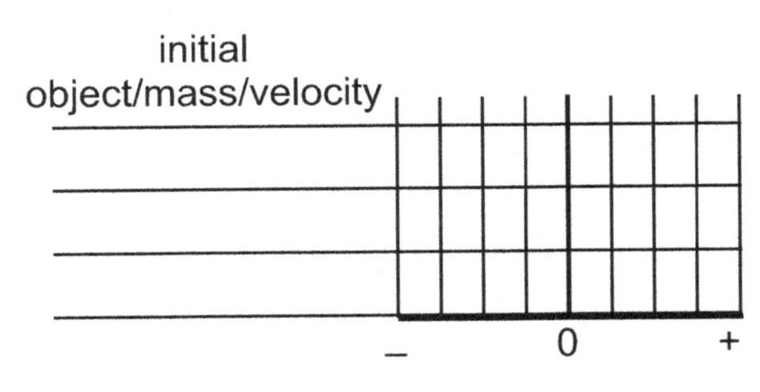

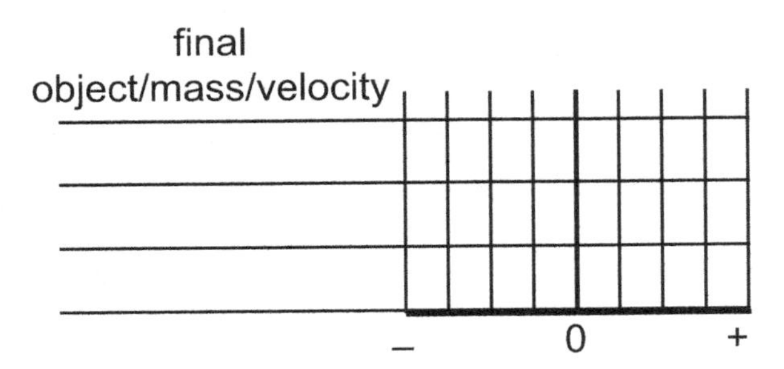

   b. Momentum conservation equation:

   c. Find the final velocity of the car.

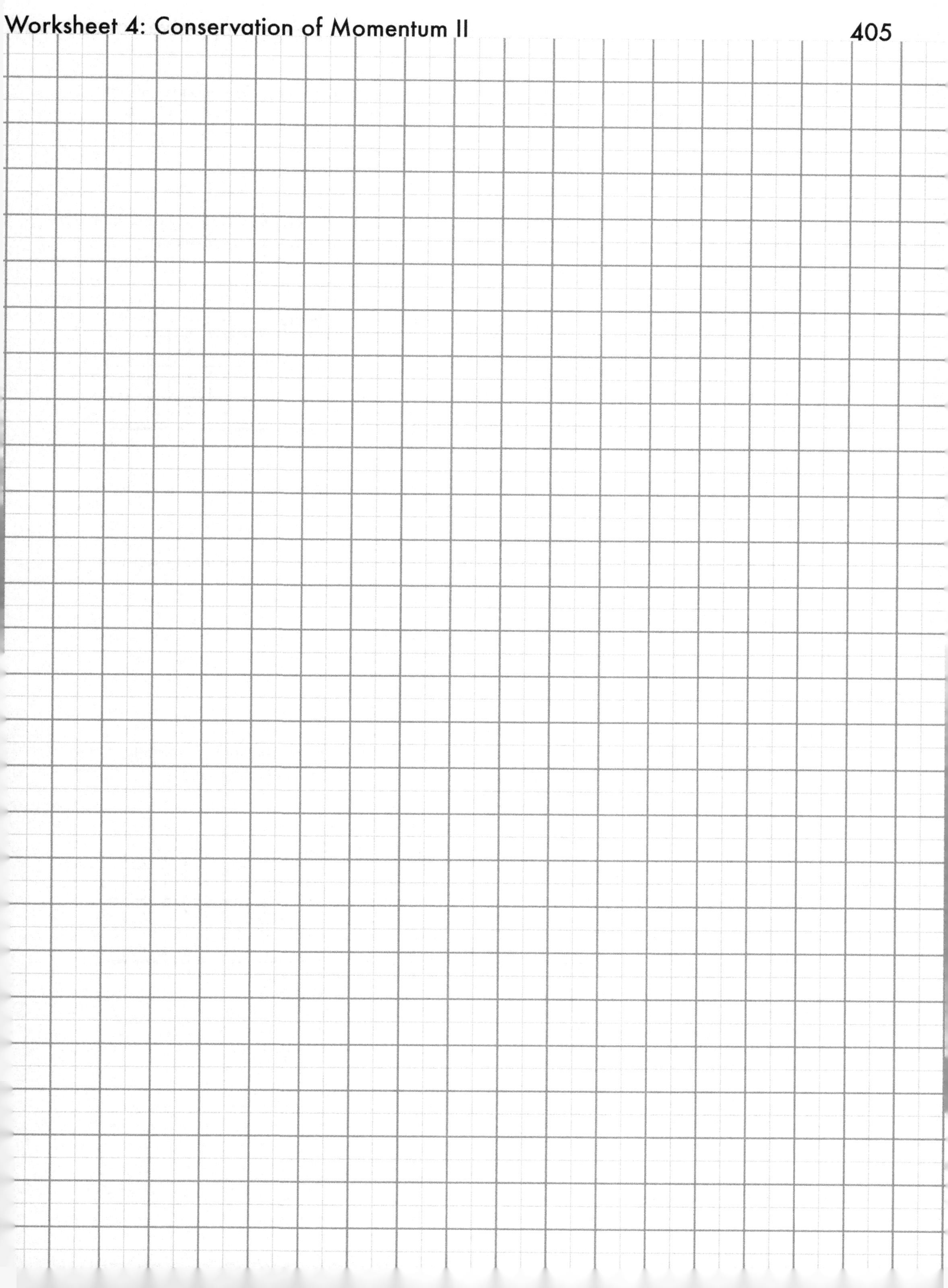

3. When radium-226 decays, it becomes radon-222 by ejecting an alpha particle - two protons and two neutrons (a helium nucleus).

→ decay occurs →

^{226}Ra ^{222}Rn ^{4}He

   a. Complete a qualitative momentum conservation diagram for the radioactive decay of radium-226. (Recall from chemistry that the isotopic number of an element is related to its mass.)

event:

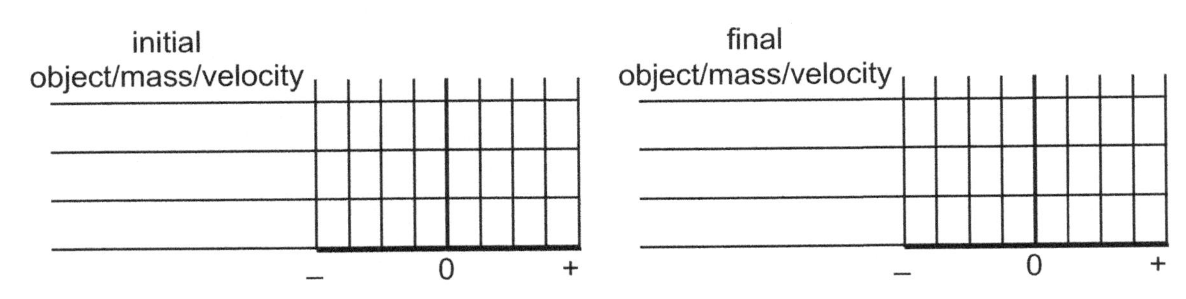

   b. Momentum conservation equation:

   c. How many times larger will the final velocity of the alpha particle be compared to the final velocity of the radon-222?

4. An apple falls from a tree.
   a. Complete a **qualitative** conservation of momentum diagram where the apple is initially attached to the tree and the final situation is just before the apple hits the ground.

event:

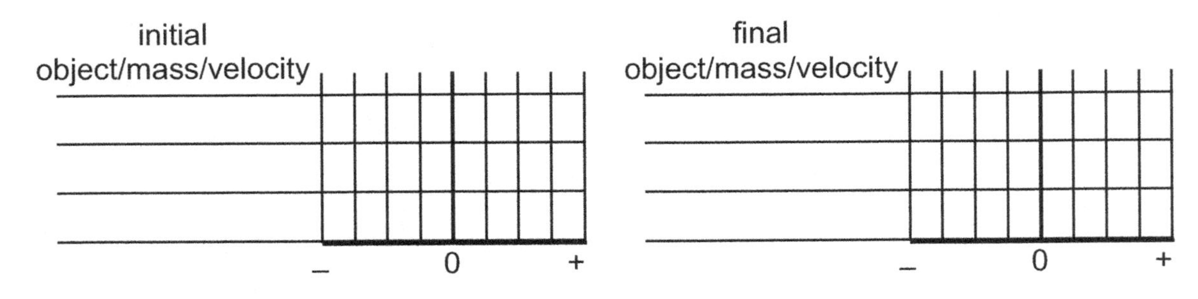

   b. Momentum conservation equation:

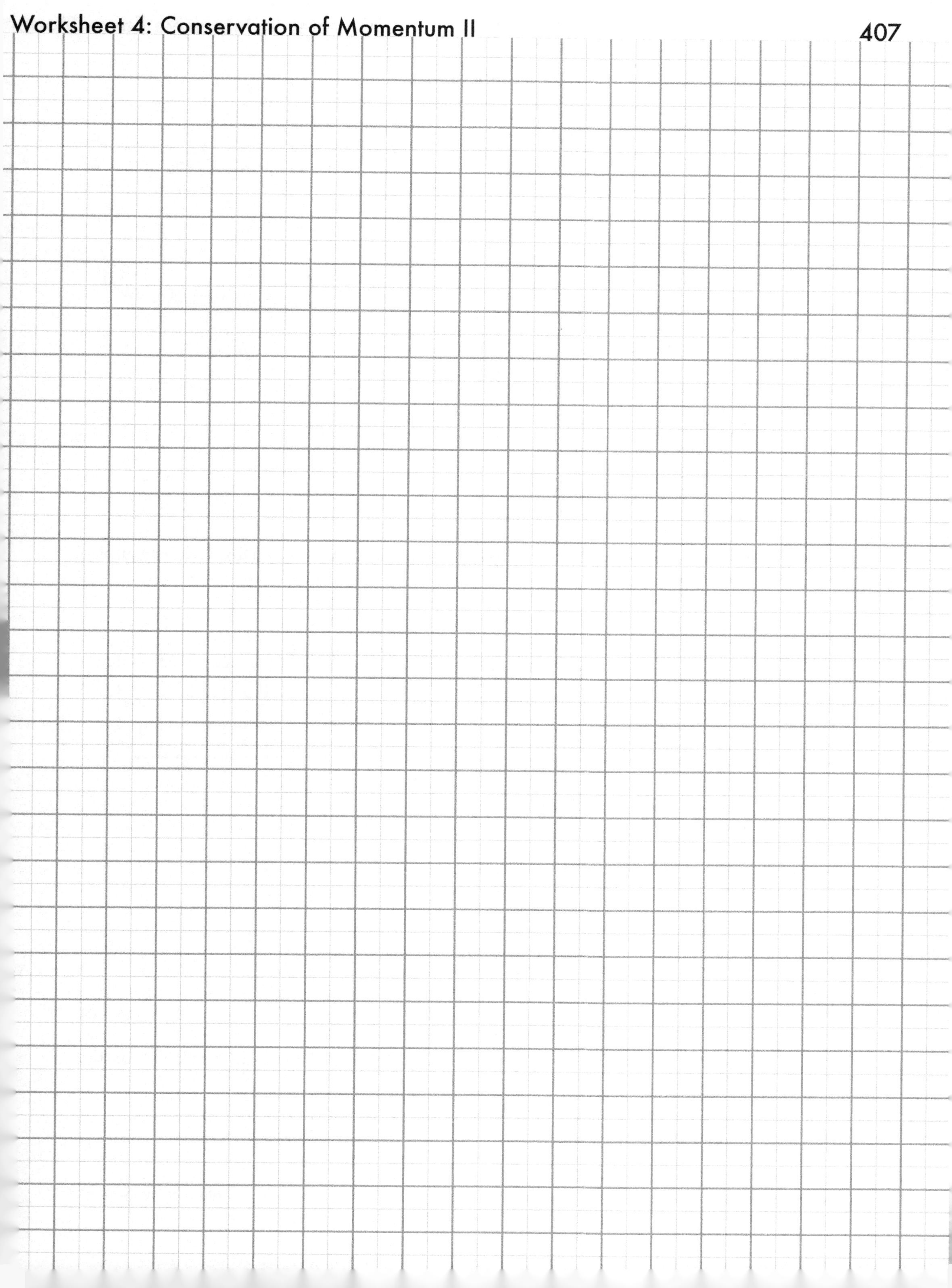

5. Airplanes maneuver on the ground by using thrust from their jets or propellers. A fully loaded, 396,900 kg Boeing 747-400 gets a total of 1100 kiloNewtons of thrust from its jet engines. (Data from Boeing's website.) Takeoff speed depends on a number of factors like air temperature, airplane weight, and airport elevation, but let us say that liftoff will occur at 170 mph.

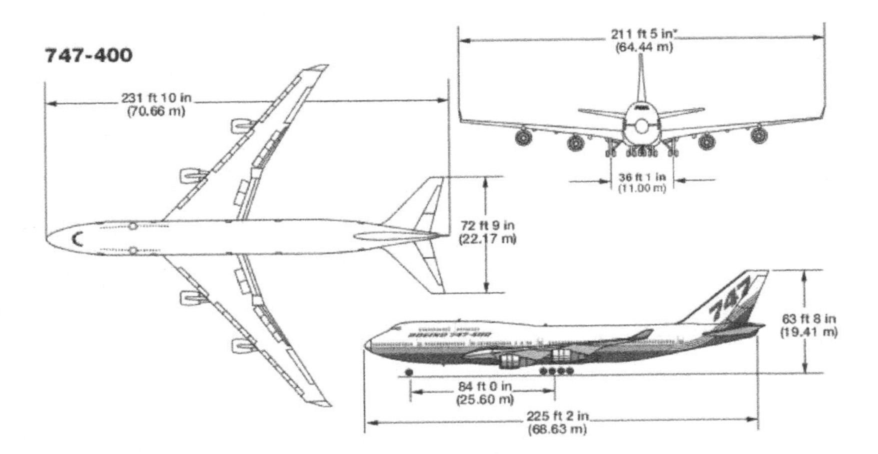

a. Determine the time the plane takes to go from 0 to 170 mph. (1 mile = 1600 meters)

b. Complete a conservation of momentum diagram showing how the initially stationary airplane gets to takeoff speed.

event:

initial
object/mass/velocity

– 0 +

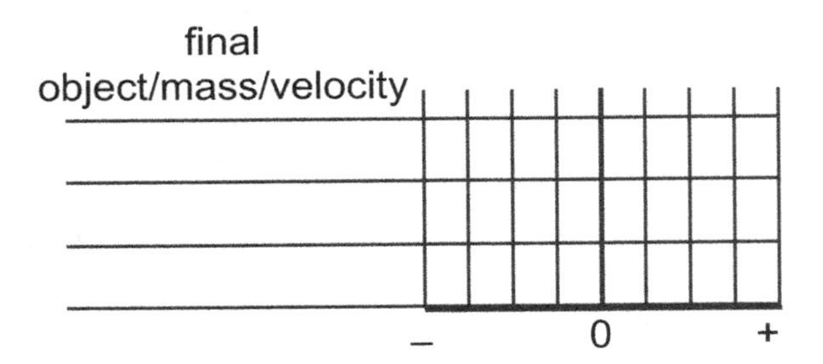

c. Momentum conservation equation:

d. Determine the momentum of the airplane at takeoff.

e. Calculate the impulse the plane receives from the engines during takeoff.

f. What additional information would be needed to calculate the velocity of the exhaust gasses from the engines?

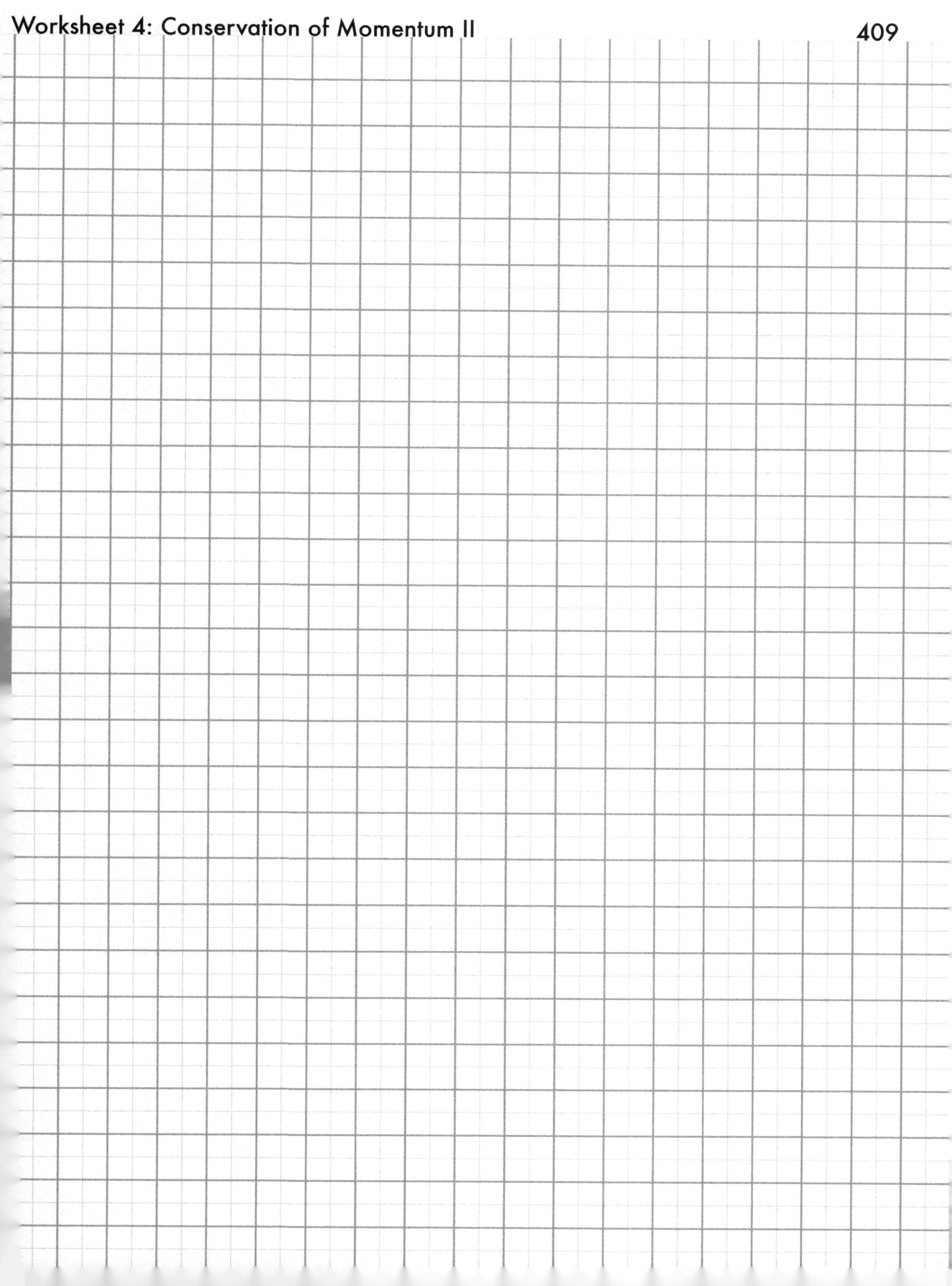

Review Problems

1. A ball of mass 3.0 kg, moving at 2.0 m/s eastward, strikes head-on a ball of mass 1.0 kg that is moving at 2.0 m/s westward. The balls stick together after the impact. Complete the momentum conservation diagram. What is the magnitude and direction of the velocity of the combined mass after the collision?

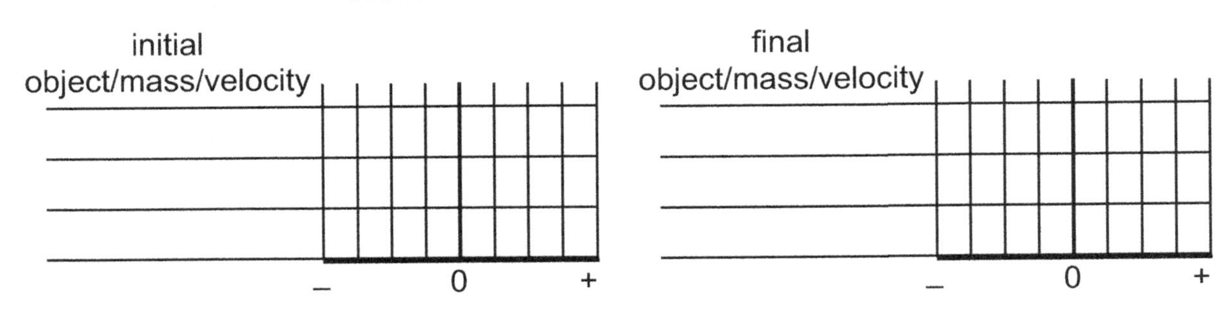

2. One way of measuring the muzzle velocity of a bullet is to fire it horizontally into a massive block of wood placed on a cart. Assuming no friction, we then measure the velocity with which the wood containing the bullet and cart begin to move. In one experiment the bullet had a mass of 7.5 g and the wood and its cart had a mass of 5.0 kg. After the shot, the cart, wood, and bullet moved at a constant speed, traveling 2.4 m in 4.0 s. From these data, complete a momentum conservation diagram and determine the original speed of the bullet.

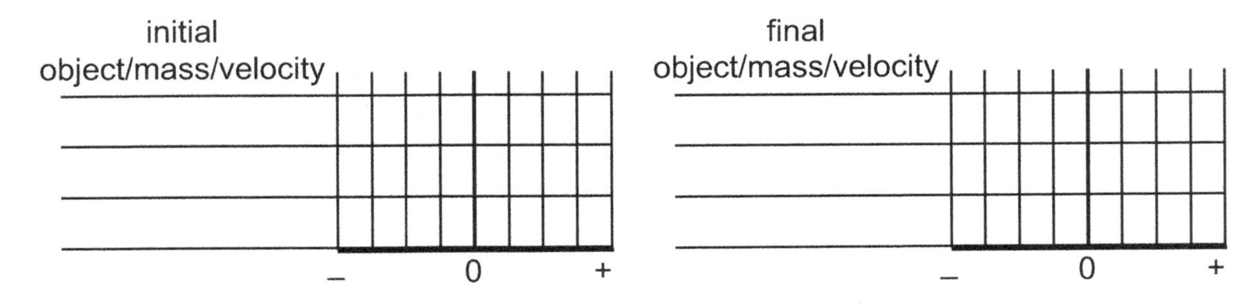

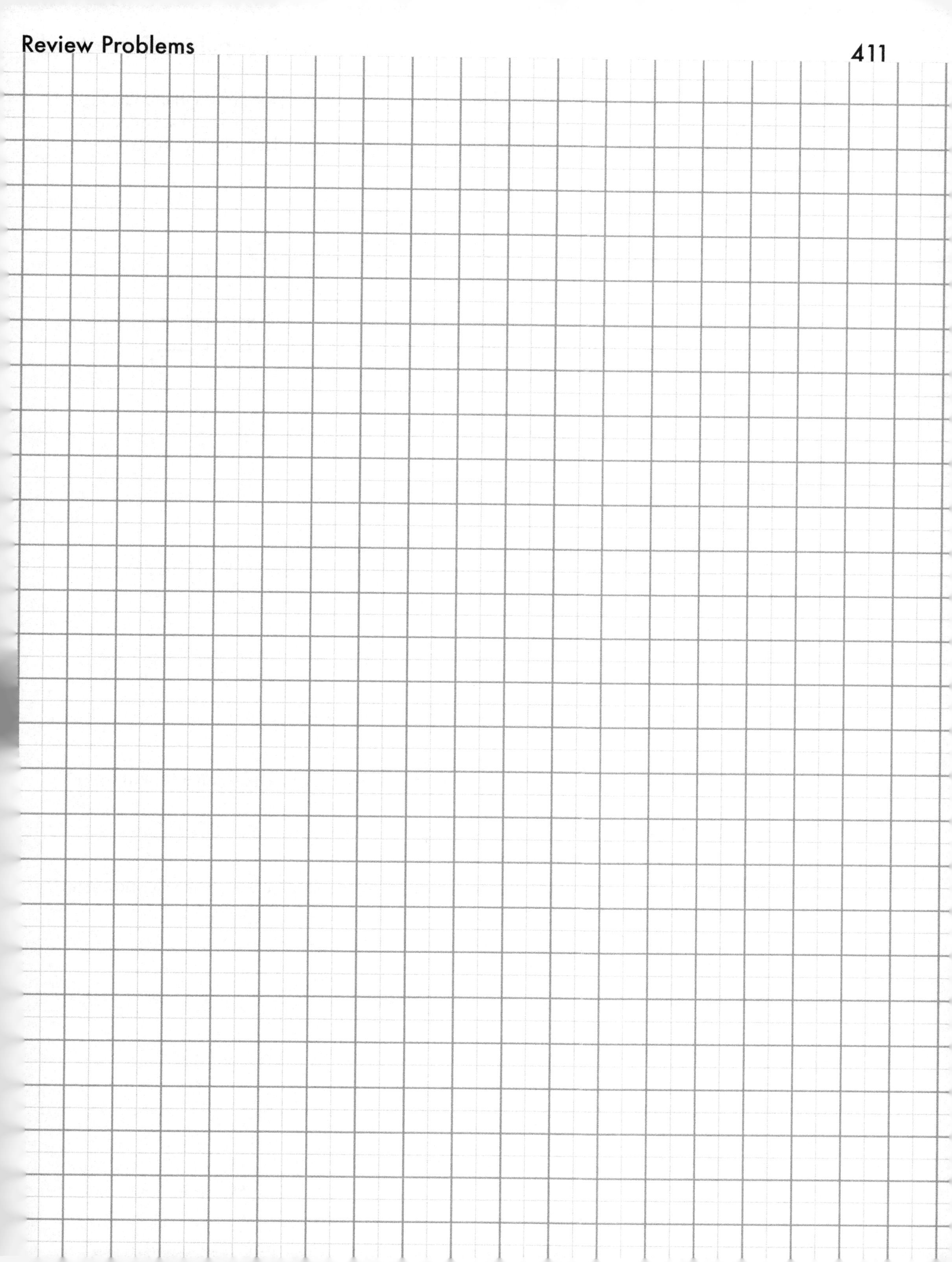

3. A raft of mass 180 kg carries two swimmers of mass 50. kg and 80. kg. The raft is initially floating at rest. The two swimmers simultaneously dive off opposite ends of the raft, each with a horizontal velocity of 3.0 m/s. Complete the momentum conservation diagram and determine the final velocity and direction the raft.

event:

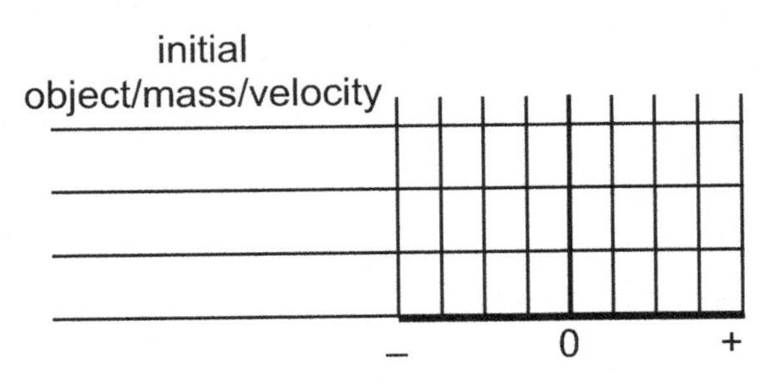

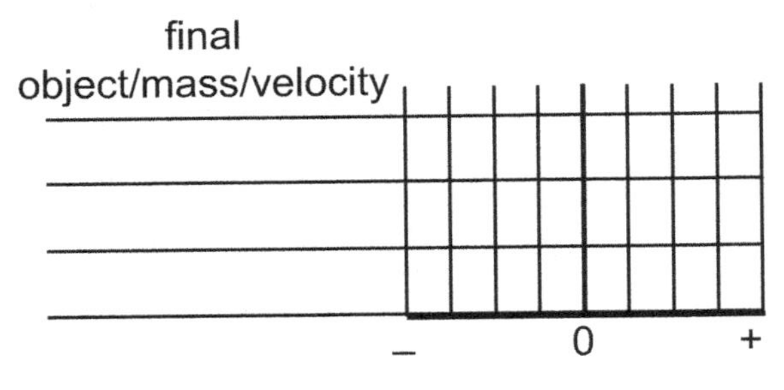

4. Comment on the advisability of attempting to jump from a rowboat to a dock that seems just within jumping distance.

5. a. Why is it difficult for a fire-fighter to hold a hose that ejects large amounts of high-speed water?

b. Calculate the force needed to hold a 6.0 cm diameter fire hose in place when the water flow rate is 110 m^3/hour. (density of water: 1000 kg/m^3)

6. A sailboat is stalled on a lake on a windless day. The skipper's only piece of auxiliary equipment is a large fan, which can either be set up to blow air into the sail or the fan can be pointed the off of the back of the boat with the sail taken down. Will either technique get the boat to shore? Which technique would work best? Explain your answer in terms of impulse and momentum.

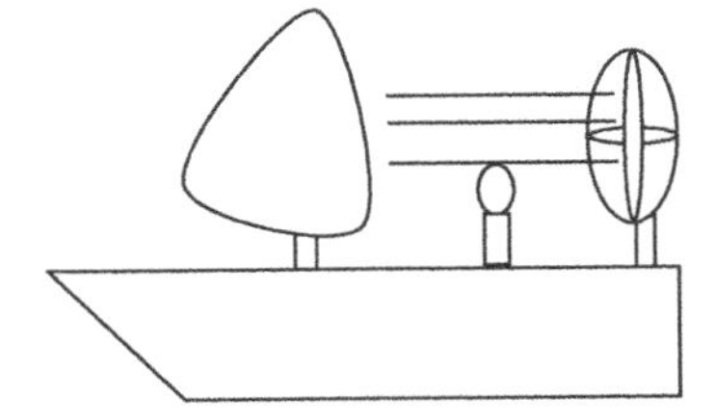

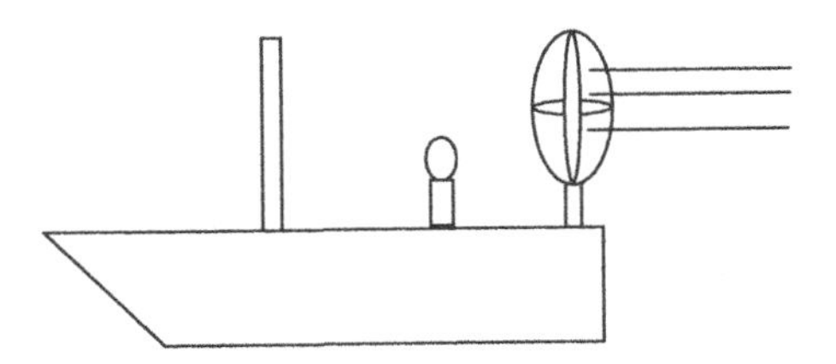

7. a. When a bug smacks into your windshield, which gets hit harder, the bug or the windshield? Justify your answer.

b. Which will experience the greatest change in momentum? Justify your answer.

c. Which will experience the greatest acceleration? Justify your answer.

8. Accident investigators come upon the following scene involving a collision between two cars of similar mass. Both drivers had intended to travel through the intersection without turning.

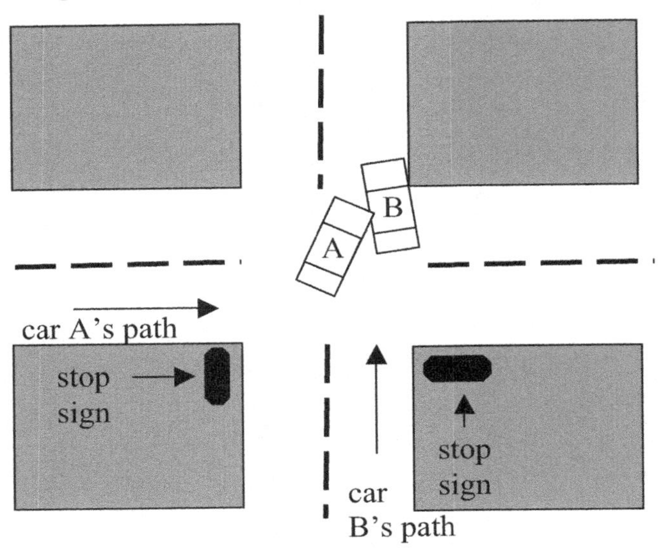

Driver A says that after stopping at the stop sign and then proceeding, car B ran the stop sign so there was no time to stop before hitting the side of car B.

Driver B says that after stopping at the stop sign and then proceeding, car A came out of nowhere, evidently running the stop sign and T-boning car B.

a. Which car ran the stop sign? Explain your answer in terms of our momentum studies.

b. Sketch a picture of how the cars would have come to rest had the driver's story that ran the stoplight been true.

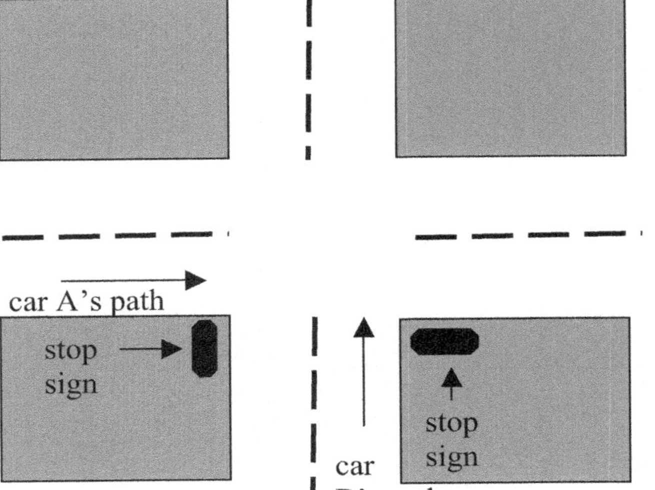

c. Briefly explain why the cars end up where you drew them.

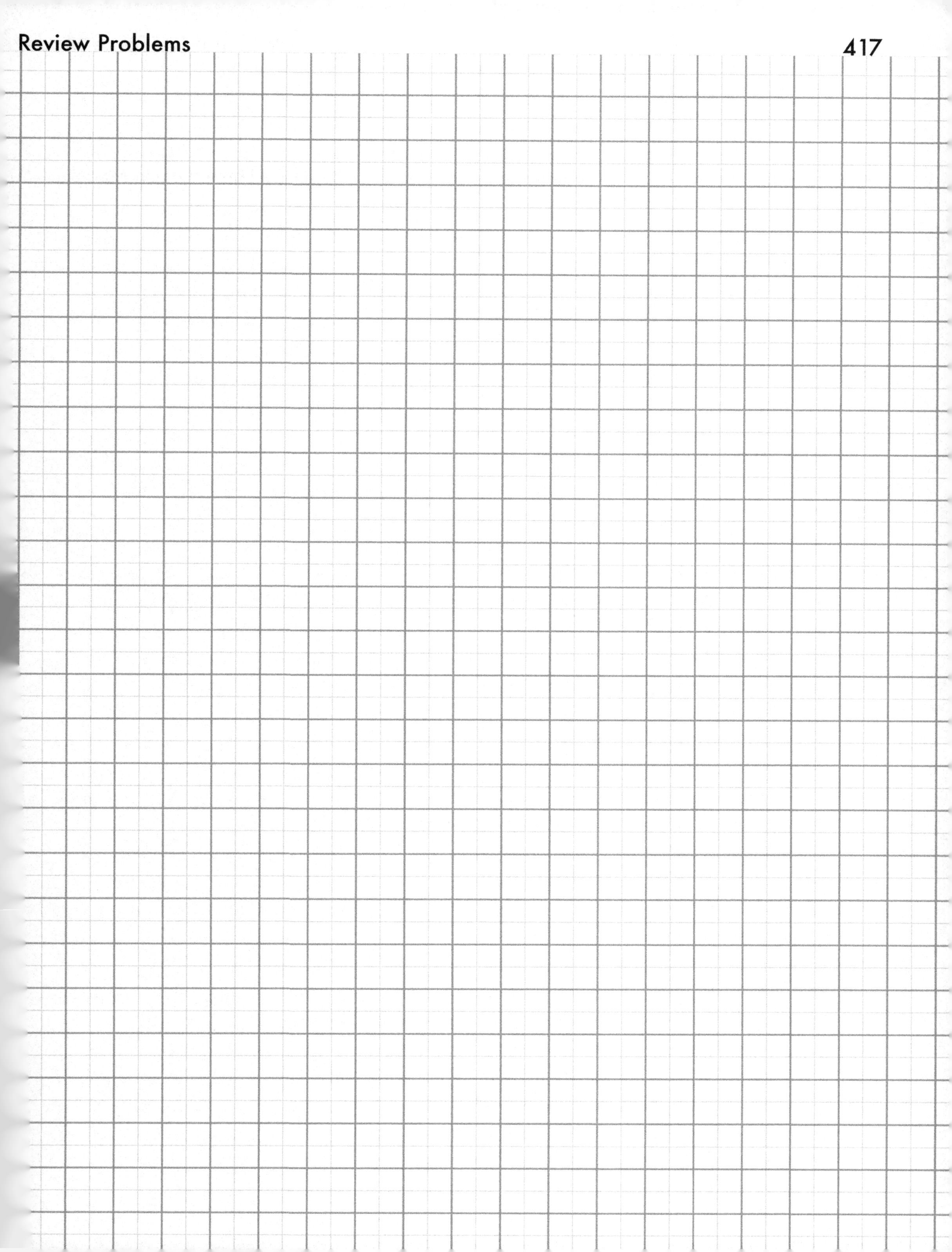

Model Summary

This is a place to summarize different representations of the Impulsive Force Particle Model

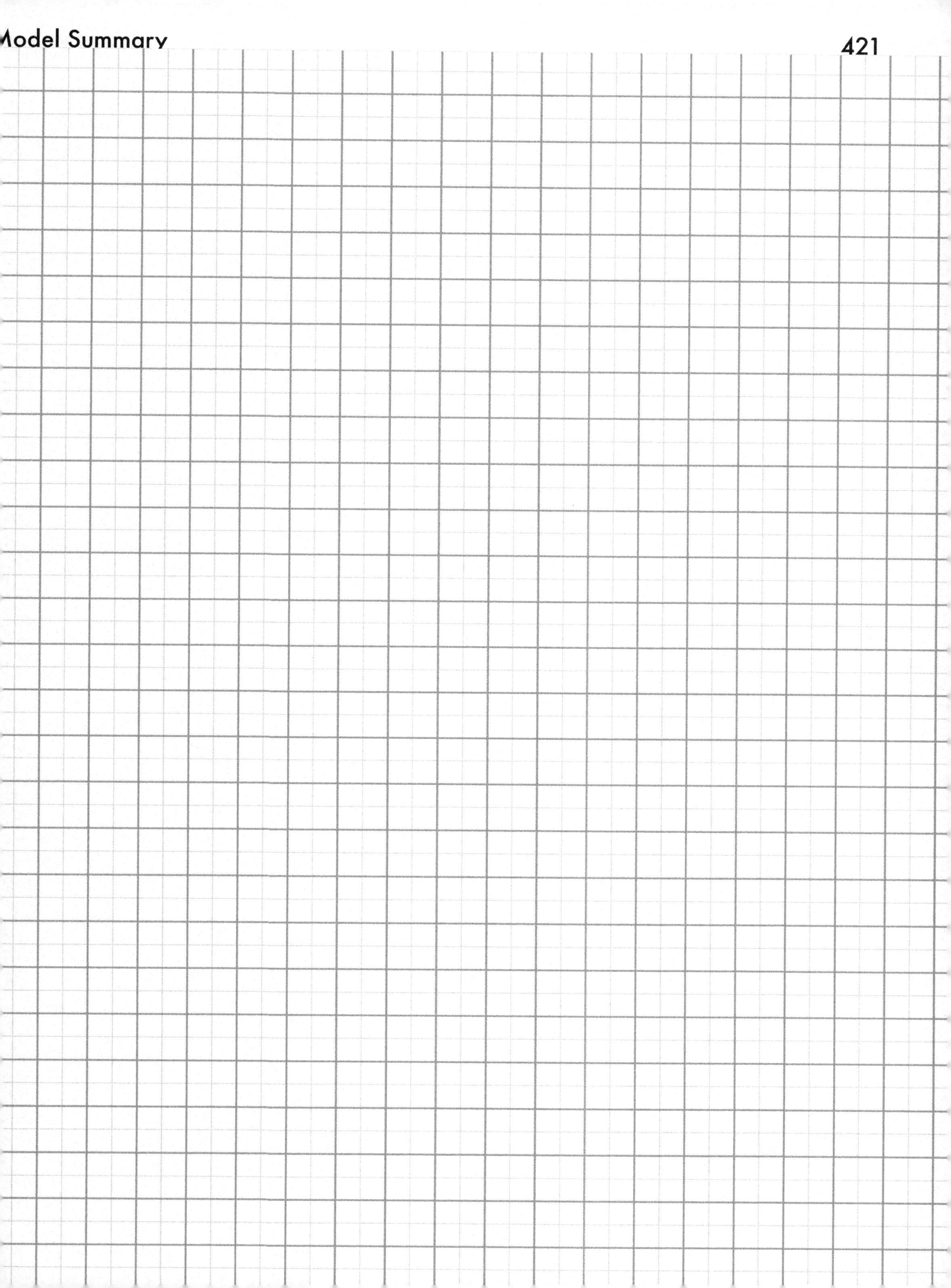

Resources

http://modelinginstruction.org/

socraticbrain.org/mechanics

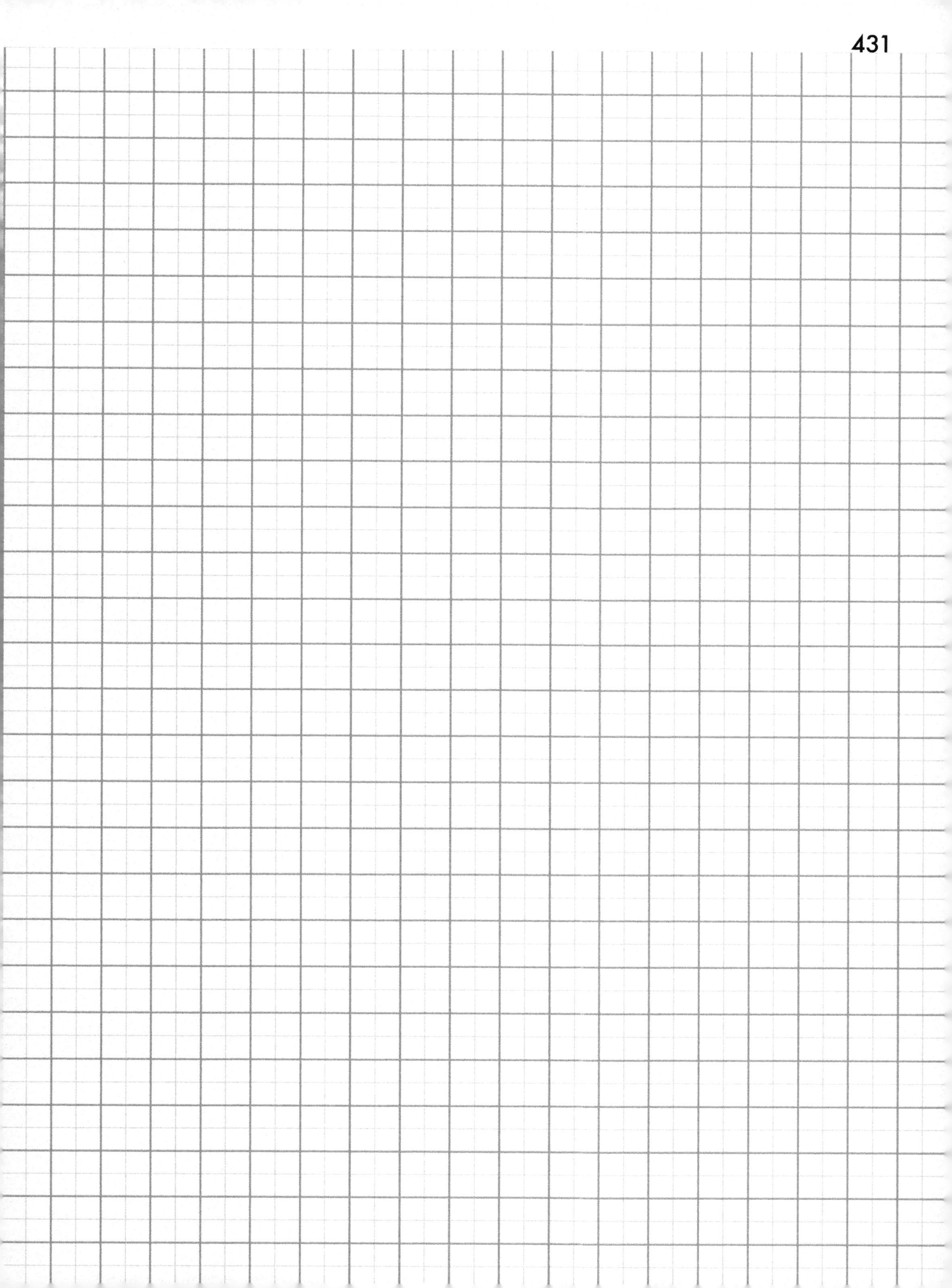

About the American Modeling Teachers Association (AMTA)

Mission AMTA is a professional organization of teachers, by teachers and for teachers who utilize Modeling Instruction in their physics, chemistry, biology, physical science and middle school teaching practice. Its mission is to provide professional development for teachers in the Modeling Method of Instruction, to provide resources that support the use of Modeling Instruction in science and mathematics classrooms, and to support and enable collaboration among Modelers. AMTA strives to foster brilliant teaching and deep learning.

History In the early 1990s, after a decade of education research to develop and validate Modeling Instruction, physicist David Hestenes was awarded a series of grants from the National Science Foundation to spread the Modeling Instruction program nationwide. At the expiration of 16 years of continuous NSF funding, AMTA was created by teachers who did not want to see these reforms die. They took on and scaled up the work begun by ASU Modeling Instruction Program, providing professional development, curriculum resources and a national virtual community of over 10,000 teachers dedicated to addressing the nation's Science, Technology, Engineering, and Mathematics (STEM) education crisis.

As of 2017, 12,000 teachers have participated in summer workshops to learn to use Modeling Instruction, including roughly 10% of US high school physics teachers. It is estimated that Modeling teachers reach more than 100,000 students each year. Each summer approximately 1200 teachers are trained in nearly 80 workshops offered across the country. This training consists of intensive 60-90 hour professional development summer workshops or distance learning courses that engage teachers from diverse teaching backgrounds and school communities to learn to use Modeling pedagogy in their classrooms.

With the teacher's guidance students build useful, flexible conceptual tools and practices solving real problems. MI applies structured inquiry techniques to help students develop the skills: mathematical modeling, proportional reasoning, quantitative estimation and technology, data collection and analysis (building, testing, elaboration and deployment of conceptual models). MI is a teaching pedagogy that aligns with many state and national standards (NGSS) and has demonstrated its effectiveness for decades.

HOW EFFECTIVE IS MODELING INSTRUCTION?

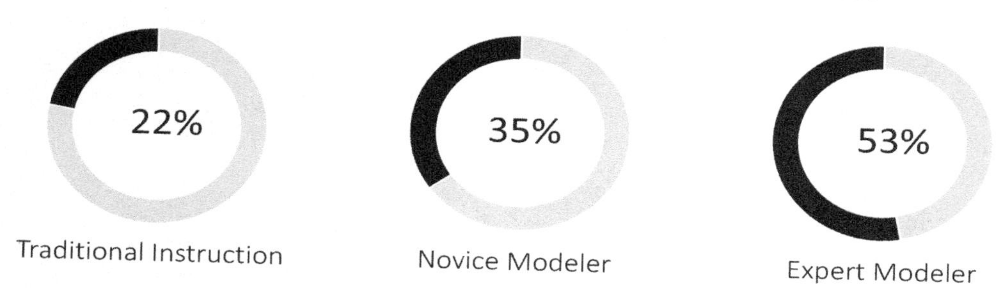

In comparison to traditional instruction, under expert modeling instruction high school students average more than two standard deviations higher on a standard instrument for assessing the gain in conceptual understanding of physics.

Modeling Instruction is a method of teaching that has been the subject of an evolving program of research and professional development since 1980. It started in undergraduate and high school physics classrooms and has expanded to include chemistry, physical science, biology and middle school science.

Students enter the physics classroom with an extensive collection of common sense beliefs and intuitions about how the physical world works based on years of personal experience. Unfortunately many of these beliefs are incompatible with physical laws. Unless instruction takes into account and explicitly addresses these naïve beliefs, learning physics can be impenetrable to many students. Modeling Instruction addresses this weakness in traditional instruction, providing students with necessary structure—models—to construct, refine and apply their own conceptual tools—tools for thinking.

Studies documenting the effectiveness of Modeling Instruction in physics date back to 1990 and continue to this day. In every published study, Modeling students have significantly outperformed students taught in more traditional instructional settings. The NSF-funded Modeling Instruction Project found that trained Modeling teachers' students scored one to two standard deviations higher on the Force Concept Inventory (the most widely used assessment of physics conceptual knowledge in the world) than their traditionally taught peers. In one early study high school students in a Modeling Physics class outperformed undergraduate introductory physics students at elite universities.

Teachers who are trained in Modeling Instruction transform their classrooms into collaborative learning environments in which students learn to work together to construct, refine and apply descriptive and explanatory conceptual models in much the same way that scientists do in their laboratories.

Over 100,000 physics students in the US learn physics from a physics teacher trained in Modeling Instruction every year. Teachers trained in the use of Modeling Instruction have been found to be significantly more confident in their use of the science and engineering practices recommended in national and state standards documents. In addition, they are more apt to be thought leaders in their department, school and region. If your teacher is a Modeler, you will experience an interactive, engaging learning environment that embodies the most effective practices science education research has identified in the last 50 years.

Made in the USA
Coppell, TX
10 September 2021